Integrated **3** Mathematics

Authors

Senior Authors

Rheta N. Rubenstein
Timothy V. Craine
Thomas R. Butts

Kerry Cantrell
Linda Dritsas
Valarie A. Elswick
Joseph Kavanaugh
Sara N. Munshin
Stuart J. Murphy
Anthony Piccolino
Salvador Quezada
Jocelyn Coleman Walton

McDougal Littell
A Houghton Mifflin Company
Evanston, Illinois   Boston Dallas Phoenix

Authors

Senior Authors

Rheta N. Rubenstein Associate Professor of Education, University of Windsor, Windsor, Ontario

Timothy V. Craine Assistant Professor of Mathematical Sciences, Central Connecticut State University, New Britain, Connecticut

Thomas R. Butts Associate Professor of Mathematics Education, University of Texas at Dallas, Dallas, Texas

Kerry Cantrell Mathematics Department Head, Marshfield High School, Marshfield, Missouri

Linda Dritsas Mathematics Coordinator, Fresno Unified School District, Fresno, California

Valarie A. Elswick Mathematics Teacher, Roy C. Ketcham Senior High School, Wappingers Falls, New York

Joseph Kavanaugh Academic Head of Mathematics, Scotia-Glenville Central School District, Scotia, New York

Sara N. Munshin Mathematics Teacher, Theodore Roosevelt High School, Los Angeles, California

Stuart J. Murphy Visual Learning Specialist, Evanston, Illinois

Anthony Piccolino Assistant Professor of Mathematics and Computer Science, Montclair State College, Upper Montclair, New Jersey

Salvador Quezada Mathematics Teacher, Theodore Roosevelt High School, Los Angeles, California

Jocelyn Coleman Walton Educational Consultant, Mathematics K-12, and former Mathematics Supervisor, Plainfield High School, Plainfield, New Jersey

All authors contributed to the planning and writing of the series. In addition to writing, the Senior Authors played a special role in establishing the philosophy of the program, planning the content and organization of topics, and guiding the work of the other authors.

Field Testing The authors give special thanks to the teachers and students in classrooms nationwide who used a preliminary version of this book. Their suggestions made an important contribution to its development.

ISBN: 0-395-64448-8   123456789 VH 99 98 97 96 95

Welcome to Integrated Mathematics 3!

A Strong Foundation

Integrated Mathematics 3 builds on the mathematical topics and problem solving techniques in *Integrated Mathematics 1* and *Integrated Mathematics 2*. This three-year series provides a strong foundation for more advanced courses in mathematics and the many other fields that require quantitative reasoning and decision-making skills.

Mathematical Strands

You can learn more with *Integrated Mathematics* because the mathematical topics are integrated. Over a three-year period, this program teaches all the essential topics in a contemporary Algebra 1/Geometry/Algebra 2 sequence, plus many other interesting topics.

> Algebra and Geometry are taught in each of the three years.

> Topics from Logical Reasoning, Measurement, Probability, Statistics, Discrete Mathematics, and Functions are interwoven throughout.

$p \rightarrow q$

(r, θ)

Course Goals

This new program has been written to prepare you for success in college, in careers, and in daily life in the 21st century.

It helps you develop the ability to:

➤ **Explore and solve mathematical problems**

➤ **Think critically**

➤ **Work cooperatively with others**

➤ **Communicate ideas clearly**

Advantages of this Program

Integrated Mathematics develops clear understanding of topics and strong problem solving skills by giving you opportunities to:

➤ **Get actively involved in learning**

➤ **Study meaningful mathematics**

➤ **See connections among different branches of mathematics**

➤ **Try a wide variety of types of problems, including real-world applications and long-term projects**

➤ **Use calculators and computers**

Contents

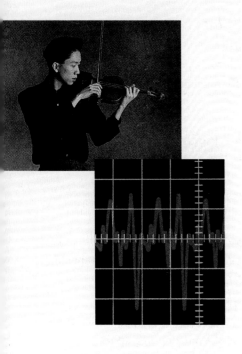

Unit 4   Sequences and Series

Unit 5	Exponential and Logarithmic Functions

Unit Project 5 ·········· **Music** **264**

Unit 10 Periodic Models

Unit Project
10 Cycles **538**

Table of Contents

Integrated Mathematics | Topic Spiraling

This chart shows how mathematical strands are spiraled over the three years of the *Integrated Mathematics* program.

	Course 1	Course 2	Course 3
Algebra	Linear equations Linear inequalities Multiplying binomials Factoring expressions	Quadratic equations Linear systems Rational equations Complex numbers	Polynomial functions Exponential and logarithmic functions Radical functions Parametric equations
Geometry	Angles, polygons, circles Perimeter, circumference Area, surface area Volume	Similar and congruent figures Geometric proofs Coordinate geometry Transformational geometry	Inscribed polygons Tangents to circles Transforming graphs Vectors, polar coordinates
Statistics, Probability	Analyzing data and displaying data Experimental and theoretical probability Geometric probability	Sampling methods Simulation Binomial distributions Compound events	Standard deviation Normal distribution Conditional probability z-scores
Logical Reasoning	Conjectures Counterexamples If-then statements	Inductive and deductive reasoning Valid and invalid reasoning Postulates and proof	Identities Contrapositive and inverse Comparing proof methods
Discrete Math	Discrete quantities Matrices to display data Lattices	Matrix operations Transformation matrices Counting techniques	Sequences and series Recursion Network diagrams
Trigonometry	Right-triangle ratios: sine, cosine, tangent Solving right triangles Tangent ratio as slope	Applying properties of special right triangles: 30° - 60° - 90° 45° - 45° - 90°	Circular trigonometric functions and graphs Modeling periodic situations Law of cosines, law of sines

What Students are Saying...

$T <^H_T$

Who has the **BEST IDEAS** about how mathematics should be taught? Students and teachers, of course! That is why preliminary versions of this book were tried out by thousands of students and their teachers in CLASSROOMS NATIONWIDE. The suggestions from these students and teachers have been incorporated into this book. Here is what some of the students who have already studied this course have said.

I enjoy doing the Explorations and solving application problems that relate to my life and the world around me.

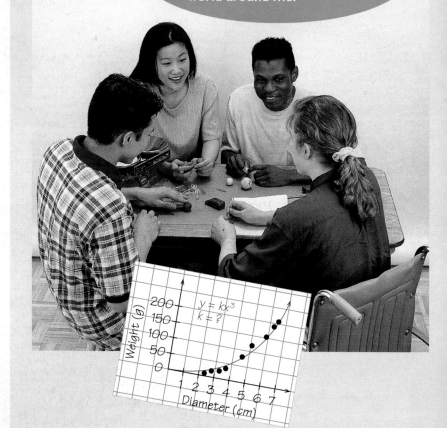

$y = kx^3$
$k = ?$

Weight (g)
200
150
100
50
0
1 2 3 4 5 6 7
Diameter (cm)

I'm really involved in math class this year. I read and think about problems, and analyze and discuss solutions with other students.

$\cos C$

Get Involved

Your Ideas are Important!

This course may be different from ones you have taken before. In this course you will be

➤ TALKING about mathematics

➤ working *together* to explore ideas

➤ gathering **DATA**

➤ looking for **patterns**

➤ making and testing **predictions**

➤ using *calculators* or **computers.**

Your ideas and viewpoints are important. Sharing them with others will help everyone learn more. So don't hold back. Jump right in and get involved.

Guide to Your Course

The next ten pages will give you an overview of the organization of your book and a preview of what you will be learning in the course. They will help you get off to a good start.

Solving problems is more interesting when you can try different methods and use different types of mathematics.

$P(E)$

rand
.7455607728
.8559005971
.2253600617
.469229188
.6866902136
.0849241336

$n!$

After studying Integrated Mathematics, my expectations have changed. I am considering careers that require more advanced mathematics because now I know I can learn it.

$M = \begin{bmatrix} 3 & 0 & 3 \\ 0 & 9 & 0 \end{bmatrix}$

ABC

I never realized math was used in so many different subjects — science, social studies, business education, art, music, literature, and sports.

Unit Projects

Each unit begins with a project that sets the stage for the mathematics in the unit. The project gives you a chance to **apply** what you are learning right away. As you study the unit, you will gather the **INFORMATION** and develop the SKILLS to complete the project. The first three pages of each unit help you get started.

Project Theme

Each project has a theme, like music, that relates the mathematics of the unit to daily life and to careers.

unit 5

Exponential and Logarithmic Functions

If you wanted to write a song for the whole world to sing, what musical system would you use? In China most music is written in a five-note scale. Traditional European music is based on an eight-note octave. In India the raga is an important musical form. Ragas use scales with various sequences of five, six, or seven notes.

To uncover the secrets of the great violin makers of the past, scientist and violin maker Carleen M. Hutchins has handcrafted over 400 instruments in the last 40 years. When a violin is played, the vibrating strings cause both the wooden walls of the violin and the air inside to vibrate. By analyzing these vibrations, Carleen M. Hutchins has worked out basic rules for making violins.

Different instruments sound different because of the blend of higher tones, or overtones, produced with each note. In 1965 the first electronic synthesizer to produce music with vibrating electric circuits was invented. Synthesizers can imitate all the instruments of the orchestra.

Unit Project 5

Making Music with Mathematics

Your project is to give a lecture/performance that demonstrates how mathematics and music are related. Following the guidelines in the Working on the Unit Project exercises, your group should make two sets of panpipes and two simple guitars. You should describe how you built your instruments, use them to play music, and explain how they produce musical notes.

Describe at least two examples of the relationship between mathematics and music.

This wooden harp is from Zaire. African harps like this traditionally played a vital role in the lives of millions of people. Many harp songs tell of historical events or legends.

On a stringed instrument like a violin or a guitar, one way to raise the pitch, or produce a higher note, is to shorten or tighten a string. Another way is to use a thinner string.

Shortening the column of air that vibrates when a musician blows into a wind instrument like a flute or panpipe raises the pitch.

264

265

Getting Started

For this project you should work in a group of four students. Here are some ideas to help you get started.

• Collect the materials and tools—plastic drinking straws, wood, strong nylon fishing line, several large screw eyes, a screwdriver, and pliers—that you will need to build your instruments.

• As a group, decide which instrument each member will make.

• Plan to meet to listen to recordings of many different kinds of music. Notice which instruments are used on the recordings and try to listen for them as the music plays.

Starting the Project

At the beginning of each unit, there is a description of the project, hints for getting started, and questions to get you thinking and talking about the project.

Working on the Unit Project

Your work in Unit 5 will help you to make your musical instruments and prepare your lecture/performance.

Related Exercises:
Section 5-1, Exercises 32, 33
Section 5-2, Exercise 22
Section 5-3, Exercises 48–52
Section 5-4, Exercise 34
Section 5-5, Exercise 34
Section 5-6, Exercises 46, 47
Section 5-7, Exercise 48
Section 5-8, Exercise 32

Alternative Projects p. 323

Can We Talk MUSIC

➤ What kind of music do you like? What instruments do the members of your favorite band play?

➤ Have you ever attended a live performance by an orchestra or listened to a recording of an orchestra? If you did, were you able to hear the individual instruments when all the musicians were playing together?

➤ The ridges on the neck of a guitar are called *frets*. As they play, most guitarists will hold strings down by pressing at various frets. What effect do you think this has on the sound produced? Why?

➤ If you play an instrument, discuss what you like about it. Is it easy to learn? Does your music teacher ever talk about mathematics in relation to the music?

266   **Unit 5** Exponential and Logarithmic Functions

Working on the Unit Project

In each section of the unit, there are exercises to help you complete your work on the project.

Unit Project 5

Completing the Unit Project

Now you are ready to complete your musical instruments and plan your lecture/performance.

Your completed project should include these things:

➤ two handmade panpipes and two handmade simple guitars

➤ drawings of your panpipes and guitars with descriptions of how you built them and how they are played

➤ a written report describing two examples of how mathematics is related to music

➤ a musical performance involving all four of your handmade instruments

Look Back
Was the panpipe or the guitar easier to make? to play? to understand in terms of mathematics? Why?

Completing the Unit Project

After you complete the unit, you can finish the project and present your results. Then you are ready to look back over what you learned.

Alternative Projects

Project 1: Mathematics and My Musical Instrument

If you play a musical instrument, prepare a lecture/performance in which you demonstrate and discuss how mathematical models are used in making and playing it.

Project 2: Applying Exponential and Logarithmic Functions

Choose one of the applications you saw in this unit, such as the Richter scale or carbon dating. Find out more about the topic and the mathematics involved. Prepare a presentation for your class.

Unit 5 Completing the Unit Project   323

Unit Projects

Section Organization

The organization of material within sections is patterned after the way that you learn: Ideas are introduced. You **EXPLORE** them, **think** about them, and TALK about them with other students. You check that you **UNDERSTAND** them by working through some sample problems. Before going on, you pause and look back at what you have learned.

Application A problem situation connects the mathematics you will be studying to real-world applications.

Focus This is what you will be doing in the lesson.

Talk it Over What do *you* think? Share your ideas. Talking them over can help you deepen your understanding.

Sample 1

In 1980 Colorado's population was about 2.8 million. Since then, the population has increased by about 1.5% each year.

a. Write an exponential function to model the population growth of Colorado.

b. If the population continues to grow at this rate, when will the population of Colorado reach 4 million people?

Denver International Airport, on the world's largest airport site, was planned to accommodate predicted growth in the number of daily passengers.

Samples Samples and Responses show ways to think through and solve exercises and problems. Use them when you study.

Sample Response

a. **Step 1** Find the growth factor *b*.

$$\text{population at end of each year} = \text{100\% of population at start of year} + \text{1.5\% of population at start of year}$$

$$= \text{101.5\% of population at start of year}$$

The growth factor *b* is 101.5%, or 1.015.

Step 2 Model the growth with an exponential function.

Let *y* = the population after *x* years. ⟶ $y = ab^x$ ⟵ Let *x* = the number of years since 1980.

$= (2.8)(1.015)^x$

Substitute **2.8** for the initial value *a* and 1.015 for the growth factor *b*.

b. **Method ❶** Use a graph.

Graph the equation $y = (2.8)(1.015)^x$.
Since an *x*-value of zero represents 1980, an *x*-value of 24 represents the year 2004. The population of Colorado will be about 4 million in the year 2004.

Read the value of *x* when *y* ≈ 4.

X = 24   Y = 4.0026079

Method ❷ Use recursion.

Enter the initial amount 2.8 and repeatedly multiply it by the growth factor 1.015.

```
2.8
                    2.8
Ans *1.015
                  2.842
               2.88463
            2.92789945
            2.971817942
```

Count the number of times —24— that you press ENTER to reach 4 million.

24 years after 1980 represents the year 2004. The population of Colorado will be about 4 million in the year 2004.

268   **Unit 5** Exponential and Logarithmic Functions

Key Concepts are highlighted to make it easier for you to learn and to review.

$X_{(.}^{.} \triangle ab$

EXPONENTIAL FUNCTIONS

Exponential Growth
$y = ab^x, b > 1$
Example: $y = (5)(1.2)^x$

Exponential Decay
$y = ab^x, 0 < b < 1$
Example: $y = (5)(0.5)^x$

Sample 2

The average amount of fuel used annually by each car in the United States has decreased by about 2% each year since 1980, when it was about 591 gallons.

a. Write an exponential function to model this situation.

b. Estimate the average number of gallons of gasoline used by a car in 1987.

Sample Response

a. $y = ab^x$ ⟵ Let *x* = the number of years since 1980. Let *y* = the average number of gallons of gasoline used.

$= (591)b^x$ ⟵ Substitute 591 for the initial amount *a*.

$= (591)(0.98)^x$ ⟵ The expression (1 − 0.02) represents a 2% decrease. Substitute 0.98 for *b*.

b. **Problem Solving Strategy:** Use a graph.

Graph the equation $y = (591)(0.98)^x$.
The initial value occurs in 1980, so an *x*-value of zero represents 1980.

An *x*-value of 7 represents 1987.
Read the value of *y* when *x* = 7.

In 1987, each car in the United States used an average of about 513 gallons of gasoline.

X = 7   Y = 513.06219

Look Back

Describe a function that models exponential decay. How is this function like an exponential growth function? How is it different?

▶ Now you are ready for:
Exs. 17–33 on pp. 272–274

270   **Unit 5** Exponential and Logarithmic Functions

Look Back Think over what you have learned. How do the different ideas in the lesson tie together? How do they relate to what you learned earlier?

Section Organization

Exercises and Problems

Each section has a wide variety of exercises and problems. Some **practice** and **EXTEND** the concepts and skills you have learned. Others apply the concepts to everyday situations and explore **connections** to other subject areas and to careers. The problems help you sharpen your **THINKING** and **problem solving** skills.

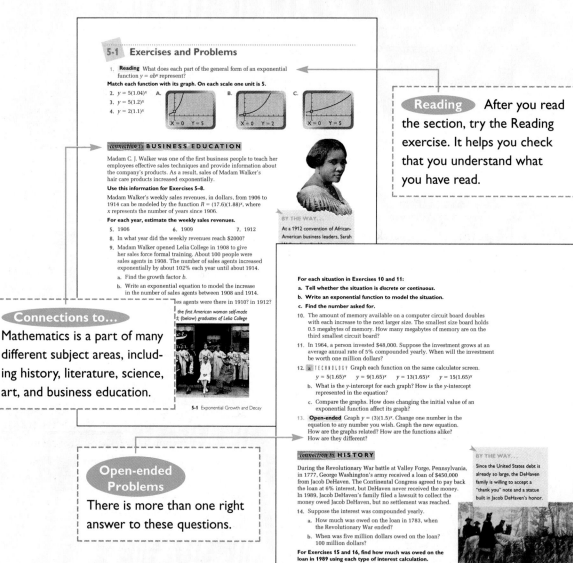

5-1 Exercises and Problems

1. **Reading** What does each part of the general form of an exponential function $y = ab^x$ represent?

Match each function with its graph. On each scale one unit is 5.

2. $y = 5(1.04)^x$ A.   B.   C.

3. $y = 5(1.2)^x$

4. $y = 2(1.1)^x$

X = 0   Y = 5   X = 0   Y = 2   X = 0   Y = 5

connection to BUSINESS EDUCATION

Madam C. J. Walker was one of the first business people to teach her employees effective sales techniques and provide information about the company's products. As a result, sales of Madam Walker's hair care products increased exponentially.

Use this information for Exercises 5–8.

Madam Walker's weekly sales revenues, in dollars, from 1906 to 1914 can be modeled by the function $R = (17.6)(1.88)^x$, where x represents the number of years since 1906.

For each year, estimate the weekly sales revenues.

5. 1906   6. 1909   7. 1912

8. In what year did the weekly revenues reach $2000?

9. Madam Walker opened Lelia College in 1908 to give her sales force formal training. About 100 people were sales agents in 1908. The number of sales agents increased exponentially by about 102% each year until about 1914.

   a. Find the growth factor b.

   b. Write an exponential equation to model the increase in the number of sales agents between 1908 and 1914.

   ...les agents were there in 1910? in 1912?

   the first American woman self-made ... (below) graduates of Lelia College

5-1 Exponential Growth and Decay

BY THE WAY...
At a 1912 convention of African-American business leaders, Sarah ...

For each situation in Exercises 10 and 11:

a. **Tell whether the situation is discrete or continuous.**

b. **Write an exponential function to model the situation.**

c. **Find the number asked for.**

10. The amount of memory available on a computer circuit board doubles with each increase to the next larger size. The smallest size board holds 0.5 megabytes of memory. How many megabytes of memory are on the third smallest circuit board?

11. In 1964, a person invested $48,000. Suppose the investment grows at an average annual rate of 5% compounded yearly. When will the investment be worth one million dollars?

12. **a TECHNOLOGY** Graph each function on the same calculator screen.

   $y = 5(1.65)^x$ $y = 9(1.65)^x$ $y = 13(1.65)^x$ $y = 15(1.65)^x$

   b. What is the y-intercept for each graph? How is the y-intercept represented in the equation?

   c. Compare the graphs. How does changing the initial value of an exponential function affect its graph?

13. **Open-ended** Graph $y = (3)(1.5)^x$. Change one number in the equation to any number you wish. Graph the new equation. How are the graphs related? How are the functions alike? How are they different?

connection to HISTORY

During the Revolutionary War battle at Valley Forge, Pennsylvania, in 1777, George Washington's army received a loan of $450,000 from Jacob DeHaven. The Continental Congress agreed to pay back the loan at 6% interest, but DeHaven never received the money. In 1989, Jacob DeHaven's family filed a lawsuit to collect the money owed Jacob DeHaven, but no settlement was reached.

14. Suppose the interest was compounded yearly.

   a. How much was owed on the loan in 1783, when the Revolutionary War ended?

   b. When was five million dollars owed on the loan? 100 million dollars?

For Exercises 15 and 16, find how much was owed on the loan in 1989 using each type of interest calculation.

15. Suppose the 6% annual interest is compounded yearly.

16. Suppose the 6% annual interest is compounded daily.

17. **a TECHNOLOGY** Graph each function on the same calculator screen.

   $y = 5(0.9)^x$ $y = 5(0.09)^x$

   b. What effect does changing 5 to −5 have on each graph?

   c. What effect does adding 1 to each value of b have on each graph?

BY THE WAY...
Since the United States debt is already so large, the DeHaven family is willing to accept a "thank you" note and a statue built in Jacob DeHaven's honor.

Without the loan from Jacob DeHaven, Washington's troops may not have had enough food and supplies to survive the winter.

272   Unit 5 Exponential and Logarithmic Functions

Reading After you read the section, try the Reading exercise. It helps you check that you understand what you have read.

Connections to...
Mathematics is a part of many different subject areas, including history, literature, science, art, and business education.

Open-ended Problems
There is more than one right answer to these questions.

Ongoing **ASSESSMENT**

24. **Open-ended** Describe a situation that can be modeled by each of the following: *discrete exponential growth, continuous exponential growth, discrete exponential decay, continuous exponential decay*. Sketch a graph for each example.

Review **PREVIEW**

Evaluate each series, if the sum exists. *(Section 4-7)*

25. $\sum_{n=0}^{\infty} (1.03)^n$

26. $\sum_{t=1}^{\infty} \left(\frac{1}{3}\right)^t$

27. $\sum_{n=1}^{\infty} -5(0.003)^{n-1}$

28. Can the sum of the interior angle measures of a regular polygon be 655°? Why or why not? *(Section 3-4)*

Simplify. Write answers with positive exponents. *(Toolbox Skill 14)*

29. $(3x^2)(5x^{-3})$

30. $5t(s^{-1}t^{-2})^{-2}$

31. $\dfrac{p^{-1}q^{-2}}{p^{-3}}$

Working on the Unit Project

The *pitch* of a note is how high or low the note sounds to a listener. Pitch depends on frequency. The frequencies of musical notes in a scale form a geometric sequence.

32. Suppose there were a musical instrument whose notes are related to one another by the function $f(n) = 20(2)^n$, where n is the number of the note in the sequence, and the frequency of the note is measured in hertz (Hz).

    a. Find $f(1)$, the frequency of the note with the lowest pitch.

    b. Find the frequency for the next seven notes in the instrument's sequence.

    c. Graph the function. How does the frequency of a note change as the pitch of a note gets higher?

    d. The human ear can hear sounds in the range 20–20,000 Hz. What problem can you foresee in terms of the instrument described above?

An electronic representation of a 440 Hz note produced by a vibrating violin string

This C note is one octave higher than middle C.

33. In the music of Europe and the United States, the frequency of a note is double the frequency of the same note one *octave* lower. One of the C notes on a piano has a frequency of 130.8 Hz. Find the frequency of the C note that is one octave higher.

This note is middle C.

5 Exponential and Logarithmic Functions

18. Suppose you repeat the Exploration using 30 dice and remove a die if a 6 lands face up.

    a. Write an equation to model the number of dice remaining after each toss.

    b. Write an equation to model the number of dice remaining after each toss if you remove a die if either a 1 or a 6 is face up.

    c. Graph each of the equations you wrote in parts (a) and (b) on the same axes. How are the graphs alike? How are they different?

19. a. **Writing** Compare the functions $y = (3)(1.25)^x$ and $y = (3)(0.75)^x$. How are the functions alike? How are they different?

    b. Graph each of the functions in part (a) on the same set of axes. Describe each graph. What point(s) do the graphs have in common?

Career After reaching a peak level, the concentration of a medication in a person's bloodstream decreases exponentially. Pharmacists can use an exponential model to determine the concentration level.

20. A medication for treating skin infections is available in three strengths. In each model, t represents the number of hours since the medication reached its peak and y represents the concentration of the medication in the blood in micrograms per milliliter (µg/mL).

weakest strength	medium strength	greatest strength
$y = (0.8)(0.84)^t$	$y = (1.6)(0.84)^t$	$y = (3.2)(0.84)^t$

    a. Graph each equation on the same set of axes. What do the y-intercept values represent in this situation?

    b. How long does it take for each strength to reach a concentration of 0.1 µg/mL, the level at which the medication is considered cleared from a person's system?

21. The concentration of a stomach medication in a person's bloodstream in nanograms per milliliter (ng/mL) can be represented by the function $y = (492.5)(0.79)^t$, where t represents the number of hours since the medication reached its peak concentration.

    a. Graph the equation.

    b. Find the peak concentration.

    c. Find the time when half of the peak concentration remains. This is the medication's half-life.

    d. Use the information from the photo and your answer to part (c) to estimate when the stomach medication is cleared from a patient's blood stream.

Pharmacists multiply a medication's half-life by five to estimate when a medication is cleared from a patient's blood stream.

22. Repeat Exercise 21 for a hypertension medication whose concentration, in ng/mL, can be modeled by the equation $y = (115)(0.95)^t$.

23. Repeat Exercise 21 for an allergy medication whose concentration, in ng/mL, can be modeled by the equation $y = (263)(0.92)^t$.

5-1 Exponential Growth and Decay

273

Exercises and Problems

Explorations

Explorations are an important part of this course. They will help you discover, understand, and connect mathematical ideas. In the Explorations, you will be gathering **data**, looking for **patterns**, and making **generalizations**. You will be working with others and sharing your ideas.

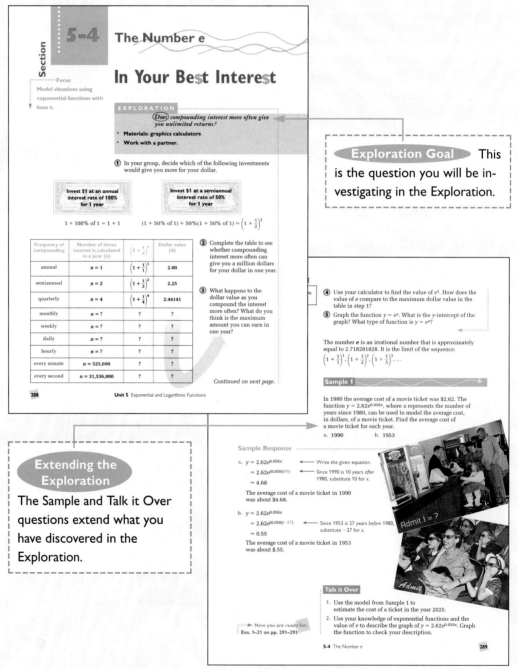

Section **5-4**

The Number e

In Your Be$t Intere$t

Focus
Model situations using exponential functions with base e.

EXPLORATION

Does compounding interest more often give you unlimited returns?

• **Materials:** graphics calculators
• **Work with a partner.**

① In your group, decide which of the following investments would give you more for your dollar.

| Invest $1 at an annual interest rate of 100% for 1 year |
| Invest $1 at a semiannual interest rate of 50% for 1 year |

$1 + 100\%$ of $1 = 1 + 1$ $(1 + 50\%$ of $1) + 50\%(1 + 50\%$ of $1) = \left(1 + \frac{1}{2}\right)^2$

Frequency of compounding	Number of times interest is calculated in a year (n)	$\left(1 + \frac{1}{n}\right)^n$	Dollar value (A)
annual	$n = 1$	$\left(1 + \frac{1}{1}\right)^1$	2.00
semiannual	$n = 2$	$\left(1 + \frac{1}{2}\right)^2$	2.25
quarterly	$n = 4$	$\left(1 + \frac{1}{4}\right)^4$	2.44141
monthly	$n = ?$	?	?
weekly	$n = ?$	?	?
daily	$n = ?$	?	?
hourly	$n = ?$	?	?
every minute	$n = 525,600$	?	?
every second	$n = 31,536,000$	?	?

② Complete the table to see whether compounding interest more often can give you a million dollars for your dollar in one year.

③ What happens to the dollar value as you compound the interest more often? What do you think is the maximum amount you can earn in one year?

Continued on next page.

288   **Unit 5** Exponential and Logarithmic Functions

Exploration Goal This is the question you will be investigating in the Exploration.

---

④ Use your calculator to find the value of e^1. How does the value of e compare to the maximum dollar value in the table in step 1?

⑤ Graph the function $y = e^x$. What is the y-intercept of the graph? What type of function is $y = e^x$?

The number e is an irrational number that is approximately equal to 2.718281828. It is the limit of the sequence:

$$\left(1 + \frac{1}{1}\right)^1, \left(1 + \frac{1}{2}\right)^2, \left(1 + \frac{1}{3}\right)^3, \ldots$$

Sample 1

In 1980 the average cost of a movie ticket was $2.62. The function $y = 2.62e^{0.058x}$, where x represents the number of years since 1980, can be used to model the average cost, in dollars, of a movie ticket. Find the average cost of a movie ticket for each year.
a. 1990   b. 1953

Sample Response

a. $y = 2.62e^{0.058x}$ ◄— Write the given equation.
   $= 2.62e^{(0.058)(10)}$ ◄— Since 1990 is 10 years *after* 1980, substitute 10 for x.
   ≈ 4.68

The average cost of a movie ticket in 1990 was about $4.68.

b. $y = 2.62e^{0.058x}$
   $= 2.62e^{(0.058)(-27)}$ ◄— Since 1953 is 27 years *before* 1980, substitute -27 for x.
   ≈ 0.55

The average cost of a movie ticket in 1953 was about $.55.

Talk it Over

1. Use the model from Sample 1 to estimate the cost of a ticket in the year 2025.

2. Use your knowledge of exponential functions and the value of e to describe the graph of $y = 2.62e^{0.058x}$. Graph the function to check your description.

▶ Now you are ready for:
Exs. 1–21 on pp. 291–293

5-4 The Number e   289

Extending the Exploration

The Sample and Talk it Over questions extend what you have discovered in the Exploration.

Review and Assessment

With this book you **review** and **ASSESS** your progress as you go along. In each unit there are one or two Checkpoints for self-assessment, plus a thorough Unit Review and Assessment at the end.

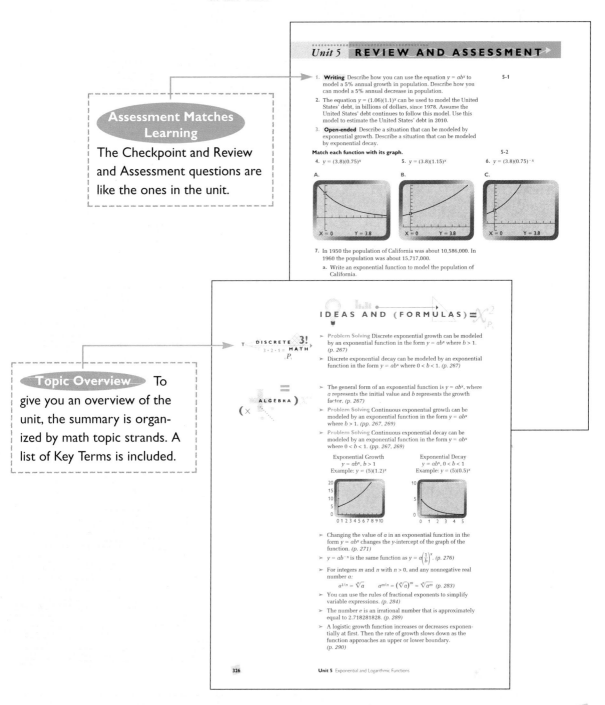

Assessment Matches Learning

The Checkpoint and Review and Assessment questions are like the ones in the unit.

Topic Overview To give you an overview of the unit, the summary is organized by math topic strands. A list of Key Terms is included.

Unit 5 REVIEW AND ASSESSMENT

1. **Writing** Describe how you can use the equation $y = ab^x$ to model a 5% annual growth in population. Describe how you can model a 5% annual decrease in population.   5-1

2. The equation $y = (1.06)(1.1)^x$ can be used to model the United States' debt, in billions of dollars, since 1978. Assume the United States' debt continues to follow this model. Use this model to estimate the United States' debt in 2010.

3. **Open-ended** Describe a situation that can be modeled by exponential growth. Describe a situation that can be modeled by exponential decay.

Match each function with its graph.   5-2

4. $y = (3.8)(0.75)^x$ 5. $y = (3.8)(1.15)^x$ 6. $y = (3.8)(0.75)^{-x}$

A.   B.   C.

7. In 1950 the population of California was about 10,586,000. In 1960 the population was about 15,717,000.

  a. Write an exponential function to model the population of California.

IDEAS AND (FORMULAS)

DISCRETE MATH

➤ **Problem Solving** Discrete exponential growth can be modeled by an exponential function in the form $y = ab^x$ where $b > 1$. (p. 267)

➤ Discrete exponential decay can be modeled by an exponential function in the form $y = ab^x$ where $0 < b < 1$. (p. 267)

ALGEBRA

➤ The general form of an exponential function is $y = ab^x$, where a represents the initial value and b represents the growth factor. (p. 267)

➤ **Problem Solving** Continuous exponential growth can be modeled by an exponential function in the form $y = ab^x$ where $b > 1$. (pp. 267, 269)

➤ **Problem Solving** Continuous exponential decay can be modeled by an exponential function in the form $y = ab^x$ where $0 < b < 1$. (pp. 267, 269)

Exponential Growth
$y = ab^x, b > 1$
Example: $y = (5)(1.2)^x$

Exponential Decay
$y = ab^x, 0 < b < 1$
Example: $y = (5)(0.5)^x$

➤ Changing the value of a in an exponential function in the form $y = ab^x$ changes the y-intercept of the graph of the function. (p. 271)

➤ $y = ab^{-x}$ is the same function as $y = a\left(\frac{1}{b}\right)^x$. (p. 276)

➤ For integers m and n with $n > 0$, and any nonnegative real number a:
$$a^{1/n} = \sqrt[n]{a} \qquad a^{m/n} = \left(\sqrt[n]{a}\right)^m = \sqrt[n]{a^m}$$ (p. 283)

➤ You can use the rules of fractional exponents to simplify variable expressions. (p. 284)

➤ The number e is an irrational number that is approximately equal to 2.718281828. (p. 289)

➤ A logistic growth function increases or decreases exponentially at first. Then the rate of growth slows down as the function approaches an upper or lower boundary. (p. 290)

326   **Unit 5** Exponential and Logarithmic Functions

Technology

In this course you will see many different ways that CALCULATORS and COMPUTERS can make exploring ideas and solving problems easier.

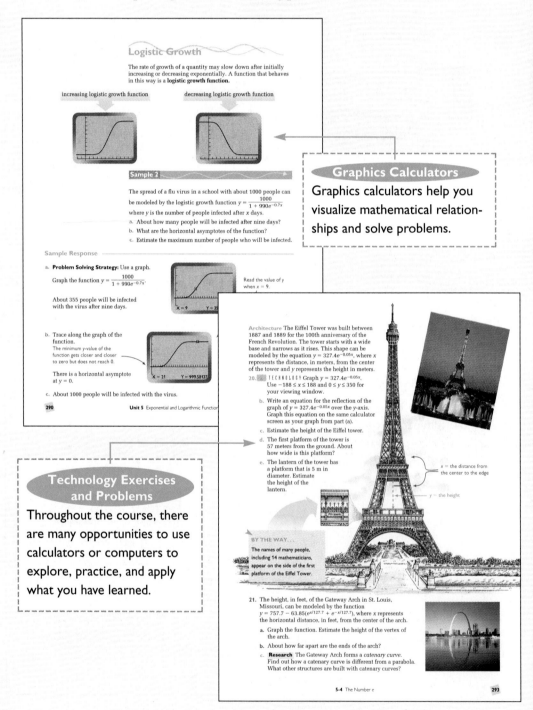

Logistic Growth

The rate of growth of a quantity may slow down after initially increasing or decreasing exponentially. A function that behaves in this way is a **logistic growth function.**

increasing logistic growth function

decreasing logistic growth function

Sample 2

The spread of a flu virus in a school with about 1000 people can be modeled by the logistic growth function $y = \dfrac{1000}{1 + 990e^{-0.7x}}$ where y is the number of people infected after x days.

a. About how many people will be infected after nine days?
b. What are the horizontal asymptotes of the function?
c. Estimate the maximum number of people who will be infected.

Sample Response

a. **Problem Solving Strategy:** Use a graph.

Graph the function $y = \dfrac{1000}{1 + 990e^{-0.7x}}$.

Read the value of y when $x = 9$.

About 355 people will be infected with the virus after nine days.

X = 9   Y = 35

b. Trace along the graph of the function.
The minimum y-value of the function gets closer and closer to zero but does not reach 0.

There is a horizontal asymptote at $y = 0$.

X = 21   Y = 999.58137

c. About 1000 people will be infected with the virus.

290   **Unit 5** Exponential and Logarithmic Functions

Graphics Calculators

Graphics calculators help you visualize mathematical relationships and solve problems.

Architecture The Eiffel Tower was built between 1887 and 1889 for the 100th anniversary of the French Revolution. The tower starts with a wide base and narrows as it rises. This shape can be modeled by the equation $y = 327.4e^{-0.05x}$, where x represents the distance, in meters, from the center of the tower and y represents the height in meters.

20. TECHNOLOGY Graph $y = 327.4e^{-0.05x}$. Use $-188 \le x \le 188$ and $0 \le y \le 350$ for your viewing window.

b. Write an equation for the reflection of the graph of $y = 327.4e^{-0.05x}$ over the y-axis. Graph this equation on the same calculator screen as your graph from part (a).

c. Estimate the height of the Eiffel tower.

d. The first platform of the tower is 57 meters from the ground. About how wide is this platform?

e. The lantern of the tower has a platform that is 5 m in diameter. Estimate the height of the lantern.

x = the distance from the center to the edge

y = the height

BY THE WAY...

The names of many people, including 14 mathematicians, appear on the side of the first platform of the Eiffel Tower.

21. The height, in feet, of the Gateway Arch in St. Louis, Missouri, can be modeled by the function $y = 757.7 - 63.85(e^{x/127.7} + e^{-x/127.7})$, where x represents the horizontal distance, in feet, from the center of the arch.

a. Graph the function. Estimate the height of the vertex of the arch.

b. About how far apart are the ends of the arch?

c. **Research** The Gateway Arch forms a *catenary curve*. Find out how a catenary curve is different from a parabola. What other structures are built with catenary curves?

5-4 The Number e   293

Technology Exercises and Problems

Throughout the course, there are many opportunities to use calculators or computers to explore, practice, and apply what you have learned.

Sample 1

The function $y = -0.014x^2 + 1.2x + 6.9$ models the relationship between MPG and driving speed for a car. Find the driving speed, to the nearest mile per hour, that maximizes MPG.

Sample Response

Student Resources Toolbox
p. 651 *Graphing*

Method ❶ Use a formula.

The function $y = -0.014x^2 + 1.2x + 6.9$ is a quadratic function, so its graph is a parabola. Since the coefficient of the x^2-term is negative, the parabola opens down. The vertex is on the line of symmetry of the parabola at the point where the value of the function is a maximum.

The speed that maximizes MPG is the x-coordinate of the vertex. To find this value, use the equation of the line of symmetry.

$x = -\dfrac{b}{2a}$ ◄—— a and b are coefficients in the general quadratic function $y = ax^2 + bx + c$.

$= -\dfrac{1.2}{(2)(-0.014)}$ ◄—— Substitute **1.2** for **b** and -0.014 for a.

≈ 42.9

A driving speed of about 43 mi/h maximizes MPG.

Method ❷ Use a graph.

Graph $y = -0.014x^2 + 1.2x + 6.9$.

The x-coordinate of this point is the driving speed that maximizes MPG.

Maximum
X = 42.857142 Y = 32.614286

Now you are ready for:
Exs. 1–11 on pp. 49–50

A driving speed of about 43 mi/h maximizes MPG.

Use Diagrams to Find Minimums

The map shows several cities in Illinois, Indiana, and Missouri, as well as the interstate highways connecting them. The driving distance between each pair of connected cities is labeled.

◄—— All distances are given in miles.

---

6. **Using Manipulatives** You w... tracing paper or wax paper, ... and a straightedge.

   a. Draw a large scale triangle on your paper.

   b. Fold each pair of sides together and crease to form the angle bisectors. Label the point of intersection of these bisectors I.

   c. Experiment with the compass opening to find the shortest distance from I to one of the sides of the triangle. Show that I is equidistant from the three sides.

   d. With I as the center, draw a circle tangent to the three sides of the triangle.

   e. **Writing** Write a short paragraph about what you learned from this activity.

7. **Open-ended** It is impossible to draw an inscribed circle inside some quadrilaterals. Make drawings or use geometric drawing software to determine which types of quadrilaterals may be circumscribed about circles.

8. A regular hexagon is circumscribed about a circle with radius 1 m.

   a. Find $m \angle AOQ$.

   b. Use trigonometry to find the length of one side of the hexagon.

   c. Find the perimeter of the hexagon.

   d. Find the area of the hexagon.

   e. Julie says the area and the perimeter of this hexagon are the same. Do you agree? Explain.

9. **Open-ended** Repeat Exercise 8 with a regular polygon with more than six sides that is circumscribed about a circle with radius 1 m.

10. $\overline{AB}$ is the side of a regular n-gon circumscribed about circle O. M is the midpoint of $\overline{AB}$.

    a. Find an expression in terms of n for $m \angle MOA$.

    b. Show that the expression you found in part (a) gives the correct value for a regular octagon (see Sample), a regular hexagon (see Exercise 8), and another regular polygon (see Exercise 9).

COMMUNITY PLANNING

Picture some barren mud flats and marshes. To this land come some exiles chased out of their city by invaders from the north. Here they build a new life and a new city full of magnificent buildings, bridges, and squares. Business and culture thrive. This unlikely success story took place over 1400 years ago. The city is Venice.

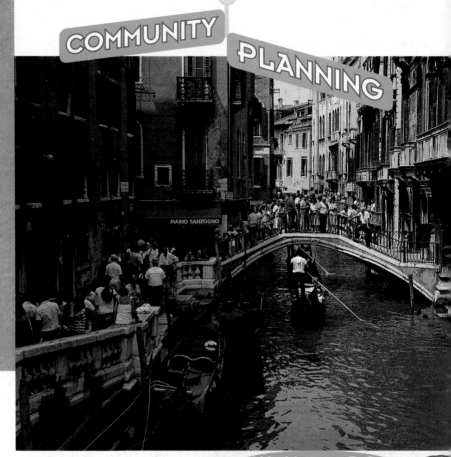

Most cities grow gradually, without any plan. A few, like Washington, D.C., and Brasília are built to a **master plan.**

The Brazilian **architect** Oscar Niemeyer designed the main public buildings of Brasília, the capital of Brazil since 1960. The city was built in the shape of an airplane.

Brasília

This early plan of Washington features a triangle formed by the White House, the Capitol, and the Washington Monument.

Washington, D.C.

Plan a Park

Your project is to plan a park and develop a proposal for funding and building it. First, you will need to survey the people in your community to find out what kind of park will meet the needs of young children through senior citizens, including people with disabilities.

Using the results of your survey, you should develop a park design and proposal. You should use at least three of these math topics from this unit:

➤ algorithms

➤ systematic lists

➤ data displays

➤ systems of equations

➤ network diagrams

➤ linear programming

You can use a scale drawing, CAD software, or a three-dimensional model to present your park design.

Parks are essential to the life of a city. This idea was promoted by landscape architect Frederick Law Olmsted, the designer of America's first park—Central Park in New York City. Olmsted's later work on the 1893 Chicago World's Fair helped set the direction for the emerging field of community planning.

Mary Pat Hodge, seated, and Marsha Johnson served as contractors for a new kind of playground.

Central Park

◄ In 1791 Benjamin Banneker was a surveyor of the land selected for the new capital of the United States.

In Fort Worth, Texas, Debbie Bradshaw and other concerned citizens brought about the construction of a playground accessible to all children. The design was modeled on Janet Simpson's design for Fantasy Landing, in Dallas, the first public playground of this kind in the United States.

Getting Started

Unit Project

For this project you should work in a group of four students. Here are some ideas to help you get started.

☞ Decide where to locate your park. You may make up a piece of land with any dimensions you choose or plan your park to fit a vacant lot in your community.

☞ Visit some parks in your area. Notice what kinds of equipment and facilities they contain and how they are arranged. Also notice who is in the park and what they are doing.

☞ Talk about what questions you should include on your survey. Brainstorm ways to reach people of different ages, cultures, and so on.

☞ Decide whether you will represent your park design with a paper-and-pencil drawing, a CAD drawing, or a three-dimensional model.

Working on the Unit Project

Your work in Unit 1 will help you plan a park.

Related Exercises:

Section 1-1, Exercise 27
Section 1-2, Exercise 30
Section 1-3, Exercise 27
Section 1-4, Exercise 31
Section 1-5, Exercise 40
Section 1-6, Exercise 31
Section 1-7, Exercise 22
Section 1-8, Exercise 23

Alternative Projects p. 61

Can We Talk COMMUNITY PLANNING

➤ How often do you use the parks in your area? What activities do you participate in when you go to a park?

➤ Some local parks and playgrounds are planned, funded, and built by volunteer community groups. Others are built by the parks department of the town or city, or the state. What are some advantages and disadvantages of both approaches?

➤ In the 17 years that it took to build New York City's Central Park, property values near the park went up by a factor of nine, but away from the park they only doubled. Studies show that property values increase when trees are planted on a city block. Why do you think this is?

➤ How are the streets in your community laid out? Do you think the area was built to a plan? Why or why not?

Algorithms

Step by Step

Section 1-1

Focus
Write, apply, and compare step-by-step procedures for solving problems.

Nijo Castle, built in 1603 by the Tokugawa shogun

Visitors to Kyoto, Japan, often use a map like this to find their way around the city.

Talk it Over

1. Give directions for walking from **Nijo Castle** to **Higashi-Hongan Temple.**

2. A tourist at point **X** walking north on Sembon-dori Avenue asked for directions to **Nishi-Hongan Temple.**

   Michiko gave these directions:
   - ➤ Turn right at Imadegawa-dori Avenue.
   - ➤ Turn right at Horikawa-dori Avenue.

   Jiro gave these directions:
   - ➤ Turn around and follow Sembon-dori Avenue past Nijo Castle to Omiya-dori Avenue.
   - ➤ Turn right at Omiya-dori Avenue.
   - ➤ Turn left at Gojo-dori Avenue.
   - ➤ Turn right at Horikawa-dori Avenue.

   a. Which directions are easier to state?

   b. Which are easier to follow?

   c. Which describe a shorter route?

   d. Which directions do you think are better? Why?

BY THE WAY...

Kyoto was the capital of Japan from 794 until 1868. It is still a cultural and artistic center.

1-1 Algorithms

3

A set of step-by-step directions for traveling from one place to another is an example of an *algorithm*. When you break down any process into steps, you are creating an **algorithm.**

Write an algorithm for parallel parking a car on the right side of the street.

Sample Response

1 Determine whether parking is permitted and whether your car will fit in the space between two cars. If the answer to either question is "No," continue looking for a parking space and repeat this step when you find a space.

2 Pull up next to the car in front of the space until the rear bumpers are side by side.

3 Shift into reverse.

4 Turn the front wheels all the way to the right.

5 Slowly back up into the parking space until your front wheels are opposite the rear bumper of the car in front.

6 Turn the steering wheel all the way to the left. Keep backing up until your car is parallel to the curb. If there is not enough room, pull out and go back to Step 2.

7 Check to see whether your car is within a foot of the curb. If it is farther away, pull out and go back to Step 2.

8 Straighten out the front wheels and center the car in the parking space.

Some algorithms, like travel directions, consist of a simple sequence of steps that you follow in order. Other algorithms, like the one for parallel parking, may ask you to make decisions or to complete a *loop.* A **loop** is a group of steps that you repeat either a certain number of times or until some condition is met.

Unit 1 Modeling Problem Situations

Talk it Over

3. In which steps of the algorithm in Sample 1 do you need to make a decision?

4. How do you know when to end each loop in Sample 1?

5. How would you change the algorithm in Sample 1 for parallel parking on the left side of a one-way street?

You can use algorithms to solve problems.

Sample 2

a. Use two different algorithms to solve the inequality $-3x + 9 < 4$.

b. **Writing** Compare the two algorithms you used in part (a).

Sample Response

a. **Method ❶** Use algebra.

$$-3x + 9 < 4$$

$$-3x < -5 \quad \longleftarrow \quad \text{Subtract 9 from both sides.}$$

$$x > \frac{5}{3} \quad \longleftarrow \quad \text{Divide both sides by } -3, \text{ and reverse the inequality symbol.}$$

The solution is all real numbers greater than $\frac{5}{3}$.

Method ❷ Use a graph.

1 Graph $y = -3x + 9$.

2 Graph $y = 4$.

Intersection
X = 1.6666667   Y = 4

3 Estimate the x-coordinate of the intersection point.

The solutions of the inequality are the values of x for which the graph of $y = -3x + 9$ is *below* the graph of $y = 4$.

The solution is all real numbers greater than about 1.7.

Describe the advantages and disadvantages of each algorithm.

b.

The algebraic method gives an exact solution, it is fast, and it is compact. However, I have to remember to reverse the inequality symbol when I divide both sides by a negative number.

The graphical method helps me see the solution region, but the boundary of the region can only be estimated.

6. What are the steps of an algorithm for using algebra to solve any linear inequality with one variable?

7. Can the steps of the algorithm in Method 2 of Sample 2 be done in a different order? If they can, what are the steps of the new algorithm?

Look Back ◄

What are some things to keep in mind when you write a set of directions for solving a problem?

1-1 Exercises and Problems

1. **Reading** How can you tell whether an algorithm contains a loop?

2. **Clothing** A *sari* is a trditional form of dress in some parts of India and Sri Lanka. It is made with a piece of cloth 5 to 7 yd long and about 40 in. wide. Some of the steps in tying and draping a sari are shown out of order. Put these steps in the correct order.

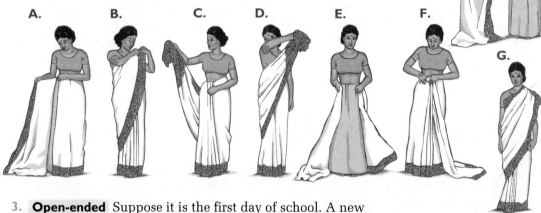

A.   B.   C.   D.   E.   F.

G.

3. **Open-ended** Suppose it is the first day of school. A new student stops you outside your mathematics classroom and asks you for directions to the main office in your school. Write directions from the classroom to the main office.

4. **Using Manipulatives** Work with another student.

   a. Draw a large triangle on a sheet of paper and cut it out.

   b. Use paper folding to construct the three medians of the triangle.

   c. Write an algorithm for the procedure you used in part (b).

   d. Use your algorithm to construct the three medians of an obtuse triangle, an acute triangle, and a right triangle by paper folding.

   e. Use your results in part (d) to make a conjecture about the intersection of the three medians of any triangle.

A *median* of a triangle is a segment from a vertex to the midpoint of the opposite side.

5. **Pottery** Santana Martinez makes coil pots in the traditional Pueblo style. The photographs show some of the key steps she follows. Put the steps in the correct order and write an algorithm for the process.

A.   B.   C.

D.   E.

F.

6. Write an algorithm to solve an equation of the form $ax + b = c$ for x using algebra.

Solve each inequality in two ways.

7. $\frac{x}{14} - 85 > 6$

8. $2x + 3 \le 17$

9. $-5x - 18 \ge 4$

10. $23 > 12 - \frac{x}{9}$

11. Susan and Ryan use different algorithms for estimating a 15% tip for a server in a restaurant. In the state where they live, there is a 5% sales tax on restaurant meals.

Susan's Algorithm	Ryan's Algorithm
1. Move the decimal point one place to the left in the total cost of the meal. 2. Find half the amount in Step 1. 3. Add the amounts in Steps 1 and 2.	Multiply the sales tax by 3.

a. Compare Susan's and Ryan's algorithms. Which do you prefer? Why?

b. Use the fact that $\frac{1}{7} \approx 14\%$ or that $\frac{1}{6} \approx 17\%$ to write another algorithm for estimating a 15% tip.

c. Compare your algorithm from part (b) to Susan's and Ryan's algorithms. Which do you prefer? Why?

12. **Open-ended** Write an algorithm for an everyday activity. Include at least one decision step and one loop in your algorithm.

Over 4000 years ago the Egyptians developed one of the earliest algorithms for multiplication. Today's computers use the idea on which the algorithm is based.

13. Explain how the Egyptian multiplication algorithm works.

14. **Writing** Compare the Egyptian multiplication algorithm to the multiplication algorithm you know. What are some advantages and disadvantages of each?

Examples

15 TECHNOLOGY Wenona used this algorithm with a graphics calculator.

    a. What procedure does Wenona's algorithm perform?

    b. Describe any loops in Wenona's algorithm.

Step 1 Enter a LIST.
Step 2 Set SUM and COUNT to 0.
Step 3 Read a number from LIST.
Step 4 Add the number in Step 3 to SUM.
Step 5 Add 1 to COUNT.
Step 6 Repeat Steps 3–5 until all the numbers in LIST have been read.
Step 7 Divide SUM by COUNT.

Ongoing **ASSESSMENT**

16. **a.** Write two different algorithms for making the change that a salesclerk gives to a customer who has made a purchase.

    b. **Writing** Compare your algorithms.

Review **PREVIEW**

48765

Factor. *(Toolbox Skill 17)*

17. $3x^2 + 4x - 7$ 18. $3x^2 + 15x + 18$ 19. $9x^2 - 64$ 20. $16x^2 + 56x + 49$

Find each number of permutations. *(Toolbox Skill 3)*

21. 4 items arranged 3 at a time   22. 6 items arranged 4 at a time   23. 9 items arranged 5 at a time

Find each number of combinations. *(Toolbox Skill 4)*

24. 7 items chosen 2 at a time   25. 12 items chosen 5 at a time   26. 5 items chosen 4 at a time

 Working on the Unit Project

27. The steps of an algorithm for planning a park are listed out of order. Put the steps in the correct order.

    A. Build the park.   **B.** Choose the location of the park.

    C. Operate the park.   **D.** Prepare a detailed design plan.

    E. Identify the need for a park.   **F.** Identify sources of funds and make a budget.

    G. Survey people in the area and use the results to develop a design concept.

Using Systematic Lists

Get Organized

EXPLORATION

How can you find all the triangles that have a given perimeter?

- **Materials: 15 toothpicks**
- **Work with another student.**

1 Try to build all the different triangles with a perimeter of 15 toothpicks. Record the number of triangles you built and the lengths of their sides. Describe any problem solving strategies and algorithms you used.

2 Compare your results with those of another group. Did you leave out any triangles with side lengths that add up to 15? If you did, how can you improve your strategy?

No triangle is possible in this case. →

In the Exploration, you probably discovered that you cannot build triangles with all combinations of side lengths. For example, you cannot build a triangle with sides that are 8 units, 5 units, and 2 units in length.

TRIANGLE INEQUALITY

The sum of the lengths of any two sides of a triangle is greater than the length of the third side.

$$AC + CB > AB$$
$$CB + BA > AC$$
$$BA + AC > CB$$

Systematic Lists

In the Exploration, you wanted to find all the possible combinations of side lengths that add up to 15. In situations like this, where there are many possibilities to explore, you can use a *systematic,* or organized, list to make sure that you do not leave out or repeat any combinations.

Sample 1

Find all the different triangles that have sides with whole-number lengths and a perimeter of 12.

Sample Response

Step 1 Make a systematic list of all possible combinations of side lengths that add up to 12.

Here is an algorithm that you can use to make a complete list in which no combinations repeat.

> Begin with 1 for the length of side 1. List in order all possible lengths for side 2. Subtract to find each length for side 3. Skip any duplicates.

Step 2 Put an "X" next to all the combinations that do not satisfy the triangle inequality stated on page 9.

There are only three different triangles that have sides with whole-number lengths and a perimeter of 12:

	Side 1	Side 2	Side 3
X	1	1	10
X	1	2	9
X	1	3	8
X	1	4	7
X	1	5	6
X	2	2	8
X	2	3	7
X	2	4	6
	2	5	5
X	3	3	6
	3	4	5
	4	4	4

Talk it Over

1. Why are there no triangles that have a perimeter of 12 and at least one side of length 1?

2. Why does the algorithm used in Sample 1 produce all possible combinations of side lengths that add up to 12?

3. Can you use the same algorithm to list all the different orderings of 12 different letters? Why or why not?

4. Describe another algorithm that you can use to solve Sample 1.

····▶ Now you are ready for:
Exs. 1–14 on p. 13

Customer	Repair	Labor (hours)
Cheney	Replace windshield	3.4
Roux	Replace oil pump	6.0
Feng	Winterize cooling system	0.5
Pinckney	Replace fuel gauge	1.9
Epstein	Replace wheel bearings and cups	3.5
Chopra	Replace disk brake pads (4 wheels)	2.4
Johnson	Replace clutch assembly	4.7
Vega	Replace clutch cable	0.8
Morgan	Replace head lamp	0.3
Benally	Replace timing cover	3.9

In many businesses, managers must make a schedule of tasks and must assign tasks to employees. Often the goal is to use the fewest number of people to complete the tasks.

Sample 2

Paula Hernandez is the manager of an automobile repair service. She lists the number of hours needed to complete the repair work on the cars waiting for service.

Each mechanic works 8 h per day and can make any repair. The repairs can be done in any order.

a. What is the least number of mechanics needed to complete all the repairs in one day?

b. How should Paula Hernandez assign the repairs so that she needs the least number of mechanics to complete all the repairs in one day?

Sample Response

a. Find the minimum number of mechanics.

$$\text{sum of all the repair times} \div \frac{\text{number of hours per day}}{\text{each mechanic works}} = \frac{\text{number of mechanics}}{\text{needed}}$$

$(3.4 + 6.0 + 0.5 + 1.9 + 3.5 + 2.4 + 4.7 + 0.8 + 0.3 + 3.9) \div 8 \approx 3.43$

At least four mechanics are needed.

b. **Problem Solving Strategy:** Make a systematic list.

Try this algorithm for assigning the repair tasks:

> Take each repair in the order listed and assign it to the first mechanic who has time to complete it.

1 Write the time for the first repair. → $3.4 + 0.5 + 1.9 + 0.8 + 0.3 = 6.9$

2 Start a second row, since $3.4 + 6.0 > 8$.

6.0

$3.5 + 2.4 = 5.9$

4.7

3.9

3 Add the next two repairs to the first row, since $3.4 + 0.5 + 1.9 < 8$.

4 Continue in the same way until all repairs are assigned.

The completed list contains five rows, so five mechanics are needed when the tasks are assigned this way.

Continued on next page.

1-2 Using Systematic Lists

11

The algorithm used on page 11 does not result in the least number of mechanics.

Try another algorithm:

1 Order the repair times from greatest to least.

6.0, 4.7, 3.9, 3.5, 3.4, 2.4, 1.9, 0.8, 0.5, 0.3

2 Take each repair task in order and assign it to the first mechanic who has time to complete it.

When you use this algorithm to assign the repairs, only four mechanics are needed.

6.0 + 1.9 = **7.9** ⟶

4.7 + 2.4 + 0.8 = **7.9** ⟶

3.9 + 3.5 + 0.5 = **7.9** ⟶

3.4 + 0.3 = **3.7** ⟶

Mechanic 1	Roux	Pinckney	
Mechanic 2	Johnson	Chopra	Vega
Mechanic 3	Benally	Epstein	Feng
Mechanic 4	Cheney	Morgan	

Talk it Over

5. Describe how to make the list for the second algorithm in Sample 2.

6. Suppose in Sample 2 Paula Hernandez did *not* need to find the least number of mechanics. Compare the two algorithms used in part (b).

7. Think of another algorithm for assigning the repairs in Sample 2. Do you think this algorithm results in the least number of mechanics? Why or why not?

8. Why would Paula Hernandez *not* be able to use the methods shown in part (b) of Sample 2 if some of the customers have to pick up their cars by noon? if more than one mechanic is needed to do some of the repairs?

Look Back

Describe at least two kinds of situations in which "Using a Systematic List" is a useful problem solving strategy. Explain why this strategy is useful in each situation you describe.

▶ **Now you are ready for:**
Exs. 15–30 on pp. 13–15

1-2 Exercises and Problems

1. **Reading** How are the lengths of the three sides of any triangle related?

For each group of measurements in Exercises 2–7, tell whether they can be the lengths of the sides of a triangle. Write *Yes* or *No*.

2. 2 ft, 7 ft, 9 ft

3. 4 in., 4 in., 6 in.

4. 12 cm, 7 cm, 15 cm

5. 7.4 m, 9 m, 14.2 m

6. 27 yd, 4 yd, 30 yd

7. $14\frac{1}{2}$ ft, 11 ft, $28\frac{1}{4}$ ft

8. Find all the sets of four whole numbers with a sum of 16.

Using Manipulatives **For Exercises 9–11, use toothpicks to build all the triangles that have whole-number side lengths and each indicated perimeter.**

9. 17

10. 24

11. 32

12. **a.** Find all the ways that you can make change for a $1 bill using quarters, dimes, and nickels.

   b. Which of the ways that you found in part (a) gives you 65¢ in exact change for a vending machine?

   c. Describe the algorithms you used in parts (a) and (b).

13. **a.** Find all isosceles triangles that have sides with whole-number lengths and a perimeter of 30.

   b. Which of the triangles you found in part (a) has the largest area?

14. **Personal Finance** Sri Iskandar is employed by a company that offers the employee savings plan described in this brochure. Find all the ways that she can contribute under 6% of her pay to the plan and still receive 3% in matching funds from the company.

15. Mel Walker collects objects that are made from cast iron. He wants to mail home the objects he bought for his collection while on vacation. The weights of the objects are:

34 lb 8 oz	26 lb 7 oz
25 lb 5 oz	43 lb 9 oz
38 lb 12 oz	30 lb 6 oz
57 lb	22 lb 8 oz
30 lb 7 oz	18 lb 14 oz

How the Plan Works
Contribute any whole percent from 1% to 15% of pay, divided in any way you wish among these three investments:
- fixed income fund
- mutual fund
- company stock

Company Matching Contributions
- The company matches contributions up to 3% of annual pay.
- Matching contributions are invested in company stock.
- The company matches 50% of your contribution to the fixed income or mutual fund, but 100% of your contribution to company stock.

The maximum weight for a parcel-post package is 70 lb. The fewer packages he mails, the lower his mailing cost will be. How can he package the objects in the least number of parcel-post packages?

16. **Business** How many groomers does Ahmad Jackson need to schedule tomorrow? At this grooming business, the groomers are part-time workers who work 3 h 30 min per day. Treatment to remove fleas takes about 15 min.

1 h 25 min to groom a long-haired dog

Jackson's Pet Grooming

Long-haired dogs to be groomed tomorrow:

Lhasa apso   groom   treat for fleas
Afghan hound   groom
cocker spaniel   groom   treat for fleas
Old English sheep dog   groom
Samoyed   groom   treat for fleas
Maltese   groom
Tibetan terrier   groom   treat for fleas

25 min to groom a cat

Jackson's Pet Grooming

Short-haired dogs to be groomed tomorrow:

basset hound   groom
Doberman pinscher   groom
Boston terrier   treat for fleas
boxer   treat for fleas
dalmatian   groom

20 min to groom a short-haired dog

Jackson's Pet Grooming

Cats to be groomed tomorrow:

Persian   groom
gray tabby   treat for fleas
Maltese   groom   treat for fleas
Manx   treat for fleas
orange tabby   groom
Siamese   groom   treat for fleas

17. **Television** Suppose a television station decides that the commercial breaks during a one-hour program cannot last longer than 2 min. The lengths of the commercials scheduled to run during the program are 60 s, 30 s, 30 s, 15 s, 30 s, 90 s, 60 s, 40 s, 30 s, 15 s, 20 s, 45 s, 60 s, 60 s, 30 s, and 90 s. The station can run the commercials at any time during the hour.

    a. How can the station schedule the commercials to minimize the number of commercial breaks during the program?

    b. **Writing** Describe the algorithm you used in part (a).

18. **Manufacturing** A sporting goods company packages baseballs in cubical boxes with edges that are 2.8 in. long. The company wants to ship the baseballs in cartons that hold four dozen baseballs.

    a. Find all possible dimensions of a shipping carton.

    b. What are the dimensions of the shipping carton that uses the least amount of material?

19. Carpentry Alyssa wants to install shelves on one wall of her bedroom. She made this sketch. How can Alyssa cut the shelves from 12 ft boards in order to use the fewest boards?

Ongoing **ASSESSMENT**

20. Writing The first algorithm used in part (b) of Sample 2 on page 11 is sometimes called the *first-fit* algorithm. The second algorithm used is sometimes called the *first-fit decreasing* algorithm. Do you think these are appropriate names for the algorithms? Why or why not?

Review **PREVIEW**

Solve each inequality in two ways. *(Section 1-1)*

21. $-6 + 4x < 11$
22. $\frac{x}{2} + 18 > -6$
23. $14 \le -3x + 8$
24. $-6x + 17 \le 2$

Find the value of x in each triangle. *(Toolbox Skill 30)*

25.

26.

27.

28.

Use deductive reasoning to reach a conclusion. *(Toolbox Skill 35)*

29. If there is heavy traffic in the city, Corey will arrive at the theater after the curtain goes up. If Corey arrives at the theater after the curtain goes up, he will have to wait until the first act ends to be seated.

 Working on the Unit Project

As you complete Exercise 30, think about how you will decide what kinds of equipment to install in the park you design.

30. A playground designer plans to include 15 pieces of equipment in a new playground. A survey of the children in the community and their parents shows that at least three swing sets, three slides, three whirligigs, and three sandboxes should be installed.

a. Find all the possible combinations of swing sets, slides, whirligigs, and sandboxes that the designer can include.

b. Suppose the survey shows that swings are twice as popular as the other types of equipment. How many of each type of equipment should the designer include?

Using Statistics

TRE/\DS

········Focus
**Use statistics and data
displays to draw
conclusions.**

Mean Monthly Temperatures (°F)

The graph for Caracas is red. The graph for Alice Springs is green.

Caracas

Alice Springs

Both Alice Springs, Australia, and Caracas, Venezuela, have a **mean,** or average, annual temperature of about 70°F. The *line graph* compares their mean monthly temperatures.

Talk it Over

1. If you want temperatures near 70°F, any time of the year, which city should you visit?

2. If you want temperatures near 70°F, which city should you visit in January? in July? Why?

3. The mean annual rainfall is 63.6 in. for Alice Springs and 213.4 in. for Caracas.

   a. Do you think it rains more every month in Caracas than in Alice Springs?

   b. Does this statistic affect your decision to visit either city? Explain.

A statistic, such as the mean, summarizes a data set. A single statistic can be misleading. It is important to examine statistics and data displays carefully before you draw any conclusions.

You can use other data displays besides line graphs. A **box-and-whisker plot** is a data display that divides a data set into four parts. Each part represents about 25% of the data. The box contains the middle 50% of the data.

Mean Monthly Temperatures in Alice Springs, Australia (°F)

The smallest data item, or **lower extreme**, is about 53.5.

The largest data item, or **upper extreme**, is about 84.

The median of the lower half of the data set, or **lower quartile**, is about 59.

The **median**, which divides the data set in half, is about 71.

The median of the upper half of the data set, or **upper quartile**, is about 81.5.

Sample 1

The box-and-whisker plots show the gas mileage for some 1993 cars. *Gas mileage* is how far a car can travel on 1 gal of gasoline.

a. Which type(s) of cars have models with low gas mileage?

b. About what percent of compact cars have higher gas mileage than any large car? Explain.

c. If you want high gas mileage, which type of car should you buy based on the box-and-whisker plots? Why?

Gas Mileage (miles per gallon)
(EPA, city and highway combined)

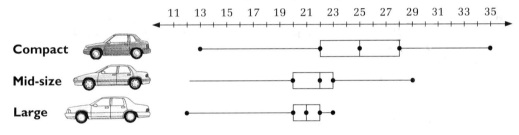

Sample Response

a. All three types of cars have models with low gas mileage. The lower extreme for all cars is about 12 or 13.

b. Between 50% and 75% of compact cars have higher gas mileage than any large car. The lower quartile for compact cars and the upper extreme for large cars are both about 23.

c. You should consider buying a compact car. Between 50% and 75% of compact cars have higher gas mileage than any large car. Since the upper quartile for compact cars and the upper extreme for mid-size cars are close together, about 25% of compact cars have higher gas mileage than any mid-size car.

Another type of data display is a *scatter plot*. A **scatter plot** is a graph that shows the relationship between two data sets.

1993 Law School Statistics		
Law school	Out-of-state tuition (dollars)	% employed 6 months after graduation
A	18,548	100
B	17,750	97
C	20,186	98
D	19,095	98
E	19,740	97
F	19,400	97
G	12,111	84
H	18,170	94
I	18,995	90
J	15,678	96
K	12,202	87
L	12,544	96
M	19,156	88
N	10,190	93
O	11,529	89
P	7,280	85
Q	17,000	94
R	13,600	88
S	17,720	92
T	9,963	80

The table shows data for 20 law schools in the United States.

a. Make a scatter plot of the relationship between out-of-state tuition and percent of graduates employed six months after graduation.

b. Describe any trends suggested by the scatter plot.

c. Explain how a person applying to law school can use this scatter plot.

Sample Response

a. Plot the ordered pairs (18,548, 100), (17,750, 97), and so on.

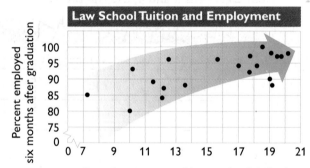

b. The scatter plot rises to the right. It appears that as out-of-state tuition increases, the percent of students employed six months after graduation also increases.

c. A person applying to law school may decide to attend a more expensive school if it means a better chance of getting a job after graduation.

Talk it Over

4. Does it matter whether you graph the percent employed on the horizontal or vertical axis?

5. If the out-of-state tuition at law school Z is $15,000, about what percent of its graduates would you expect to be employed six months after graduation?

Look Back

Do you have to put the items of a data set in numerical order to make a line graph? a box-and-whisker plot? a scatter plot? Explain.

1-3 Exercises and Problems

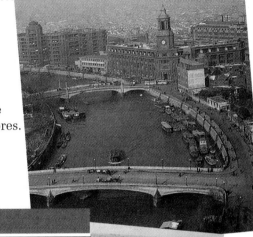

1. **Reading** How would a box-and-whisker plot for the mean monthly temperatures in Caracas differ from the one for Alice Springs? (See pages 16 and 17.)

2. Find the lower extreme, the lower quartile, the median, the upper quartile, and the upper extreme of these bowling scores.

123, 254, 100, 121, 143, 93, 205,
66, 111, 176, 89, 189, 205, 75, 100

Meteorology For Exercises 3 and 4, use the table.

Mean Monthly Temperature (°C)												
	Jan.	Feb.	Mar.	Apr.	May	June	July	Aug.	Sept.	Oct.	Nov.	Dec.
Mexico City, Mexico	12	13	16	18	20	19	18	19	18	16	14	13
Shanghai, China	-4	6	10	14	21	26	28	28	25	19	12	6

3. What is the mean annual temperature of each city?

4. a. Make a box-and-whisker plot for each city using the same number line.

   b. **Writing** Write three statements comparing the temperatures in the two cities. Use the box-and-whisker plots to justify your statements.

   c. **Open-ended** Do you think it is better to use a line graph to compare these data? Explain.

Seasonal change in Shanghai, China

For Exercises 5 and 6, use the scatter plot.

5. a. Describe any trend(s) suggested by the scatter plot.

   b. Does every refrigerator represented on the scatter plot follow the trend(s) you found in part (a)? Explain.

6. About how much would you expect to pay each year to operate a refrigerator with a freezer on top that sells for $470?

Refrigerators with a Freezer on Top

Annual operating cost (dollars) vs Price (dollars)

Television The A. C. Nielsen Company rated the prime-time television series of the four major commercial networks for the 1994 season. A higher rating indicates a larger percent of homes watching.

Network Ratings

7. Which network had the lowest rated series in 1994?

8. About what percent of NBC series had higher ratings than all Fox series in 1994? Explain.

9. Which network had the best overall prime-time ratings in 1994? Explain.

10. **Open-ended** The Nielsen rating system includes both one-hour and half-hour prime-time series. Do you think one-hour shows should be rated separately from half-hour shows? Why or why not?

Career Atmospheric scientists in California measured the thickness of the ozone layer over a city with two instruments, one in a satellite in space and one at ground level. This scatter plot compares the two readings over 100 days.

11. What do you notice about the scales on the horizontal and vertical axes?

12. a. Since the instruments measure the same thing, what do you expect about the readings from each instrument?

    b. Does the scatter plot support your expectation?

13. **Open-ended** Why do you think scientists would want to compare the readings of two instruments measuring the same thing?

Ozone Readings

Unit 1 Modeling Problem Situations

14. Group Activity Work with another student.

Sociology In a recent study of 36 United States cities, researchers measured how willing people are to help people they do not know.

a. **Research** Find the population density of each city by dividing the population by the area of the city in square miles.

b. **T E C H N O L O G Y** Use a graphics calculator or graphing software.

Alternative Approach Work with another student.

Make a scatter plot of the relationship between ranking and population density for these cities.

c. Describe any trends suggested by the scatter plot.

Volunteers serving a free Thanksgiving dinner in San Antonio, Texas

Rank	City	Rank	City	Rank	City
1	Paterson, N.J.	13	San Francisco, Cal.	25	Columbus, Ohio
2	New York City, N.Y.	14	Buffalo, N.Y.	26	Indianapolis, Ind.
3	Los Angeles, Cal.	15	Bakersfield, Cal.	27	Chattanooga, Tenn.
4	Fresno, Cal.	16	Atlanta, Ga.	28	East Lansing, Mich.
5	Philadelphia, Pa.	17	Springfield, Mass.	29	Detroit, Mich.
6	Shreveport, La.	18	San Diego, Cal.	30	St. Louis, Mo.
7	Chicago, Ill.	19	San Jose, Cal.	31	Louisville, Ky
8	Providence, R.I.	20	Dallas, Texas	32	Knoxville, Tenn.
9	Boston, Mass.	21	Santa Barbara, Cal.	33	Memphis, Tenn
10	Salt Lake City, Utah	22	Worcester, Mass.	34	Nashville, Tenn.
11	Sacramento, Cal.	23	Kansas City, Mo.	35	Houston, Texas
12	Youngstown, Ohio	24	Canton, Ohio	36	Rochester, N.Y.

Least willing to help → (rank 1)

Most willing to help → (rank 36)

Ongoing **ASSESSMENT**

15. Writing Write an algorithm for drawing a box-and-whisker plot.

Review **PREVIEW**

Find the whole-number lengths of the sides of all triangles with each indicated perimeter. *(Section 1-2)*

16. 13   **17.** 14   **18.** 18   **19.** 26

For the graph of each function in Exercises 20–22: *(Toolbox Skill 28)*

a. **Find an equation for the line of symmetry.**   b. **Find the y-intercept.**

20. $y = 4x^2 + 3x + 8$ **21.** $y = -3x^2 + 11x$ **22.** $y = 7x^2 - 5x + 1$

Solve each system of equations. *(Toolbox Skill 21)*

23. $3x - 2y = 12$
$y = 4x + 7$

24. $5x - 18 = 4y$
$y = 3x$

25. $x = 6y - 8$
$-5x + 7y = 11$

26. $x = 19 - 2y$
$x = 5y + 4$

Working on the Unit Project

As you complete Exercise 27, think about how you will use the results of your survey to make decisions about what facilities to include in your park plan.

27. **Writing** Suppose a park planner can include only three sports facilities in a new park. Which three sports should the park offer? Make at least two data displays that will help you answer. Explain your choices. The numbers in the table are in thousands.

People Who Play Selected Recreational Sports in the United States (1991)					
Sport	Male	Female	Ages 7–17	Ages 18–34	Ages 35 and over
Baseball	13,640	2,908	10,040	4,312	2,197
Softball	11,878	7,768	6,644	8,997	4,006
Basketball	19,151	6,999	12,960	9,277	3,913
Soccer	6,657	3,935	7,322	2,010	660
Swimming	30,833	35,348	20,203	21,899	24,080
Tennis	9,207	7,495	4,053	7,645	5,005
Volleyball	11,495	11,091	6,863	11,146	4,579

Unit 1 CHECKPOINT

SALAD CITY EXPRESS

GREEN SALADS
garden $1.89
Greek $2.29
chef's $2.49
salad sampler $2.99

SIDE ORDERS   sm   lg
cole slaw $.89 $1.39
potato salad $1.19 $1.59

BEVERAGES   sm   lg
herbal tea $.99 $1.49
juice $1.39 $1.89

1. **Writing** Explain why box-and-whisker plots are useful for comparing two data sets.

2. Write an algorithm for choosing a movie to see with a group of friends. Include at least one loop.   **1-1**

3. Use this menu. Suppose a meal consists of a salad, a side order, and a beverage. Find all meals that cost less than $4. Assume that prices include tax.   **1-2**

Use these box-and-whisker plots.

4. About what percent of the countries represented used less than the equivalent of 400 million metric tons of coal each year?   **1-3**

5. Describe any trends shown by the graph.

Amount of Energy Used by the Top 20 Energy-Using Countries
(equivalent of millions of metric tons of coal)

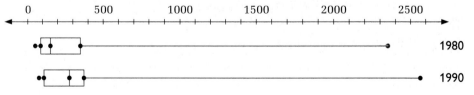

Using Graphs and Equations

Focus

Use graphs and equations
to model situations and
make decisions.

Making The Right Decision

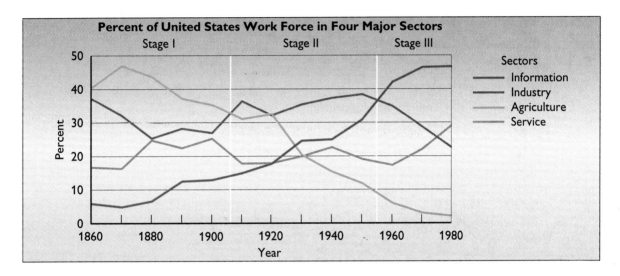

Percent of United States Work Force in Four Major Sectors

Stage I   Stage II   Stage III

Sectors
Information
Industry
Agriculture
Service

Percent

Year

The graph shows how the percent of workers in four sectors
of the United States economy changed from 1860 to 1980.

Agriculture in the United States in the
last century and today

Talk it Over

1. Why do you think Stage I is called the *Agriculture Age*?

2. a. What happens to the Agriculture and Industry graphs at
the end of Stage I?

   b. About what year did Stage I end?

3. a. What do you think Stage II is called?

   b. About what year did Stage II end?

4. What do you think Stage III is called? Why?

By comparing two graphs, you can determine when a quantity is
greater than, less than, or equal to another quantity. This can
help you make decisions.

Sample 1

Camille has saved $600 and wants to open her first checking account. Which bank offers the lowest monthly charge?

Monthly Charges

Central Bank: $6.00 plus $.35 for each check you write

Main St. Bank: $3.00 plus $.75 for each check you write

Co-op Bank: $10.00, no matter how many checks you write

Sample Response

Problem Solving Strategy: Use a graph.

Model the information with equations.

Let x = the number of checks Camille writes each month.

Let y = the total monthly charge.

$$\left.\begin{array}{l} \text{Central Bank: } y = 6 + 0.35x \\ \text{Main St. Bank: } y = 3 + 0.75x \\ \text{Co-op Bank: } y = 10 \end{array}\right\}$$ Camille's monthly charge depends on the number of checks she expects to write.

Graph the equations on the same set of axes. Find the x-coordinate of the points of intersection.

The Central Bank graph is below the others for $7.5 < x < 11.4$.

$y = 10$
$y = 6 + 0.35x$
$y = 3 + 0.75x$

Intersection
X = 7.5   Y = 8.625

Intersection
X = 11.428571   Y = 10

The Co-op Bank graph is below the others for $x > 11.4$.

The Main St. Bank graph is below the others for $0 \le x < 7.5$. Since the number of checks must be a whole number, the monthly charges at Main St. Bank are the lowest for $x \le 7$.

Camille should choose:

Main St. Bank if she expects to write 7 or fewer checks each month.

Central Bank if she expects to write 8, 9, 10, or 11 checks each month.

Co-op Bank if she expects to write 12 or more checks each month.

Talk it Over

5. Why were only the x-coordinates of the points of intersection considered? What do the y-coordinates mean in this situation?

6. Why does Camille not have to consider the intersection of the graphs of $y = 3 + 0.75x$ and $y = 10$?

Break-Even Point

BY THE WAY...

A break-even chart or graph is one of the standard tools used by economists. It shows at a glance the point where loss ends and profit begins.

Until its income exceeds its expenses, a business loses money. When its income equals its expenses, a business has reached the *break-even point.*

Sample 2

Suppose the mortgage, taxes, and insurance for a 100-room motel in Joplin, Missouri, are $120,000 per year. Each occupied room costs $25 per day to maintain. Each unoccupied room costs $5 per day to maintain. The room rental charge is $35 per day.

The motel is open 365 days a year. What must the average number of occupied rooms be each day in order for this motel business to break even at the end of a year?

Sample Response

Step 1 Separate expenses from income.

Expenses: mortgage, taxes, insurance, maintenance
Income: room rental

Step 2 Write equations to model the situation.

Let r = the average number of occupied rooms each day.

Let E = the total annual expenses.

$$E = \begin{array}{c}\text{mortgage, taxes,}\\ \text{and insurance}\end{array} + \begin{array}{c}\text{annual maintenance,}\\ \text{occupied rooms}\end{array} + \begin{array}{c}\textbf{annual maintenance,}\\ \textbf{unoccupied rooms}\end{array}$$

$$= 120{,}000 \qquad + \qquad 365 \cdot 25r \qquad + \qquad 365 \cdot 5\underbrace{(100 - r)}_{\text{number of unoccupied rooms}}$$

$$= 120{,}000 + 9125r + 182{,}500 - 1825r$$

$$= 302{,}500 + 7300r$$

Let I = annual income from room rental.

$$I = 365 \cdot 35r$$

$$= 12{,}775r$$

Step 3 Find the break-even point, when $I = E$.

Method ❶ Use a graph.

Graph the equations on the same set of axes.

The average number of occupied rooms each day should be about 55.3.

$y = 302{,}500 + 7300x$

$y = 12{,}775x$

Intersection
X = 55.25114   Y = 705833.33

The break-even point is the *x*-coordinate.

Method ❷ Use algebra.

$$302{,}500 + 7300r = 12{,}775r$$

$$55.3 \approx r$$

The average number of occupied rooms each day should be about 55.3.

7. Why can you graph both the expenses and the income equations in Sample 2 on the same set of axes?

8. Explain how to solve Sample 1 with algebra. Which method, *algebra* or *a graph*, do you prefer for Sample 1? for Sample 2?

Look Back ◄──────────────────────────────────────

Why are intersection points important when you make a decision based on a graph?

1-4 Exercises and Problems

1. **Reading** What can you find out by comparing graphs on the same set of axes?

Business The three graphs represent bids submitted to a large medical group practice by three firms that process patient bills.

➤ Physicians' Services (PS) bid a flat fee plus a charge per bill.

➤ Doctors' Service (DS) bid a flat fee less than that of PS, plus a charge per bill.

➤ Human Resources (HR) bid a charge per bill with no flat fee.

Bill Processing Bids

For Exercises 2–4, choose the letter of the graph that models each bid.

2. PS   3. DS   4. HR

5. Estimate the flat fee of the PS bid.

6. Which firm charges the most per bill? How do you know?

7. Which firm's bid is the lowest for processing 80,000 bills per year?

8. Let x = the number of bills that the medical group expects to process next year. Estimate the values of x for which the DS bid is the lowest.

Graph each pair of equations and estimate the break-even point.

9. $E = 500 + 3.5x$ 10. $E = 127 + 3x$ 11. $E = 0.52 + 0.04x$ 12. $E = 8200 + 73x$
   $I = 5x$ $I = 25x$ $I = 0.06x$ $I = 1436x$

Use algebra to find each break-even point. Round decimal answers to the nearest tenth.

13. $E = 220 + 4.3x$ 14. $E = 99 + 0.01x$ 15. $E = 725 + x$ 16. $E = 18 + 22x$
    $I = 14x$ $I = 0.28x$ $I = 6.5x$ $I = 24x$

Gourmet

12 rolls at $21 per roll

Autumn

14 rolls at $16 per roll

17. **Interior Decorating** Charlie Ruben wants to wallpaper his dining room. DJ Paperers charges $18 per hour for labor to hang plain paper such as Gourmet. An extra $5 per hour is added for patterned paper such as Autumn, since a helper is needed to finish the job in the same amount of time.

   a. Write two equations to model the cost of wallpapering Charlie Ruben's dining room with each type of paper. Be sure to include the cost of materials.

   b. Which paper is less expensive to hang if each job takes 4 h? 6 h?

18. **Consumer Economics** Anna Croft wants to rent a 15-foot truck for a day. She makes a list of rental charges at four companies.

   U-Rent: $19.95 per day plus $.59 per mile

   MacRents: $44.95 per day plus $.39 per mile

   Wiley's: $79.95 per day plus $.22 per mile

   Zeke's: $150 per day with unlimited mileage

   a. Write an equation that models each company's rental charges.

   b. Which company should she choose? Why?

connection to SCIENCE

19. A rule of thumb for converting temperatures from Celsius to Fahrenheit is to double the Celsius reading and add 30. The formula is $F = 1.8C + 32$.

   a. Write an equation that models the rule of thumb.

   b. Graph both equations on the same set of axes.

   c. Find the Celsius reading that gives the same Fahrenheit reading for both the rule of thumb and the formula.

   d. Suppose that you consider the rule of thumb estimate good only if it is within 5°F of the actual reading. Use your graph from part (b) to find the values of C that meet this condition.

   e. **Open-ended** What estimation error do you consider reasonable? What values of C meet your condition?

TECHNOLOGY NOTE

See the Technology Handbook, p. 600, for moving between graphs to see different y-values for the same x-value.

20. Alejandro earns extra money by typing papers and reports. He estimates that his per-hour cost for supplies is about $1.25. He decides to invest in a new word processor that sells for $559.

   a. Write an equation that models Alejandro's expenses.

   b. Alejandro charges $12 per hour for typing. Write an equation that models Alejandro's income.

   c. If Alejandro averages only five hours of typing per week, how many weeks will it take him to break even?

21. **Open-ended** Describe a situation that can be modeled by these expense and income equations:

$$E = 52.50 + 1.50x \qquad I = 3.25x$$

22. Recycling Cardboard that is *baled* is easier to recycle and can be sold to earn money.

Baled cardboard is compacted and bound with wire.

a. Suppose it costs $290 a month to lease a baling machine. The cost of baling wire is $3.38 per ton of cardboard, and the cost of labor is $27.30 per ton. Write an equation that models monthly costs.

b. Suppose a city receives $35 per baled ton of cardboard. Write an equation that models monthly income.

c. How many tons of cardboard does the city in part (b) have to bale each month to break even?

Ongoing **ASSESSMENT**

23. Writing How can you decide when to use a graph and when to use algebra to find a break-even point?

Review **PREVIEW**

For each data set, find the lower extreme, the lower quartile, the median, the upper quartile, and the upper extreme. *(Section 1-3)*

24. 25, 83, 44, 59, 26, 37, 49, 48, 68, 75, 39, 48   **25.** 80, 113, 140, 95, 87, 102, 117, 90, 94, 115

Find the exact measure of each unknown side in each triangle. *(Toolbox Skill 30)*

26.

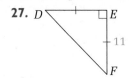

27. D ▢ E, 11, F

28. K, $5\sqrt{3}$, 60°, J ▢ L

29. Z, 22, 45°, X 45° ▢ Y

30. Add matrices B and C. *(Toolbox Skill 10)*

$$B = \begin{bmatrix} 11 & 36 & 15 \\ 2 & 34 & 8 \end{bmatrix} \quad C = \begin{bmatrix} 1.6 & 42 & 13 \\ 8 & 36 & 1 \end{bmatrix}$$

Working on the Unit Project

As you complete Exercise 31, think about how you can use graphs and equations to make the decisions needed to develop your park proposal.

31. A community group is writing a proposal for a new park. Since the park project began, the population in the area has grown. To handle the expected increase in park use, the group must add an additional employee to the proposed park staff or schedule 35 hours of overtime for the present staff. Should the group add another full-time employee or ask the present staff to work overtime? Explain your choice.

PARK WORKERS' WAGES AND HOURS
Hours: 35 hours per week
Regular hourly wages: Experienced—$8 New—$7
Overtime pay: Time-and-a-half (over 40 hours per week)
Benefits: 28% of earnings

Using Systems of Equations

Focus

Use systems of equations to solve problems.

Sound Systems

STAGE

PREMIER

PREFERRED

Suppose a concert by a popular band involves these expenses:

➤ The band charges $20,000 plus 75% of the income from ticket sales.

➤ The costs for renting a 10,000-seat auditorium and paying for security, insurance, publicity, and so on are an additional $60,000.

The concert promoter wants to sell two types of tickets, preferred and premier.

Talk it Over

1. What limits the total number of tickets that can be sold?

2. Which type of ticket should be sold at a higher price? Why?

3. What other factors, besides the expenses given above, should the concert promoter consider when setting ticket prices?

A concert promoter thinks a concert will be a sellout when tickets are priced as shown. The promoter needs to know how many of each type of ticket to sell to make a $5000 profit. Write two equations that model this situation. Use the information on page 29 about the number of seats and the expenses.

STAGE

PREMIER $36

PREFERRED $28

Sample Response

Let x = the number of preferred tickets. Let y = the number of premier tickets.

number of preferred tickets + number of premier tickets = **number of tickets sold**

$$x \quad + \quad y \quad = \quad 10{,}000 \quad \longleftarrow \text{first equation}$$

ticket income − expenses for band, auditorium, and so on = **profit**

income from $28 tickets

$$28x + 36y - [20{,}000 + 0.75(28x + 36y) + 60{,}000] = 5000 \quad \longleftarrow \text{second equation}$$

income from **$36 tickets**

These equations model the situation.

$$x + y = 10{,}000$$

$$7x + 9y = 85{,}000 \quad \longleftarrow \text{Simplify the second equation.}$$

A **system of equations** consists of two or more equations involving the same variables, as in Sample 1.

Solve the system of equations: $x + y = 10{,}000$
$7x + 9y = 85{,}000$

Sample Response

Method ❶ Use algebra.

$$y = 10{,}000 - x \quad \longleftarrow \text{Solve one equation for } y.$$

$$7x + 9(10{,}000 - x) = 85{,}000 \quad \longleftarrow \begin{array}{l}\text{Substitute } 10{,}000 - x \text{ for } y \\ \text{in the other equation.}\end{array}$$

$$x = 2500$$

$$x + y = 10{,}000$$

$$2500 + y = 10{,}000 \quad \longleftarrow \begin{array}{l}\text{To find } y, \text{ substitute} \\ 2500 \text{ for } x \text{ in either of} \\ \text{the original equations.}\end{array}$$

$$y = 7500$$

Method ❷ Use a graph.

Find the intersection point.

$7x + 9y = 85{,}000$

$x + y = 10{,}000$

Intersection
X = 2500   Y = 7500

The promoter should sell 2500 preferred tickets and 7500 premier tickets.

Matrix Equations

Student Resources Toolbox
pp. 632–634 *Operations with
Matrices*

You can write a system of linear equations as a *matrix equation*.

System of Equations	**Matrix Equation**

$$ax + by = c$$
$$dx + ey = f$$

coefficient $\begin{bmatrix} a & b \\ d & e \end{bmatrix}\begin{bmatrix} x \\ y \end{bmatrix} = \begin{bmatrix} c \\ f \end{bmatrix}$ constant
matrix   matrix

For a system with two variables,
a matrix equation has the form:
$$A\begin{bmatrix} x \\ y \end{bmatrix} = B$$

The solution of this matrix equation is $\begin{bmatrix} x \\ y \end{bmatrix} = A^{-1}B.$

inverse matrix

Sample 3

**Write the system in Sample 1 as a matrix equation and use a
graphics calculator to solve.**

T E C H N O L O G Y   N O T E

To use matrices, see Technology Handbook, p. 603.

Sample Response

System of Equations	**Matrix Equation**	**Solution of Matrix Equation**

$$x + y = 10{,}000$$
$$7x + 9y = 85{,}000$$

$\begin{bmatrix} 1 & 1 \\ 7 & 9 \end{bmatrix}\begin{bmatrix} x \\ y \end{bmatrix} = \begin{bmatrix} 10{,}000 \\ 85{,}000 \end{bmatrix}$

Enter as   Enter as
matrix *A*.   matrix *B*.

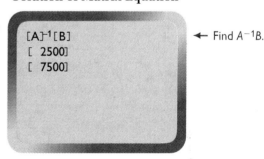

← Find $A^{-1}B$.

The resulting matrix tells you that the promoter should sell 2500 preferred
tickets and 7500 premier tickets.

······▶ **Now you are ready for:**
Exs. 1–12 on p. 34

Systems of Linear Equations with Three Variables

A linear equation with two variables, x and y, can be written in the form

$$ax + by = c.$$

A **linear equation with three variables**, x, y, and z, can be written in the form

$$ax + by + cz = d.$$

Talk it Over

4. a. Is $(-1, 2)$ a solution of $3x + 4y = 5$? Explain.

   b. Is $(-1, 2, 3)$ a solution of $3x + 4y + 2z = 11$? Explain.

   c. Is $(-1, 2, -3)$ a solution of $3x + 4y + 2z = 11$? Explain.

5. a. Is $(-1, 2)$ a solution of this system? Explain.

   $$3x + 4y = 5$$
   $$2x + 5y = 8$$

   b. Is $(-1, 2, 3)$ a solution of this system? Why?

   $$3x + 4y + 2z = 11$$
   $$2x + 5y - z = 3$$
   $$x - 2y + 4z = 6$$

This point is the graph of the *ordered triple* $(2, -3, 4)$.

You can graph a solution of a linear equation with three variables in a three-dimensional coordinate system with an x-axis, a y-axis, and a z-axis that meet at right angles at the origin O.

The graph of *all* the solutions of a linear equation with three variables is a plane. The graph of a system of three linear equations with three variables is three planes. Only those points that are common to all three planes are solutions of the system.

no common point of intersection   one common point of intersection   many common points of intersection

STAGE

VIP $52

PREMIER $36

PREFERRED $28

Suppose the promoter decides to sell three types of tickets for the concert described on page 29. The promoter wants the number of preferred tickets to equal the number of premier and VIP tickets combined. How many of each type of ticket must be sold in order to make a profit of $8000 when the concert is a sellout?

Sample Response

Let x = the number of preferred tickets, y = the number of premier tickets, and z = the number of VIP tickets.

1 Write three equations.

number of preferred tickets	+	number of premier tickets	+	number of VIP tickets	=	total number of tickets sold
x	+	y	+	z	=	10,000

ticket income − expenses for band, auditorium, and so on = profit

$$28x + 36y + 52z - [20{,}000 + 0.75(28x + 36y + 52z) + 60{,}000] = 8000$$

number of preferred tickets	=	number of premier tickets	+	number of VIP tickets
x	=	y	+	z

$$x + y + z = 10{,}000$$
$$7x + 9y + 13z = 88{,}000$$
$$x - y - z = 0$$

2 Rewrite each equation in the form $ax + by + cz = d$.

$$\begin{bmatrix} 1 & 1 & 1 \\ 7 & 9 & 13 \\ 1 & -1 & -1 \end{bmatrix} \begin{bmatrix} x \\ y \\ z \end{bmatrix} = \begin{bmatrix} 10{,}000 \\ 88{,}000 \\ 0 \end{bmatrix}$$

3 Write the matrix equation $A \begin{bmatrix} x \\ y \\ z \end{bmatrix} = B$.

$$\begin{bmatrix} x \\ y \\ z \end{bmatrix} = \begin{bmatrix} 5000 \\ 3000 \\ 2000 \end{bmatrix}$$

4 Use a graphics calculator to solve.

The promoter must sell 5000 preferred tickets, 3000 premier tickets, and 2000 VIP tickets to make a profit of $8000.

Talk it Over

6. **a.** The last equation in Sample 4 can be rewritten as $x = y + z$. Does substituting for x in the other two equations produce a system that you can solve with algebra? Explain.

   b. Is it possible to solve Sample 4 with a graphics calculator, as in Method 2 of Sample 2? Why or why not?

▶ Now you are ready for:
Exs. 13–40 on pp. 35–36

Look Back ◂

How is solving a system of linear equations with three variables like solving a system of linear equations with two variables? How is it different?

1-5 Exercises and Problems

1. **Reading** Samples 2 and 3 show three methods for solving a system of equations. Which of these methods do you prefer? Why?

2. **Open-ended** Make a chart or a concept map about methods for solving systems of equations.

Solve. When necessary, round decimal answers to the nearest tenth.

3. $3x + 2y = 1$
   $x + y = 1$

4. $x - y = 7$
   $2x + y = 2$

5. $4x + 2y = 1$
   $-6x + 4y = 9$

6. $3x - y = 12$
   $2x + 3y = 74$

7. $x + y = 7000$
   $5x + 7y = 39{,}000$

8. $2x - 3y = 5000$
   $4x - 5y = 45{,}000$

9. $0.54x + 3.2y = 7.9$
   $2.1x - 4.5y = 2.3$

10. $570x - 190y = 3400$
    $320x + 780y = 4600$

11. $\frac{3}{4}x + \frac{1}{2}y = -1$
    $\frac{5}{8}x + \frac{2}{5}y = 2$

12. **Aviation** In the atmosphere over the United States, winds generally blow from west to east. These winds affect the travel time of airplanes. A flight from San Francisco to New York may take 5.5 h, but a flight from New York to San Francisco in the same airplane may take an hour longer.

   a. The distance between San Francisco and New York is about 2800 mi. Use the formula

   distance = travel speed × time

   to write a system of two equations with two variables.

   b. Find the airplane's speed (without the wind). Round your answer to the nearest tenth.

Traveling against the wind:
$$\frac{\text{travel}}{\text{speed}} = \frac{\text{speed of}}{\text{airplane}} - \frac{\text{speed of}}{\text{wind}}$$

Traveling with the wind:
$$\frac{\text{travel}}{\text{speed}} = \frac{\text{speed of}}{\text{airplane}} + \frac{\text{speed of}}{\text{wind}}$$

For Exercises 13–15, suppose planes *P*, *Q*, and *R* represent a system of equations. Tell whether each system has a solution. Explain.

13.

14.

15.

16. **Group Activity** Work with another student.

Writing Not having his graphics calculator handy, Dana decided to solve the system shown using algebra. He began by solving the first equation for *z* in terms of *x* and *y*, but he was not sure what to do next. Show Dana how to proceed, giving him explanations along the way.

$$x + y + z = 2$$
$$x - y + z = 6$$
$$x - y - z = 8$$

$$z = -x - y + 2$$

Solve. Round decimal answers to the nearest tenth.

17. $x + y = 7$
$y + z = 8$
$x + 2z = 2$

18. $2x - y = 7$
$6x + 3z = 9$
$x + 2y + 3z = -4$

19. $5x + y + 6z = 3$
$x - y + 10z = 9$
$5x + y - 2z = -9$

20. $7x + 2y + z = -10$
$5x + 5y + z = 13$
$2x - y + z = -5$

21. $3x + y - 4z = -3$
$5x + y - z = -6$
$10x + 4y + 5z = 15$

22. $-2x + 2y + 2z = 5$
$2x + 2y - z = 3$
$2x + 4y - z = 4$

connection to **PHYSICS**

Suppose an electric circuit has three resistors wired to an 18-volt battery. To find the currents I_A, I_B, and I_C (measured in amperes) across the resistors in this circuit, you can use these laws:

Current law:	The sum of the currents entering a node equals the sum of the currents leaving the node.
Voltage law:	Around any closed loop, the sum of the voltage drops across the resistors is equal to the voltage supplied by the battery.

23. Use the current law to write an equation relating I_A, I_B, and I_C at the labeled node.

24. To calculate the voltage *V* (measured in volts) across a resistor, you use the formula $V = RI$, where the resistance *R* is measured in ohms and the current *I* is measured in amperes. Use this formula and the voltage law to write an equation for the closed loop containing resistors *A* and *B*.

25. Use the voltage law to write an equation for the closed loop running from the battery, through resistors *A* and *C*, and back to the battery.

26. Solve the system of three equations that you wrote in Exercises 23–25.

27. **Business** Koretta Jackson is the manager of *Koretta's Kitchen*, a new restaurant, which will be open from 6:00 A.M. to 11:00 P.M. daily. She must hire workers to cover three shifts.

> Shift I: 6:00 A.M.–2:00 P.M.
> Shift II: 11:00 A.M.–7:00 P.M.
> Shift III: 4:00 P.M.–12:00 midnight

She needs 11 workers during the lunch rush from 11:00 A.M. to 2:00 P.M. and 16 workers during the dinner rush from 4:00 P.M. to 7:00 P.M. Her budget allows her to hire 20 workers. How many should she hire for each shift?

Ongoing ASSESSMENT

28. **Open-ended** Write a system of three linear equations that has the solution (1, 5, 23). Check your answer by solving your system.

Review PREVIEW

Use algebra to find the break-even point when E = expenses and I = income. Round decimal answers to the nearest tenth. *(Section 1-4)*

29. $E = 187 + 5x$
    $I = 5.6x$

30. $E = 260 + 3x$
    $I = 7.34x$

31. $E = 112x - 3200$
    $I = 55x$

32. $E = 1350 - 4x$
    $I = 46x$

Solve each inequality. *(Section 1-1)*

33. $\frac{1}{2}x + 5 > 16$

34. $2(3 - x) \le 9$

35. $2x + 2.5 > -3x$

Simplify. Write answers with positive exponents. *(Toolbox Skill 14)*

36. $2c^{-1/2}d^0$

37. $(-1 + x^0)y^{-1/3}$

38. $\frac{18n^{-5}}{3}$

39. $\frac{-3}{r^{-4}}$

Working on the Unit Project

40. **Research** Write a report on the achievements of Frederick Law Olmsted. Include a discussion of some of his major park projects.

A section of Boston's "Emerald Necklace," a connected system of parks designed by Frederick Law Olmsted

1-6

Using Diagrams

BY THE WAY...

The lines of the Boston public transit system are color-coded: Green Line for "Emerald Necklace" parks of Frederick Law Olmsted; Blue Line for Atlantic coast; Red Line for crimson of Harvard University; Orange Line for area once known as "Orange."

Talk it Over

1. Which map is easier to read? Why?

2. What do the dots represent on the transit map? What does it mean when a line is drawn to connect one dot to another? What does it mean when there is no line connecting two dots?

3. Describe a route from Museum station to Airport station on the public transit system. How many stations will you stop at before you reach Airport station?

4. The transit map is an example of a *network* diagram. A dot is a **vertex of a network**, and a line connecting two dots is an **edge of a network.** Name the vertices from Kenmore to Science Park along the Green Line. How many edges are there along this route?

5. On the transit map, the distance from Park Street to Government Center is equal to the distance from Park Street to Downtown Crossing. Are these distances the same on the street map?

6. How is the transit map like the street map? How is it different?

A high school newspaper staff is making assignments for the next edition of the paper. This list shows which reporters are available to cover each event. How can the stories be assigned so that each reporter covers one event?

Student council elections	Language club's international festival	Opening performance of the school play	Regional volleyball championship	Academic banquet
Kwan	Kwan	Epstein	Cárdenas	Cárdenas
Pinnoo	Cárdenas	Cárdenas	Kwan	Epstein
Cárdenas	Epstein		Johns	
			Pinnoo	

Sample Response

Problem Solving Strategy: Use a diagram.

Step 1 List the events in one column and the reporters in another.

Step 2 Draw a vertex for each event and for each reporter. Draw an edge to connect the vertices if a reporter can cover the event.

Step 3 Assign each reporter to an event by darkening the edge connecting the reporter and the event.

> **Watch Out!**
> The point where two edges cross is not always a vertex.

1 Look for vertices that have only one edge. Johns has only one edge. Darken this edge.

2 Look at the vertices that have edges in common with "volleyball." Pinnoo has only two edges. Since Johns is covering volleyball, Pinnoo must cover the student council elections.

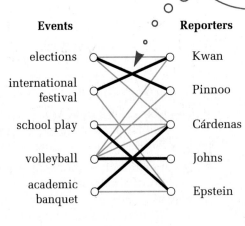

3 Look at the vertices that have edges in common with "elections." The only event that Kwan can cover is the international festival.

4 Cárdenas and Epstein can both cover the remaining stories.

This is one way to assign the reporters to cover the events:

Student council elections	International festival	School play	Volleyball tournament	Academic banquet
Pinnoo	Kwan	Epstein (or Cárdenas)	Johns	Cárdenas (or Epstein)

This table shows a nonstop flight schedule for a regional airline. Show this information in a diagram or a matrix.

Departure from ...	Provides nonstop service to...			
DSM Des Moines	Minn.-St. Paul	St. Louis		
MSP Minn.-St. Paul	Des Moines	Pittsburgh	St. Louis	
PIT Pittsburgh	St. Louis			
RDU Raleigh/Durham	Pittsburgh	St. Louis		
STL St. Louis	Des Moines	Pittsburgh	Raleigh/Durham	Minn.-St. Paul

Sample Response

Method ❶ Use a diagram.

Draw a vertex for each city of departure. Connect the vertices with edges. Place arrowheads on the edges to show the direction of the flight.

When two vertices are connected by two or more edges, draw at least one edge as a curved line.

St. Louis has service to the most destinations, so place that vertex in the center.

Method ❷ Use a matrix.

Let each row represent a city with nonstop service and each column represent a destination.

Destination

$$\begin{array}{c}\text{Departure} \\ \end{array} \begin{array}{c} \\ \text{DSM} \\ \text{MSP} \\ \text{PIT} \\ \text{RDU} \\ \text{STL} \end{array} \begin{array}{ccccc} \text{DSM} & \text{MSP} & \text{PIT} & \text{RDU} & \text{STL} \\ \left[\begin{array}{ccccc} 0 & 1 & 0 & 0 & 1 \\ 1 & 0 & 1 & 0 & 1 \\ 0 & 0 & 0 & 0 & 1 \\ 0 & 0 & 1 & 0 & 1 \\ 1 & 1 & 1 & 1 & 0 \end{array}\right] \end{array}$$

The element "1" means there is a nonstop flight from the city of departure to the destination.

The element "0" means there is no nonstop flight from the city of departure to the destination.

Talk it Over

7. How many nonstop flights depart from Des Moines? from St. Louis? How do you get this information from the diagram? from the matrix?

8. Which representation is more helpful for finding the number of nonstop flights departing from a city? Which is more helpful for finding the number of roundtrip nonstop flights? Explain your choices.

···· ► Now you are ready for: Exs. 1–17 on pp. 41–43

Sometimes it is helpful to color the vertices of a network diagram. Suppose you use different colors for vertices that are connected by edges. Then vertices that are the *same color* represent things, people, or ideas that can be grouped together.

Sample 3

Suppose an activities director at a high school is scheduling the meeting times for the school's activities. The director lists the students in each group who participate in more than one activity.

Make an activities schedule so that no activities with a member in common meet at the same time.

Band	Honor Society	Student Council	Drama Club	Language Club	Science Club	School Newspaper
Epstein	Volk	Medved	Medved	Mason	Hilbert	Kwan
Benally	Cárdenas	Volk	Mason	Hilbert	Benally	Johns
Kwan		Hayden		Johns		Cárdenas
Hayden						Epstein

Sample Response

Problem Solving Strategy: Use a diagram.

Step 1 Draw a network diagram for the activities. Connect vertices that represent activities with members in common.

Step 2 Color the diagram so that vertices that are connected by an edge have different colors. Use as few colors as you can.

  1 To start, color any vertex (for example, language club ●).

  2 Use the same color to color all vertices *not* connected to each other or the first vertex.

  3 Use a second color for one of the other vertices and repeat Step 2.

  4 Use a third color and repeat Steps 2 and 3 until all the vertices are colored.

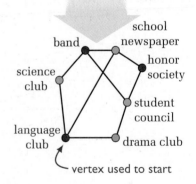

vertex used to start

One possible schedule groups together activities represented by the vertices of the same color.

Meeting time A	Meeting time B	Meeting time C
band	student council	drama club
honor society	science club	
language club	school newspaper	

9. Find another activities schedule by coloring the diagram differently.

10. How do you think you can find all the possible schedules?

Look Back ←

······► Now you are ready for:
Exs. 18–31 on pp. 43–44

How can a diagram help you organize information? How can coloring a diagram help you analyze information?

1-6 Exercises and Problems

1. **Reading** Which vertex in Sample 1 has the most edges connected to it? What does the number of edges connected to a vertex represent in this situation?

Use a matrix to represent the connections among the vertices of each diagram.

2.

3.

4.

Draw a diagram to show how the points in each matrix are connected.

5.
$$\begin{array}{c@{\ }c@{\ }c@{\ }c@{\ }c} & W & X & Y & Z \\ W & 0 & 1 & 1 & 1 \\ X & 1 & 0 & 0 & 1 \\ Y & 1 & 0 & 0 & 0 \\ Z & 1 & 1 & 0 & 0 \end{array}$$

6.
$$\begin{array}{c@{\ }c@{\ }c@{\ }c@{\ }c@{\ }c} & A & B & C & D & E \\ A & 0 & 1 & 1 & 0 & 1 \\ B & 1 & 0 & 0 & 1 & 0 \\ C & 1 & 0 & 0 & 1 & 0 \\ D & 0 & 1 & 1 & 0 & 0 \\ E & 1 & 0 & 0 & 0 & 0 \end{array}$$

7.
$$\begin{array}{c@{\ }c@{\ }c@{\ }c@{\ }c@{\ }c} & J & K & L & M & N \\ J & 0 & 0 & 0 & 1 & 1 \\ K & 0 & 0 & 1 & 1 & 1 \\ L & 0 & 1 & 0 & 1 & 0 \\ M & 1 & 1 & 1 & 0 & 1 \\ N & 1 & 1 & 0 & 1 & 0 \end{array}$$

Each diagram matches a student with his or her preferences. Assign each task so that every student participates in one activity.

8. **Yearbook Staff Committees**

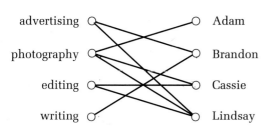

9. **Volunteer Club—Two Students per Location on Saturday**

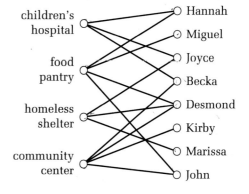

Career Architects may draw a network diagram called an *access graph* to analyze the floor plan for a house or a building. In an access graph, each room is represented by a vertex and each edge connects two vertices when you can walk directly from one room to the other without passing through another room.

10. Suppose a client gives an architect the following preferences for the design of a restaurant.

Room	Has access to...
waiting area	dining room, function room, public restrooms
kitchen	dining room, employees' restrooms, function room
dining room	waiting area, kitchen, patio for outdoor dining
function room	waiting area, kitchen
patio for outdoor dining	dining room
employees' restrooms	kitchen
public restrooms	waiting area

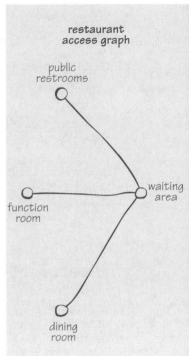

restaurant access graph

a. Complete the access graph to show the connections between the rooms.

b. Do you think there is more than one possible graph? Explain.

For Exercises 11–13, draw an access graph for each plan of a traditional dwelling unit in Burkina Faso in west Africa.

11.

12.

13.

14. a. Draw an access graph for each house plan.

A.

B.

C.

b. How are your access graphs alike? Do you see any patterns?

c. How are the house plans alike? How are they different?

15. **Writing** Each diagram shows the passes that led to a goal during a hockey game.

First period **Second period** **Third period**

a. Describe how each goal was scored.

b. Show the information from each diagram in a matrix. For each matrix, explain what each row and each column represent.

c. Were any player(s) in all three plays? If so, which ones? Do you think it is easier to find out using the diagrams or the matrix? Why?

16. a. Draw a network diagram to represent the nonstop airline service shown.

b. How many nonstop flights are there?

c. Which airport is used the most by this airline?

Departure from ...	Provides nonstop service to ...		
Albuquerque	Salt Lake City	Denver	
Denver	Aspen	Cheyenne	Salt Lake City
Aspen	Denver		
Salt Lake City	Albuquerque	Denver	Cheyenne
Cheyenne	Denver	Aspen	

17. a. Use the flight schedule from Exercise 16. Make a matrix, M, to represent the nonstop service.

b. TECHNOLOGY Use matrix multiplication to find M^2. This matrix will tell you the cities connected by a one-stop flight. A "1" means there is a one-stop, or 2-leg, flight. A "2" or "3" means there are two or three one-stop flights. A "0" means there are no one-stop flights. List all the one-stop flights. For each flight, tell where each stop occurs. (*Note*: Do not list flights that return to the city of departure.)

In Exercises 18 and 19, an edge is drawn between two vertices when two or more students are in the same class. How can exams be scheduled so that no student has a conflict?

18. **11th Grade Classes**

19. **12th Grade Classes**

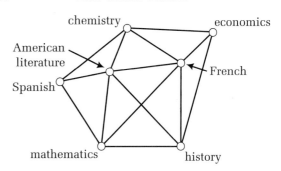

Chemistry In this table, a check (✔) means the chemicals in two groups can be stored together. A dash (—) means they cannot be stored together.

20. a. Represent the information in a network diagram.

b. What does each vertex of your diagram represent? What does each edge represent?

c. Find a way to group the chemicals for storage. How many storage areas are needed?

Can be stored with . . .

Chemical

	Inorganic acids	Organic acids	Caustics	Amines and alkanolamines	Halogenated compounds	Alcohols and glycols	Phenols
Inorganic acids	✔	—	—	—	—	—	✔
Organic acids	—	✔	—	—	✔	✔	✔
Caustics	—	—	✔	✔	—	✔	—
Amines and alkanolamines	—	—	✔	✔	—	✔	—
Halogenated compounds	—	✔	—	—	✔	✔	✔
Alcohols and glycols	—	✔	✔	✔	✔	✔	✔
Phenols	✔	✔	—	—	✔	✔	✔

Ongoing **ASSESSMENT**

21. **Open-ended** Make an access graph of a building you are familiar with. Which rooms have access to the greatest number of other rooms? the least?

Review **PREVIEW**

Solve. (Section 1-5)

22. $-x - 3y - 2z = 1$
$3x + 2y - z = -3$
$-2x + y - 3z = 8$

23. $-2x - y - 3z = -10$
$-x + 2y - z = -10$
$4x - 3y - 2z = -5$

24. $-2x + y + z = -2$
$-x + 5y - 3z = 13$
$2x + 2y - z = 2$

Find each distance. (Toolbox Skill 31)

25. DG
26. LP
27. BT
28. KM
29. TK
30. CP

 Working on the Unit Project

As you complete Exercise 31, think about how you can use network diagrams to design a park.

31. The table shows the amount of sunlight each type of flower needs.

Daffodil	Petunia	Begonia	Dahlia	Fuschia	Geranium	Impatiens
full sun	full sun	partial sun or shade	full sun or partial sun	partial sun	full sun	partial sun or shade

a. Show this information in a network diagram.

b. Show this information in a matrix.

c. Use your diagram or matrix to group together at least two types of flowers to plant in flower beds receiving each amount of sunlight.

d. **Writing** Do you think it is easier to see how to group the flowers in a diagram or in a matrix? Why?

Maximizing and Minimizing

Peak Performance

Stickers on new cars give values for MPG (miles per gallon of gasoline) for city and highway driving.

Use these two estimates to compare with other models.

Average estimate for city driving

Average estimate for highway driving

These numbers represent a range of fuel economy that most drivers achieve with this particular model.

These numbers represent the range of fuel economy for other models in this size class.

This fuel cost is based on 15,000 miles per year.

Compare this vehicle with others by using the **FREE GAS MILEAGE GUIDE** available in the dealer showroom.

CITY MPG

HIGHWAY MPG

Actual Mileage will vary with options, driving conditions, driving habits and vehicle's condition. Results reported to EPA indicate that the majority of vehicles with these estimates will achieve between

13 and **18** mpg in the city, and between

21 and **28** mpg on the highway.

For Comparison Shopping, all vehicles classified as **COMPACT** have been issued mileage ratings ranging from **12** to **37** mpg city and **20** to **40** mpg highway.

Estimated Annual Fuel Cost: $942

Talk it Over

The table gives the MPG for an average car at various speeds.

x = speed (mi/h)	y = MPG
15	21.0
25	30.0
35	33.6
45	33.5
55	30.3
65	24.9
75	20.0

1. What happens to MPG as the speed of a car increases?

2. Do you think a car has a **maximum**, or greatest, MPG? Why or why not? If so, at what speed(s) do you think the maximum MPG occurs?

3. Do you think a car has a **minimum**, or least, MPG? Why or why not? If so, at what speed(s) do you think the minimum MPG occurs?

In many situations it is important to make a quantity as large or as small as possible. For example, business managers want to make decisions that maximize income and minimize expenses. Drivers often want to maximize gas mileage or minimize the distance or time of a trip.

The function $y = -0.014x^2 + 1.2x + 6.9$ models the relationship between MPG and driving speed for a car. Find the driving speed, to the nearest mile per hour, that maximizes MPG.

Sample Response

Student Resources Toolbox
p. 651 *Graphing*

Method ❶ Use a formula.

The function $y = -0.014x^2 + 1.2x + 6.9$ is a quadratic function, so its graph is a parabola. Since the coefficient of the x^2-term is negative, the parabola opens down. The vertex is on the line of symmetry of the parabola at the point where the value of the function is a maximum.

The speed that maximizes MPG is the x-coordinate of the vertex. To find this value, use the equation of the line of symmetry.

$$x = -\frac{b}{2a}$$ ← a and b are coefficients in the general quadratic function $y = ax^2 + bx + c$.

$$= -\frac{1.2}{(2)(-0.014)}$$ ← Substitute **1.2** for b and -0.014 for a.

$$\approx 42.9$$

A driving speed of about 43 mi/h maximizes MPG.

Method ❷ Use a graph.

Graph $y = -0.014x^2 + 1.2x + 6.9$.

The x-coordinate of this point is the driving speed that maximizes MPG.

Maximum
X = 42.857142 Y = 32.614286

······▶ **Now you are ready for:**
Exs. 1–11 on pp. 49–50

A driving speed of about 43 mi/h maximizes MPG.

Use Diagrams to Find Minimums

The map shows several cities in Illinois, Indiana, and Missouri, as well as the interstate highways connecting them. The driving distance between each pair of connected cities is labeled.

← All distances are given in miles.

4. Use the map on page 46. Suppose you want to travel from St. Louis to Danville using interstate highways.

   a. What do you think is the shortest route between the two cities? What is the length of this route?

   b. Describe the method you used in part (a) to find the route you think is shortest.

Sample 2 shows how to use an algorithm to find the minimum distance between two points.

Sample 2

Find the shortest route on interstate highways from St. Louis to Danville. Use the map on page 46.

Sample Response

Problem Solving Strategy: Use a diagram.

1 Draw a network diagram that models the map. Each vertex represents a city. Each edge represents an interstate highway. Distances do not need to be drawn to scale.

The red edges join labeled and unlabeled vertices.

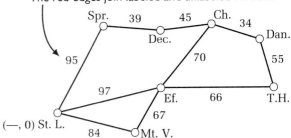

2 Label the starting point, St. Louis, with the ordered pair $(—, 0)$.

3 For each edge that connects a labeled and an unlabeled vertex, find this sum:

$$s = \frac{\text{second entry of ordered}}{\text{pair for labeled vertex}} + \frac{\text{length}}{\text{of edge}}$$

Find s for each red edge.
St. L. to Spr.: $0 + 95 = 95$
St. L. to Ef.: $0 + 97 = 97$
St. L. to Mt. V.: $0 + 84 = 84$ ◀—— This is the least sum.

Write the ordered pair (St. L., 84) next to "Mt. V."

4 Choose the edge from Step 3 that has the minimum sum s. Label the unlabeled vertex of that edge with this ordered pair:

(label of the other vertex of the edge, s)

5 Repeat Steps 3 and 4 until the vertex for Danville is labeled.

This is the least sum.
Find s for each red edge.
St. L. to Spr.: $0 + 95 = 95$
St. L. to Ef.: $0 + 97 = 97$
Mt. V. to Ef.: $84 + 67 = 151$

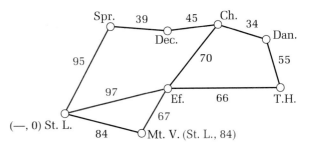

Write the ordered pair (St. L., 95) next to "Spr."

Continued on next page.

6 When the vertex for Danville is labeled, use the ordered pairs to find the shortest route from St. Louis to Danville.

Starting from Danville, use the first coordinates of the ordered pairs to backtrack to St. Louis. This gives the shortest route.

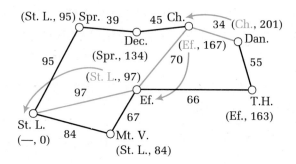

The shortest route from St. Louis to Danville on interstate highways is St. Louis to Effingham to Champaign to Danville.

Talk it Over

Questions 5–8 are about Sample 2.

5. What is the length of the shortest route from St. Louis to Danville? What is the relationship between this length and the second entry of the ordered pair for Danville?

6. Why is the first entry of the ordered pair for St. Louis a dash instead of a vertex label?

7. How many times must you perform Steps 3 and 4 to find the shortest route from St. Louis to Danville?

8. Can you use the network diagram to find the shortest route from St. Louis to Terre Haute? from Springfield to Terre Haute? Why or why not?

Look Back

How can you use graphs of functions and network diagrams to maximize and minimize quantities?

·····► Now you are ready for:
Exs. 12–22 on pp. 50–52

1-7 Exercises and Problems

1. **Reading** Describe one situation in which you want to maximize a quantity. Describe one situation in which you want to minimize a quantity.

For each quadratic function in Exercises 2–7:

a. Tell whether the function has a *maximum value* or a *minimum value*.

b. Find the value of *x* that maximizes or minimizes the function.

c. Find the function's maximum or minimum value.

2. $y = x^2 + 2x - 8$

3. $y = 3x^2 - 12x + 1$

4. $y = -x^2 + 14x - 40$

5. $y = -2.5x^2 - 15x + 3$

6. $y = 0.2x^2 + 1.4x + 6$

7. $y = -\frac{2}{3}x^2 + \frac{1}{6}x + \frac{1}{2}$

Distance Traveled by a Baseball Batted at 110 mi/h

Distance (feet) — Batting angle (degrees)

8. **Baseball** Use the graph.

   a. Describe what happens to the distance traveled by a baseball as the batting angle increases.

   b. What batting angle maximizes the distance a baseball travels? What is the maximum distance?

   c. **Writing** Why does the graph have a horizontal intercept at (90, 0)?

connection to **BIOLOGY**

0.1466

Many birds migrate over long distances. Keeping energy use to a minimum during flights makes stored fat last longer, so the birds need to stop to feed less often. By controlling their flight speed, birds minimize the energy they use.

9. **Career** Zoologists gather data about the amount of oxygen birds use in flight as a measure of the amount of energy birds use. The amount of oxygen used by one type of parakeet from Australia each hour during flight is given by the function

   $$f(s) = 1.96s^2 - 130s + 2920$$

   where *s* is the flight speed in kilometers per hour (km/h) and $f(s)$ is measured in milliliters (mL).

   a. Find the flight speed that minimizes the amount of oxygen used each hour.

   b. **Writing** Explain why the average amount of oxygen this type of parakeet uses for every kilometer of distance it travels is given by the function

   $$g(s) = \frac{f(s)}{s}$$

   where *f* is the function shown above.

   c. TECHNOLOGY Use a graphics calculator or graphing software. Graph $y = g(s)$. Is there a speed *s* that minimizes this function? Explain.

10. **Writing** Do you think a migrating bird should minimize the amount of oxygen it uses per unit of time or per unit of distance traveled? Explain.

11. **Manufacturing** Suppose a food manufacturer is designing a
can to hold 500 cm³ of soup. To minimize tin and steel costs,
the can's radius r and height h should be chosen so that the
surface area of the can is as small as possible.

a. The volume V of a cylindrical can is given by the formula
$$V = \pi r^2 h.$$
Use the fact that $V = 500$ cm³ to express h in terms of r.

b. The surface area S of a cylindrical can is given by the
formula
$$S = 2\pi r^2 + 2\pi rh.$$
Use your expression for h from part (a) to write S as a
function of r.

c. **TECHNOLOGY** Use a graphics calculator or graphing software.
Graph the function you wrote in part (b). Find the radius that
minimizes the surface area of the soup can. Then use your
expression for h from part (a) to find the height that minimizes
the surface area.

**For each network diagram, find the shortest route from vertex A to
vertex Z.**

12.

13.

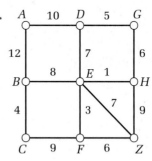

14. A classic puzzle problem asks you to suppose you need to transport a
wolf, a goat, and a cabbage across a river by boat. You can take only one
of them across at a time. The wolf and the goat cannot be left alone on the
same side of the river. Also, the goat and the cabbage cannot be left alone
on the same side. Write instructions for transporting the wolf, goat, and
cabbage across the river so that the number of trips is minimized. How
many trips are needed?

15. **Group Activity** Work with another student. You will need a large piece of smooth, heavy-weight cardboard; nylon fishing line; a metal washer; and three identical plastic mugs.

    a. On the cardboard, mark three widely spaced points A, B, and C that are the vertices of an acute scalene triangle.

    b. Mark the point P that you think minimizes this sum:

    $$d = d_A + d_B + d_C$$

    Find the value of d for the point P you chose.

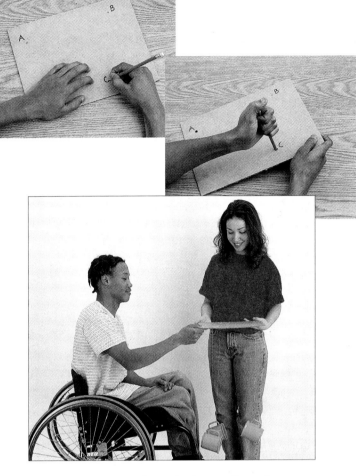

    c. Punch holes through the cardboard at points A, B, and C. Cut three equal lengths of nylon fishing line. Thread one piece through each hole and tie one end to a washer, as shown in the diagram. Tie the other end of each piece of string to one of the three mugs.

    d. Hold the piece of cardboard above the ground so that the mugs are hanging freely. Shake the cardboard gently until the washer settles down. Mark the point P' where the center of the washer ends up. This point minimizes the sum d in part (b).

    e. Find the value of d for your point P'. Compare this value of d with the value you found in part (b).

    f. Use a protractor to measure $\angle AP'B$, $\angle AP'C$, and $\angle BP'C$. What do you notice about the angle measures?

    g. **Open-ended** Describe a real-life problem that you can solve using this activity.

16. Write a matrix that shows the connections among the vertices in this network diagram. *(Section 1-6)*

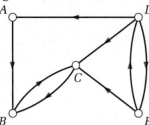

17. Use this matrix to draw a network diagram showing the connections among vertices P, Q, R, and S. *(Section 1-6)*

$$\begin{array}{c} \\ P \\ Q \\ R \\ S \end{array}\begin{array}{c} \begin{array}{cccc} P & Q & R & S \end{array} \\ \left[\begin{array}{cccc} 0 & 1 & 1 & 0 \\ 1 & 0 & 0 & 1 \\ 0 & 1 & 0 & 1 \\ 1 & 0 & 1 & 0 \end{array}\right] \end{array}$$

Graph each system of inequalities. *(Toolbox Skill 27)*

18. $y \geq 2x$
    $y \leq -3x - 1$

19. $x \geq 5$
    $y < 2x - 4$

20. $y \leq 3x + 2$
    $y \geq -2x + 7$

21. $y + \frac{1}{2}x < 1$
    $x + 2y \leq 6$

Working on the Unit Project

As you complete Exercise 22, think about how you can use the strategies presented in this section to maximize and minimize quantities related to your park proposal.

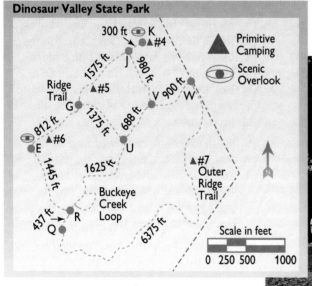

22. Use the map. All distances are given in feet. Find the shortest route from point Q to campsite #4.

Linear Programming

········Focus

Use systems of inequalities
to model situations and
find maximum and
minimum values.

A WINNING Combination

Advertise on WMMR	One 60-second ad costs ...
Morning (A.M.)	$200
Afternoon/evening (P.M.)	$50

Talk it Over

1. Look at WMMR's rate sheet. Why do you think A.M. ads are more expensive than P.M. ads?

2. Suppose you are the marketing manager for a store that sells casual clothing. Would you advertise a sale on WMMR in the morning? in the afternoon/evening? Why?

3. For each combination, find the total number of ads and the total cost of running the ads.

   a. ten A.M. ads and twelve P.M. ads

   b. six A.M. ads and ten P.M. ads

   c. ten A.M. ads and eight P.M. ads

   d. two A.M. ads and twenty P.M. ads

4. A **linear combination** is an expression in the form $ax + by$. Let x = the number of A.M. ads. Let y = the number of P.M. ads. Tell what each linear combination represents.

   a. $x + y$

   b. $200x + 50y$

5. You decide on two conditions. To which linear combination, $x + y$ or $200x + 50y$, does Condition 1 apply? Condition 2?

6. Which combination(s) of ads in question 3 meet(s) at least one of the conditions? Which meet(s) both conditions?

7. Can either x or y be negative in this situation? Why or why not?

Condition 1
You will spend
at most $2200.

Condition 2
You will run
at most 20 ads.

Any condition that must be met by a variable or by a linear combination of variables is a **constraint.**

$$x \geq 0 \quad \longleftarrow \quad \text{The number of A.M. ads cannot be negative.}$$

$$y \geq 0 \quad \longleftarrow \quad \text{The number of P.M. ads cannot be negative.}$$

$$x + y \leq 20 \quad \longleftarrow \quad \text{The total number of ads must be less than or equal to 20.}$$

$$200x + 50y \leq 2200 \quad \longleftarrow \quad \text{The total cost of the ads must be less than or equal to \$2200.}$$

You can use a *system of linear inequalities* to express all the constraints on the numbers of ads.

The graph of the solution of the system of inequalities includes all points that represent possible combinations of ads that meet all the constraints. The graph is called the **feasible region.**

Sample 1

Student Resources Toolbox
p. 644 *Solving Inequalities*

Graph the feasible region for the system of inequalities shown above. Label each vertex with its coordinates.

Sample Response

You must find the points that make all four inequalities true.

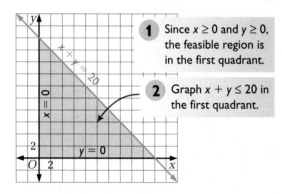

1 Since $x \geq 0$ and $y \geq 0$, the feasible region is in the first quadrant.

2 Graph $x + y \leq 20$ in the first quadrant.

$200x + 50y = 2200$

3 Identify points in the blue shaded region that also make $200x + 50y \leq 2200$ true.

The feasible region consists of all points on or inside quadrilateral $ABCO$. You can find the coordinates of each vertex by solving a system of equations.

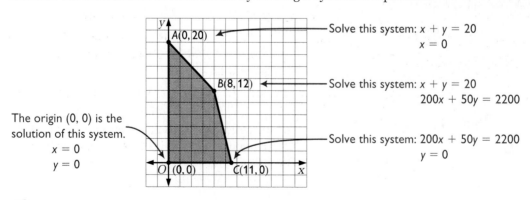

Solve this system: $x + y = 20$
$x = 0$

Solve this system: $x + y = 20$
$200x + 50y = 2200$

The origin $(0, 0)$ is the solution of this system.
$x = 0$
$y = 0$

Solve this system: $200x + 50y = 2200$
$y = 0$

8. Find the total number of ads represented by each vertex of *ABCO* and the total cost of running the ads.

9. Does every point in the feasible region in Sample 1 represent a possible combination of ads? Explain.

Now you are ready for:
Exs. 1–9 on pp. 57–58

The rate sheet on page 53 has another column of information that shows how many people, on average, are listening to WMMR at any one time.

Advertise on WMMR	One 60-second ad costs ...	and is heard by ...
Morning (A.M.)	$200	90,000 people
Afternoon/evening (P.M.)	$50	30,000 people

Given the original constraints, you want as many people as possible to hear the ads. You must find the *maximum-listeners point*. This is the point in the feasible region (see Sample 1) that represents the combination of ads that reaches the most listeners.

10. Find the total number of listeners reached by the combination of ads represented by each point.

    a. (0, 10)   b. (1, 7)   c. (2, 4)

11. The graph shows the feasible region found in Sample 1 and the line $90,000x + 30,000y = T$ for several values of T.

    a. What does T represent?

    b. Where are all the points in question 10 located?

    c. Use the graph to find another combination of ads that reaches the same number of listeners as the combinations of ads in question 10.

12. Use the graph to find a combination of ads that reaches each number of listeners.

    a. 600,000   b. 990,000

    c. 1,080,000   d. 1,260,000

13. a. Describe what happens to the line $90,000x + 30,000y = T$ as the number of listeners increases.

    b. Explain why B is the maximum-listeners point.

    c. How many A.M. ads and how many P.M. ads should you run to reach the maximum number of listeners? What is the maximum number of listeners?

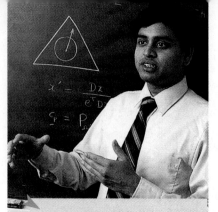

The process used to find the combination of ads that maximizes the number of listeners is an example of **linear programming.**

In this situation, the maximum-listeners point is one of the vertices of the feasible region. This is an example of the *corner-point principle* of linear programming.

Sample 2

Use the WMMR rate sheet on page 55. Suppose that you choose these constraints for one day of radio advertisements.

Constraint 1	Constraint 2	Constraint 3
You will run at most twenty ads.	You will run at least as many A.M. ads as P.M. ads.	You want to reach at least 720,000 listeners.

How many A.M. ads and how many P.M. ads should you run in order to minimize the total cost? How much will the ads cost?

BY THE WAY...

In 1984 Narendra Karmarkar created a high-speed computer algorithm for linear programming that solves a problem with 800,000 variables in 10 hours.

Sample Response

1 Represent the constraints with a system of linear inequalities.

Let x = the number of A.M. ads
Let y = the number of P.M. ads.

$$x + y \leq 20 \quad \longleftarrow \quad \text{Constraint 1}$$
$$x \geq y \quad \longleftarrow \quad \text{Constraint 2}$$
$$90{,}000x + 30{,}000y \geq 720{,}000 \quad \longleftarrow \quad \text{Constraint 3}$$
$$x \geq 0 \quad \longleftarrow \quad \text{Include inequalities}$$
$$y \geq 0 \qquad \qquad \text{that show that}$$

that show that x and y cannot be negative.

2 Graph the feasible region and find the coordinates of its vertices.

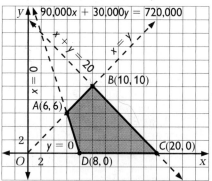

3 Write a linear combination that represents the total cost of the ads.

$$200x + 50y$$

4 Use the corner-point principle.

The minimum cost occurs at a vertex of the feasible region.

Find the total cost for the combination of ads represented by each vertex.

The minimum cost occurs → at A(6, 6).

Vertex	Total cost (dollars)
(x, y)	**200x + 50y**
$A(6, 6)$	$200(6) + 50(6) = 1500$
$B(10, 10)$	$200(10) + 50(10) = 2500$
$C(20, 0)$	$200(20) + 50(0) = 4000$
$D(8, 0)$	$200(8) + 50(0) = 1600$

You should run six A.M. ads and six P.M. ads. The ads will cost $1500.

LINEAR PROGRAMMING

You can use linear programming:

➤ when you can represent the constraints on the variables with a system of linear inequalities, and

➤ when the goal is to find the maximum or minimum value of a linear combination of the variables.

CORNER-POINT PRINCIPLE

Any maximum or minimum value of a linear combination of the variables will occur at one of the vertices of the feasible region.

·····➤ **Now you are ready for:**
: **Exs. 10–23 on pp. 59–60**

Look Back ←

Explain the meaning of each of these terms in your own words: *linear combination*, *constraint*, and *feasible region*.

1-8 Exercises and Problems

1. Rosario goes to the post office to buy aerograms and pre-stamped postcards to use when she writes to her friends and family in Mexico.

   Let a = the number of aerograms Rosario buys.
   Let p = the number of postcards Rosario buys.

   a. Write a linear combination for the total cost of the aerograms and postcards Rosario buys.

   b. Rosario has $8.10 in her wallet. Write an inequality that represents this constraint on a and p.

   c. Rosario plans to write to at least eight people this weekend. Write an inequality that represents this constraint on a and p.

   d. Write two more inequalities that represent other constraints on a and p. (*Hint:* Can either a or p be negative in this situation?)

   e. Graph the feasible region that represents all possible combinations of numbers of aerograms and postcards that Rosario can buy. Label each vertex with its coordinates.

   f. Choose a point of the feasible region that is not a vertex. Find the total cost at that point.

2. Use the feasible region graphed in Sample 1.

   a. **Reading** Which vertex of the feasible region represents the maximum number of ads that can be run in the morning? in the afternoon/evening?

   b. Do you think either of these options is a good choice? Explain.

Graph the feasible region for each system of inequalities. Label each vertex with its coordinates.

3. $x \geq 0$
$y \geq 0$
$x + y \leq 6$
$12x + 6y \leq 48$

4. $1 \leq c \leq 4$
$c + d \leq 14$
$d \geq 2c$

5. $a \geq 0$
$2 \leq b \leq 8$
$10a + 5b \geq 30$
$2a + b \leq 12$

6. $x \geq 0$
$y \geq 1$
$x + y \geq 5$
$40x + 10y \geq 80$

7. Manufacturing A chemical company manufactures two silicon compounds using the raw materials shown in the table.

  a. For each raw material, write a linear combination that represents the total amount (in kilograms) of the raw material needed to manufacture c kg of silicon carbide and t kg of silicon tetrachloride.

  b. The manufacturer has in stock 105 kg of silica, 84 kg of carbon, and 126 kg of chlorine. Write a system of inequalities that represents all the constraints in this situation.

Raw material	Amount (kg) needed to make 1 kg of …	
	silicon carbide	silicon tetrachloride
silica	1.5	0.35
carbon	0.6	0.14
chlorine	0	0.84

BY THE WAY...

Some silicon compounds are used to make silicon chips for computers, calculators, radios, and televisions.

8. Fitness Emilio tries to meet several goals each time he works out on the ski machine and the treadmill. He drew this graph of the feasible region that represents all possible workouts that allow him to meet his goals.

  a. What does the linear combination $8s + 5t$ represent? What does the linear combination $s + t$ represent?

  b. Write a system of inequalities that represents the feasible region.

  c. Describe the goal (constraint) represented by each inequality in part (b).

9. a. For each workout represented by a vertex of $ABCD$, find the total length of the workout, the amount of time spent on each machine, and the number of Calories burned during the workout.

  b. **Writing** Explain why Emilio might choose the workout represented by B over the workout represented by A. Explain why Emilio might choose the workout represented by C over the workout represented by D.

10. **Agriculture** Rhonda Neilson will plant at most 100 acres of her farm with barley and corn. She can spend up to $8400 to grow these two crops.

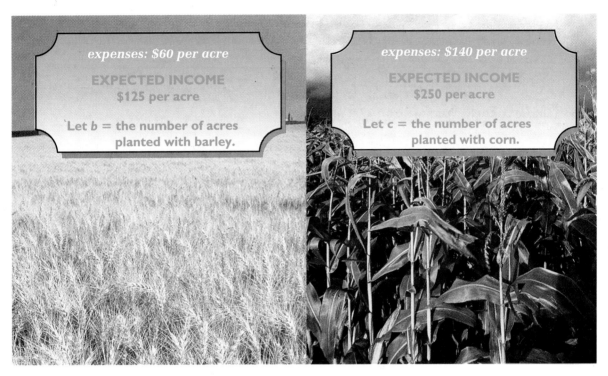

expenses: *$60 per acre*

EXPECTED INCOME
$125 per acre

Let *b* = the number of acres planted with barley.

expenses: *$140 per acre*

EXPECTED INCOME
$250 per acre

Let *c* = the number of acres planted with corn.

a. Write a system of inequalities that represents all the constraints on the number of acres that will be used for each crop on Rhonda Neilson's farm.

b. Graph the feasible region and find the coordinates of its vertices.

c. What does the linear combination $125b + 250c$ represent?

d. Graph the line $125b + 250c = 20,000$ on the same set of axes you used in part (b).

e. **Writing** What does your graph in part (d) tell you about the farm's total income from barley and corn? Explain how you know.

f. How many acres of each crop should Rhonda Neilson plant in order to maximize the income? What is the maximum income?

11. Use the situation described in Exercise 7. Suppose the company sells silicon carbide for $320/kg and silicon tetrachloride for $250/kg. How many kilograms of each product should the company manufacture in order to maximize income? What is the maximum income?

12. **Business** A small business produces oak chairs and walnut chairs.

➤ The business can make at most 20 chairs per week.

➤ Materials cost $100 per oak chair and $150 per walnut chair.

➤ The business has a budget of $2400 per week for materials.

➤ Each oak chair sells for $400 and each walnut chair for $500.

How many of each type of chair should the business make each week to maximize income?

13. a. **Open-ended** Use the information in the tables to create and solve a linear programming problem about an exercise routine that consists of two types of exercise. Make up constraints on time and Calories burned.

Calories Burned During Exercise						
Type of exercise	aerobics	swimming	squash	walking	jogging	bicycling
Cal/min	5	7	12	6	8	10

b. **Group Activity** Work with another student.

Trade the problems you wrote in part (a). Solve the problem you receive.

Ongoing ASSESSMENT

14. **Writing** Explain how systems of inequalities are used in linear programming.

Review PREVIEW

15. The function $y = -0.036x^2 + x + 6$ models the relationship between the height y of a soccer ball in feet and the horizontal distance x in feet that the ball travels after being struck at an angle of 45° and an initial speed of 30 ft/s. What is the maximum height of the ball and how far has it traveled horizontally when it reaches this height? Round answers to the nearest foot. *(Section 1-7)*

Suppose you roll one red die and one green die. Find each probability.
(Toolbox Skill 7)

16. P(red 3 and green 3)   17. P(odd red and green 5)   18. P(odd red and odd green)

Find the surface area and volume of a sphere with each indicated radius or diameter. *(Toolbox Skill 29)*

19. radius: 4.5 cm   20. diameter: 72 in.   21. diameter: 18 m   22. radius: 13 ft

Working on the Unit Project

As you complete Exercise 23, think about how you can use linear programming in the creation of your park proposal.

23. **Writing** Suppose you plan to include in your park a large field that can be used for both touch football and field hockey games in the fall. Explain how you can use the information below to decide how many hours per week to schedule each sport in order to make the most profit from the use of the field.

➤ hours per week that the field can be used   ➤ hourly personnel costs for both games

➤ hourly maintenance costs for both games   ➤ weekly budget for personnel costs

➤ weekly maintenance budget   ➤ admission charges for both games

Completing the Unit Project

Now you are ready to complete your park proposal. Your completed proposal should include these things:

> ➤ **a copy of your survey asking the people of your community what they want in a park**

> ➤ **a written summary of the survey results**

> ➤ **a scale drawing, a CAD drawing, or a three-dimensional model of your park plan**

> ➤ **an explanation of how you used three of the math topics from this unit in your project**

> ➤ **a written description of your park and an explanation of how it meets the needs of the people in your community**

Look Back ◄

How did you use topics in mathematics from previous courses in your work on this project?

Alternative Projects

Project 1: Management Science

Write a report on linear programming. Include the contributions of George Dantzig, Narendra Karmarkar, and L. G. Khachian. Describe several business applications, including airline scheduling and the routing of information transmitted over complex communications networks. Also discuss the simplex and ellipsoid methods for finding the corner point that represents maximum profit in cases where there are so many corner points that you cannot test them all.

Project 2: Secret Codes

Huffman codes represent one way to use network diagrams to send messages in secret codes. Find out how to use Huffman codes. Write an article explaining how to code and decode messages with them.

1. **a.** Write two algorithms for solving a system of two linear equations with two variables.

   b. **Writing** Compare your algorithms.

   1-1

2. Solve the inequality $3x > 7 + 10x$ in two ways.

3. What are the lengths of the sides of all the triangles that have sides whose lengths are whole numbers and a perimeter of 22?

   1-2

4. **a.** What conclusion(s) can you draw from the scatter plot?

   b. Does each conclusion you drew apply to every SLR zoom lens in the scatter plot? Why or why not?

   1-3

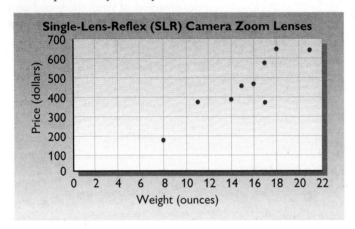

5. Robert DiNucci must select a monthly calling plan for local telephone service for his new apartment. He expects to limit local calls to Zone 1.

   1-4

Measured Service	Unlimited Service	Measured Circle Service
$6.39 per month plus 2.6¢ per min for local calls in Zone 1	$12.59 per month for local calls in Zone 1	$9.25 per month for up to two hours of local calls in Zone 1 plus 5.8¢ per min for local calls in Zone 1 after two hours

   a. For how many minutes per month of local calls in Zone 1 is Measured Service the least expensive?

   b. For how many minutes per month of local calls in Zone 1 is Unlimited Service the most expensive?

   c. Which plan should Robert DiNucci choose in order to pay as little as possible for local phone service? Explain.

Solve. Round decimal answers to the nearest tenth.

1-5

6. $x - 3y - z = 1$
    $2x + y + z = 3$
    $x + 2y + 2z = 0$

7. $2x + z = 1$
    $3y + 2z = -2$
    $-3x + y - z = -3$

8. $x - y + 2z = 1$
    $-x + 3y + z = 5$
    $-2x + y - z = 4$

9. a. **Open-ended** Describe a situation that can be modeled by this network diagram.

   b. Write a matrix that represents the connections in the diagram in part (a).

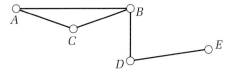

1-6

10. A landscape architect's plan for this flower bed states that the flowers in bordering sections are different colors. Show how to follow this plan using the least number of colors.

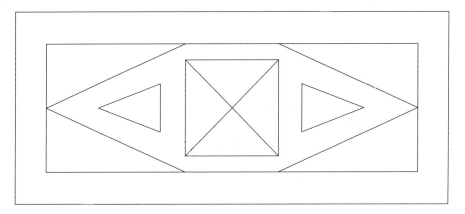

For each quadratic function in Questions 11–13:

1-7

a. **Tell whether the function has a *maximum value* or a *minimum value*.**

b. **Find the value of *x* that maximizes or minimizes the function.**

c. **Find the function's maximum or minimum value.**

11. $y = 2x^2 - 5x + 11$ 12. $y = -x^2 + 3x - 2$ 13. $y = -1.1x^2 - 4.5x + 2.3$

14. Katie Stein is a sales representative whose territory is Arizona and New Mexico. Her daily travel expenses average $120 in Arizona and $100 in New Mexico. She receives an annual travel allowance of $18,000. She must spend at least 50 days in Arizona and 60 days in New Mexico. If sales average $3000 per day in Arizona and $2800 per day in New Mexico, how many days should she spend in each state to maximize sales?

1-8

15. **Self-evaluation** Which of the problem-solving strategies presented in this unit have you used before? Which, if any, are new to you? Do you think your work in this unit has made you a better problem-solver? Explain.

16. **Group Activity** Work in a group of three students.

   Use this system of equations.

   $$16x - 2.4y = 147$$
   $$5.8x + 9y = 258$$

   a. One student should solve the system by graphing, another by algebra, and the third by matrices.

   b. Compare your solutions. Explain any differences.

   c. Compare the three algorithms the group used to solve the system.

IDEAS AND (FORMULAS)=x^2

$_5P_5$

ALGEBRA

➤ You can solve a linear inequality in one variable with algebra and with a graph. *(p. 5)*

➤ **Problem Solving** To solve certain problems modeled by two or more linear equations, you can find the intersection point of the graphs of the equations. *(p. 24)*

➤ To find a break-even point where income is equal to expenses, you can use algebra or a graph. *(p. 25)*

➤ You can use algebra or a graph to solve a system of two linear equations. *(p. 30)*

GEOMETRY

➤ The triangle inequality states that the sum of the lengths of any two sides of a triangle must be greater than the length of the third side. *(p. 9)*

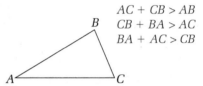

$$AC + CB > AB$$
$$CB + BA > AC$$
$$BA + AC > CB$$

➤ Three planes can have no point of intersection, one point of intersection, or many points of intersection. *(p. 32)*

no common point
of intersection

one common point
of intersection

many common points
of intersection

DISCRETE MATH

➤ Sometimes there is more than one possible algorithm for solving a problem. Algorithms may contain loops. *(p. 4)*

➤ **Problem Solving** You can use a systematic list to be sure that you do not leave out or repeat any possible solutions of a problem. *(p. 10)*

➤ A matrix equation can be used to solve a system of two or more linear equations. *(pp. 31, 33)*

➤ **Problem Solving** Network diagrams can be used to solve some problems that involve connections. The direction of the connections can also be represented in network diagrams. *(pp. 38, 39, 40)*

Unit 1 Modeling Problem Situations

➤ You can use matrices whose elements are only "0" or "1" to represent situations that involve connections. A "0" means there is no connection. A "1" means there is a connection. *(p. 39)*

➤ Problem Solving Sometimes it is useful to color the vertices of a network diagram in order to solve a problem that involves groupings. *(p. 40)*

➤ The region formed by the graphs of a system of linear inequalities that represent all the constraints on a situation is the feasible region that includes all possible solutions. *(p. 54)*

➤ You can find the maximum or minimum value of a linear combination by using linear programming. *(p. 56)*

➤ The corner-point principle states that for a linear programming problem, any maximum or minimum value of a linear combination $ax + by$ will occur at one of the vertices of the feasible region. *(p. 56)*

STATISTICS & PROBABILITY

➤ Line graphs drawn on the same set of axes can be used to compare data sets in order to make a decision. *(p. 16)*

➤ Box-and-whisker plots drawn under the same number line can be used to compare data sets in order to make a decision. *(p. 17)*

➤ A scatter plot that compares two data sets can be used to make a decision. *(p. 18)*

············ **Key Terms**

- **algorithm** (p. 4)
- **box-and-whisker plot** (p. 17)
- **lower extreme** (p. 17)
- **scatter plot** (p. 18)
- **inverse matrix, A^{-1}** (p. 31)

- **edge of a network** (p. 37)
- **linear combination** (p. 53)
- **linear programming** (p. 56)

- **loop** (p. 4)
- **median** (p. 17)
- **upper quartile** (p. 17)
- **system of equations** (p. 30)
- **linear equation with three variables** (p. 32)
- **maximum** (p. 45)
- **constraint** (p. 54)

- **mean** (p. 16)
- **upper extreme** (p. 17)
- **lower quartile** (p. 17)
- **matrix equation** (p. 31)
- **vertex of a network** (p. 37)

- **minimum** (p. 45)
- **feasible region** (p. 54)

BICYCLING

What's a good way to avoid rush-hour traffic? Ride a bike! In China, Japan, Germany, and the Netherlands — countries with a high percent of bicycle owners — specially designed roads make it convenient for commuters to bike to work.

bike trails

W&OD Railroad Park in Falls Church, Virginia

Cyclists are getting **on track** —railroad tracks! In 1963, naturalist May Theilgaard Watts had the idea of replacing abandoned railroad tracks with paths for walking and riding bicycles. Trails in almost every state now connect cities to towns and go through state and national forests.

Pedals are added. Riders slide the pedals from front to back to move the rear wheel.

1840

A chain connects the pedals to the back wheel making a more efficient, safer bicycle.

1885

1790

The first bicycles had no pedals. They were called "hobbyhorses".

1870

The front wheel is made larger than the rear wheel so riders can go faster.

Make a Pedal Pitch

Your project is to give a presentation about bicycles to children in your community.

Each group member will choose one aspect of bicycling and plan to present information on it. For example, you may choose bicycle safety, bicycling for exercise, bike racing, or the physics of bicycles.

As you complete the "Working on the Unit Project" exercises in this unit, decide how you will use the information in your presentation. Save your work to support the data you present.

Bike racing tracks are made of asphalt, clay, concrete, or wood. Most racers prefer the smooth finish of a wood track, like the one in the Major Taylor **Velodrome** in Indianapolis, named after the cyclist who was the first African-American world champion in any sport.

race tracks

Bicycles are built to resemble motorcycles, with wide tires and heavy frames.

1933

1981

The mountain bicycle combines wide tires with high-technology construction.

Solid disk wheels improve the aerodynamics of racing bicycles.

1990

Future

Superconductive magnets that power the pedals and hold up the rims promise lighter weight and better aerodynamics.

67

Getting Started

For this project you should work in a group of four students. Here are some ideas to help you get started.

☞ Decide which topics you want to discuss. You may want to look at the "Working on the Unit Project" exercises at the end of each section for ideas. Decide which group member will present each topic.

☞ Make a preliminary outline of your presentation. Discuss each group member's role in the presentation. Plan to meet later to finalize your outline.

☞ In your group discuss how you can use posters, diagrams, and props to make your descriptions and explanations as clear and complete as possible.

☞ Plan to research your topics. You can use books about bicycles or talk to cyclists or bicycle experts in your community.

Working on the Unit Project

Your work in Unit 2 will help you prepare your presentation.

Related Exercises:

Section 2-1, Exercise 40
Section 2-2, Exercise 35
Section 2-3, Exercise 30
Section 2-4, Exercise 24
Section 2-5, Exercises 35, 36
Section 2-6, Exercises 48, 49
Section 2-7, Exercise 27
Section 2-8, Exercises 23–25

Alternative Projects p. 132

Can We Talk BICYCLING

➤ There are twice as many bicycles in the world as cars. Why do you think there are more bicycles?

➤ What are the advantages of commuting to school or work by bicycle? What are the disadvantages? What are some other uses of bicycles in your community?

➤ Why do you think there are special bicycles for racing and for traveling on dirt roads?

➤ What safety hazards do you need to watch for while riding a bicycle?

➤ What protective equipment do you think cyclists should wear? Why?

What Is a Function?

It All ◀ Depends

Your fastest walking speed in miles per hour depends on your leg length in feet.
Maximum speed = $\sqrt{32 \times \text{length}}$

A dictionary pairs words with their meanings.

ıriccıon

Fri·day [fráɪdɪ] *s.* viernes.
fried [fraɪd] *adj.* frito; freído; *p.p. de* **to fry.**
friend [frend] *s.* amigo, amiga.
friend·li·ness [fréndlɪnɪs] *s.* afabilidad; amistad.
friend·ly [fréndlɪ] *adj.* amistoso, afable, amigable; ɔicio, favorable; *adv.* amistosamente.
·ship [fréndʃɪp] *s.* amistad.
frighten [fráɪtn] v. espantar, asustar, atemorizar;

The area of a circle depends on its radius.

$A = 9\pi \qquad A = 4\pi \qquad A = 8$

Everybody has a birthday.

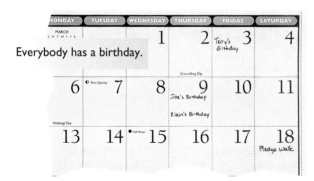

The minimum distance needed to stop a car depends on how fast it is moving.

Every real number except 0 has a reciprocal.

x	$\frac{1}{x}$
-2	-0.5
-1	-1
0	undefined
1	1
2	0.5

Each of these relationships has two variables. A variable that determines, or controls, another variable is called a *control variable*. A variable that is determined by, or depends on, another variable is called a *dependent variable*.

In the relationship between speed and stopping distance, the control variable is the speed of the car and the dependent variable is the distance needed to stop.

A *function* is a relationship for which each value of the control variable is paired with *only one* value of the dependent variable.

One word may have more than one meaning. This does not represent a function.

A person's birthday can be on only one date. This does represent a function.

wind [wind] *s.* viento, aire; resuello;—**instrument** instrumento de viento; **to get—of** barruntar; tener noticia de.

wind [waind] *v.* enredar; devanar, ovillar; (*watch*) dar cuerda a (*un reloj*); (*road*) serpentear (*un camino*); dar vueltas; *s.* vuelta; recodo.

TUESDAY	WEDNESDAY	THURSDAY	FRIDAY	SATURDAY
			Mom's Birthday	1	2
5	6 Full Moon	7	8	9

Domain and Range

The **domain of a function** is all possible values of the control variable. The **range of a function** is all possible values of the dependent variable.

Sample 1

Does this table represent a function? If so, find its domain and range.

Tune-ups	
4 cylinders	$49.95
6 cylinders	$59.95
8 cylinders	$69.95

Sample Response

Each value of the control variable (number of cylinders) is paired with only one value of the dependent variable (cost of tune-up). This table represents a function.

The domain is all values of the control variable: 4, 6, 8.

The range is all values of the dependent variable: 49.95, 59.95, 69.95.

Talk it Over

Questions 1–3 refer to the functions shown on page 69.

1. In the relationship between fastest walking speed and length of legs, which is the dependent variable?

2. What is the domain of the reciprocal function?

3. What is the range of the birthday function?

Notation for Functions

When a variable y is a function of a variable x, you can use **function notation:**

dependent variable (output) ⟶ $y = f(x)$ ⟵ The notation $f(x)$ is read "f of x."

control variable (input)

function name (Other letters can be used.)

This means that y represents the value of the function f for a value of x.

When a function has a rule for pairing x-values with y-values, you can write:

$$y = f(x) = \text{rule}$$

For example, if the reciprocal function is named f,

Watch Out!

$f(x)$ does *not* mean f times x.

$$y = f(x) = \frac{1}{x}.$$

This statement is usually written in one of these ways:

$$y = f(x) \qquad y = \frac{1}{x} \qquad f(x) = \frac{1}{x}$$

The *values of a function* are the numbers in its range. One value of the reciprocal function is $f(2) = 0.5$.

Read "$f(2) = 0.5$" as

"f of 2 equals 0.5."

"the value of f at 2 is 0.5."

Sample 2

a. Use $f(x) = 3x^2 - 1$. Find $f(2)$ and $f(a)$.

b. Use $A(r) = \pi r^2$. Find $A(0.5)$ and $A(3 + x)$. Leave your answer in terms of π.

Sample Response

a. $f(x) = 3x^2 - 1$

$f(2) = 3(2)^2 - 1$ ⟵ Substitute 2 for x.

$\quad = 11$ ⟵ Simplify.

$f(x) = 3x^2 - 1$

$f(a) = 3a^2 - 1$ ⟵ Substitute a for x.

b. $A(r) = \pi r^2$

$A(0.5) = \pi(0.5)^2$ ⟵ Substitute 0.5 for r.

$\quad = \pi(0.25)$

$\quad = 0.25\pi$

$A(r) = \pi r^2$

$A(3 + x) = \pi(3 + x)^2$ ⟵ Substitute $3 + x$ for r.

$\quad = \pi(9 + 6x + x^2)$

$\quad = 9\pi + 6\pi x + \pi x^2$

4. Write a rule for $C(r)$, the circumference of a circle as a function of the radius.

5. The birthday function is $B(\text{person}) = \text{date}$. What is $B(\text{you})$?

6. The minimum stopping distance function on page 69 is defined by the equation $y = x + \dfrac{x^2}{20}$.

   a. Choose a name for the function and write it in function notation.

   b. What is the value of the function at 0? How does the graph on page 69 show this?

▶ Now you are ready for:
Exs. 1–20 on pp. 73–75

Graphs and Functions

You can represent functions with graphs.

On a coordinate grid, the domain is on the *x*-axis and the range is on the *y*-axis.

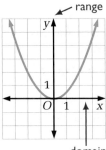

If no vertical line crosses a graph in two or more points, the graph represents a function.

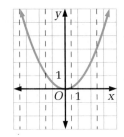

The minimum stopping distance function on page 69 is an example of a **one-to-one function.** Each member of the range is paired with exactly one member of the domain. If no horizontal line crosses the graph of a function in two or more points, the function is one-to-one.

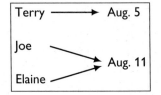

The birthday function is an example of a **many-to-one function.** A member of the range (a date) may be paired with more than one member of the domain (people).

a. Is the function $f(x) = x^2$ *one-to-one* or *many-to-one*?

b. Find the domain and range of f.

72   **Unit 2** Exploring and Applying Functions

a. Write the function as $y = x^2$. Graph the function.

The graph shows two different domain values, 2 and −2, paired with the same range value 4. The function is many-to-one.

b. Any real number can be squared. The domain is all real numbers.

The square of any number is nonnegative. The range is all positive real numbers and zero. You can also describe the range by writing $y \geq 0$.

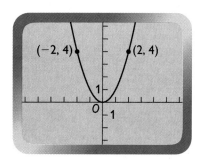

Look Back ◄——

:·····► **Now you are ready for:**
: **Exs. 21–40 on pp. 75–76**

How can you tell if a graph or a table of values represents a function?

2-1 Exercises and Problems

1. a. **Reading** Give an example of a relationship on pages 69–70 that is not a function.

 b. Explain how you can tell it is not a function.

2. a. Does this cast list represent a function? Explain why or why not.

 b. If so, what are the domain and range of the function?

3. Does this table give a person's phone number as a function of his or her name? Explain why or why not.

A Raisin in the Sun
a play by Lorraine Hansberry

The Cast, in order of appearance

Ruth Younger	Libra Woods
Travis Younger	Kyle Turner
Walter Lee Younger	Warren Moore
Beneatha Younger	Denise Loundes
Lena Younger	Kenyatta Johnson
Joseph Asagai	Steven Taylor
George Murchison	Jerome Roberts
Karl Lindner	Richard Wilson
Bobo	Teritus Fortune

TECHNICAL CREW LIST

NAME	PHONE
Giles	555-5678 (workshop)
	555-7325 (house)
Isaac	555-2587
Kalisha	555-1234 (home)
	555-5432 (work)

4. **Writing** The domain of a sales relationship is *merchandise items* and the range is their *prices*.

   a. Explain why, in any one store, customers expect the relationship to be a function.

   b. Explain why, in any one city, this relationship is probably not a function.

5. a. Use the diagram to explain why the area of an equilateral triangle is given by $A(s) = \dfrac{\sqrt{3}}{4}s^2$.

   b. Does this relationship represent a function?

   c. What is the control variable? the dependent variable?

   d. What are the domain and range of the function?

6. Write a rule for $S(e)$, the surface area of a cube as a function of the length of one edge.

7. Write a rule for $V(e)$, the volume of a cube as a function of the length of one edge.

For each function:

a. **Find $f(2)$.**   b. **Find $f(-4)$.**   c. **Find $f(a + b)$.**

8. $f(x) = 6x^2$

9. $f(s) = \dfrac{1}{s + 1}$

10. $f(x) = \dfrac{2x}{3 + x}$

11. $f(t) = |t|$

12. $f(x) = 3x + 4$

13. $f(x) = 4x^2 - 3x + 1$

Career Very hot or very cold temperatures can affect the length of a steel tape measure. A surveyor can find out how the length of the tape measure changes by using a formula. For a tape calibrated at 68°F, the formula is:

$$C(T) = 0.00000645L(T - 68)$$

$C(T)$ is the change in the length of the tape, L is the original length of the tape, and T is the temperature at which the surveyor uses the tape.

14. Explain why the temperature is the control variable in this situation.

15. a. Write a formula for the change in the length of a tape originally 100 ft long.

    b. Suppose the tape is used at a temperature of 16°F. Use your formula to find the length of the tape.

16. The *truth function*, *T*, assigns the value 1 (true) or 0 (false) to statements. For example, *T*(All squares are rectangles.) = 1 and *T*(All circles are squares.) = 0. What are the domain and range of the truth function?

Find each value of the truth function, which is defined in Exercise 16.

17. *T*(All rectangles are parallelograms.)

18. $T(\text{If } -2x \geq -6, \text{ then } x \geq 3.)$

19. $T(\text{If } x < 0, \text{ then } \sqrt{x} \text{ is not a real number.})$

20. *T*(All parallelograms are squares.)

Tell whether each graph represents a function.

21.

22.

23.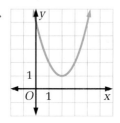

24. **Open-ended** Draw a graph that does not represent a function.

25. **Writing** A function can also be represented by a *mapping diagram,* in which two vertical number lines represent the domain and range. Akeem drew mapping diagrams for three relationships. Which is a *one-to-one function*, which is a *many-to-one function*, and which is *not a function*? Explain your answer.

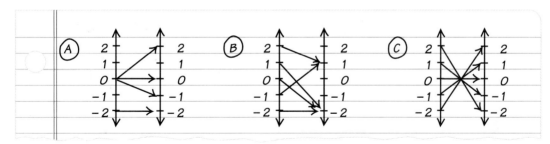

For Exercises 26–29, tell whether each function is *one-to-one* or *many-to-one*. Explain your answer.

26.

27.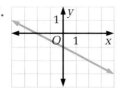

28. $g(x) = \frac{3}{5}x$

29. $c(x) = x^3$

30. **Reading** How does the graph in Sample 3 show that the range of *f* is the nonnegative real numbers?

31. Find the domain and range of the function shown in Exercise 23.

32. Find the domain and range of $f(x) = \sqrt{x}$.

Shipping and Handling

The chart below shows how much your shipping and handling will be.

Order size	Shipping charges
$ 30.00 – 49.99	$ 7.35
$ 50.00 – 99.99	$ 8.60
$100.00 – 149.99	$10.30
$150.00 – 199.99	$13.10
$200.00 – 299.99	$16.45
$300.00 – 499.99	$22.80
$500.00 – 749.99	$30.65
$750.00 – 999.99	$48.45
$1,000 – 2,000.00	$58.65

33. **Writing** Describe a function that could represent the information in this mail-order catalog shipping chart. Include in your description a discussion of domain, range, and whether the function is one-to-one.

Review **PREVIEW**

Graph the feasible region for each system of inequalities. Label each vertex with its coordinates. *(Section 1-8)*

34. $x \geq 0$
    $y \geq 0$
    $x - y \leq 4$

35. $y \leq 0$
    $y \leq \frac{3}{2}x + 3$
    $y \leq -x + 1$

36. $x \geq 2$
    $2 \leq y \leq 5$
    $y \leq -\frac{1}{2}x + 10$

37. Write an algorithm for preparing for your mathematics class. *(Section 1-1)*

38. Solve the inequality $8 < 3x - 10$. *(Section 1-1)*

39. Find the value of y in the equation $y = \frac{1}{4}x - 3$ when $x = -3$. *(Toolbox Skill 12)*

Working on the Unit Project

40. The diameter of the circle made by the front wheel of your bicycle depends on how much you turn the handlebars.

angle of turn

circle made by front wheel

   a. Is the relationship between the angle of the turn and the diameter of the circle a function? Explain why or why not.

   b. **Open-ended** What do you think is a reasonable domain for the relationship? Explain your choice.

Angle	Diameter
0°	—
10°	461 in.
20°	234 in.
30°	160 in.
40°	124 in.

2-2 Linear Functions

Focus
Use linear functions to describe situations. Find the domain and range of a linear function.

When you are camping high up in the Swiss Alps, water boils at a lower temperature than it does when you are camping in Death Valley. This happens because altitude affects the boiling temperature of water.

PLACE	Altitude (feet)	Boiling temperature of water (°F)
Cartagena, Colombia	Sea level (0 ft)	212
Fribourg, Switzerland	1929	209
Kimberley, South Africa	4013	205
Colorado Springs, United States	6012	201
Thimphu, Bhutan	7950	198

TECHNOLOGY NOTE

See the Technology Handbook, p. 605, for graphing a fitted line.

Talk it Over

1. Make a scatter plot of the data in the table. Use altitude as the control variable. What pattern do you see in the graph?

2. Does the graph represent a function? Explain why or why not.

3. a. Use your graph to estimate the boiling temperature of water when the altitude is 7000 ft.

   b. Draw a fitted line through the points on your graph. Use it to estimate the altitude when the boiling temperature is 207°F.

4. Where does the line cross the vertical axis? What does this point represent?

Some relationships, such as the one between altitude and boiling temperature, can be modeled by *linear functions*.

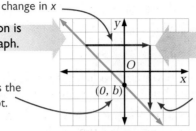

change in x

You can tell that a function is linear by looking at its graph. The graph is a line.

You can also look at how f(x) changes when x changes by a constant amount: The change is constant.

The value of b is the vertical intercept.

(0, b)

change in f(x)

$$m = \frac{\text{change in } f(x)}{\text{change in } x}$$

The ratio of the change in f(x) to the change in x is the slope, m. Any **linear function** can be written in the form $f(x) = mx + b$.

Sample 1

a. Use the information in the table on the previous page. Describe how the boiling temperature of water changes in relation to altitude.

b. Write an equation for the boiling temperature of water as a function of altitude.

Sample Response

a. Let a = the altitude (in feet).

Let $T(a)$ = the temperature (in degrees Fahrenheit) as a function of altitude.

Use any two pairs of data in the table.
For example, use Fribourg (1929, 209) and Thimphu (7950, 198).

$$m = \frac{\text{change in } T(a)}{\text{change in } a}$$

The slope describes how $T(a)$ changes as a changes.

change in a

change in T(a)

$$= \frac{198 - 209}{7950 - 1929}$$

$$= \frac{-11}{6021}$$

$$\approx -0.0018$$

If the altitude *increases* by 1 ft, the boiling temperature of water *decreases* by about 0.0018°F.

b. $\begin{pmatrix} \text{Boiling} \\ \text{temperature at} \\ \text{any altitude} \end{pmatrix} = \begin{pmatrix} \text{Boiling} \\ \text{temperature} \\ \text{at sea level} \end{pmatrix} + \begin{pmatrix} \text{Change in boiling} \\ \text{temperature per} \\ \text{foot of altitude} \end{pmatrix} \times \begin{pmatrix} \text{Altitude} \\ \text{(in ft)} \end{pmatrix}$

$\quad T(a) \quad = \quad 212 \quad + \quad (-0.0018)a$

If the altitude is a, then the boiling point of water is $T(a) = -0.0018a + 212$.

5. How does the equation $T(a) = -0.0018a + 212$ in Sample 1 show that the boiling temperature of water *decreases* as the altitude *increases*? How does the graph show this? How does the table of data show it?

6. Cathie found an equation for the function in Sample 1 this way after finding the slope. Explain Cathie's method.

7. Choose two other data points from the table on page 77. Use them to find the equation for the boiling temperature of water as a function of altitude. Is your answer the same as the one in Sample 1?

$m = -0.0018$
$f(x) = mx + b$
$T(a) = -0.0018a + b$
$198 = -0.0018(7950) + b$
$198 = -14.31 + b$
$212 \approx b$
An equation of the function is
$T(a) = -0.0018a + 212$.

Tell whether each function is linear. Explain how you know.

8. $f(x) = \frac{1}{2}x - 13$ **9.** $y = 4x$ **10.** $g(x) = x^2 + 0.6$

Sample 2

Use $f(x) = \frac{1}{3}x + 17$.

a. Find $f(9)$.   **b.** Find x when $f(x) = -1$.

Sample Response

a. Substitute 9 for x in the function.

$$f(x) = \frac{1}{3}x + 17$$

$$f(9) = \frac{1}{3}(9) + 17$$

$$= 20$$

b. Substitute -1 for $f(x)$ in the function and solve for x.

$$f(x) = \frac{1}{3}x + 17$$

$$-1 = \frac{1}{3}x + 17$$

$$-18 = \frac{1}{3}x \qquad \longleftarrow \text{Subtract 17 from both sides.}$$

$$-54 = x \qquad \longleftarrow \text{Multiply both sides by 3.}$$

11. Describe how you can use the equation from Sample 1 to find the boiling temperature of water at an altitude of 10,000 ft. Find this temperature.

12. Describe how you can use the equation from Sample 1 to find the altitude of Shiraz, Iran, where the boiling temperature of water is 185°F. Find the altitude of Shiraz.

▶ **Now you are ready for:**
Exs. 1–19 on pp. 81–82

Domain and Range of a Linear Function

Any value of x can be substituted into $f(x) = mx + b$. This means that the domain of a linear function consists of all real numbers. Any value of $f(x)$ can be produced by the formula. This means that the range of a linear function also consists of all real numbers when $m \neq 0$.

Watch Out!
When a function represents an everyday situation, there may be limits on the domain and range.

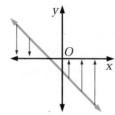

The graph of a linear function shows that the domain covers the entire x-axis.

The graph also shows that the range covers the entire y-axis.

29,028 ft above sea level

1312 ft below sea level

Dead Sea   **Mount Everest**

Sample 3

The altitude of Mount Everest, the highest place on Earth, is 29,028 ft. The lowest place on the surface of Earth is the Dead Sea, 1312 ft below sea level.

Use this information to find the domain and range of $T(a) = -0.0018a + 212$ on the surface of Earth.

Sample Response

The domain is all possible values for a: $-1312 \leq a \leq 29{,}028$.

The range is all possible values for $T(a)$ over this domain.

When $a = -1312$:
$$T(a) = -0.0018(-1312) + 212$$
$$\approx 214.36$$

range of the function

When $a = 29{,}028$:
$$T(a) = -0.0018(29{,}028) + 212$$
$$\approx 159.75$$

domain of the function

The range is about $160 \leq T(a) \leq 214$.

Unit 2 Exploring and Applying Functions

LINEAR FUNCTIONS

A linear function has the form $f(x) = mx + b$.

slope ⟶   ⟵ vertical intercept

$$m = \frac{\text{change in } f(x)}{\text{change in } x}$$

$$b = f(0)$$

The graph of a linear function is a line.

change in x

change in $f(x)$

$(0, b)$

Look Back ⟵

⟶ **Now you are ready for:**
Exs. 20–35 on pp. 82–84

How many data points do you need to find the equation of a linear function? Why?

2-2 Exercises and Problems

1. **Reading** How can you tell that a function is linear?

Tell whether each graph represents a linear function.

2.

3.

4.

5.
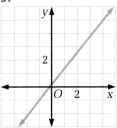

6. **a.** Which of the graphs in Exercises 2–5 represent a direct variation?

   b. Suppose the slope of a direct variation is m. Write an equation for this direct variation.

Student Resources
p. 672 *Visual Glossary of Functions*

Tell whether each function is linear. If it is, find $f(2)$, $f(-2)$, and $f(a + b)$.

7. $f(x) = 2 - x^2$

8. $f(x) = -3x - 6$

9. $f(a) = 4 + 10a$

10. $f(x) = x^3 - x$

11. $f(x) = \frac{3}{2}x + 4$

12. $f(d) = \frac{1}{d}$

Use the table of shoe sizes for Exercises 13–15.

13. Suppose a woman's American shoe size is 8. What European size would you recommend in a walking shoe?

14. Do you think the relationship in the table is an example of a linear function? Why?

15. Use the table to write an equation for European women's shoe sizes as a linear function of American women's shoe sizes.

Women's Shoe Sizes	
American	European
5	36
7	38
9	40
11	42

Write an equation for each function in the form $f(x) = mx + b$.

16. $f(3) = 9$, $f(5) = 15$

17. $f(-2) = 4$, $f(2) = -16$

18. $f(0) = 5$, $f(-5) = 10$

19. $f(10) = 4$, $m = \frac{1}{2}$

20. Each graph is an example of a *constant function*.

  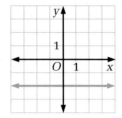

   a. Do the graphs represent linear functions?

   b. What is the slope of each graph?

   c. Suppose a constant function intersects the *y*-axis at $(0, c)$. Write an equation for this constant function.

   d. What is the domain of a constant function? What is the range of a constant function?

   e. **Open-ended** Give an everyday example of a constant function.

21. The number of chirps made by a snowy tree cricket can be modeled by a linear function of temperature. At 68°F, these crickets chirp 116 times per minute; at 80°F, they chirp 164 times per minute.

   a. Write an equation for $C(T)$, the number of chirps as a function of temperature.

   b. Find $C(90)$. What does it represent?

   c. Most crickets do not begin chirping until the temperature is about 39°F. Suppose that the highest temperature at which snowy tree crickets chirp is 105°F. Find the domain and range of $C(T)$.

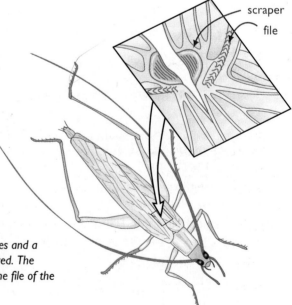

scraper

file

Each wing has a "file" with crossridges and a "scraper" that is hard and sharp-edged. The scraper of either wing rubs against the file of the other to produce a chirping sound.

22. When you fill a car's gas tank, the amount of gasoline in the tank is a function of the time the pump has been on. Suppose a pump fills an empty tank at a rate of 3.9 gal/min and the tank holds up to 13.5 gal of gasoline.

    a. Write an equation for the amount of gas in the tank as a function of time.

    b. What are the domain and range in this situation?

connection to **LITERATURE**

In 1861 Samuel White Baker and Florence von Sass Baker set out on a journey to search for the lake at high altitude that is the source of the Nile River. Their travels are recorded in Samuel Baker's journal, *The Albert N'Yanza, Great Basin of the Nile.*

"The river was about 180 to 200 yards in width, but much obstructed with rocks and islands; the stream ran at about four miles per hour; and the rapids and falls were so numerous that the roar of water had been continuous throughout our march from Murchison's Falls. By observations of Casella's thermometer I made the altitude of the river level at the island of Patooan 3,195 feet; thus from this point to the level of the Albert Lake at Magungo there was a fall of 475 ft . . . ."

After recording the altitude at several points along the river, Samuel Baker comments:

"These observations were extremely satisfactory, and showed that the thermometer behaved well at every boiling, as there was no confusion of altitudes, but each corroborated the preceding."

For Exercises 23–25, use the formulas from Sample 1 on page 78.

23. Why do you think it was important for the Bakers to take measurements at different points along the river?

24. **Writing** Explain how the Bakers could use the boiling temperature of water to find the altitude.

25. For a decrease in altitude of 475 ft, what is the change in the boiling temperature of water?

26. In his journal, Samuel Baker states, "Thus Victoria is the first source; but from the Albert the river issues at once as the great White Nile." The altitude of Albert Lake is 2021 ft. Find the boiling temperature of water there.

27. Use the function $g(x) = 3x + 2$.

    a. Show that $g(y) + g(z) \neq g(y + z)$.

    b. Show that $g(y) \cdot g(z) \neq g(y \cdot z)$.

Murchison's Falls

28. Use the function $f(x) = mx + b$.

    a. Show that $f(y) + f(z) \neq f(y + z)$.   **b.** Show that $f(y) \cdot f(z) \neq f(y \cdot z)$.

Ongoing **ASSESSMENT**

29. **Writing** Does this table represent a linear function? Describe two ways you can tell.

x	y
−2	−8
0	−7
3	−5.5
7	−3.5
12	−1

Review **PREVIEW**

30. Use the function $f(x) = x^3 - x$. Find $f(5)$, $f(-1)$, and $f(2a)$. *(Section 2-1)*

31. Explain what the corner-point principle is. *(Section 1-8)*

Write an inequality to describe each graph. *(Toolbox Skill 27)*

32.   −15 −10 −5 0 5 10   **33.**   −10   0   10   **34.**   −4 −3 −2 −1 0 1 2 3

Working on the Unit Project

Use your group's bicycle or go to a bicycle shop.

35. The diagrams show the position of the chain in the highest and lowest gears of a multispeed bicycle.

IN HIGHEST GEAR

rear gear

front gear

IN LOWEST GEAR

rear gear

front gear

    a. Choose a gear on your bicycle. When your bicycle is in this gear, how many teeth are in the front gear? How many teeth are in the rear gear?

    b. The ratio $\dfrac{\text{teeth in front gear}}{\text{teeth in rear gear}}$ is the number of turns the rear wheel makes for one full turn of the pedals. Find this ratio for the gear that you chose in part (a).

    c. Write an equation for the number of turns of the back tire as a function of the number of turns of the pedals for the gear you chose.

    d. Describe how you could use the function you wrote for part (c) to find the speed of your bicycle as a function of the number of turns of the pedals. (*Hint:* The circumference of the rear tire is the distance your bicycle travels for one full turn of the rear wheel.)

Piecewise and Absolute Value Functions

PIECE IT TOGETHER

Average Resting Heart Rate by Age

(0, 112)

(20, 72)   (50, 72)

Heart rate (beats/min)

Age (years)

BY THE WAY...

The typical heart rate for adults is 72 beats per minute. But doctors consider resting rates from 60–100 beats per minute within normal range. Athletic training slows the heart rate. Many athletes have resting rates from 40–60 beats per minute.

Talk it Over

1. Tell how a person's heart rate changes over the course of his or her lifetime. Refer to the graph.

2. Does the graph represent a function? Why or why not?

3. Do you think the graph can be described by a single equation? Explain.

Express heart rate as a function of age.

Sample Response

Problem Solving Strategy: Break the problem into parts.

Separate the heart rate graph into two pieces. For each piece, write an equation and give the ages to which the equation applies.

Find the slope of the line segment.

$$\text{slope} = \frac{72 - 112}{20 - 0} = \frac{-40}{20} = -2$$

The vertical intercept is 112. An equation for this piece is:

$$h(a) = -2a + 112$$

This piece represents a constant function. An equation for this piece is:

$$h(a) = 72$$

You can combine the two equations using this notation:

$$h(a) = \begin{cases} -2a + 112 & \text{if } 0 \le a \le 20 \\ 72 & \text{if } a > 20 \end{cases}$$

Talk it Over

4. Use the function from Sample 1 to predict the heart rate of a person 4 years old, 15 years old, and 50 years old.

5. a. Etenia's resting heart rate is 90 beats/min. What equation can you solve to estimate Etenia's age?

   b. Solve your equation from part (a).

The heart rate function in Sample 1 is an example of a *piecewise function*. A **piecewise function** is a function defined by two or more equations. Each equation applies to a different part of the function's domain.

Texas Automobile Rules — Liability/Private Passenger Rates		Harris County
Territory		
Type or Class	**Use or Status**	
No operator over 65	pleasure	$421
No operator over 65	work (more than 50% of the time)	484
No operator over 65	work (less than 50% of the time)	421
Males under 21	owner or principal operator	1495
Males between 21 and 25	owner or principal operator	926
Males under 21	not owner or principal operator	1212

The table shows average annual car insurance premiums for male drivers living in Harris County, Texas. The minimum age for a regular driver's license is 16.

a. Express the premiums for the highlighted categories as a function of the age of a male driver.

b. Graph the function in part (a).

Sample Response

a. Let a be the age of the driver, and let $p(a)$ be the premium in dollars. The rule for $p(a)$ consists of one equation for each of the three categories.

$$p(a) = \begin{cases} 1495 & \text{if } 16 \leq a < 21 \\ 926 & \text{if } 21 \leq a \leq 25 \\ 421 & \text{if } 25 < a \leq 65 \end{cases}$$

b. Graph each equation in the rule for $p(a)$ over the appropriate part of the domain.

The closed circle at (25, 926) means this point *is* part of the graph.

The open circle at (25, 421) means this point *is not* part of the graph.

Age of Male Drivers in Texas (owners or principal operators)

▶ Now you are ready for: Exs. 1–11 on pp. 89–90

Absolute Value Functions

The function d in Exercise 10 on page 90 pairs each real number x with its *absolute value*, written $|x|$. The **absolute value** of a number can be defined by this piecewise rule:

$$|x| = \begin{cases} x & \text{if } x \geq 0 \\ -x & \text{if } x < 0 \end{cases}$$

the original value if x is non-negative

the opposite of the original value if x is negative

2-3 Piecewise and Absolute Value Functions

Graph $y = |x + 2|$.

Sample Response

Write $y = |x + 2|$ in piecewise form:

Solve each inequality for x.

$$y = \begin{cases} x + 2 & \text{if } x + 2 \geq 0 \\ -(x + 2) & \text{if } x + 2 < 0 \end{cases}$$

or

$$y = \begin{cases} x + 2 & \text{if } x \geq -2 \\ -x - 2 & \text{if } x < -2 \end{cases}$$

Graph $y = x + 2$ and $y = -x - 2$ over the appropriate parts of the x-axis:

For $x < -2$, graph $y = -x - 2$.

For $x \geq -2$, graph $y = x + 2$.

$y = |x + 2|$

$(-2, 0)$

The function in Sample 3 is called an *absolute value function*.

ABSOLUTE VALUE FUNCTIONS

An **absolute value function** is a function that has a variable within the absolute value symbol.

Example

$y = 2|x + 1| - 4$

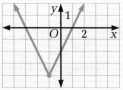

Student Resources Toolbox
p. 649 *Graphing*

Talk it Over

6. a. Graph $y = |x| + 2$. Compare this graph with the graph of $y = |x + 2|$ in Sample 3.

   b. For which values of x is $|x + 2| = |x| + 2$?

7. Graph $y = |2x|$ and $y = 2|x|$ on the same set of axes. What do you notice about the two graphs? Compare the graphs with the graph of $y = |x|$.

8. Repeat question 7 for the graphs of $y = |-2x|$ and $y = -2|x|$.

······▶ Now you are ready for:
Exs. 12–30 on pp. 90–92

Look Back ◀

Explain why an absolute value function is a piecewise function.

2-3 Exercises and Problems

1. **Reading** Explain the meaning of this heart rate function from Sample 1:

$$h(a) = \begin{cases} -2a + 112 & \text{if } 0 \le a \le 20 \\ 72 & \text{if } a > 20 \end{cases}$$

Write a rule for a piecewise function for each graph.

2.

3.

4.
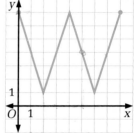

Graph each piecewise function.

5. $f(x) = \begin{cases} 4 & \text{if } 0 \le x < 3 \\ 8 & \text{if } x \ge 3 \end{cases}$

6. $g(t) = \begin{cases} 5 & \text{if } t \le -2 \\ -\dfrac{3}{2}t + 2 & \text{if } t > -2 \end{cases}$

7. $y = \begin{cases} x & \text{if } x < 0 \\ 2 & \text{if } x = 0 \\ x + 4 & \text{if } x > 0 \end{cases}$

8. $y = \begin{cases} 9 & \text{if } x < -3 \\ x^2 & \text{if } -3 \le x \le 3 \\ 9 & \text{if } x > 3 \end{cases}$

9. **Consumer Economics** The graph shows the monthly cost of Zachary's long-distance calling plan as a function of the length of time he talks on the telephone.

   a. Write a piecewise function for the graph.

   b. Find the cost of calling long-distance for 1.5 hours per month.

   c. Zachary wants his monthly long distance telephone bill to be no more than $20. Find the maximum length of time he can call long-distance.

Monthly Cost of Long-Distance Calling

2-3 Piecewise and Absolute Value Functions

10. a. Let d be a function that pairs a real number x with its distance from 0 on a number line. Copy and complete the table.

x	$d(x)$
-3	?
-2	?
-1	?
0	?
1	?
2	?
3	?

The distance from -3 to 0 is 3 units, so $d(-3) = 3$.

The distance from 2 to 0 is 2 units, so $d(2) = 2$.

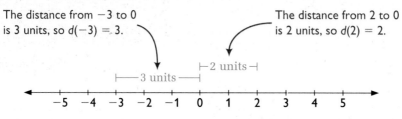

├── 2 units ──┤

├─── 3 units ───┤

b. Use your completed table to graph $y = d(x)$. Describe the graph, and give the domain and range of d.

c. Complete each sentence with *equal* or *opposites*.

If x is a negative number, then x and $d(x)$ are __?__.

If x is a nonnegative number, then x and $d(x)$ are __?__.

d. Write a piecewise rule for d.

TECHNOLOGY NOTE

On many graphics calculators, you enter piecewise functions such as

$$y = \begin{cases} 3x & \text{if } x < 2 \\ x - 1 & \text{if } x \geq 2 \end{cases}$$

like this:

$$y = 3x(x < 2) + (x - 1)(x \geq 2)$$

11. Michelle Jacobson received job offers from two department stores, Clothing Galore and Fits You Right. Clothing Galore offered Michelle a 4% commission on all sales. Fits You Right offered her $1000 per month plus a 2% commission on all sales over $15,000.

a. Express Michelle's possible monthly earnings at Clothing Galore as a function of her sales.

b. Express Michelle's possible monthly earnings at Fits You Right as a function of her sales.

c. Graph the functions from parts (a) and (b) on the same set of axes.

d. **Writing** Based on your graphs, which job do you think Michelle should accept? Explain your reasoning.

CLOTHING GALORE
Position Available

Position: Sales Associate

Salary: 4% commission on all sales

Responsibilities: Waiting on customers, assisting customers with clothing
ng ou

Fits You Right
Sales Assistant

$1000 per month + 2% commission on monthly sales over $15,000

Duties include helping shoppers in selecting clothing, posting sales, maintaining a neat and organized area including changing rooms and merchandise, cashing out at the end of shift.

Contact Personnel on the 3rd floor

Graph each absolute value function.

12. $y = |x + 1|$

13. $y = |x - 1|$

14. $y = 2|x| + 3$

15. $y = 2|x + 3|$

16. $y = 3|x - 4| - 2$

17. $y = -4|x + 2| + 1$

Depth finders Using an electronic device called a *depth finder*, the captain of a fishing boat measures the water depth to be 550 ft. Assume that the difference of the actual and measured depths is at most 5% of the actual depth.

18. **a.** The *absolute difference* between x and *any* fixed number a is given by the equation $y = |x - a|$. Write a function $f(x)$ that gives the absolute difference of the actual depth x and the measured depth.

b. You write "5% of the actual depth x" as $0.05x$. Graph the function from part (a) and $f(x) = 0.05x$ on the same axes.

c. What are the intersection points? What do these values mean?

screen display

BY THE WAY...

A depth finder measures water depth by producing pulses of sound just below the water's surface. The water depth can be calculated based on the time it takes for the sound pulses to echo off the bottom of the body of water and return to the ship.

TECHNOLOGY NOTE

On many graphics calculators, you enter $y = |x - 550|$ as $y = \text{abs}(x - 550)$.

connection to **PHYSICS**

The path of the billiard ball in the diagram is described by this equation:

$$y = (\tan d°)|x - a|$$

19. Suppose $a = 4.5$. For what value of d will the ball go into the corner pocket?

20. Suppose $d = 40$. For what value of a will the ball go into the corner pocket?

21. Suppose the ball is initially located at the point (2, 5). For what values of a and d will the ball go into the corner pocket?

Ongoing ASSESSMENT

22. Open-ended Alberta fills a glass with water, adds two ice cubes, and uses a straw to drink the water. Sketch a piecewise graph that you think could give the height of the water in the glass as a function of time. State the action associated with each piece of the graph.

Review PREVIEW

Write an equation for each function in the form $f(x) = mx + b$. *(Section 2-2)*

23. $f(-2) = -10$, $f(2) = 2$

24. $f(0) = 5$, $f(7) = \frac{3}{2}$

What name best describes each quadrilateral? *(Glossary)*

25.

26.

27.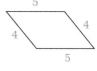

Solve each quadratic equation. *(Toolbox Skill 22)*

28. $x^2 + 3x + 1 = 0$

29. $4x^2 - 7 = 2x$

2 Working on the Unit Project

30. During the summer, Juanita likes to mountain bike. The graph shows the distance she travels on one trail as a function of time.

   a. Write a piecewise function for the graph and give the function's domain and range.

   b. How long does it take Juanita to complete the trail? How long does it take her to reach the halfway mark of the trail?

   c. Is Juanita's speed constant? How can you tell by looking at the graph? What might be reasons for any change in speed?

1. **Writing** Describe how to use the vertical line test to determine whether a graph is a function. Why does this test work?

   2-1

2. Does the table below represent a function? If so, what are its domain and range?

Soft Drinks	
12 oz	$.75
20 oz	$1.00
32 oz	$1.50

3. **a.** Write a rule for $V(r)$, the volume of a cone as a function of its radius. The height of the cone is 9 in.

   b. Find $V(2.5)$ and $V(7x)$.

4. Is the function $f(x) = x^2 + 5$ *one-to-one* or *many-to-one*? Explain your answer.

5. A cablevision company charges its subscribers a monthly fee of $24.28 for its basic service. The company also offers an additional Pay-per-Watch movie service that costs $4.99 per movie.

   2-2

   a. Write a rule for the monthly cable fee as a function of the number of movies ordered.

   b. Suppose Julie orders 5 movies this month. How much will she pay this month for her cable service?

   c. Ferris budgets $45 per month for his cable service. How many movies can he order each month?

   d. Suppose the cablevision company increases the monthly fee for basic service by $3. How does that affect the number of movies Ferris can order?

6. $f(-6) = 7$ and $f(3) = 4$. Write an equation for $f(x)$ in the form $f(x) = mx + b$.

7. A supermarket has a discount on "family packs" of meat. Chicken costs $2.00/lb for packages over 5 lb. Smaller packages are $2.50/lb. Express the cost as a function of weight.

   2-3

8. Graph the functions $y = |x - 3|$ and $y = |x| - 3$ on the same set of axes. How are the graphs related?

Quadratic Functions

POWER FALL

$t = 0$ s
$d = 0$ ft

$t = 0.5$ s
$d = 4$ ft

t is the time since the clam was dropped.

d is the distance the clam has fallen in t seconds.

$t = 1$ s
$d = 16$ ft

$t = 1.5$ s
$d = 36$ ft

Some species of gulls use a clever technique for eating clams and other shellfish. In order to break a clam's shell, a gull will pick up the clam with its beak, fly into the air, and drop the clam onto a rock. If the shell does not break, the gull will drop the clam from greater heights until it is successful.

Talk it Over

1. a. How far does the clam in the diagram fall from $t = 0$ s to $t = 0.5$ s? from $t = 0.5$ s to $t = 1$ s? from $t = 1$ s to $t = 1.5$ s?

   b. Is d a linear function of t? Why or why not?

   c. Make a scatter plot of the data pairs (t, d), and connect the plotted points with a smooth curve. Does your graph support your answer to part (b)? Explain.

2. In 1604, the Italian scientist Galileo Galilei observed that the distance traveled by any falling object varies directly with the *square* of the time the object falls.

   a. Use Galileo's observation to write an equation relating d, t, and a variation constant k.

   b. Use a point (t, d) from the diagram to find k.

The distance traveled by any falling object is given by this *quadratic function*:

$$d(t) = 16t^2$$

This function gives $d(t)$ in feet. — t must be in seconds.

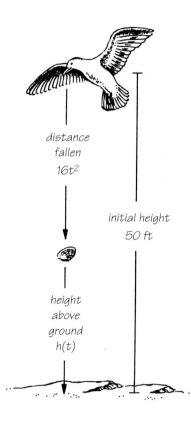

distance
fallen
$16t^2$

initial height
50 ft

height
above
ground
$h(t)$

Suppose a gull drops a clam from a height of 50 ft.

a. Express the height of the clam above the ground as a function of time.

b. Graph the function in part (a). What are the domain and range of the function?

Sample Response

a. **Problem Solving Strategy:** Use a diagram.

Let $h(t)$ = the height of the clam after t seconds.

$$\begin{pmatrix} \text{distance clam} \\ \text{has fallen} \end{pmatrix} + \begin{pmatrix} \text{height of clam} \\ \text{above ground} \end{pmatrix} = \begin{pmatrix} \text{initial height} \\ \text{of clam} \end{pmatrix}$$

$$16t^2 + h(t) = 50$$
$$h(t) = -16t^2 + 50$$

b. Graph the related function $f(x) = -16x^2 + 50$. Then look at which part of the graph is the graph of the function $h(t) = -16t^2 + 50$.

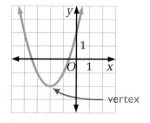

The clam is dropped. ———→

The graph of the clam height function is in the first quadrant.

The clam hits the ground at $h(t) = 0$.

Domain: $0 \le t \le 1.7$ Range: $0 \le h(t) \le 50$

QUADRATIC FUNCTIONS

A quadratic function has the form:

$$f(x) = ax^2 + bx + c$$

where a, b, and c are constants and $a \ne 0$.

The graph is a parabola.

The sign of a determines whether the parabola opens upward or downward.

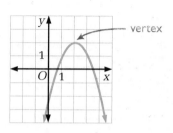

Case 1: $a > 0$
The parabola opens upward.
The vertex is the lowest point.

Case 2: $a < 0$
The parabola opens downward.
The vertex is the highest point.

The Height of a Thrown Object

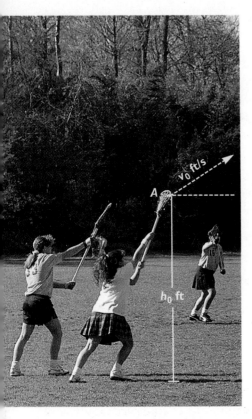

In the function in Sample 1, $f(x) = -16x^2 + 50$, the initial height, h_0, is 50 feet.

If you throw an object instead of dropping it, the object's height in feet after t seconds is given by this equation:

$$h(t) = -16t^2 + (v_0 \sin A)t + h_0 \quad \longleftarrow \quad h_0 \text{ is the object's initial height (in feet).}$$

v_0 is the object's initial speed (in feet per second).

A is the angle at which the object is thrown with respect to the horizontal.

Sample 2

A lacrosse player uses a stick with a pocket on one end to throw a ball toward the opposing team's goal. Suppose the ball leaves a player's stick from an initial height of 7 ft, at a speed of 90 ft/s, and at an angle of 30° with respect to the horizontal.

a. Express the height of the ball as a function of time.

b. When is the ball 25 ft above the ground?

Sample Response

a. Use the equation for the height of a thrown object.

$$h(t) = -16t^2 + (v_0 \sin A)t + h_0$$
$$= -16t^2 + (90 \sin 30°)t + 7 \quad \longleftarrow \quad \text{Substitute } 90 \text{ for } v_0, 30° \text{ for } A, \text{ and } 7 \text{ for } h_0.$$
$$= -16t^2 + 45t + 7$$

b. Solve the equation $h(t) = -16t^2 + 45t + 7$ when $h(t) = 25$.

Method 1

Problem Solving Strategy: Use a graph.

1 Graph $y = -16x^2 + 45x + 7$ and $y = 25$ on the same set of axes.

Intersection
X = .48291958 Y = 25

2 Find each point of intersection. The x-coordinates of these points are about 0.5 and 2.3.

Intersection
X = 2.3295804 Y = 25

The ball is 25 ft above the ground after about 0.5 s and about 2.3 s.

Method ❷

Problem Solving Strategy: Use a formula.

$-16t^2 + 45t + 7 = 25$ ⟵ First write the equation in the form $at^2 + bt + c = 0$.

$-16t^2 + 45t - 18 = 0$ ⟵ Subtract 25 from both sides.

Then solve the equation using the quadratic formula.

$$t = -\frac{b}{2a} \pm \frac{\sqrt{b^2 - 4ac}}{2a}$$

$$= -\frac{45}{2(-16)} \pm \frac{\sqrt{(45)^2 - 4(-16)(-18)}}{2(-16)} \quad \text{⟵ Substitute } -16 \text{ for } a, \\ 45 \text{ for } b, \text{ and } -18 \text{ for } c.$$

$$= \frac{45}{32} \pm \frac{\sqrt{873}}{-32}$$

$$\approx 1.41 \pm (-0.92)$$

$$\approx 0.49 \text{ or } 2.33$$

The ball is 25 ft above the ground after about 0.5 s and about 2.3 s.

Talk it Over

3. In Sample 2, which method do you prefer? Why?

4. Use a graphics calculator to determine when the lacrosse ball reaches its maximum height. Find the maximum height.

5. Does the graph of $h(t) = -16t^2 + 45t + 7$ show the path of the lacrosse ball through the air? Explain.

6. Is the graph of the function one-to-one? Explain.

BY THE WAY...

Modern lacrosse is based on a game first played by the Iroquois people of New York and Canada. The Iroquois called their game *baggataway* or *tewaraathon*.

Look Back ⟵

List at least two ways in which quadratic functions differ from linear functions.

2-4   Exercises and Problems

1. **Reading** Look at the picture of the gull and clam on page 94. How far does the clam fall in 1.5 s?

Tell whether each function is a quadratic function. For each quadratic function:

a. Find $f(3)$, $f(-3)$, and $f(a + b)$.

b. Graph $f(x)$.

2. $f(x) = 1.5x^2$

3. $f(x) = 2x^2 + 3x - 2$

4. $f(x) = \dfrac{1}{2x^2 + 3x - 2}$

5. $f(x) = 5 - 7x^2$

6. $f(x) = (x - 4)^3$

7. $f(x) = (x - 4)^2$

8. Suppose a gull drops a clam from a height of 40 ft.

   a. Express the height of the clam above the ground as a function of time.

   b. Graph the function in part (a).

   c. When does the clam hit the ground?

9. Suppose the lacrosse ball in Sample 2 is thrown from an initial height of 6 ft, at a speed of 120 ft/s, and at an angle of 10° with respect to the horizontal.

   a. Express the height of the ball above the ground as a function of time.

   b. When is the ball 5 ft above the ground?

   c. TECHNOLOGY Use a graphics calculator to determine when the ball reaches its maximum height. What is the maximum height?

10. Suppose an automatic pitching machine releases a baseball parallel to the ground at a height of 5 ft and at an initial speed of 70 mi/h. At the same instant, a second baseball is dropped from the same initial height.

   a. Express the height of the pitching machine's baseball as a function of time. (Use the formula on page 96 and an angle of 0°.)

   b. Express the height of the dropped baseball as a function of time. (Use the formula on page 94.)

   c. **Writing** What do you notice about the functions from parts (a) and (b)? What does the relationship between the functions mean in this situation?

11. **Career** An engineer designing a curved road must make the curve's radius large enough so that car passengers are not pulled to one side as they go around the curve at the posted speed. The minimum radius for passenger comfort is given by this function:

   $$r(s) = 0.334s^2$$

   $r(s)$ is the curve's radius in feet. s is the expected speed of traffic in miles per hour.

   a. Copy and complete the table.

   b. Calculate the ratios $\dfrac{r(10)}{r(5)}$, $\dfrac{r(20)}{r(10)}$, and $\dfrac{r(40)}{r(20)}$.
   Based on your calculations, by what factor does the minimum radius increase when the expected speed of traffic doubles?

   c. Show that doubling the traffic speed *always* produces the result you observed in part (b).
   $\left(Hint: \text{Use the ratio } \dfrac{r(2s)}{r(s)}.\right)$

s (mi/h)	$r(s)$ (ft)
5	?
10	?
?	133.6
?	534.4

History of Mathematics The Indian mathematician Sridhara gave this derivation of the quadratic formula around A.D. 1025.

$ax^2 + bx + c = 0$	← Start with the general quadratic equation.
$ax^2 + bx = -c$	← Subtract c from both sides.
$4a^2x^2 + 4abx = -4ac$	← Multiply both sides by $4a$.
$4a^2x^2 + 4abx + b^2 = b^2 - 4ac$	← Add b^2 to both sides.
$(2ax + b)^2 = b^2 - 4ac$	← Factor the left side of the equation.
$2ax + b = \pm\sqrt{b^2 - 4ac}$	← Take the square root of both sides.
$2ax = -b \pm \sqrt{b^2 - 4ac}$	← Subtract b from both sides.
$x = \dfrac{-b \pm \sqrt{b^2 - 4ac}}{2a}$	← Divide both sides by $2a$.

12. Look at the fourth and fifth equations in Sridhara's derivation. Show that these equations are equivalent by expanding the product $(2ax + b)^2$.

13. Why is the condition $a \neq 0$ necessary in the quadratic formula?

14. Use the quadratic equation $2x^2 + 5x + 3 = 0$.

   a. What are the values of a, b, and c for this equation?

   b. Solve $2x^2 + 5x + 3 = 0$ by following the steps to the right of the equations in Sridhara's derivation.

   c. Solve $2x^2 + 5x + 3 = 0$ by substituting the values of a, b, and c directly into the quadratic formula. Are your solutions the same as those for part (b)?

15. **Research** Write a short report on Sridhara's life and mathematical work.

16. Cochita wants to build a rectangular corral for her horse. Three sides of the corral will be wooden fencing. The wall of the canyon will form the fourth side. Cochita has 200 ft of fencing and wants to build the largest corral possible.

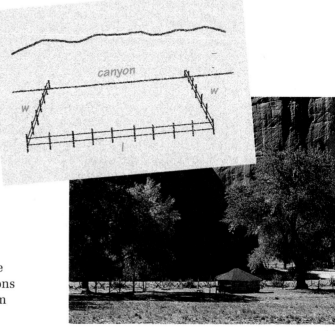

   a. Express the area A of Cochita's corral in terms of the length l and width w.

   b. Express l in terms of w.

   c. Express A as a function of w alone. Is the function $A = f(w)$ a quadratic function?

   d. Graph $A = f(w)$. What values of w and l maximize the corral's area? What is the maximum area?

   e. Suppose Cochita's corral does not have to be rectangular. Does the corral whose dimensions you found in part (d) still have the maximum possible area?

17. **Writing** The function $h(t) = -16t^2 + (v_0 \sin A)t + h_0$ for the height of a thrown object is based on the assumption that there is no air resistance. Do you think the function will overestimate or underestimate an object's actual height at a given instant? Explain.

18. Find the mean, median, and mode of these test scores: 85, 56, 89, 92, 84, 100, 75, 72, 81, 69. *(Toolbox Skill 1)*

Graph each function. *(Section 2-3)*

19. $y = \begin{cases} x + 3 & \text{if } x < 0 \\ 5 & \text{if } x = 0 \\ 2x - 1 & \text{if } x > 0 \end{cases}$

20. $f(x) = -3\,|x + 2| - 1$

Factor. *(Toolbox Skill 17)*

21. $x^2 + 2x - 24$

22. $6a^2 - a - 15$

23. $25x^3 - 100x$

Working on the Unit Project

24. In 1992, only about 20% of adults and 5% of children wore protective helmets while bicycling. In this exercise, you will investigate what happens if you fall without a helmet.

   a. When a person of average height sits on a bicycle, the person's head is about 5.3 ft above the ground. Suppose such a person falls from a bicycle at rest. Use the function $d(t) = 16t^2$ to estimate the time it takes for the person's head to hit the ground.

   ventilation hole
   allows air to flow under helmet

   outer shell
   protects liner

   b. The function $v(t) = 32t$ gives the speed $v(t)$ in feet per second of an object that falls for t seconds. Estimate the speed at which the head of the person in part (a) hits the ground.

   c. **Open-ended** A cyclist not wearing a helmet will generally have lasting brain damage if the cyclist's head hits the ground at more than 18 ft/s. Based on your answer to part (b), do you think wearing a helmet is a good idea? Explain.

   shock-absorbing liner
   crumples to absorb impact

   sizing pad
   provides better fit and allows air space between the head and helmet

   straps and buckle
   adjust for secure fit

Polynomial Functions

More POWER To You

Recognize, evaluate, and graph direct variation functions and polynomial functions.

EXPLORATION

How is the weight of a ball related to its diameter?

- **Materials: modeling clay, thin probe (for example, a straightened paper clip), ruler, spring or balance scale, graphics calculator**
- **Work in a group of four students.**

Try to make the ball as round as possible.

(1) Make eight balls of clay of different sizes. Use the probe to measure the diameter of each ball.

Mark or hold this point.

Measure the part of the probe that was inside the ball of clay.

Measure the diameter in three different directions. Find the mean of the three diameters. Record your data in a table.

(2) Weigh each ball on the scale. Record the weights in the table.

(3) Make a scatter plot of the ordered pairs (diameter, weight). Describe the shape of the graph.

(4) Use the statistical functions of a graphics calculator to find an equation that models the data in the scatter plot. Use the calculator's "power regression" model. Write down the equation.

(5) Suppose you could make perfect measurements in steps 1 and 2. The equation that you found in step 4 would have the form $f(x) = kx^3$. How close to 3 is the exponent in your equation? What is the value of k in your equation?

DIRECT VARIATION FUNCTIONS

A direct variation function has the form
$$f(x) = kx^n$$
where n is a positive integer and $k \neq 0$.

The exponent, n, is the degree of the function.

A snake
that is 0.4 m long
weighs 27.7 g.

Sample 1

The weight, w, of an adult male hognose snake varies directly with the cube of its length, l. Write a direct variation function that describes weight in terms of length.

Sample Response

Problem Solving Strategy: Use an equation.

$$w(l) = kl^3 \quad \longleftarrow \quad \text{Use the general form for direct variation with the cube.}$$

$$27.7 = k(0.4)^3 \quad \longleftarrow \quad \text{Substitute the values you know.}$$

$$27.7 = k(0.064)$$

$$432.8 \approx k$$

The function is $w(l) = 432.8l^3$.

Talk it Over

Use the graphs of $y = x$, $y = x^2$, $y = x^3$, $y = x^4$, and $y = x^5$.

    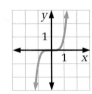

1. Explain why each function is a direct variation function. Give the degree of each function.

2. Which of the functions are one-to-one?

3. What kind of symmetry does each graph have?

4. The functions $f(x) = x$, $f(x) = x^3$, and $f(x) = x^5$ are *odd functions*. What do their graphs have in common?

5. The functions $f(x) = x^2$ and $f(x) = x^4$ are *even functions*. What do their graphs have in common?

The sum of one or more direct variation functions is a **polynomial function.** The sum may also include a constant function. An example of a polynomial function is

$$P(x) = x^4 + 16x^3 + 5x^2 - 13x + 6.$$

The coefficients of a polynomial function are real numbers, and the exponents are whole numbers. The **degree of a polynomial function** is the largest exponent.

Sample 2

Use the polynomial function $P(x) = 2x^4 + 0.2x^3 - x^2 + 1.$

a. Find $P(-2)$.　　　　　　　**b.** Find $P(3a)$.

Sample Response

a. 　$P(x) = 2x^4 + 0.2x^3 - x^2 + 1$

$P(-2) = 2(-2)^4 + 0.2(-2)^3 - (-2)^2 + 1$　　⟵—— Substitute -2 for x.

$= 2(16) + 0.2(-8) - 4 + 1$　　⟵—— Simplify.

$= 32 + (-1.6) - 4 + 1$

$= 27.4$

b. 　$P(x) = 2x^4 + 0.2x^3 - x^2 + 1$

$P(3a) = 2(3a)^4 + 0.2(3a)^3 - (3a)^2 + 1$　　⟵—— Substitute $3a$ for x.

$= 2(81a^4) + 0.2(27a^3) - 9a^2 + 1$　　⟵—— Simplify.

$= 162a^4 + 5.4a^3 - 9a^2 + 1$

Talk it Over

6. Use the function $f(x) = \frac{1}{2}x - 4$.

   a. Is f a polynomial function? What is its degree? What other type of function is this?

   b. Find x so that $f(x) = -1$.

7. Use the function $g(x) = -x^2 + 3x - 1$.

   a. Is g a polynomial function? What is its degree? What other type of function is this?

   b. Find x so that $g(x) = -1$.

8. Use the function in Sample 2. Suppose you wanted to find x so that $P(x) = -1$. What method could you use?

······▶ **Now you are ready for:**
⋮ **Exs. 1–21 on pp. 105–107**

Zeros of a Function

Sometimes polynomials are written in factored form. For example, you can write the volume of the prism below as the sum of the volumes of the four smaller prisms or as the product of the length, width, and height of the large prism.

The volume of this piece is $2x^2$.

The volume of this piece is $6x$.

The volume of this piece is x^3.

The volume of this piece is $3x^2$.

Volume $= x^3 + 5x^2 + 6x$

Volume $= x(x + 3)(x + 2)$

The polynomial $V(x) = x(x + 3)(x + 2)$ is in factored form. The factored form of a polynomial function tells you the *zeros of the function*. A **zero of a function** is a value of x that makes $f(x)$ equal to zero. You can use the zeros to graph the function.

Sample 3

Graph the function $V(x) = x(x + 3)(x + 2)$.

Sample Response

Method ❶ Graph the function by hand.

Step 1 Find the zeros of the function.

$V(x) = 0$ when $x = 0$, $x = -3$, or $x = -2$.
The graph crosses the x-axis at $(0, 0)$, $(-3, 0)$, and $(-2, 0)$.

Step 2 Substitute values of x that are between and beyond the zeros to see the shape of the graph.

x	y
-4	-8
-2.5	0.625
-1	-2
1	12

Step 3 Graph all the points that you found and connect them with a smooth curve.

Unit 2 Exploring and Applying Functions

Method ❷ Use a graphics calculator or graphing software.

Enter the polynomial in factored form or as a sum:

$y = x(x + 3)(x + 2)$ or $y = x^3 + 5x^2 + 6x$.

Talk it Over

9. The dimensions of a prism must be positive. Which points of the graph in Sample 3 represent this?

10. Describe how to use the graph in Sample 3 to find x when the volume of the prism is 40.

POLYNOMIAL FUNCTIONS

A polynomial function has the form

$P(x) = a_n x^n + a_{n-1} x^{n-1} + a_{n-2} x^{n-2} + \ldots + a_1 x + a_0$

The exponents are whole numbers.

n is the degree of the polynomial.

The coefficients are real numbers.

Example

$P(x) = 3x^5 + x^3 - 4x^2 + 1$

The factored form of a polynomial gives the zeros of the function. You can use the zeros to sketch a graph of the function.

Look Back ←

⋯▶ **Now you are ready for:**
Exs. 22–36 on pp. 107–109

Use examples to explain why constant functions, linear functions, quadratic functions, and direct variation functions are types of polynomial functions.

2-5 Exercises and Problems

1. **Reading** What is the value of k for each of the direct variation functions in the graphs on page 102?

Tell whether each direct variation function is *one-to-one*.

2. $f(x) = 0.2x^3$

3. $g(x) = 1.2x^4$

4. $r(x) = 0.75x$

For Exercises 5–8, write an equation in the form $f(x) = kx^n$ for each direct variation function.

5. $k = 0.8$ and $n = 3$ 6. $k = 1$ and $f(6) = 36$ 7. $f(2) = 8$ and $n = 4$

8. $f(0.3) = 45$ and $f(x)$ varies directly with the square of x

9. Suppose a ball of clay with a diameter of 1 in. weighs 0.41 oz. Write a formula for the weight of the ball as a function of the diameter.

Student Resources Toolbox
p. 652 *Formulas*

10. **Driving** A driver's reaction distance, r, varies directly with the speed, s, of the car.

    a. Write an equation for r as a function of s. Use k as the constant.

    b. Suppose the reaction distance for a driver traveling 30 mi/h is 33 ft. Find the value of k. Rewrite your function using this value of k.

    c. For what speed is the reaction distance 50 ft?

11. **Trains** Taking curves at high speeds raises the average speed of a train, but passengers do not like how it feels. The force (F) you feel when a train goes around a curve depends on your mass (m), the radius of the curve (r), and the square of the train's velocity (v).

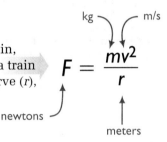

$$F = \frac{mv^2}{r}$$

kg — m/s

newtons — meters

a. Suppose the same passenger goes around the same curve at different velocities. Explain why this represents direct variation with the square of the velocity.

b. Suppose the passenger has a mass of 60 kg and the radius of the turn is 9 m. Write a direct variation function that describes force in terms of velocity.

c. Use your equation to find the force on the passenger when the velocity is 9 m/s.

d. **Research** Find out what a *newton* is and after whom it is named.

> **BY THE WAY...**
>
> New passenger cars for trains are designed to tilt as they round corners in order to cancel out 70% of the force experienced by riders.

12. **Medicine** The blood flow in an artery varies directly with the fourth power of the radius of the artery.

a. The radius of the aorta, a coronary artery, is about 1.2 cm at one point. The blood flow at that point is about 225 mL/min (milliliters per minute). Write a direct variation function that describes blood flow in terms of radius.

b. Farther away from the heart, the radius of the aorta is 0.86 cm. Find the blood flow at that point.

Tell whether each function is a polynomial function. If your answer is *No*, give a reason.

13. $g(x) = \frac{1}{2}x^3 - 5x$

14. $h(a) = 6^a - a^6$

15. $a(c) = c^{-2} + c^4 + 2c^5$

16. Use the function $f(x) = 1.5x - 7$.

a. What is the degree of f? What are two different names for this type of function?

b. Find $f(6)$ and $f(0)$.

c. Find x so that $f(x) = -22$.

17. Use the function $g(x) = x^2 + 3x$.

a. What is the degree of g? What are two different names for this type of function?

b. Find $g(-5)$ and $g\left(\frac{1}{2}\right)$.

c. Find x so that $g(x) = 0$.

For each polynomial function, write the degree and find the given value.

18. $f(x) = x^3 - 3x^2 + 2x - 1; f(2)$

19. $g(x) = 3x - x^2 + x^4 - 2x^3; g(1)$

20. $h(x) = x^5 - x^3 + 1; h(3)$

21. $f(x) = 2x^4 - x^2 + 1; f(-1)$

For Exercises 22–25:

a. **Find the zeros of each function.**

b. **Graph each polynomial function.**

22. $f(x) = x(x - 2)(x + 3)$

23. $g(x) = (x - 1)(x - 3)^2$

24. $h(x) = x(x^2 - x - 6)$

25. $r(x) = x^4 - 4x^3 + 4x^2$

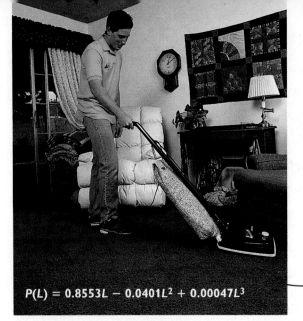

P(L) = 0.8553L − 0.0401L² + 0.00047L³

Noise Level A social scientist found that the percent (*P*) of people who are "highly annoyed" by noise from household appliances, traffic, airports, and so on depends on the decibel level (*L*) of the noise.

26. What percent of people are highly annoyed by a noise level of 80 decibels?

27. What percent of people are highly annoyed by a noise level of 0 decibels? What does this tell you about the graph of this polynomial?

A vacuum cleaner makes a noise of approximately 80 decibels.

28. Anne wrote a formula for the number of diagonals of a polygon.

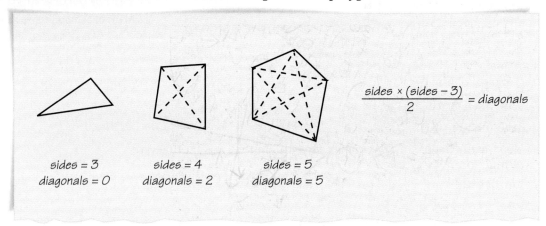

$$\frac{sides \times (sides - 3)}{2} = diagonals$$

sides = 3
diagonals = 0

sides = 4
diagonals = 2

sides = 5
diagonals = 5

a. Write Anne's formula as a polynomial function for the number of diagonals in terms of the number of sides. What is its degree? What is its domain?

b. How many diagonals does an octagon have?

c. A polygon has 135 diagonals. How many sides does it have?

Ongoing ASSESSMENT

29. a. **Open-ended** Write equations for at least ten different polynomial functions of varying degrees.

b. TECHNOLOGY Use a graphics calculator or graphing software to graph the functions. Record the degree of each polynomial function and how many *turning points* the function has.

c. Make a conjecture about the relationship between the number of turning points and the degree of the polynomial function.

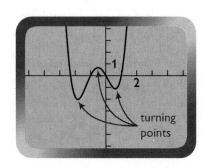

turning points

30. Suppose a pebble falls from a height of 75 ft. Express the height of the pebble above the ground as a function of time. *(Section 2-4)*

Tell whether each group of measurements can be the lengths of the sides of a triangle. Write *Yes* or *No*. *(Section 1-2)*

31. 7 mm, 8 mm, 19 mm   32. 1 in., 0.5 in., 0.75 in.   33. 10 yd, 10 yd, 10 yd

34. Is this statement *true* or *false*: $\sqrt{25 \cdot 16} = \sqrt{25} \cdot \sqrt{16}$? *(Toolbox Skill 19)*

•••
Working on the Unit Project

If there were no friction from the air or the road, a cyclist would coast forever at a constant speed. A cyclist must supply energy to maintain a constant speed, however. The power (in watts) that a 75 kg rider on a 10 kg bicycle must supply to maintain a constant speed is $P = 0.2581v^3 + 3.509v$, where v is the speed in meters per second.

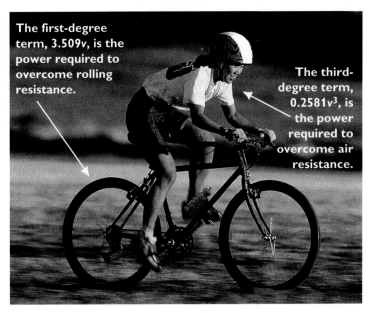

The first-degree term, 3.509v, is the power required to overcome rolling resistance.

The third-degree term, 0.2581v³, is the power required to overcome air resistance.

35. In a two-hour bicycle race, Bonnie rides at an average speed of 11 m/s (25 mi/h).

   a. How much power must she supply to ride at this speed?

   b. How much of the power is used to overcome rolling resistance? How much is used to overcome air resistance?

   c. Which do you think is more important to a bicycle racer, rolling resistance or air resistance? Describe two things a racer could do in order to reduce the effect of the resistance.

36. When Arlean rides her bike to school, she supplies 0.1 horsepower (74.6 watts) to the bicycle in order to keep it moving at a constant speed. Use a graphics calculator to determine Arlean's speed when she rides to school.

2-6 Radical Functions

········Focus
Explore functions that
involve radicals. Use these
functions to solve problems.

Natural FORCES

A tsunami is an ocean wave with tremendous power. These waves move at speeds of up to 600 mi/h. The speed, *s*, of a tsunami in miles per hour is a function of the depth, *d*, of the ocean in feet.

$$s(d) = 3.86\sqrt{d}$$

A copy of The Great Wave Off the Coast of Kanagawa *by the Japanese artist Hokusai*

Depth *d* (feet)	Speed *s(d)* (mi/h)
100	?
200	?
346	?
5000	?
10,000	?
20,000	?
34,600	?

Talk it Over

1. The ocean depth in the Kuril Trench east of Japan is 34,600 ft. As you move toward the Japanese island of Hokkaido, the depth decreases rapidly. Suppose an earthquake occurs along the Kuril Trench and causes a tsunami.

   a. Use the function $s(d) = 3.86\sqrt{d}$. Complete the table by calculating the speed of the resulting tsunami as it moves toward Hokkaido. Round decimals to the nearest tenth.

   b. Use your table to compare the speeds of a tsunami at depths of 100 ft and 10,000 ft. Compare the speeds at 346 ft and at 34,600 ft. What do you notice?

2. a. Use the function $s = 3.86\sqrt{d}$. Write and simplify an expression for $s(100d)$.

   b. Use your result in part (a) to compare the speeds of a tsunami as it moves from one place in the ocean to another 100 times as deep.

   c. Does your answer in part (b) agree with your answer to part (b) of question 1? Explain.

Student Resources Toolbox
p. 642 *Algebraic Expressions*

Map showing stations in the Tsunami Warning Center's network.

BY THE WAY...

Tsunami is a Japanese word that means "harbor wave." A tsunami occurs when a large area of the ocean floor, often at the bottom of a deep trench, shifts suddenly. This shift causes huge amounts of water to move, creating a wave that can reach a height of over 100 ft!

Sample 1

What is the ocean depth where the speed of a tsunami is 400 mi/h? Round your answer to the nearest foot.

Sample Response

Problem Solving Strategy: Use a formula.

$$s(d) = 3.86\sqrt{d}$$ ← The speed of a tsunami is a function of depth.

$$400 = 3.86\sqrt{d}$$ ← Substitute 400 for $s(d)$.

Solve for d.

Method ❶ Use a graph.

Graph $y = 3.86\sqrt{x}$ and $y = 400$ on the same set of axes and find the point of intersection.

A tsunami travels at 400 mi/h where the ocean is about 10,739 ft deep.

Intersection
X = 10738.543 Y = 400

Method ❷ Use algebra.

$$400 = 3.86\sqrt{d}$$

$$103.63 \approx \sqrt{d}$$ ← Divide both sides by 3.86.

$$10,739.18 \approx d$$ ← Square both sides.

A tsunami travels at 400 mi/h where the ocean is about 10,739 ft deep.

2-6 Radical Functions

111

To solve an equation in which a variable appears under a radical symbol, you need to get the radical alone on one side of the equation. Remember that $\sqrt{x}$ means the positive square root of x.

Sample 2

Solve $\sqrt{x + 7} - 1 = x$.

Sample Response

Method ❶ Use algebra.

$$\sqrt{x + 7} - 1 = x$$
$$\sqrt{x + 7} = x + 1 \qquad \longleftarrow \text{ Get the square root term alone on one side.}$$
$$x + 7 = x^2 + 2x + 1 \qquad \longleftarrow \text{ Square both sides.}$$
$$0 = x^2 + x - 6 \qquad \longleftarrow \text{ Subtract } (x + 7) \text{ from both sides.}$$
$$0 = (x + 3)(x - 2) \qquad \longleftarrow \text{ Factor or use the quadratic formula.}$$
$$x + 3 = 0 \quad \text{or} \quad x - 2 = 0 \qquad \longleftarrow \text{ Set each factor equal to 0.}$$
$$x = -3 \quad \text{or} \quad x = 2 \qquad \longleftarrow \text{ Solve for } x.$$

Check

$$\sqrt{x + 7} - 1 = x \qquad \longleftarrow \text{ Use the } \textit{original} \text{ equation.} \longrightarrow \sqrt{x + 7} - 1 = x$$
$$\sqrt{-3 + 7} - 1 \overset{?}{=} -3 \qquad \longleftarrow \text{ Substitute a solution for } x. \longrightarrow \sqrt{2 + 7} - 1 \overset{?}{=} 2$$
$$\sqrt{4} - 1 \overset{?}{=} -3 \qquad\qquad\qquad\qquad\qquad\qquad \sqrt{9} - 1 \overset{?}{=} 2$$
$$2 - 1 \neq -3 \qquad\qquad\qquad\qquad\qquad\qquad 3 - 1 = 2 \ ✔$$

-3 is not a solution.   2 is a solution.

The solution is 2.

Method ❷ Use a graph.

Graph $y = \sqrt{x + 7} - 1$ and $y = x$ on the same set of axes and find all points of intersection.

Intersection
X = 2   Y = 2

The solution is 2.

In Sample 2, squaring both sides of the equation produced a value for x that is not a solution of the original equation. Such an answer is called an **extraneous solution**.

Talk it Over

3. How does the graph in Method 2 of Sample 2 show that -3 is an extraneous solution?

4. Why does the graph of $y = \sqrt{x + 7} - 1$ stop at $(-7, -1)$?

Radical Functions

A function like $s(d) = 3.86\sqrt{d}$ is a *radical function*. A **radical function** is a function that has a variable under a radical symbol. In this book, assume that the domains and ranges of all functions are real numbers.

PROPERTIES OF RADICALS

Examples

$\sqrt[n]{b} = x$ when $x^n = b$ $\sqrt[4]{16} = 2$ because $2^4 = 16$

└─You read this as "the nth root of b."

$$\sqrt[n]{b^n} = \begin{cases} b & \text{when } n \text{ is odd} \\ |b| & \text{when } n \text{ is even} \end{cases}$$

$\sqrt[5]{(-7)^5} = -7$

$\sqrt[4]{(-7)^4} = |-7| = 7$

$\sqrt[n]{ab} = \sqrt[n]{a} \cdot \sqrt[n]{b},$ for all values of a and b when n is odd $\sqrt[3]{8x^3} = \sqrt[3]{8} \cdot \sqrt[3]{x^3} = 2x$

for positive values of a and b when n is even $\sqrt[4]{256x^4} = \sqrt[4]{256} \cdot \sqrt[4]{x^4} = 4|x|$

Sample 3

Simplify.

a. $\sqrt[4]{(-3)^4}$ b. $\sqrt[3]{(t-5)^3}$ c. $\sqrt[6]{(2-x)^6}$

Sample Response ···

a. $\sqrt[4]{(-3)^4} = |-3|$ ◄──── $\sqrt[n]{b^n} = |b|$ when n is even
     $= 3$

b. $\sqrt[3]{(t-5)^3} = t - 5$ ◄──── $\sqrt[n]{b^n} = b$ when n is odd

c. $\sqrt[6]{(2-x)^6} = |2 - x| = \begin{cases} 2 - x & \text{when } x \le 2 \\ -(2 - x) = x - 2 & \text{when } x > 2 \end{cases}$

2-6 Radical Functions   **113**

Find the domain and range of each function.

a. $f(x) = \sqrt{x + 1}$ b. $f(x) = \sqrt[3]{x + 1}$

Sample Response

a. Graph $y = \sqrt{x + 1}$.

Range: $y \geq 0$

Domain: $x \geq -1$

b. Graph $y = \sqrt[3]{x + 1}$.

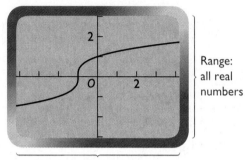

Range: all real numbers

Domain: all real numbers

TECHNOLOGY NOTE

To enter radicals, see p. 596 of the Technology Handbook.

Talk it Over

5. Jane found the domain of $f(x) = \sqrt{x + 1}$ in this way:

   $(x + 1)$ *cannot be negative.*

   $x + 1 \geq 0$

   $x \geq -1$

   Explain her reasoning.

6. Discuss the differences in the domains and ranges of the two functions of Sample 4.

X, ∆ab

RADICAL FUNCTIONS

A radical function is a function that has a variable under a radical symbol.

Examples $f(x) = \sqrt{x}$ $f(x) = \sqrt[3]{x - 1}$

·····▶ Now you are ready for:
Exs. 18–49 on pp. 116–118

Look Back ◂───

Describe how to use the expression under the radical symbol and the value of *n* to find the domain of a radical function.

2-6 Exercises and Problems

Find $f(x)$ when $x = 2$. Round decimals to the nearest tenth.

1. $f(x) = 2\sqrt{5x}$

2. $f(x) = -3\sqrt{x + 4}$

$-3\sqrt{6}$

3. $f(x) = -\sqrt{x - 1} + 6$

Find s when $t = 5$.

4. $t + 1 = 4\sqrt{s}$

5. $t = \sqrt{-5s + 31}$

6. $-4t + 2 = -\sqrt{s + 1}$

7. Make a table of values for $f(x) = \sqrt{25x}$ and $f(x) = 5\sqrt{x}$. What do you notice? Explain.

8. **Using Manipulatives** Work with another student.

a. Cut out a 6 in. by 2.5 in. piece of paper. Hold the piece of paper just above your partner's hand so that it will fall between your partner's thumb and forefinger. Drop the paper. Did your partner catch the paper?

b. Switch roles. Did you catch the paper?

c. Repeat parts (a) and (b) with a ruler. The zero mark on the ruler should be just between the catcher's fingers. Record the measurement at the point where the ruler is caught.

d. The time it takes to see the ruler falling and to catch it is called *reaction time*. It is modeled by the equation $t = \sqrt{\dfrac{d}{192}}$, where t = time in seconds and d = distance of fall in inches. Use your answers from part (c) to find the reaction times for you and your partner.

e. What is the maximum possible reaction time to still catch the paper in part (a)?

$, 0$

Zero mark between the fingers

9. **Writing** Tell whether the statement $\sqrt{a + b} = \sqrt{a} + \sqrt{b}$ is *True* or *False*. Explain your answer.

10. **Reading** How can you tell if a solution of a radical equation is an extraneous solution?

Solve.

11. $\sqrt{x} = 2x$

12. $\sqrt{x} = x - 2$

13. $a = \sqrt{7a - 12}$

14. $\sqrt{5x - 6} = 2x$

15. $\sqrt{z + 2} - 2 = z$

16. $x\sqrt{x + 13} - 1 = x$

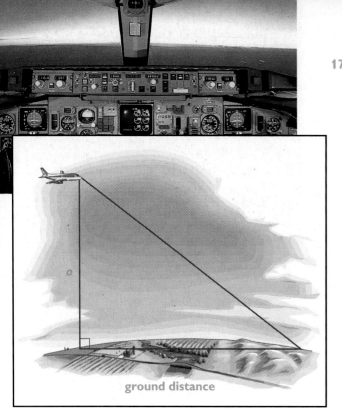
ground distance

17. **Viewing Distance** When you are flying in an airplane, the distance you can see is modeled by the formula $v = \sqrt{1.5a}$, where v = the viewing distance to the horizon in miles and a = the altitude in feet.

a. Suppose you are in an airplane and flying over your hometown at an altitude of 31,680 ft. What is the viewing distance to the horizon? Round your answer to the nearest mile.

b. The ground distance along Earth's surface can be approximated by a straight line. Use the Pythagorean theorem to find the ground distance in miles from your hometown to the point you can see on the horizon. Round your answer to the nearest mile.

c. **Research** Use an atlas or a map and the information from part (b) to find out what cities or towns are within your viewing distance at 31,680 ft over your hometown.

18. The statement $\sqrt{ab} = \sqrt{a} \cdot \sqrt{b}$ is true when a and b are positive.

a. Show that $\sqrt{4 \cdot 16} = \sqrt{4} \cdot \sqrt{16}$.

b. Show that $\sqrt{-4 \cdot 16} = \sqrt{-4} \cdot \sqrt{16}$.

c. Compare the value of $\sqrt{-4 \cdot (-16)}$ with the value of $\sqrt{-4} \cdot \sqrt{-16}$.

d. Tell whether the statement $\sqrt{ab} = \sqrt{a} \cdot \sqrt{b}$ is true when a and b are negative.

Student Resources Toolbox
p. 643 *Algebraic Expressions*

Simplify.

19. $\sqrt{64x^2}$

20. $\sqrt[4]{a^4}$

21. $\sqrt[3]{343p^3}$

22. $\sqrt[3]{-64a^3}$

23. $\sqrt[4]{(-2)^4}$

24. $\sqrt{(5 - h)^2}$

25. $\sqrt{75x^2}$

26. $\sqrt[5]{-(x + 1)^5}$

Graph each function, and then find the domain and range.

27. $f(a) = 3\sqrt{4a}$

28. $t = \sqrt{s} + 3.9$

29. $y = \sqrt{x - 9}$

30. $y = \sqrt{2x}$

31. $y = \sqrt{2x + 2}$

32. $y = \sqrt{2x} + 2$

33. Find the domain of $y = \sqrt{-5x}$ without graphing.

Find the domain and range of each function.

34. $f(x) = \sqrt[3]{4x}$

35. $y = 2\sqrt[3]{x} - 1.8$

36. $y = \sqrt{-x}$

37. $s(t) = -3\sqrt{t} + 1$

38. $d = -\sqrt[3]{g} + 5$

39. $f(x) = \sqrt[3]{x - 7}$

40 **TECHNOLOGY** Graph $y = \sqrt[n]{x}$ for several values of n. What conclusion(s) can you make about the domain and range of radical functions when n is odd? when n is even?

Unit 2 Exploring and Applying Functions

Sailing Yachts that race must meet design requirements. In 1989, the International America's Cup
Class (IACC) rules included this formula:

$$\frac{L + 1.25\sqrt{S} - 9.8\sqrt[3]{D}}{0.388} \leq 42$$

S = the area of
the sails in square
meters, $S \leq 300$ m²

D = the volume
of water the
yacht displaces
in cubic meters

L = the length of
the yacht in meters, $L \leq 22$ m

41. Suppose you design a yacht with length
20.8 m and sail area 285 m². It displaces
a volume of water equal to 21.4 m³. Will
your yacht meet the IACC requirements?

42. Suppose a designer maximizes the length of
the yacht and the area of the sails. Estimate the
minimum volume of water the yacht can displace.

43. Suppose a designer decides not to maximize the
length of the yacht and the area of the sails. Does
the minimum amount of water the yacht can
displace go up or down? Explain.

BY THE WAY...

America's Cup is an international
sailing competition. The trophy,
also called America's Cup, is
named after the yacht, *America*,
which won the first race held in
1851. It is the oldest trophy in
international sports.

Ongoing **ASSESSMENT**

44. **Group Activity** Work in a group of three students.

  a. Without graphing, decide whether these functions are
  equivalent to $y = x$:
  $$y = \sqrt{x^2} \qquad\qquad y = (\sqrt{x})^2$$

  b. One of you should graph $y = x$. Another should graph $y = \sqrt{x^2}$.
  The third person should graph $y = (\sqrt{x})^2$.

  c. Compare your graphs. Was the decision you made in part (a) correct?

  d. Graph $y = \sqrt[3]{x^3}$ and $y = (\sqrt[3]{x})^3$. Compare these graphs to the
  graph of $y = x$.

  e. Make a conjecture about the functions $y = x$, $y = \sqrt[n]{x^n}$, and
  $y = (\sqrt[n]{x^n})^n$. Test your conjecture for different values of n.

Review **PREVIEW**

45. a. Graph the function $P(x) = x(x - 4)(x + 10)$. *(Section 2-5)*

  b. What are the zeros of the function in part (a)?

46. Find the lower extreme, the lower quartile, the median, the upper
quartile, and the upper extreme of these batting averages. *(Section 1-3)*

    0.325, 0.249, 0.311, 0.188, 0.190, 0.234,
    0.214, 0.171, 0.202, 0.190, 0.298, 0.249

47. What is the only value of x not in the domain of $f(x) = \dfrac{1}{1 - x}$?
Explain. *(Section 2-1)*

Bicycle racecourses have *banked*, or sloped, curves. This helps keep the tires perpendicular to the road around a curve to prevent skidding. The approximate speed at which a bicyclist should enter a curve banked at $b°$ is given by the formula at the right.

48. How fast should a bicyclist enter a 12° banked curve with a radius of 40 m?

49. a. Suppose you design a racetrack that has a curve with a radius of 80 m. You want the average speed on this part of the track to be 11 m/s. At what angle should you bank the curve?

   b. You decide to design another curve and bank it at 7°. You want the average speed on this part of the track to be 12 m/s. With what radius should you design the curve?

$v = \sqrt{0.171rb}$

v = the speed in meters per second

r = the radius of the curve in meters

$b°$ = the measure of the angle at which the curve is banked

Unit 2   CHECKPOINT 2

1. **Writing** Compare the graphs of quadratic functions with the graphs of square root functions. How are their shapes alike? How are they different?

2. Suppose a squirrel drops an acorn from a branch at a height of 60 ft.   **2-4**

   a. Express the height of the acorn above the ground as a function of time.

   b. Graph the function in part (a).

3. A baseball pitcher throws a ball from an initial height of 4 ft, at a speed of 120 ft/s, and at an angle of 1.5° with respect to horizontal.

   a. Use the equation $h(t) = -16t^2 + (v_0 \sin A)t + h_0$ to express the height of the ball as a function of time.

   b. When is the ball 1.5 ft above the ground?

4. Use the polynomial function $P(x) = x^3 - 9x^2 + 18x$.   **2-5**

   a. Find $P(-3)$ and $P(4b)$.   b. Graph $P(x)$.

5. Use the function $f(x) = 4.2\sqrt{x}$. Solve for x when $f(x) = 200$.

Solve.

6. $\sqrt{2x - 1} = x$ 7. $\sqrt{11x + 3} = 2x$

Graph each function, and then find the domain and range.   **2-6**

8. $f(x) = \sqrt{x - 3}$ 9. $f(b) = \sqrt[3]{b}$

Rational Functions

MAP-IT-OUT

··········Focus

Understand how rational functions are different from other types of functions. Use rational functions to solve problems.

BY THE WAY...

The Iroquois/Mohawk trail was originally a footpath for the Iroquois Confederacy. Runners, traveling 100 mi a day, used the trail to carry messages between the Native American nations of the confederacy from Buffalo to Albany.

It is about a 300-mile trip across New York state from Buffalo to Albany along the Iroquois/Mohawk Trail.

Talk it Over

1. Complete the table for a 300-mile trip.

2. **a.** Write an equation that relates speed, time, and distance.

   b. Solve your equation for t. Since you know the distance for this trip, what does the time of the trip depend on?

   c. Why is the function in part (b) not a polynomial function?

Speed s (miles per hour)	Time t (hours)
25	?
40	?
55	?
65	?

2-7 Rational Functions

119

The function you wrote in part (b) of question 2 is an example of a *rational function*. A function that is defined by a *rational expression* is called a **rational function**. A **rational expression** is the quotient of two polynomials. Here are some other rational functions:

$$f(x) = \frac{1}{x} \qquad g(x) = \frac{x^2 + 4}{x + 2}$$

Sample 1

Use the rational function $f(x) = \dfrac{x^2 - 2x + 3}{x - 1}$.

a. Find $f(4)$. **b.** Find x when $f(x) = 3$.

Sample Response

a. $f(x) = \dfrac{x^2 - 2x + 3}{x - 1}$

$f(4) = \dfrac{4^2 - 2(4) + 3}{4 - 1}$

$= \dfrac{11}{3}$

Student Resources Toolbox
p. 646 *Solving Equations and Inequalities*

b. $f(x) = \dfrac{x^2 - 2x + 3}{x - 1}$

$3 = \dfrac{x^2 - 2x + 3}{x - 1}$ ⟵ Substitute 3 for $f(x)$.

$3x - 3 = x^2 - 2x + 3$ ⟵ Multiply both sides by $x - 1$.

$0 = x^2 - 5x + 6$ ⟵ Subtract $3x - 3$ from both sides.

$0 = (x - 3)(x - 2)$ ⟵ Factor or use the quadratic formula.

$x = 3$ or $x = 2$ ⟵ Solve for x.

Talk it Over

3. In part (b) of Sample 1, why do you subtract $3x - 3$ from both sides?

4. What happens when you try to find $f(1)$ for the function in Sample 1?

Sample 2

Roy took two tests and his average is 63. If he scores 100 on the rest of his tests, how many more tests does Roy need to take to raise his average to 85?

Roy's average is the sum of all his scores divided by the total number of tests.

Let t = the number of tests Roy needs.

Let $a(t)$ = the average of his test scores.

average of first two scores — score on each of the remaining tests

$$a(t) = \frac{2 \cdot 63 + t \cdot 100}{t + 2}$$

total number of tests

Substitute 85 for $a(t)$.

$$85 = \frac{2 \cdot 63 + t \cdot 100}{t + 2}$$

$$85(t + 2) = 126 + 100t \qquad \longleftarrow \text{Multiply both sides by } t + 2.$$

$$2.93 \approx t \qquad \longleftarrow \text{Solve for } t.$$

Roy must score 100 on three more tests to raise his average to 85.

Talk it Over

5. Why can you use the expression $2 \cdot 63$ for the sum of Roy's first two test scores even though you do not know his actual scores?

6. Suppose Roy has scores of 52 and 74 on his first two tests, but the teacher decides not to include the lowest score. How does the function in Sample 2 change?

Graphs of Rational Functions

There is not a single shape that describes the graphs of all rational functions. The shape of the graph of a rational function depends on the degrees of the polynomials in the numerator and in the denominator.

Sample 3

a. **Graph $f(x) = \frac{1}{x - 1}$.**

b. **Find the domain and range of $f(x)$.**

a. **Method ①** Sketch the graph by hand. Make a table of values.

Problem Solving Strategy: Break the problem into parts.

Step 1 When $x = 1$, $f(x)$ is undefined since the denominator is 0. No point on the graph of $f(x)$ lies on the line $x = 1$. Graph a dashed vertical line at $x = 1$ as a reminder.

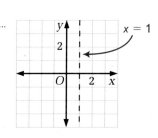

Continued on next page.

Step 2 Look at what happens to $f(x)$ as the value of x gets very close to 1.

x	approach 1 from the left →			← approach 1 from the right		
x	0.99	0.999	0.9999	1.0001	1.001	1.01
f(x)	−100	−1000	−10,000	10,000	1000	100

As x approaches 1 from either direction, $|f(x)|$ becomes very large.

Step 3 Look at what happens to $f(x)$ as the value of x gets very far from 1.

x	← get farther from 1 to the left			get farther from 1 to the right →		
x	−1,000,000	−100,000	−10,000	10,000	100,000	1,000,000
f(x)	−0.000001	−0.00001	−0.0001	0.0001	0.00001	0.000001

As x gets farther away from 1 in either direction, $|f(x)|$ approaches zero, but never equals zero.

Step 4 Graph the trend that the points in Steps 2 and 3 suggest.

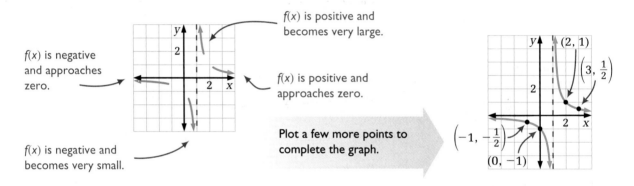

$f(x)$ is positive and becomes very large.

$f(x)$ is negative and approaches zero.

$f(x)$ is positive and approaches zero.

$f(x)$ is negative and becomes very small.

Plot a few more points to complete the graph.

Method ❷ Use a graphics calculator.

Enter the equation $y = \dfrac{1}{x-1}$. (Some graphics calculators, when in Connected mode, will draw a line connecting the separate parts of a graph. To avoid this, use Dot mode.)

b. Look at the graph of $f(x)$. The domain is all real numbers except 1. The range is all real numbers except 0.

In Method 1 part (a) of Sample 3, the x-axis and the dashed line are called *asymptotes*. **Asymptotes** are lines that a graph approaches more and more closely. Asymptotes are helping lines used in graphing. They are usually graphed as dashed lines because they are not part of the graph.

Talk it Over

7. Explain why the value of the function in Sample 3 cannot be zero.

8. How can you find the domain of the function in Sample 3 without graphing?

9. The graph of the function in Sample 3 has both a vertical and a horizontal asymptote. What is an equation of the horizontal asymptote?

10. How are the asymptotes and the domain and range of a rational function related?

RATIONAL FUNCTIONS

A rational function is defined by the quotient of two polynomials.

Examples

Suppose the numerator and denominator have no common factor. Then the shape of the graph is a **hyperbola** whenever the numerator has degree 0 or 1 and the denominator has degree 1.

$$f(x) = \frac{x + 6}{x + 1}$$

$$f(x) = \frac{5x^2}{x^2 + 1}$$

asymptote

asymptote

Look Back

Draw a concept map for these types of functions: *absolute value functions*, *rational functions*, *quadratic functions*, *radical functions*, and *polynomial functions*.

Exercises and Problems

1. **Reading** Why are asymptotes usually graphed as dashed lines?

Find $f(x)$ when $x = -2$.

2. $f(x) = \dfrac{x - 4}{2x}$

3. $f(x) = \dfrac{x^2 + 4x - 7}{x^3 + 5}$

4. $f(x) = \dfrac{x^3 - 10}{x^2 - x}$

Find t for the given value of $g(t)$.

5. $g(t) = \dfrac{t - 1}{t - 5}$; $g(t) = -3$

6. $g(t) = \dfrac{t^2 - 5}{t + 3}$; $g(t) = -2$

7. $g(t) = \dfrac{t^2 - 2t + 3}{t + 2}$; $g(t) = 6$

8. $g(t) = \dfrac{2t^2 + 8t - 40}{t - 4}$; $g(t) = 5$

9. Anabel took two tests this semester and her average is 75. If she scores 100 on the rest of her tests, how many more tests does Anabel have to take to raise her average to 90?

10. **Writing** Explain why $f(x) = \dfrac{\sqrt{x - 5}}{x}$ is not a rational function.

For Exercises 11–18:

a. **Graph the function.**

b. **Write the equations of all asymptotes of the graph.**

c. **Find the domain and range of the function.**

11. $f(x) = \dfrac{2}{x - 1}$

12. $g(x) = \dfrac{x}{x - 2}$

13. $y = \dfrac{2x - 1}{x}$

14. $r(x) = \dfrac{6x^2}{x^2 + 1}$

15. $f(x) = \dfrac{1}{1 - x^2}$

16. $f(x) = \dfrac{x^2}{3 - x}$

17. $d(x) = \dfrac{-2x^2}{x^2 + 4}$

18. $f(x) = \dfrac{1}{x^2 - x - 6}$

19. **Open-ended** Write a rational function whose domain is all real numbers.

connection to **PHYSICS**

20. A *lever* is a bar that pivots at a point called the *fulcrum*. Suppose a mass of 20 grams is placed 30 cm from the fulcrum. A second mass, m, is placed d cm from the fulcrum at the other end. The function that models this situation is $d = \dfrac{600}{m}$.

a. Suppose the second mass is also 20 g. How far from the fulcrum should the second mass be placed to balance the lever?

b. Suppose the second mass is more than 20 g. Should this mass be placed more or less than 30 cm from the fulcrum to balance the lever?

c. Suppose the second mass placed 20 cm from the fulcrum balances the lever. How many grams is this mass?

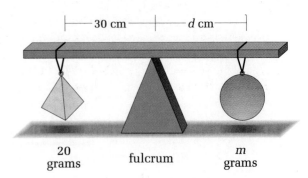

Unit 2 Exploring and Applying Functions

shuttle orbit 300 mi
above Earth

Earth
radius
4000 mi

21. The radius of Earth is about 4000 mi. On or near Earth, the weight, *w*, of an object depends on how far the object is from the center of Earth. The weight of an object is modeled by the function

$$w = \frac{(4000)^2 s}{(4000 + h)^2},$$

where *h* = the height above sea level in miles, and *s* = the weight on Earth at sea level in pounds.

a. The Space Shuttle orbiter weighs about 190,000 lb at sea level. The orbiter is in orbit when it is about 300 mi above Earth. What does the orbiter weigh while in orbit?

b. Suppose an astronaut inside the orbiter weighs 110 lb when the shuttle is in orbit. What is the astronaut's weight on Earth at sea level?

BY THE WAY...

Mae Jemison was the first African American woman to venture into space. As a Science Mission Specialist aboard the *Space Shuttle Endeavor*, she performed experiments on the effects of weightlessness and gravity.

Ongoing **ASSESSMENT**

22. **Writing** Describe how rational functions are different from linear functions. Include in your description a discussion of graphs and domain and range.

Review **PREVIEW**

Solve. *(Section 2-6)*

23. $\sqrt{9x - 20} = x$ **24.** $\sqrt{x + 3} = 2x$

25. Write $f(x) = |3x - 12|$ as a piecewise function. *(Section 2-3)*

26. Use $g(x) = 2x + 1$. Find $g\left(\frac{a}{2}\right)$. *(Section 2-2)*

 Working on the Unit Project

27. **Research** Talk to an expert at a local bicycle store or read a book about bicycles to find out about shifting gears on a bicycle. What factors affect how often a rider should shift gears? What are the road or weather conditions that require high gears? low gears?

Combining Functions

Watt Comes Out?

Sunshine on a rooftop in Santa Fe, New Mexico, may input 1000 watts of solar power to each square meter of solar panels. Suppose the solar panels can convert 12% of the solar power into electric power.

Diagram of a Solar Cell

SUNSHINE

NEGATIVE LAYER
POSITIVE LAYER

ELECTRON FLOW

Talk it Over

1. Let A = the area of the solar panels in square meters. Let s = the total number of watts of solar power input to the panels. Write a formula for s as a function of A.

2. Let p = the total number of watts of electric power generated by solar panels on the rooftop. Write a formula for p as a function of s.

3. Using the results of questions 1 and 2, write a formula for p as a function of A.

4. How many watts of electric power can solar panels with an area of 2 m² generate on a sunny rooftop in Santa Fe?

BY THE WAY...

In 1948, architect Eleanor Raymond and chemist/engineer Maria Telkes collaborated to build the first solar-heated house.

You expressed p as a function of s, and s as a function of A. You combined the functions to find p as a function of A.

The new function $p(s(A))$ is called the **composite** of $p(s)$ and $s(A)$.

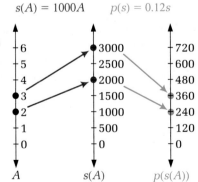

$$s(A) = 1000A \qquad p(s) = 0.12s$$

THE COMPOSITE OF TWO FUNCTIONS

The composite of two functions f and g is the function $f(g(x))$, which is read, "f of g of x."

You write $(f \circ g)(x)$, which is read "the composite of f and g."

To find $(f \circ g)(x)$, you find $g(x)$ first and then find $f(x)$ for that value.

Watch Out!
$f \circ g$ does not mean the product of f and g.

Sample 1

Use the functions $h(x) = x^2 + x$ and $k(x) = 6x$.

a. Find $(h \circ k)(x)$.   b. Find $(h \circ k)\left(\dfrac{1}{3}\right)$.

Sample Response

a. $(h \circ k)(x) = h(k(x))$ ← Use the definition of the composite of two functions.

$= h(6x)$ ← Substitute $6x$ for $k(x)$.

$= (6x)^2 + 6x$ ← Substitute $6x$ for x in the rule for $h(x)$.

$= 36x^2 + 6x$ ← Simplify.

b. $(h \circ k)\left(\dfrac{1}{3}\right) = 36 \cdot \left(\dfrac{1}{3}\right)^2 + 6 \cdot \dfrac{1}{3}$ ← Substitute $\dfrac{1}{3}$ for x in the rule that you found in part (a).

$= 36 \cdot \dfrac{1}{9} + 2$

$= 6$

Talk it Over

5. In Sample 1, how are the range of $k(x)$ and the domain of $(h \circ k)(x)$ related?

6. Sandra's work is shown. Explain how she found $(h \circ k)\left(\dfrac{1}{3}\right)$.

7. Use the functions $f(x) = x^2 - 1$ and $g(x) = 1 - 2x$.

a. Find a function rule for $(f \circ g)(x)$.

b. Find a function rule for $(g \circ f)(x)$.

c. Do you think that $(f \circ g)(x)$ and $(g \circ f)(x)$ are always equal? Explain.

$(h \circ k)(\tfrac{1}{3}) = h(k(\tfrac{1}{3}))$

$k(\tfrac{1}{3}) = 6 \cdot \tfrac{1}{3} = 2$

$h(2) = 2^2 + 2 = 4 + 2 = 6$

Jason is providing supplies for a morning canoe trip. He plans to have 2 bottles of flavored water for each person and 10 extra bottles. Each bottle costs $.60. Write a function for the total cost of the water in terms of the number of people on the canoe trip.

Sample Response

1 Write the cost as a function of the number of bottles.

Let b = the number of bottles.
Let C = the total cost in dollars.
$$C(b) = 0.6b$$

2 Write the number of bottles as a function of the number of people on the trip.

Let p = the number of people on the trip.
$$b(p) = 2p + 10$$

3 Write the cost as a function of the number of people.

$$(C \circ b)(p) = C(b(p))$$
$$= C(2p + 10)$$
$$= 0.6(2p + 10)$$
$$= 1.20p + 6$$

Talk it Over

8. What are the control variable and the dependent variable of each function? Which functions have the same domain?

9. Leah says that the domain of the cost function is the range of the number-of-bottles function. Do you agree or disagree? Explain your answer.

Look Back

Explain how to find the composite of two functions.

2-8 Exercises and Problems

For Exercises 1–6, use the functions $f(x) = \sqrt{x}$, $g(x) = 2x$, and $h(x) = 3x^2 - 2$.
Find each function rule or value.

1. $(f \circ g)(x)$

2. $(g \circ h)(x)$

3. $(h \circ g)(x)$

4. $(f \circ g)(8)$

5. $(g \circ h)(-2)$

6. $(h \circ g)(1)$

7. Reading How do you read $f(g(x))$ and $(f \circ g)(x)$?

8. a. Express the area A of a circle as a function of the radius r.

   b. Express the radius as a function of the circumference C.

   c. Write an expression for area as a function of the circumference of a circle.

9. The tax on a restaurant bill is 5%. A customer leaves a tip that is three times the tax on the bill.

   a. Express the tax p as a function of the amount on the bill.

   b. Express the tip t as a function of the tax.

   c. Write a function for the tip in terms of the bill.

$k(x) = x + 1$ $h(k) = \frac{1}{k}$

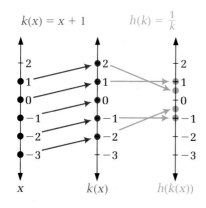

10. Writing This mapping diagram shows how to find the value of the composite of h and k. Choose one value of x from the first number line and explain how to find the corresponding value of $h(k(x))$.

11. Lily has a coupon for $10 off at a stereo store. An ad for the store says that there is a 5% discount on any purchase.

   a. Let x be the price of an item. What does the function $c(x) = x - 10$ represent? What does the function $d(x) = 0.95x$ represent?

   b. Suppose Lily uses the 5% discount on an item, then uses the coupon on the same item. Write the price that she pays as a function of x.

   c. Suppose Lily uses the coupon first, then the discount. Write the price that she pays as a function of x.

   d. Find $(c \circ d)(x)$ and $(d \circ c)(x)$. Which of these is the function you wrote for part (b)? Which is the function you wrote for part (c)? Explain.

12. Use the functions $f(x) = \frac{1}{2}x + 4$ and $g(x) = 2x - 8$.

   a. Find $(f \circ g)(x)$ and $(g \circ f)(x)$. What do you notice?

   b. **Open-ended** The function $I(x) = x$ is called the *identity function*. Write rules for two other functions whose composite is the identity function.

The table contains data about the respiratory systems of eleven wild and domestic African animals.

genet cat

Animal	Body mass (kg)	Lung volume (mL)	Maximum oxygen use $\left(\dfrac{mL}{s}\right)$
dwarf mongoose	0.418	27.4	0.89
banded mongoose	1.14	63.3	2.17
genet cat	1.415	86.8	2.41
suni	3	208.7	4.83
Grant's gazelle	10	562	9.03
wildebeest	102	7,678	75.7
waterbuck	126	9,383	102.6
eland	240	10,668	143.3
African goat	21.9	1,355	19.2
African sheep	22	1,662	15.3
Zebu cattle	151	8,036	68

Grant's gazelle

13. **a.** Make a scatter plot of the data in the first two columns. Use body mass, *m*, as the control variable.

b. Draw a fitted line through the points on your graph.

c. Using your fitted line, write a rule for $v(m)$, lung volume as a function of body mass.

wildebeest

d. Repeat parts (a) and (b) for the last two columns of data. Use lung volume, *v*, as the control variable.

waterbuck

e. Using your fitted line from part (d), write a rule for $u(v)$, maximum oxygen use as a function of lung volume.

f. Write a rule for the composite function $u(v(m))$.

g. Use your rule from part (f) to estimate the maximum oxygen use of a camel whose body mass is 234.5 kg.

14. **a.** Ann Martin used the data in the table and data for eleven other African mammals. She found these relationships among body mass (*m*), lung volume (*v*), and maximum oxygen use (*u*):

$$u(v) = 0.009v + 3.36$$

$$v(m) = 58.19m + 106.66$$

Write a rule for the composite function $u(v(m))$.

b. **Writing** Use the rule you wrote in part (a) to estimate the maximum oxygen use for the eland and the dwarf mongoose in the table. Explain why Ann's equations may give better estimates of some data items than others. Compare the estimated values to the corresponding values in the table.

In Exercises 15–18, add, subtract, multiply, or divide the functions. Use $f(x) = x^2 - 5x + 4$, $g(x) = 2x - 2$, **and** $h(x) = x^2 - x$.

Student Resources Toolbox
p. 635 *Algebraic Expressions*

Example:

$$g(x) - f(x) = (2x - 2) - (x^2 - 5x + 4)$$
$$= 2x - 2 - x^2 + 5x - 4$$
$$= -x^2 + 7x - 6$$

Example:

$$\frac{f(x)}{h(x)} = \frac{x^2 - 5x + 4}{x^2 - x}$$
$$= \frac{(x - 4)(x - 1)}{x(x - 1)} = \frac{x - 4}{x}; x \neq 1$$

15. $f(x) + g(x)$ **16.** $f(x) - h(x)$ **17.** $\dfrac{f(x)}{g(x)}$ **18.** $g(x) \cdot h(x)$

Ongoing **ASSESSMENT**

19. Group Activity Work with another student.

a. Write rules for two different functions, $f(x)$ and $g(x)$.

b. One student should find $f \circ g$ and the other should find $g \circ f$. Exchange papers and check each other's work.

c. Which of the composite functions in part (b) was easier to find? Why?

Review **PREVIEW**

20. Find the domain and range of $k(x) = \dfrac{4}{2 - x}$. *(Section 2-7)*

21. Use the function $f(x) = x^2 - 3x + 2$. Find $f(3)$ and $f(2a)$. *(Section 2-1)*

22. Tell which of these sets of three measures provides enough information to prove that two triangles are congruent: SSS, SSA, ASA, AAS, AAA, SAS *(Postulates and Theorems, p. 670)*

Working on the Unit Project

The average speed v, in meters per second, of a rider in a 40 km bicycle race is given by the function $v(t) = \dfrac{40{,}000}{t}$, where t is the total time in seconds that it takes the rider to complete the course.

Racer	Time
Racer 1	1 h 12 min
Racer 2	1 h 14 min
Racer 3	1 h 17 min

Suppose the racecourse is flat and the cyclists ride at a constant speed. The power P in watts that a cyclist supplies to a bicycle is given by the function $P(v) = 0.2581v^3 + 3.509v$. Use the table.

23. What was Racer 1's average speed during the race?

24. How much power did Racer 1 supply to the bicycle?

25. a. Find $(P \circ v)(t)$. Explain what this function represents.

b. Use your formula for $P(t)$ to find the power that Racer 2 supplied to the bicycle.

Completing the Unit Project

Now you are ready to organize your information and make your presentation.

If possible, schedule time at a local elementary school to make your presentation. Make sure that each group member has the information, props, diagrams, and so on needed to make the presentation. Decide on the order of the topics.

Your presentation should include these things:

➤ an overview of the bicycle project

➤ each group member's presentation, including at least three posters, diagrams, or props

➤ a summary of what you have discussed

➤ time for questions from the audience

Look Back ◀

Write an evaluation of your presentation. What went well? What would you do differently? How would you change your presentation for a different age group?

Alternative Projects

Project 1: Graphs

Look through books, magazines, and newspapers for graphs of polynomial and piecewise functions. What situations do they describe? Collect several of them and prepare a brief description of how each function is used.

Project 2: Falling Objects

The functions in Section 2-4 that describe the height of an object do not include the force of air resistance. Find out how air resistance affects the velocity of a falling object. Experiment with different objects to find the constant of air resistance. Describe your results, using diagrams and function notation as needed.

1. Does this table represent a function? Explain why or why not.

Popcorn	
small	$1.55
medium	$1.95
large	$2.45

2-1

2. Erin buys gasoline at a self-service station for $1.17/gal.

   a. Write a rule for $C(g)$, the cost of buying g gallons of gasoline, as a function of price.

   b. Suppose the gasoline tank of Erin's car holds 12 gal. What are the domain and range of the function in part (a)?

3. Find $f(-2)$ and $f(a - b)$ for $f(z) = \dfrac{2}{z + 4}$.

Write an equation for each function in the form $f(x) = mx + b$.

2-2

4. $f(9) = 5$, $m = \dfrac{1}{9}$

5. $f(2) = 3$, $f(6) = -3$

6. Write a piecewise function for the graph.

2-3

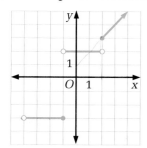

7. Jamelle drops a ball from an initial height of 4 ft.

2-4

   a. Use the model $h(t) = -16t^2 + h_0$ to express the height of the ball as a function of time.

   b. After 0.25 s, what is the height of the ball?

   c. When is Jamelle's ball 2 ft above the ground?

8. Find $f(2)$ and $f(-2)$ for $f(x) = x^2 + 5x - 14$.

9. The volume (V) of a sphere varies directly with the cube of its diameter (d^3). When $V = 288\pi$, $d = 12$. Write a direct variation function that expresses V as a function of d.

2-5

10. Use the function $f(x) = 7x^4 - 4x^2 - 12$.

    a. What is the degree of f?   **b.** Find $f(1)$.

11. Simplify $\sqrt{12a^2}$.

2-6

12. Solve $x = \sqrt{2x - 1}$.

13. Use the function $f(x) = \dfrac{x^2 - x - 12}{5x + 9}$.

2-7

    a. Find $f(2)$.   **b.** Find x when $f(x) = 10$.

14. Writing Monica has played 19 basketball games and averaged 22 points per game. She has one game left and must average at least 23.2 points per game in order to win her league's scoring title. Do you think she can win the title? Explain.

15. $f(x) = 3x$ and $g(x) = \frac{1}{x}$. Find $(f \circ g)(x)$.

2-8

16. a. Graph each function and find its domain and range.

$$f(x) = |x + 2| \qquad f(x) = 2\sqrt{x + 1} \qquad f(x) = \frac{10}{x - 5} \qquad f(x) = x(x + 4)(x + 6)$$

b. Writing Describe one way in which each graph is different from the others.

17. Open-ended Use this *Venn diagram* to make three statements about the relationships between some of the functions you have studied in this unit.

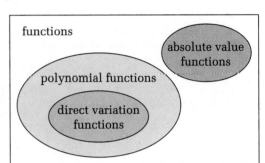

18. Self-evaluation Which topic in this unit would you spend some time reviewing? Why?

19. Group Activity Work in a group of four students.

Use the fact that the volume of a submerged object is equal to the volume of water that it displaces.

a. One pair of students should measure the volume of an object shaped like a sphere, such as a golf ball or softball, by submerging it in water in a straight-sided bucket or a plastic wastebasket. To estimate the volume of water displaced, you can use the formula $V = Bh$, where B is the area of the base of the bucket or wastebasket and h is the rise in the height of the water.

b. The other pair of students should measure the diameter of the spherical object by placing it between two books and measuring the distance between them. You can use the direct variation formula $V = \frac{4}{3}\pi r^3$, where V is the volume and r is the radius, to find the volume of the spherical object.

c. Repeat parts (a) and (b) for several spherical objects.

d. Compare results using the two methods. Which do you think is more accurate? Why?

IDEAS AND (FORMULAS)

➤ The domain of a function is all possible values of the control variable. *(p. 70)*

➤ The range of a function is all possible values of the dependent variable. *(p. 70)*

➤ A function can be written in function notation, $y = f(x)$. *(p. 71)*

➤ A function may have the same output for many different inputs but may not have more than one output for one input. *(p. 72)*

➤ One-to-one functions have one input for each output. *(p. 72)*

➤ Linear functions have the form $f(x) = mx + b$. The slope is m and the vertical intercept is b. *(p. 78)*

➤ A piecewise function has different equations for different parts of its domain. *(p. 86)*

➤ An absolute value function is a special type of piecewise function. *(p. 87)*

➤ You can model the height of an object that is dropped or thrown with a quadratic function. *(pp. 94, 96)*

➤ Direct variation functions have the form $f(x) = kx^n$ where n is a positive integer and $k \neq 0$. *(p. 102)*

➤ Polynomial functions are the sum of one or more direct variation functions or a constant function. *(p. 103)*

➤ A zero of a function is a value of x that makes $f(x)$ equal to zero. *(p. 104)*

➤ Radical functions are functions with a variable under the radical symbol. *(p. 113)*

➤ Rational functions are defined by rational expressions. *(p. 120)*

➤ The composite of two functions is written $f \circ g$. You can find the composite by finding $f(g(x))$. *(p. 127)*

GEOMETRY ▶

➤ Functions can be used to describe geometric relationships such as area and volume. *(p. 71)*

➤ The graph of a linear function is a line. *(p. 81)*

➤ The graph of a quadratic function is a parabola. *(p. 95)*

➤ Asymptotes are used as helping lines when graphing a rational function. *(p. 123)*

➤ The graphs of some rational functions are hyperbolas. *(p. 123)*

$(x, y) = (\cos \theta, \sin \theta)$

TRIGONOMETRY ▶

90° 180° 270° 360°

tan

2π

➤ The angle at which an object is thrown affects the height of the object. *(p. 96)*

········**Key Terms**

- **domain of a function** (p. 70)
- **one-to-one function** (p. 72)
- **piecewise function** (p. 86)
- **degree** (p. 103)
- **radical function** (p. 113)
- **asymptote** (p. 123)

- **range of a function** (p. 70)
- **many-to-one function** (p. 72)
- **absolute value function** (p. 88)
- **zero of a function** (p. 104)
- **rational function** (p. 120)
- **hyperbola** (p. 123)

- **function notation ($f(x)$)** (p. 71)
- **linear function** (p. 78)
- **polynomial function** (p. 103)
- **extraneous solution** (p. 112)
- **rational expression** (p. 120)
- **composite** (p. 126)

Should a girl be allowed to play on a boys' team in a sport where there is no girls' team, or vice versa? Would you go to court to sue for the right to try out for a school team?

You will use the witness statements on pages 136–138 to help you develop your case for or against the Springfield school system.

Justice

Sarah Wilkins, a junior, played soccer for many years before moving to Springfield last year. When she learned there was no girls' team at Springfield High School, she went to the tryouts for the boys' team, but the soccer coach would not let her try out.

Sarah decided to file a suit against the Springfield school system for sex discrimination. She cited the law shown below.

Title IX of the 1972 Educational Amendments states, in part:

No person in the United States shall, on the basis of sex, be excluded from participation in, be denied the benefits of, or be subjected to discrimination under any education program or activity receiving Federal financial assistance . . .

❝ I have coached boys' soccer for eight years. In previous years, a sign-up sheet for girls interested in playing soccer did not get enough signatures to support developing a girls' team. I know that boys play rough and think they may assume a girl is weaker than they are. I think some boys would be embarrassed by being on a team with a girl, or ashamed of losing to a girl. **❞**

*Springfield High School
Boys' Soccer Coach*

*Superintendent of the
Springfield School System*

Lawyer for the Defense

❝ I believe that a girl should not play on the boys' soccer team. As superintendent of schools, I am concerned about the safety of all students, and fear that Sarah might be injured. The Springfield school system complies with Title IX guidelines because it offers a field sport for girls: field hockey. I think Sarah should join the girls' field hockey team. **❞**

State Your Case

Your project is to prepare a legal brief for the case of Wilkins vs. Springfield School System. A **brief** is an outline that lists your main lines of reasoning in a case, along with supporting evidence. It is sometimes filed by an attorney before arguing a case in court.

Your brief should include these things:

BRIEF

➤ an opening statement

➤ questions you plan to ask witnesses

➤ questions you plan to ask witnesses for the opposing side during cross-examination

➤ the law as it applies to your case

➤ the reasoning you will use to convince others that the evidence presented justifies your position according to the law

➤ counterarguments you will make to your opponent's case

➤ closing arguments

Sarah Wilkins
Junior, Springfield High School

❝ I began playing soccer at age 10 at an all-girls school. I hoped to continue playing in college, and feel that I must play in high school to get an athletic scholarship. I am a good player and am not afraid of playing with and against boys. I think I should be able to try out for the boys' soccer team. I do not think it is fair to ask me to play a different sport. ❞

❝ Soccer has been a way for my daughter to excel. Her attitude toward studying and doing homework improved when she began playing soccer. I know that playing soccer is important to her. I am concerned that boys might tease her if she joined the boys' team, but I am more concerned about the bad effects that not playing might have on her. ❞

Sarah Wilkins's father

Lawyer for the Plaintiff

137

Sarah's Former Soccer Coach

" I was Sarah's soccer coach at another school for the past seven years. I have watched Sarah improve her soccer playing and was happy to present her with a Most Valuable Player award. I think Sarah is as good a player as most boys her age, and as good as many college-aged women players. These next two years are important ones for Sarah to continue developing her skills. "

Senior and Captain of the Boys' Soccer Team

" I believe that adding a girl to my soccer team will ruin team spirit. Teamwork requires cooperation, and not all boys will support a girl team member. Part of the experience of being on a team— analyzing our mistakes together —will be ruined by the presence of a girl. I also expect other teams in the league may make fun of my team. "

For this project you should work in a group of four students. Half the groups will be assigned to work for the plaintiff, and half for the defense. Here are some ideas to help you get started.

☞ Read the law that applies to the case. Discuss how you might convince a jury or judge that your case is supported by the law.

☞ Look at the witness statements on this page and pages 136 and 137. Discuss the evidence you think the witnesses might offer to support the plaintiff or the defendant.

☞ Discuss the case with your team. What are the strengths of the witnesses you have? What are their weaknesses? What other witnesses, if any, do you think you can use to support your case?

☞ Visit a courtroom during a trial that is open to the public, or watch a trial on TV. Talk about the kinds of reasoning that lawyers use to convince a judge or a jury.

Working on the Unit Project

Your work in Unit 3 will help you see how reasoning is used in arguing a court case.

Related Exercises:

Section 3-1, Exercise 36
Section 3-2, Exercise 20
Section 3-3, Exercise 24
Section 3-4, Exercise 22
Section 3-5, Exercise 22
Section 3-6, Exercise 21
Section 3-7, Exercise 22
Section 3-8, Exercise 16
Section 3-9, Exercise 28

Alternative Projects p. 199

Can We Talk Justice

➤ Why do you think a person might not be selected as a juror for this case by the lawyers for the defense? by the lawyers for the plaintiff?

➤ Attorneys use reasoning to try to convince a jury. What role, if any, do you think emotions play in a courtroom?

➤ What do you think the outcome of this case should be? What do you think would happen if this case occurred at your school?

➤ Discuss the impact of pre-trial publicity and/or cameras in the courtroom on the outcome of a trial that has been in the news recently.

3-1 Implications and Proof

Focus
Review proofs and explore
the relationship between
implications and their
converses, inverses, and
contrapositives.

ON THE DIAGONAL

EXPLORATION

(How) do properties of diagonals determine quadrilaterals?

- **Materials: straws or stirrers cut to unequal lengths**
- **Work in a group of four students.**

(1) Take two straws of unequal length. Find their midpoints. Make an x so the straws intersect at their midpoints. Draw the figure you get by joining the endpoints. What kind of quadrilateral is it?

(2) Repeat step 1 using a different angle at the point of intersection.

(3) Compare your results with other members of your group. Make a conjecture about what you observe.

(4) Repeat steps 1 and 2 using two straws of equal length. Make a conjecture about the kind of quadrilaterals you can draw by joining the endpoints.

(5) Using the two straws of equal length from step 4, make an x so the straws do not intersect at their midpoints. Draw the figure you get by joining the endpoints. Do you have a special quadrilateral?

Talk it Over

Remember that the *converse* of an if-then statement is formed by interchanging the hypothesis (the "if" part) and conclusion (the "then" part). State the converse of each statement. Do you think each converse is true? Why or why not?

1. If a quadrilateral is a parallelogram, then the diagonals bisect each other.

2. If a quadrilateral is a rectangle, then the diagonals are equal in length.

Writing Proofs

The converse of a true statement is not necessarily true. To be sure that a converse is true, you must prove it.

Synthetic proof is a proof built using a system of postulates and theorems in which the properties of figures, but not their actual measurements, are studied.

JUSTIFICATIONS FOR SYNTHETIC PROOF

To prove a theorem, you may use the following as justifications:

➤ given statements

➤ definitions

➤ postulates

➤ previously proved theorems

A list of postulates and previously proved theorems is on page 668–671.

Sample 1

Prove that if the two diagonals of a quadrilateral bisect each other, then the quadrilateral is a parallelogram.

Sample Response

Given $AE = CE$, $BE = DE$

Prove $ABCD$ is a parallelogram.

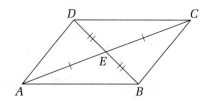

Plan Ahead

Show that $\triangle ABE$ and $\triangle CDE$ are congruent, so $m \angle 3 = m \angle 4$, which means that $\overline{AB} \parallel \overline{CD}$.

Repeat with $\triangle ADE$ and $\triangle CBE$, to show that $m \angle 7 = m \angle 8$, which means that $\overline{AD} \parallel \overline{BC}$.

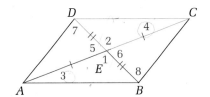

Show Your Reasoning

....

Statements	**Justifications**
1. $AE = CE$ and $BE = DE$	1. Given
2. $m \angle 1 = m \angle 2$	2. Vertical ∠s are = in measure.
3. $\triangle ABE \cong \triangle CDE$	3. SAS (Steps 1 and 2)
4. $m \angle 3 = m \angle 4$	4. Corresponding parts of ≅ △ are = in measure.
5. $\overline{AB} \parallel \overline{CD}$	5. If two lines are intersected by a transversal and alternate interior ∠s are = in measure, then the lines are ∥.
6. $m \angle 5 = m \angle 6$	6. Vertical ∠s are = in measure.
7. $\triangle ADE \cong \triangle CBE$	7. SAS (Steps 1 and 6)
8. $m \angle 7 = m \angle 8$	8. Corresponding parts of ≅ △ are = in measure.
9. $\overline{AD} \parallel \overline{BC}$	9. If two lines are intersected by a transversal and alternate interior ∠s are = in measure, then the lines are ∥.
10. $ABCD$ is a parallelogram.	10. Definition of parallelogram (Steps 5 and 9)

Talk it Over

3. In the plan for the proof, one goal is to show that $\overline{AB} \parallel \overline{CD}$. Which steps in the proof show this?

4. Another goal in the plan for the proof is to show that $\overline{AD} \parallel \overline{BC}$. Which steps in the proof show this?

BISECTING DIAGONALS THEOREM

Theorem 3.1 If the two diagonals of a quadrilateral bisect each other, then the quadrilateral is a parallelogram.

······▶ **Now you are ready for:**
Exs. 1–15 on pp. 143–144

Implications

If-then statements are called **implications** and can be represented in symbols. $p \rightarrow q$ is read "p implies q" or "if p, then q."

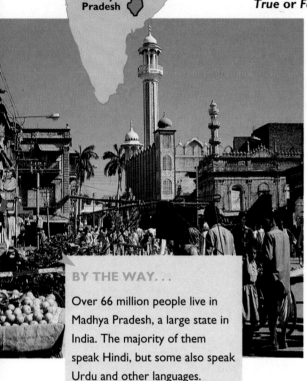

INDIA

Madhya Pradesh

Sample 2

Use the map to determine whether each implication is *True* or *False*.

a. If you live in Madhya Pradesh, then you live in India. ($p \rightarrow q$)

b. If you live in India, then you live in Madhya Pradesh. ($q \rightarrow p$)

c. If you do not live in Madhya Pradesh, then you do not live in India. (not $p \rightarrow$ not q)

d. If you do not live in India, then you do not live in Madhya Pradesh. (not $q \rightarrow$ not p)

Sample Response

a. True. The map shows that any person, X, who lives in Madhya Pradesh must also live in India, because Madhya Pradesh is a state in India.

b. False. Many residents of India do not live in Madhya Pradesh. This is the *converse* of the first implication.

c. False. Many people do not live in Madhya Pradesh but still live in India. This is the *inverse* of the original implication.

d. True. Any person, Y, who lives outside India cannot possibly live inside Madhya Pradesh. This is the *contrapositive* of the original implication.

X Lab

IMPLICATIONS

Original Implication	**Converse**
$p \rightarrow q$ If p, then q.	$q \rightarrow p$ If q, then p.
Contrapositive	**Inverse**
not $q \rightarrow$ not p If not q, then not p.	not $p \rightarrow$ not q If not p, then not q.
An implication and its contrapositive are either *both true* or *both false*. They are logically equivalent.	The converse and inverse of an implication are not necessarily true just because the implication is true.

······▶ Now you are ready for:
Exs. 16–36 on pp. 144–146

Look Back ◀─

State the converse, inverse, and contrapositive of the theorem in this section. Determine which of these are true.

3-1 Exercises and Problems

1. In the Exploration and in Sample 1, you used inductive and deductive reasoning. Give an example of each.

2. **Reading** The word *synthetic* has a special meaning in geometry. What is it? Give another meaning for the word *synthetic* in a different context.

3. **Writing** Describe how this object demonstrates something you discovered in the Exploration.

For each pair of triangles in Exercises 4–7:

a. **Can you use the given information to prove that two triangles are congruent? Write Yes or No.**

b. **If your answer to part (a) is Yes, what postulate or theorem would you use to prove the triangles are congruent?**

4.   5.   6.   7.

For each postulate or theorem in Exercises 8–10:

a. **State the converse.**

b. **Tell whether the converse is *True* or *False*.**

c. **If your answer to part (b) is *False*, give a counterexample.**

8. If two parallel lines are intersected by a transversal, then corresponding angles are equal in measure.

9. If two lines are intersected by a transversal and alternate interior angles are equal in measure, then the lines are parallel.

10. If a quadrilateral is a rhombus, then its diagonals are perpendicular to each other.

11. Give a justification for each step in this flow proof of the statement:
If a quadrilateral is a parallelogram, then opposite sides are equal
in measure.

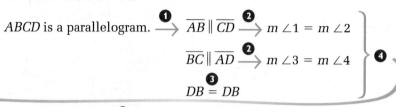

Given $ABCD$ is a parallelogram.

Prove $AB = CD$ and $BC = AD$

$$ABCD \text{ is a parallelogram.} \xrightarrow{\textbf{1}} \overline{AB} \parallel \overline{CD} \xrightarrow{\textbf{2}} m\angle 1 = m\angle 2$$

$$\overline{BC} \parallel \overline{AD} \xrightarrow{\textbf{2}} m\angle 3 = m\angle 4$$

$$DB = DB \quad \textbf{3}$$

$$\textbf{4}$$

$$\xrightarrow{} \triangle ABD \cong \triangle CDB \xrightarrow{\textbf{5}} AB = CD \text{ and } BC = AD$$

12. Rewrite the flow proof in Exercise 11 in two-column form.

13. **a.** State the converse of the theorem proved in Exercise 11.

   b. Prove the converse in a two-column proof. (*Hint:* Use the same pair of
congruent triangles and SSS.)

14. Prove that the diagonals of a parallelogram bisect each other.

Given Parallelogram $ABCD$ with diagonals intersecting at E

Prove $AE = CE$ and $BE = DE$

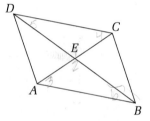

Plan Ahead

Prove $\triangle AEB \cong \triangle CED$ by using ASA and the theorem
proved in Exercise 11.

15. Prove that if a parallelogram is a rectangle, then its diagonals are
equal in measure. Use the theorem proved in Exercise 11.

Geography For each map in Exercises 16–18:

a. Write an implication suggested by the map.

b. Write the contrapositive of your implication.

16.

17.

18.

          Unit 3 Logical Reasoning and Methods of Proof

For each implication, state its converse, inverse, and contrapositive. Determine which are *True* and which are *False*. If *False*, give a counterexample.

Margaret Chase Smith

19. If two lines are perpendicular, then they form right angles.

20. If two triangles are congruent, then they are similar.

21. **Research** If a compound is a sugar, then it contains carbon.

22. **Research** If a football team scores a touchdown, then the team adds six points to its score.

23. **Open-ended** State three theorems that have been previously proved. Make three new statements by forming the contrapositives of the proved theorems. How do you know that the three new statements are also true?

24. **Writing** A friend insists that the converse and inverse of any implication are either both true or both false. Explain why you agree or disagree.

connection to **SOCIAL STUDIES**

Article I Section 3 of the United States Constitution states:

No Person shall be a Senator who shall not have attained to the Age of Thirty years.

25. **a.** Complete this implication: "If a person has not attained to the age of thirty years, then __?__."

   b. State the contrapositive of the implication.

26. If a person is a Representative in Congress, then he or she must be at least twenty-five years old. Rewrite this statement in the language used in the United States Constitution.

For Exercises 27–29, let $p \rightarrow q$ be the implication "If today is Monday, then tomorrow is Tuesday."

27. Show that the inverse of the converse of the implication $p \rightarrow q$ is the same as the contrapositive of $p \rightarrow q$.

28. Find the converse of the contrapositive of the implication $p \rightarrow q$. What is the relationship of your answer to the original implication $p \rightarrow q$?

29. Find the inverse of the inverse of the implication $p \rightarrow q$. What do you notice?

30. **Group Activity** Work in a group of three students. Rotate roles so that you get to play each role.

    Student 1: Write an implication but do not show it to the others.

    Student 2: Pick one of the three words *converse*, *inverse*, or *contrapositive* and announce it to everyone.

    Student 1: Write the converse, inverse, or contrapositive as chosen by Student 2 and give it to Student 3.

    Student 3: State the original implication.

Review **PREVIEW**

31. Use the functions $f(x) = x + 1$ and $g(x) = x^2$. Find $(f \circ g)(x)$. *(Section 2-8)*

Find the reflection of each point about the y-axis. *(Toolbox Skill 38)*

32. $(4, 6)$ 33. $(-3, 0)$ 34. (a, b)

35. Find the distance between points $P(6, 0)$ and $Q(0, 3)$. *(Toolbox Skill 31)*

Working on the Unit Project

DNA fingerprinting laboratory

36. A blood sample is often a critical piece of evidence in a trial. Suppose blood found at the scene of a burglary presumably belongs to the burglar. The police announce to the press: "If this blood came from the suspect, then the suspect's blood group matches the blood group of the sample."

    a. Write the converse and the contrapositive of the above implication.

    b. Which statement, the converse or the contrapositive, could be used most convincingly in a court of law? Which side, the prosecution or the defense, could use that statement?

Coordinate and Synthetic Proof

WILL YOUR PROOF HOLD UP?

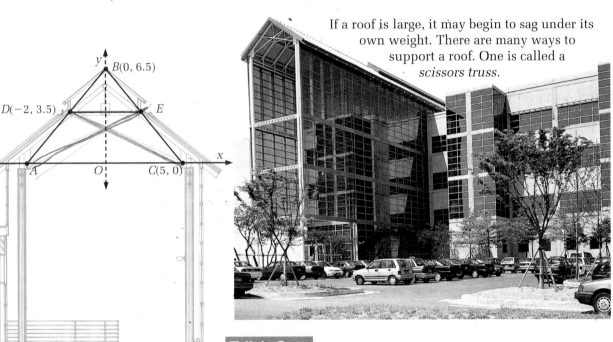

If a roof is large, it may begin to sag under its own weight. There are many ways to support a roof. One is called a *scissors truss*.

$D(-2, 3.5)$ $B(0, 6.5)$ E A O $C(5, 0)$

Talk it Over

1. Figure *ADEC* is a trapezoid where $\overline{DE} \parallel \overline{AC}$. Both $\triangle ABC$ and trapezoid *ADEC* have a line of symmetry. $\triangle ABC$ is an isosceles triangle. Do you think trapezoid *ADEC* should be called an *isosceles trapezoid*? Why or why not?

2. What are the coordinates of points *E* and *A*?

3. Support beams $\overline{DC}$ and $\overline{AE}$ are the diagonals of trapezoid *ADEC*. How could you use coordinates to find out whether support beams $\overline{DC}$ and $\overline{AE}$ are the same length?

4. A **median of a triangle** is a segment joining a vertex to the midpoint of the opposite side. How could you use coordinates to determine whether $\overline{DC}$ and $\overline{AE}$ are medians of $\triangle ABC$?

Student Resources Toolbox
p. 654 *Formulas and Relationships*

You can use *coordinate proof* or synthetic proof to show that the medians to the legs of an isosceles triangle are equal in measure. **Coordinate proof** is a proof based on a coordinate system in which all points are represented by ordered pairs of numbers.

JUSTIFICATIONS FOR COORDINATE PROOF

In addition to the justifications allowed for synthetic proofs, you may use the following as justifications in coordinate proofs:

➤ the distance and midpoint formulas

➤ Parallel lines have the same slope.

➤ Perpendicular lines have slopes that are negative reciprocals of each other.

➤ A geometric figure may be placed anywhere in the coordinate plane.

Show that the medians drawn to the legs of an isosceles triangle are equal in measure.

Sample Response

Method ❶ Write a coordinate proof.

Step 1 Since every isosceles triangle has a line of symmetry, you can place the triangle on coordinate axes so that the y-axis is the line of symmetry. Use variables to describe the coordinates of each vertex.

$R(0, 2b)$ ⟵ ——— Let R have coordinates $(0, 2b)$.

Choose $2a$ and $2b$ rather than a and b to make calculations with midpoints easier.

Let Q have coordinates $(2a, 0)$.

$P(-2a, 0)$ $Q(2a, 0)$

P has coordinates $(-2a, 0)$ since it is the reflection of Q over the y-axis.

Step 2 Use the midpoint formula to find the midpoints of the legs.

$$\text{Midpoint} = \left(\frac{x_1 + x_2}{2}, \frac{y_1 + y_2}{2}\right)$$

$$\text{Midpoint of } \overline{PR} = T\left(\frac{-2a + 0}{2}, \frac{0 + 2b}{2}\right) = T(-a, b)$$

$$\text{Midpoint of } \overline{QR} = S\left(\frac{2a + 0}{2}, \frac{0 + 2b}{2}\right) = S(a, b)$$

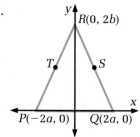

Step 3 The medians are $\overline{QT}$ and $\overline{PS}$. Use the distance formula to show that $QT = PS$.

Distance $= \sqrt{(x_2 - x_1)^2 + (y_2 - y_1)^2}$

$QT = \sqrt{(-a - 2a)^2 + (b - 0)^2} = \sqrt{9a^2 + b^2}$

$PS = \sqrt{[a - (-2a)]^2 + (b - 0)^2} = \sqrt{9a^2 + b^2}$

Therefore $QT = PS$ and the two medians are equal in measure.

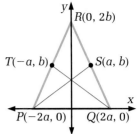

Method ❷ Write a synthetic proof.

Given Isosceles $\triangle PQR$ with $PR = QR$ and medians $\overline{PS}$ and $\overline{QT}$

Prove $PS = QT$

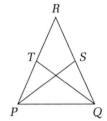

Plan Ahead

Show in a flow proof that $\triangle PQS \cong \triangle QPT$, and then use the fact that corresponding parts of congruent triangles are equal in measure.

Show Your Reasoning

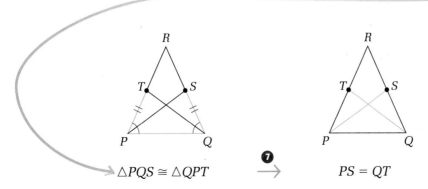

You will provide justifications in Exercise 5.

ISOSCELES TRIANGLES AND ISOSCELES TRAPEZOIDS

Theorem 3.2 In an isosceles triangle, the medians drawn
to the legs are equal in measure.

Definition An isosceles trapezoid is a trapezoid with a line of
symmetry that passes through the midpoints of
the bases.

$AE = BD$

Theorem 3.3 In an isosceles trapezoid,

(1) the legs are equal in measure,

(2) the diagonals are equal in measure, and

(3) the two angles at each base are equal in measure.

$AD = BC$

$AC = BD$

$m \angle A = m \angle B$
$m \angle D = m \angle C$

You will use both coordinate and synthetic methods in
Exercise 11 to prove Theorem 3.3.

Look Back

In what ways are isosceles triangles and isosceles trapezoids
alike? In what ways are they different?

3-2 Exercises and Problems

1. **Reading** How can you use coordinate
geometry to show that two segments are
equal in measure?

2. In pentagon *GHJKL*, the *y*-axis is a line of
symmetry. Find the coordinates of *H* and *L*.

**Architecture Use the illustration of the scissors
truss on page 147.**

3. Use coordinates to determine whether support
beams $\overline{DC}$ and $\overline{AE}$ are the same length.

4. Use coordinates to determine whether $\overline{DC}$ and
$\overline{AE}$ are medians of $\triangle ABC$.

5. Provide justifications for the statements of the
synthetic proof in Method 2 of the Sample on
page 149.

(Measurements are in inches.)

(−9, 56) R   Q (9, 56)

(−18, 37)   (18, 37)

S (−34, 0)   O   C(5, 0)   P (34, 0)

Use this picture of a swing.

6. Does the frame of the swing at the left have a line of symmetry? Justify your answer.

7. Show that the sides are the same length.

8. The diagonal supports keep the frame steady. Show that the supports are the same length.

9. The frame would be sturdier if the supports were at the diagonals of trapezoid *PQRS*. Why do you think that the supports were not placed at the diagonals?

10. The triangle in Method 1 of the Sample Response on page 148 has coordinates $P(-2a, 0)$, $Q(2a, 0)$, and $R(0, 2b)$. Show that this triangle is isosceles by showing that $PR = QR$.

11. In isosceles trapezoid *PQRS* the *y*-axis is a line of symmetry that passes through the midpoints of the bases.

    a. Use the coordinates of isosceles trapezoid *PQRS* to show that $\overline{PS}$ and $\overline{QR}$ are equal in measure. (Part (1) of Theorem 3.3)

    b. Show that the diagonals, $\overline{PR}$ and $\overline{QS}$, are equal in measure. (Part (2) of Theorem 3.3)

    c. Use pairs of overlapping congruent triangles in a synthetic proof to show that $m \angle SPQ = m \angle RQP$ and $m \angle QRS = m \angle PSR$. (Part (3) of Theorem 3.3.)

12. **Writing** Explain why it would be difficult to write a coordinate proof of part (3) of Theorem 3.3.

Diagram: $S(-b, c)$ $R(b, c)$ $P(-a, 0)$ O $Q(a, 0)$

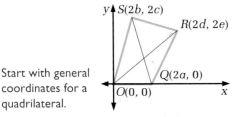

S(2b, 2c)   R(2d, 2e)   Q(2a, 0)   O(0, 0)

Start with general coordinates for a quadrilateral.

S(2b, 2c)   R(?, ?)   Q(2a, 0)   O(0, 0)

13. In this exercise you will write a coordinate proof of Theorem 3.1: If the two diagonals of a quadrilateral bisect each other, then the quadrilateral is a parallelogram.

    a. Find the coordinates of the midpoint of $\overline{OR}$.

    b. Find the coordinates of the midpoint of $\overline{QS}$.

    c. $\overline{OR}$ bisects $\overline{QS}$, so their midpoints have the same coordinates. Complete:

    $$d = \underline{\ ?\ } \text{ and } e = \underline{\ ?\ }.$$

    d. Rewrite the coordinates of *R* in terms of *a*, *b*, and *c*. Then show that quadrilateral *OQRS* is a parallelogram. (*Hint:* Show that opposite sides are parallel because they have the same slope.)

3-2 Coordinate and Synthetic Proof

14. **Writing** Which proof of Theorem 3.1 do you prefer, the synthetic proof on pages 140 and 141 of Section 3-1, or the coordinate proof in Exercise 13? Why?

15. **Architecture** The Kpelle people of Liberia build round houses and rectangular houses of wood. To make a rectangle, they lay two poles of equal length on the ground, one across the other intersecting at their midpoints. The ends of the poles are the corners of a rectangle.

A F R I C A

Liberia

a. Write a conjecture that justifies the Kpelle construction method.

b. Prove your conjecture from part (a).

Ongoing ASSESSMENT

16. **Open-ended** Decide whether you would use a coordinate proof or a synthetic proof to prove each conjecture. Give a reason for your answer.

a. In every square, a segment that connects the midpoints of two opposite sides has the same length as a side of the square.

b. The measure of each exterior angle of an equilateral triangle is 120°.

Review PREVIEW

17. Write the contrapositive of the following statement: "If a quadrilateral is a square, then it is a rectangle." *(Section 3-1)*

18. Write true sentences of the form "All _?_ are _?_" using the following pairs of words: *(Toolbox Skill 34, Glossary)*

a. rhombuses, squares

b. parallelograms, quadrilaterals

c. parallelograms, rectangles

19. Write a definition for the word *parallelogram* using the phrase "if and only if." *(Toolbox Skill 34, Glossary)*

Working on the Unit Project

20. In a courtroom, as in mathematics, there is often more than one way to argue a case. Outline two or more plans for how you can argue your case.

Another Look at Definitions

On Your Own Terms

To attract customers, the manager of a bookstore sets up a small refreshment counter and sells hot drinks, lemonade, and pastry. The manager has provided tables and chairs in a corner of the store where customers can eat a snack and enjoy a book.

No commercial establishment may sell meals to be consumed on its premises without having obtained a restaurant license from the Department of Public Health.

The City Health Inspector visits the bookstore and tells the manager to apply for a restaurant license. The inspector cites a city law.

The manager tells the inspector that a bookstore operator does not need a restaurant license. They take the matter to court and argue over how the city law should be interpreted.

Talk it Over

1. Read the section of the city law cited above. List the terms whose definition you must know to decide whether the bookstore manager must apply for a restaurant license.

2. Write a definition for each of the terms listed in question 1.

3. On the basis of your definitions, decide whether the bookstore manager must apply for a restaurant license.

4. Compare your decision with the decisions of your classmates.

Inclusive and Exclusive Definitions

Definitions are important in interpreting matters of law. In mathematics, definitions are equally important. A good mathematical definition should be clear and easy to interpret.

A trapezoid is a quadrilateral with one pair of parallel sides.

In quadrilateral $MNRS$, $\overline{MN} \parallel \overline{SR}$. Is $MNRS$ a trapezoid? The discussion of the students below shows that there may not be a simple answer.

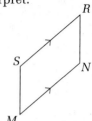

> $MNRS$ must be a trapezoid, because it does have one pair of parallel sides, $\overline{MN}$ and $\overline{SR}$.

> But $MNRS$ could have another pair of parallel sides, $\overline{MS}$ and $\overline{NR}$. I'd call $MNRS$ a parallelogram.

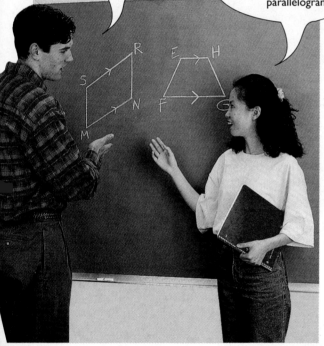

Talk it Over

5. Do you agree with what Silas says about $MNRS$?

6. Do you agree with Carly's response?

7. Silas tells Carly, "A parallelogram has *at least* one pair of parallel sides, so it is a trapezoid." Do you agree or disagree? Explain.

Using Silas's definition of *trapezoid*, which of these statements are true?

8. All parallelograms are trapezoids.

9. All rectangles are trapezoids.

10. All squares are trapezoids.

11. All kites are trapezoids.

Carly interprets "one" to mean "exactly one," but Silas says it means "at least one." To settle the dispute you must agree on which interpretation to use. This book will use this definition:

> A **trapezoid** is a quadrilateral with *at least one* pair of parallel sides.

With this definition, you can conclude that $MNRS$ must be a trapezoid, regardless of whether $\overline{MS}$ and $\overline{NR}$ are also parallel.

Because the new definition of trapezoid *includes* parallelograms as trapezoids, it is called an **inclusive definition.** Carly's definition *excludes* parallelograms and is called an **exclusive definition.**

A Quadrilateral Chart

With the inclusive definition of trapezoid, a parallelogram may be considered as one kind of trapezoid. In the previous section you saw examples of another special trapezoid, the isosceles trapezoid.

Sample

Explain why this statement is true: If a quadrilateral is a rectangle, then it is an isosceles trapezoid.

Sample Response

Suppose the rectangle is named *PQRS*. All rectangles are parallelograms, and all parallelograms are trapezoids. So *PQRS* is a trapezoid.

You can place *PQRS* so that the *y*-axis is a line of symmetry through the midpoints of $\overline{PQ}$ and $\overline{SR}$. So *PQRS* is an isosceles trapezoid.

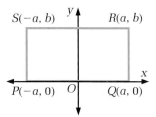

This chart shows the relationships among the quadrilaterals you have now studied. Figures in the quadrilateral chart inherit all the properties of figures above them to which they are linked.

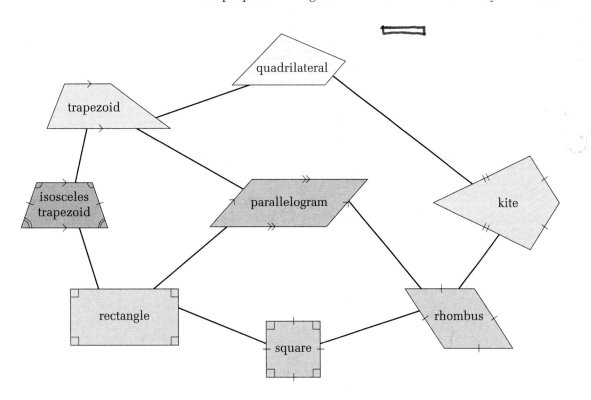

Look Back ◄─────────────────────────────────────

Why is it important to have clear definitions? Give mathematical and nonmathematical examples to explain your answer.

··

3-3 Exercises and Problems

1. **Driver's Licenses** Suppose the law where you live reads as follows:

   > • No person shall be eligible for a driver's license if he or she is less than 16 years old.
   >
   > • No person under the age of 18 shall be eligible for a driver's license without having successfully completed a state-approved course in driver education, consisting of at least 30 hours of instruction, under the supervision of a qualified instructor.

   a. Identify the words or phrases in this law that you feel need to be well defined in order for this law to be interpreted.

   b. Write a good definition for one of the words or phrases you listed in part (a).

For each sentence in Exercises 2–6, tell whether the word *one* means "exactly one" or "at least one."

2. To graduate from high school you must pass one art course.

3. Each senior is entitled to one free guest pass to the senior luncheon.

4. The equation $2x + 5 = 9$ has one solution.

5. An even number has one factor that is a power of two.

6. Through a point not on a line, one line may be drawn perpendicular to the given line.

7. This book uses an *inclusive* definition of trapezoid: A trapezoid is a quadrilateral with *at least one* pair of parallel sides. Some other books use an *exclusive* definition: A trapezoid is a quadrilateral with *exactly one* pair of parallel sides.

   a. Which figures are trapezoids if you use the inclusive definition?

   b. Which figures are trapezoids if you use the exclusive definition?

I   II   III   IV   V

Exercises 8 and 9 contain applications of inclusive and exclusive definitions in two situations.

8. **Movie Theaters** A movie theater charges one rate for children and another rate for teenagers. Children are defined as people who are at least 6 years old but under 13. Teenagers are from age 13 through age 19. Does the definition of "child" include or exclude "teenager"?

9. **Open-ended** Write an inclusive definition for "packaging that uses recycled material." Then write an exclusive definition.

10. **Reading** Review the definitions of *polynomial function* and *rational function* from Unit 2. Does the set of rational functions include or exclude the set of polynomial functions?

For Exercises 11–14, tell whether each statement is *True* or *False*, using the definitions from this book.

11. All squares are isosceles trapezoids.

12. Every trapezoid is a parallelogram.

13. If a kite is a rhombus, then it is a square.

14. If a quadrilateral is a rectangle, then it is a trapezoid.

15. Figures in the quadrilateral chart inherit properties of figures above them to which they are linked. Show that rectangles have each of the three properties of isosceles trapezoids listed in Theorem 3.3.

100% OF THE PLASTIC IN THIS PRODUCT, INCLUDING THE TIES, IS MADE FROM POST-CONSUMER RECYCLED PLASTIC

Box made of recycled fiber, including a minimum of 74% post-consumer fiber

THE BOARD USED IN THIS CARTON IS MADE WITH 100% RECYCLED FIBER. MINIMUM 35% POST-CONSUMER CONTENT.

Bottle made with **25% RECYCLED PLASTIC***

*Post-Consumer Plastic

For Exercises 16–18, write a definition for each type of polygon using a biconditional statement. For example, a quadrilateral is a parallelogram *if and only if* it has two pairs of parallel sides.

16. trapezoid   17. isosceles trapezoid   18. kite

Ongoing **ASSESSMENT**

For Exercises 19 and 20, use this information.

Sometimes two different definitions can describe exactly the same figure. Here are two definitions of *rectangle*.

Definition 1: A rectangle is a quadrilateral with four right angles.

Definition 2: A rectangle is a parallelogram with at least one right angle.

19. Using Definition 1, prove this statement in a paragraph proof: If a quadrilateral is a rectangle, then it is a parallelogram.

20. Using Definition 2, prove this statement in a paragraph proof: If a quadrilateral is a rectangle, then it has four right angles.

21. Show that the quadrilateral *PQRS* with vertices $P(-1, -2)$, $Q(0, 0)$, $R(2, 1)$, and $S(1, -1)$ is a rhombus. *(Section 3-2)*

22. Write an algorithm for finding a specific book at a library. *(Section 1-1)*

23. a. Use quadrilateral *ABCD* to complete each statement.

$m \angle A + m \angle 1 + m \angle 3 = \underline{\;?\;}$

$m \angle C + m \angle 2 + m \angle 4 = \underline{\;?\;}$

$m \angle 1 + \underline{\;?\;} = m \angle CDA$

$m \angle 3 + m \angle 4 = \underline{\;?\;}$

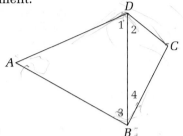

b. Use the results in part (a) to show that

$m \angle A + m \angle ABC + m \angle C + m \angle CDA = 360°$.

c. State the theorem that part (b) proves. *(Theorems, pp. 668-671)*

 Working on the Unit Project

24. At the beginning of this section, you saw that in law as well as in mathematics, certain words require precise definitions. Choose two or three words that are relevant to your case and explain why their definitions may help determine the outcome.

Unit 3 **CHECKPOINT 1**

1. Writing Explain how to tell the difference between the inverse and the contrapositive of an implication. **3-1**

2. State the inverse of this implication: If a quadrilateral is a rectangle, then its diagonals are equal in measure. Is the inverse true?

Tell whether each triangle with the given vertices is **3-2**
isosceles. Use both the distance formula and symmetry
to justify your answer.

3. $D(-6, 0)$, $E(5, 0)$, $F(0, 3)$ **4.** $J(-4, 5)$, $K(0, -2)$, $L(4, 5)$

Tell whether each statement is *True* or *False*. **3-3**

5. All rectangles are isosceles trapezoids.

6. All isosceles trapezoids have two lines of symmetry.

Angles in Polygons

One Thing Leads To Another

.... **Focus**

Find formulas for the sums of interior and exterior angle measures in polygons.

quadrilateral

pentagon

hexagon

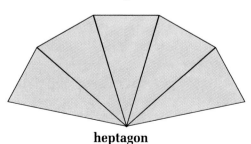
heptagon

Student Resources Toolbox
p. 668 *Postulates and Theorems*

You know a theorem of geometry that states:

The sum of the measures of the angles of a triangle is 180°.

You can use this fact to find the sum of the angle measures of any polygon.

Talk it Over

Use the drawings to answer question 1.

1. What is the sum of the angle measures of any quadrilateral? any pentagon? any hexagon? any heptagon?

2. Complete the chart. Look for patterns.

Name of polygon	Number of sides, n	Sum of angle measures $S(n)$
Triangle	3	$180° = (180°)$
Quadrilateral	4	$\underline{?} = \underline{?}\ (180°)$
Pentagon	5	$\underline{?} = \underline{?}\ (180°)$
Hexagon	6	$\underline{?} = \underline{?}\ (180°)$
Heptagon	7	$\underline{?} = \underline{?}\ (180°)$
Octagon	8	$\underline{?} = \underline{?}\ (180°)$

3. Find a general formula for the function $S(n)$, the sum of the angle measures of a polygon with n sides. Explain why you think this formula will work for *all* polygons.

The Sum of the Measures of the Angles of a Polygon

You may have conjectured that in a polygon with n sides, the sum of the measures of the angles is given by the formula

$$S(n) = (n - 2)180°.$$

This formula works for polygons with 3, 4, 5, 6, and 7 sides, but how can you be sure that it will work for *all* values of n? A proof of the conjecture uses a technique called *mathematical induction*.

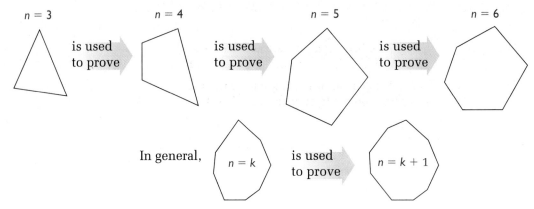

$n = 3$ is used to prove $n = 4$ is used to prove $n = 5$ is used to prove $n = 6$

In general, $n = k$ is used to prove $n = k + 1$

To show that the pattern will continue forever, you must show that you can always use the current case, $S(k) = (k - 2)180°$, to prove the next case, $S(k + 1) = ([k + 1] - 2)180°$.

Sample 1

Suppose that the formula $S(n) = (n - 2)180°$ gives the sum of the angle measures for a polygon with k sides. Show that the formula gives the sum of the angle measures for a polygon with $k + 1$ sides.

Sample Response

Draw a diagonal of the $(k + 1)$-gon to form a triangle and a k-gon.

The sum of the angle measures of the k-gon is $(k - 2)180°$.

$$S(k + 1) = (k - 2)180° + 180°$$
$$= (k - 2 + 1)180°$$
$$= ([k + 1] - 2)180°$$

The sum of the angle measures of the triangle is $180°$.

The last expression is equal to $(n - 2)180°$ when $n = k + 1$, so the formula $S(n) = (n - 2)180°$ works for the $(k + 1)$-gon if it works for the k-gon.

Talk it Over

4. Explain how $(k - 2)180° + 180°$ can be rewritten as $(k - 2 + 1)180°$ in Sample 1 using the distributive property.

5. In Sample 1, the case of $n = k$ is used to prove the case of $n = k + 1$. How does Sample 1 convince you that $S(n) = (n - 2)180°$ for all integral values of n greater than 3?

INTERIOR AND EXTERIOR ANGLE MEASURES IN POLYGONS

Theorem 3.4 The sum of the angle measures of an n-gon is given by the formula $S(n) = (n - 2)180°$.

Theorem 3.5 The sum of the exterior angle measures of an n-gon, one angle at each vertex, is 360°.

$m \angle 1 + m \angle 2 + m \angle 3 = 180°$
$m \angle 4 + m \angle 5 + m \angle 6 = 360°$

You will prove Theorem 3.5 in Exercise 11.

Regular Polygons

A polygon is a **regular polygon** if and only if all its sides are equal in measure and all its angles are equal in measure.

Sample 2

Find the measure of each interior and each exterior angle of the regular octagon.

Sample Response

First find the sum of the interior angle measures.

$S(n) = (n - 2)180° = (8 - 2)180° = 6(180°) = 1080°$

Since the eight interior angles are equal in measure, the measure of each angle is $\frac{1080°}{8} = 135°$.

The sum of the exterior angles is 360°. Since each exterior angle is a supplement of one of the interior angles, the eight exterior angles are equal in measure. The measure of each exterior angle is $\frac{360°}{8} = 45°$. (Also, $180° - 135° = 45°$.)

Octagonal barn dating from 1873

Look Back

Explain how to find the measure of an interior angle of a
regular polygon. How do you find the measure of an exterior
angle?

3-4 Exercises and Problems

1. **Reading** Is a square a regular polygon? Explain.

2. **a.** Explain why this pentagon is not a regular polygon.

   b. Find the measures of the angles of the pentagon and
   show that their sum is 540°.

3. Can each figure be a regular polygon? Explain.

   a. rectangle   **b.** rhombus   **c.** trapezoid

4. Use the formula $S(n) = (n - 2)180°$ for the sum of the angle measures of a
   polygon.

   a. Explain why $n = 2$ and $n = 6.5$ are not in the domain of $S(n)$.

   b. Find the domain and range of $S(n)$.

   c. What kind of function is $S(n)$?

Coins Find the measures of each interior and each exterior angle of the
regular polygon on each coin.

5.

7-gon from
Sierra Leone

6.

8-gon
from Netherlands Antilles

7.

9-gon from
Portugal

8.

10-gon from
Tanzania

9.

11-gon
from Canada

10.

12-gon from
South Vietnam

11. Complete this proof of Theorem 3.5: The sum of the exterior angle measures of an n-gon, one angle at each vertex, is 360°.

> **Given** a polygon with n sides
>
> $S(n)$ = the sum of the interior angle measures.
>
> $E(n)$ = the sum of the exterior angle measures.

> **Prove** $E(n) = 360°$

a. At each vertex, the sum of the measures of the interior angle and one exterior angle is 180°. Justification: __?__

b. Based on part (a), what is the combined sum of interior and exterior angle measures in a polygon with n vertices? $(S(n) + E(n) = $ __?__ $)$

c. Substitute $(n - 2)180°$ for $S(n)$ in the equation you wrote in part (b) and solve for $E(n)$. $E(n) = $ __?__

12. a. Find the domain and range of $E(n)$ in Exercise 11.

b. What kind of function is $E(n)$?

13. Let $X(n)$ represent the measure of one exterior angle of a regular polygon of n sides. Let $I(n)$ represent the measure of one interior angle of a regular polygon of n sides.

a. Find algebraic expressions for $X(n)$ and $I(n)$.

b. What kind of functions are $X(n)$ and $I(n)$?

c. Sketch graphs of $X(n)$ and $I(n)$.

14. **Writing** Explain how these dominos are like a proof that uses mathematical induction.

15. The diagrams suggest that the sum of the first n odd integers is n^2.

a. Draw the next two pictures in the sequence.

b. The sum of the first n odd integers is given by the function $F(n) = 1 + 3 + 5 + \ldots + (2n - 1)$. What does $2n - 1$ represent?

c. Suppose $F(k) = k^2$ is a formula for the sum of the first k odd integers. Show that $F(k + 1) = (k + 1)^2$.

d. Do you think the statement $F(n) = n^2$ is true for all positive integers n? Explain.

1 + 3 + 5

9

1 + 3

4

1

1

16. **Group Activity** Work in a group of five students.

a. Complete the table showing the number of handshakes if everyone shakes hands once with every person.

b. Show that $H(p) = \dfrac{p(p-1)}{2}$ for $p = 2, 3, 4,$ and 5.

c. Suppose a sixth person joins your group. How many more handshakes will there be as you welcome the sixth person?

d. Suppose k people all shake hands with each other, for a total of $H(k) = \dfrac{k(k-1)}{2}$ handshakes. One more person walks into the room and shakes hands with everyone.

Show that $H(p) = \dfrac{p(p-1)}{2}$ when $p = k + 1$.

e. **Writing** How many handshakes will there be if everyone in your class shakes hands once with everyone else? Explain.

Number of people	Number of handshakes
p	$H(p)$
2	?
3	?
4	?
5	?

Ongoing **ASSESSMENT**

17. **Writing** Explain why it is possible to create a regular polygon with exterior angles that measure 15°, but it is not possible to create a regular polygon with exterior angles that measure 25° or 35°.

Review **PREVIEW**

Tell whether each statement is *True* or *False*. *(Section 3-3)*

18. Every square is a trapezoid.

19. If a quadrilateral is a rhombus, then it is a trapezoid.

20. Solve $\sqrt{-x + 13} = x - 1$. *(Section 2-6)*

21. Which of the following show(s) a perpendicular bisector of $\overline{PQ}$? Explain. *(Glossary, Toolbox Skill 33)*

a.   b.   c.   d.

 Working on the Unit Project

22. You have learned to use both inductive and deductive reasoning. Give examples of how both types of reasoning can be used in your brief.

3-5

Inscribed Polygons

Focus
Examine relationships
between inscribed polygons
and circles.

STRIKE A CHORD

EXPLORATION

Can a circle be drawn through the vertices of any triangle?

- **Materials: rulers, compasses**
- **Work in a group of four students.**

① On a sheet of paper, draw an acute scalene triangle and label it $\triangle ABC$.

② Fold the paper so that A lies directly on top of C. The line formed by the crease of the paper is the perpendicular bisector of $\overline{AC}$.

③ Fold the paper again to find the perpendicular bisectors of $\overline{BC}$ and $\overline{AB}$.

④ Label the point O where the three perpendicular bisectors intersect. With a compass, see if you can draw a circle with center O that passes through A, B, and C.

⑤ Repeat steps 1–4 for an obtuse scalene triangle.

⑥ Discuss these questions in your group.

   a. Why does the crease made in step 2 produce the perpendicular bisector of $\overline{AC}$?

   b. Make a conjecture about where the center of the circle would lie if $\triangle ABC$ were a right triangle.

   c. If $\triangle ABC$ is scalene, none of the perpendicular bisectors passes through a vertex. Would this be so with an isosceles triangle? with an equilateral triangle?

perpendicular bisector of $\overline{AB}$

perpendicular bisector of $\overline{BC}$

perpendicular bisector of $\overline{AC}$

$\overline{AB}$ is a chord of circle O.

Inscribed Triangles

The triangles in the Exploration are **inscribed** in the circles you drew. The circles are **circumscribed** about the triangles. The sides of the triangles are segments joining two points on the circle. Such segments are called **chords** of the circle.

The Exploration suggests it is always possible to circumscribe a circle about a triangle. The point where the perpendicular bisectors of the sides meet is the center of the circumscribed circle.

Sample 1

Prove that the perpendicular bisector of a chord of a circle passes through the center of the circle.

Sample Response

Given $\overline{CD}$ is a chord of circle O.
Line t is the perpendicular bisector of $\overline{CD}$.

Prove O lies on the perpendicular bisector of $\overline{CD}$.

Plan Ahead

Show that $OC = OD$, and therefore O lies on the perpendicular bisector of $\overline{CD}$.

> C and D both lie on circle O, since $\overline{CD}$ is a chord of circle O.
>
> Since O is the center of the circle, $\overline{OC}$ and $\overline{OD}$ are radii of circle O.
>
> By definition, all radii of a circle are equal in measure, so O is the same distance from points C and D.
>
> The perpendicular bisector theorem (p. 669) states that if a point is the same distance from both endpoints of a segment, then it lies on the perpendicular bisector of the segment. Therefore O lies on the perpendicular bisector of $\overline{CD}$.

PERPENDICULAR BISECTOR OF A CHORD

Theorem 3.6 The perpendicular bisector of a chord of a circle passes through the center of the circle.

$\overleftrightarrow{CD}$ is a perpendicular bisector of $\overline{AB}$.

▶ Now you are ready for:
Exs. 1–5 on pp. 168–169

Although every triangle may be inscribed in a circle, not all polygons have this property.

Any regular polygon, however, can be inscribed in a circle. An example is regular pentagon *DEFGH* inscribed in circle *O*.

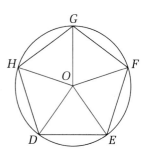

Talk it Over

1. In the regular pentagon shown, which triangles are congruent? How do you know that they are congruent?

2. Find the measures of the angles at center *O*.

Central Angles and Arcs

A **central angle** of a circle is an angle with its vertex at the center of the circle. The measure of an arc *intercepted* (cut off) by a central angle is equal to the measure of that central angle.

Arcs may be classified according to their measures in degrees. A major arc is named with three letters to distinguish it from the minor arc with the same endpoints.

CLASSIFICATIONS OF ARCS

minor arc	semicircle	major arc
$m \overset{\frown}{PR} < 180°$	$m \overset{\frown}{STU} = 180°$	$180° < m \overset{\frown}{VWX} < 360°$

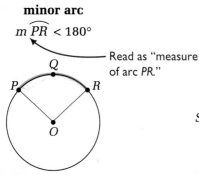

Read as "measure of arc *PR*."

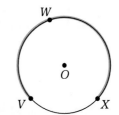

Name with two or three letters: $\overset{\frown}{PR}$ or $\overset{\frown}{PQR}$. Equal in measure to central angle *POR*.

Name with three letters: $\overset{\frown}{STU}$. $\overline{SU}$ is a diameter.

Name with three letters: $\overset{\frown}{VWX}$.

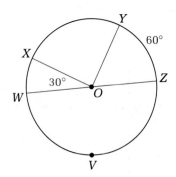

Find the measure of each arc or angle.

a. $\overset{\frown}{WX}$ b. $\angle YOZ$

c. $\overset{\frown}{WVZ}$ d. $\overset{\frown}{XY}$

Sample Response

a. The measure of a minor arc is equal to the measure of its central angle, so $m\,\overset{\frown}{WX} = 30°$.

b. The measure of a central angle is equal to the measure of the arc it intercepts, so $m\,\angle YOZ = 60°$.

c. The measure of a semicircle is 180°, so $m\,\overset{\frown}{WVZ} = 180°$.

d. The sum of the arcs of a circle is 360°.
$m\,\overset{\frown}{XY} = 360° - (30° + 180° + 60°) = 90°$

Look Back ◄──────

······► **Now you are ready for:**
Exs. 6–22 on pp. 169–171

Based on what you have learned in this section, what types of polygons may be inscribed in a circle?

3-5   Exercises and Problems

1. In the Exploration you were asked to make a conjecture about where the center of the circumscribed circle lies for a right triangle. Draw a right triangle and its circumscribed circle to test your conjecture.

2. **Reading** P, Q, and R lie on circle O.

   a. What name is given to the segments $\overline{PQ}$, $\overline{QR}$, and $\overline{RP}$?

   b. Where do the perpendicular bisectors of $\overline{PQ}$ and $\overline{QR}$ meet?

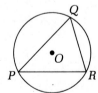

3. **Writing** Explain why you agree or disagree with this statement: "For every triangle there is a point that is equidistant from all three vertices."

4. A circle with equation $x^2 + y^2 = 100$ has its center at the origin O and radius 10.

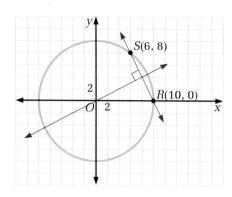

   a. Show that the points $R(10, 0)$ and $S(6, 8)$ lie on the circle.

   b. Find the midpoint of $\overline{RS}$.

   c. Find the slope of $\overline{RS}$ and the slope of a line perpendicular to $\overline{RS}$.

   d. Find an equation of the perpendicular bisector of $\overline{RS}$.

   e. Show that the perpendicular bisector of $\overline{RS}$ passes through the center of the circle (Theorem 3.6).

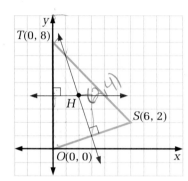

5. In coordinate geometry it is possible to inscribe a triangle in a circle by finding the equation of the circle. Start with $\triangle OST$ with vertices $O(0, 0)$, $S(6, 2)$, and $T(0, 8)$.

   a. Find the midpoints of $\overline{OT}$ and $\overline{OS}$.

   b. The perpendicular bisector of $\overline{OT}$ is a horizontal line. Find its equation.

   c. Find an equation of the perpendicular bisector of $\overline{OS}$.

   d. Find the coordinates of H, the point where these two perpendicular bisectors intersect.

   e. Find the distance from H to each vertex and the equation of the circle with center H passing through O, S, and T.

   f. Find an equation of the perpendicular bisector of $\overline{ST}$ and show that it also passes through H.

Find the measure of each arc or angle.

   6. $\overset{\frown}{CD}$

   7. $\angle AOB$

   8. $\overset{\frown}{AED}$

connection to **GEOGRAPHY**

9. Distances traveled by ships are usually measured in *nautical miles* rather than the more familar *statute* (land) *miles*.

One nautical mile is defined as the length of $\frac{1}{60}^\circ$ of arc of Earth's circumference.

   a. Find Earth's circumference in nautical miles.

   b. Use the fact that one nautical mile is about 1.15 statute miles to find Earth's circumference and diameter in statute miles.

(Not drawn to scale)

10. Using number lines like the one shown, graph the sets of measures (in degrees) for:

0°   60°   120°   180°   240°   300°   360°

   a. all possible major arcs

   b. all possible minor arcs

11. Make a concept map for what you have learned about central angles and arcs.

12. A regular polygon with 15 sides is inscribed in a circle. Find the degree measure of each intercepted arc.

13. Equilateral $\triangle ABC$ is inscribed in circle O. Find each measure.

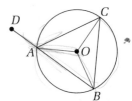

   a. $m \angle AOB$ b. $m \overset{\frown}{AB}$

   c. $m \angle OAB$ d. $m \angle DAC$

14. A regular polygon with n sides is inscribed in a circle. Prove that the measure of a central angle is equal to the measure of one of the exterior angles of the polygon.

15. The Cherokee people had a system of government based on seven clans. Their council house consisted of seven sections, one for each clan, and its shape was a regular *heptagon*. Find the measure of each central angle of this figure.

BY THE WAY...

This design symbolizes the seven clans of the Cherokee people. The number 7 is sacred to the Cherokee. Besides having 7 clans, they use 7 kinds of wood to kindle the fire in their 7-sided council house, and they have 7 yearly festivals.

16. An almost-regular heptagon can be constructed using a rope with 13 equally-spaced knots. Form isosceles triangles with sides measuring 4 units, 4 units, and 5 units and a common central vertex. The outer vertices of the triangles mark the vertices of a heptagon.

Show that this method produces a central angle which is within one degree of the angle needed for a true regular heptagon. (*Hint:* Draw a right triangle and use one of the trigonometric ratios.)

17. **Using Manipulatives** A regular hexagon can be constructed by compass and straightedge alone. Draw a circle and choose a point A on the circle. With the same radius as the circle, draw arcs at points B, C, D, E, and F on the circle. Join these points to form hexagon ABCDEF. Connect all points to the center O. Show that each central angle formed is 60° and that ABCDEF is a regular hexagon.

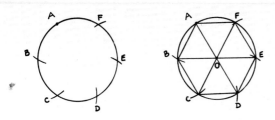

Ongoing **ASSESSMENT**

18. **Open-ended** Some quadrilaterals can be inscribed in a circle, but others cannot, as this parallelogram demonstrates. Make drawings or use geometric drawing software to determine which types of quadrilaterals can be inscribed in circles.

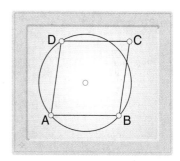

Review **PREVIEW**

19. What is the measure of an interior angle in a regular 13-gon? *(Section 3-4)*

20. Triangles ABC and DEF are similar triangles. What must be true about their corresponding angles? about their corresponding sides? *(Toolbox Skill 32)*

21. Find the value of each unknown angle measure. *(Toolbox Skill 30)*

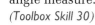

Working on the Unit Project

22. Read these simplified rules of evidence that will be used in deciding your case. Are these rules more like postulates or theorems in mathematics? Explain.

Simplified rules of evidence

1. Evidence must be relevant to the case.

2. Leading questions are not permitted on direct examination.

3. Lawyers must formally introduce physical evidence.

4. Hearsay testimony is not permitted.

The complete rules of evidence can be found in legal periodicals, historical documents, statutes, and trial records.

Arcs and Angles

BEST SEATS IN THE HOUSE

Helen and Tim are trying to decide where to sit in a theater.

"I want to sit close enough to get a good view of the stage," says Helen.

"But if we sit too close, we won't be able to see the whole stage at once," replies Tim.

Helen and Tim decide that at point *B*, their viewing angle for the stage is just right. They decide that the seats near *B* are the "best seats in the house."

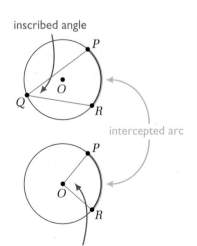

inscribed angle

intercepted arc

central angle

Talk it Over

1. Which point, *A*, *B*, or *C*, has the largest viewing angle for the stage? Which point has the smallest?

2. Are there any other places Helen and Tim can sit in the theater with the same viewing angle for the stage as point *B*? If so, where do you think these points are located?

The answer to question 2 is related to a theorem about inscribed angles in circles. An **inscribed angle** is an angle formed by two chords that intersect at a point on a circle. The arc that lies within an inscribed angle is called its **intercepted arc.**

You have learned that a minor arc is measured by finding its central angle, the angle formed by two radii from the center to the endpoints of the arc. The degree measure of an arc may be written near the center of the circle or along the arc itself.

Prove that the measure of an inscribed angle of a circle is equal to half the measure of its intercepted arc.

Sample Response

Given $\angle BAC$ is inscribed in circle O.

Prove $m \angle BAC = \frac{1}{2} m \,\overset{\frown}{BC}$

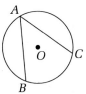

Plan Ahead

Show that $m \angle BAC = \frac{1}{2} m \angle BOC$. Then use the fact that $m \angle BOC = m \,\overset{\frown}{BC}$ and use the substitution property.

Show Your Reasoning

Draw $\overline{BC}$ and radii $\overline{OA}$, $\overline{OB}$, and $\overline{OC}$.
$\triangle AOB$, $\triangle BOC$, and $\triangle COA$ are isosceles.
Mark equal angles using $x°$, $y°$, and $z°$.

In $\triangle ABC$, $2x + 2y + 2z = 180$.
In $\triangle BOC$, $2x + m \angle BOC = 180$.
So, $2x + m \angle BOC = 2x + 2y + 2z$.
Using algebra and substitution,
$m \angle BOC = 2y + 2z$.

Since $m \angle BAC = y + z$ and $m \angle BOC = 2y + 2z$,
$m \angle BOC = 2 \, m \angle BAC$.

Since the measure of an arc is equal to
the measure of its central angle,
$m \,\overset{\frown}{BC} = m \angle BOC = 2 \, m \angle BAC$.
Therefore, $\frac{1}{2} m \,\overset{\frown}{BC} = m \angle BAC$.

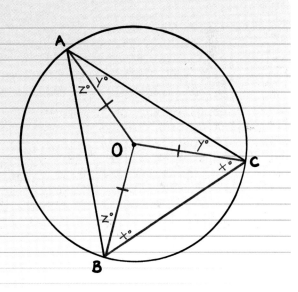

This proof assumes that point O lies inside $\angle BAC$. The theorem is also true when point O lies on a side of the angle or outside the angle. You will prove this in Exercises 7 and 8.

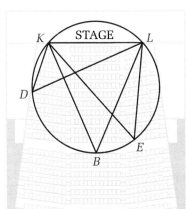

> **Talk it Over**
>
> 3. In the diagram in Sample 1, what is the intercepted arc for $\angle BCA$?
>
> 4. What kind of arc is intercepted by an inscribed angle of 90°?
>
> 5. In the figure, why do $\angle D$, $\angle B$, and $\angle E$ all have the same measure?

INSCRIBED ANGLE THEOREMS

Theorem 3.7 The measure of an inscribed angle of a circle is equal to half the measure of its intercepted arc.

Theorem 3.8 An inscribed angle whose intercepted arc is a semicircle is a right angle.

Theorem 3.9 If two inscribed angles in the same circle intercept the same arc, then they are equal in measure.

Theorem 3.7

Theorem 3.8

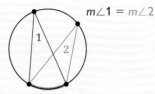

Theorem 3.9

You can use the theorems above to find angle measures and arc measures.

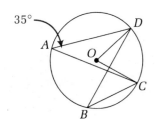

Sample 2

O is the center of the circle at the left. In circle O, $m \angle A = 35°$. Find each angle or arc measure.

a. $m \angle B$

b. $m \overset{\frown}{CD}$

c. $m \overset{\frown}{DAC}$

d. $m \angle COD$

Sample Response

a. $\angle A$ and $\angle B$ intercept the same arc, $\overset{\frown}{CD}$, so $m \angle A = m \angle B = 35°$.

b. The measure of an inscribed angle is half the measure of its intercepted arc, so $m \overset{\frown}{CD} = 2\, m \angle A = 70°$.

c. $\overset{\frown}{DAC}$ is a major arc. Since the measure of the entire circle is 360°,
$m \overset{\frown}{DAC} = 360° - m \overset{\frown}{CD} = 360° - 70° = 290°$.

d. $\angle COD$ is a central angle and equal in measure to its intercepted arc, so
$m \angle COD = m \overset{\frown}{CD} = 70°$.

Look Back

When are two inscribed angles in a circle equal in measure? When a central angle and an inscribed angle intercept the same arc, how are their measures related?

3-6 Exercises and Problems

1. **Reading** What is the difference between an inscribed angle and a central angle?

Find all the missing measures of angles and arcs.

2.

3.

4.

5. **Using Manipulatives** You can simulate the "best seat in the house" problem with a paper model of the theater and viewing angle.

   a. On one sheet of paper draw a segment to represent the stage.

   b. On another sheet of paper draw a viewing angle of 30° and cut it out.

   c. Place the viewing angle at many different positions, each time with the endpoints of the stage lying on the sides of the angle. Draw a dot next to the vertex of the viewing angle each time. What do you notice?

   d. Predict the result if you use a viewing angle of 45° instead of 30°. Cut out a viewing angle of 45° and check your prediction.

6. *DEFGH* is a regular pentagon inscribed in a circle.

   a. Find the measures of $\overarc{DE}$, $\overarc{EF}$, and $\overarc{FG}$.

   b. Use the results of part (a) to find $m \angle DHG$.

   c. Find $m \angle DHG$ by another method.

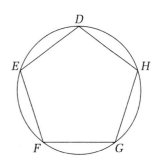

7. Here is a diagram for a proof of Theorem 3.7 for the case where the center of the circle lies *on one of the sides* of the angle. Write a proof.

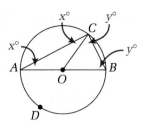

> **Given** ∠*BAC* is inscribed in circle *O*.

> **Prove** $m \angle BAC = \frac{1}{2} m \widehat{BC}$

Plan Ahead

Show that $m \angle AOC = 2y$, $m \angle BOC = 2x$, and $x + y = 90°$.

8. Here is a diagram for a proof of Theorem 3.7 for the case where the center of the circle lies *outside* the angle.

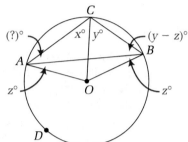

a. Write $m \angle BAC$ in terms of x and z.

b. Prove that $m \angle BAC = \frac{1}{2} m \widehat{BC}$.

Plan Ahead

Use $\triangle BOC$ to show that $2y + m \angle BOC = 180°$. Then write an equation based on the sum of the angle measures in $\triangle ABC$. Show that $m \angle BOC = 2x - 2z = 2m \angle BAC$.

9. **Group Activity** Work in a group of four students. Each of you should carry out steps 1–4. You will need protractors and compasses.

Step 1: Draw a circle of any size and mark its center. Draw points *A*, *B*, *C*, and *D* anywhere on the circle. Connect them to form quadrilateral *ABCD*.

Step 2: Find the measures of $\widehat{AB}$, $\widehat{BC}$, $\widehat{CD}$, and $\widehat{DA}$. The sum of these measures should be 360°.

Step 3: Find the measures of ∠*DAB* and ∠*DCB*.

Step 4: Find the measures of ∠*ABC* and ∠*ADC*.

What relationship do you find between opposite angles of your quadrilaterals? State your conjecture as a theorem and prove it.

10. Theorem 3.8 can be illustrated using coordinates of points on the circle with equation $x^2 + y^2 = 25$.

a. Show that each of these points lies on the circle: $P(-5, 0)$, $Q(5, 0)$, $A(-4, 3)$, $B(-3, 4)$, $C(0, 5)$, $D(3, 4)$, $E(4, 3)$.

b. Find the slopes of $\overline{PA}$, $\overline{PB}$, $\overline{PC}$, $\overline{PD}$, and $\overline{PE}$.

c. Find the slopes of $\overline{QA}$, $\overline{QB}$, $\overline{QC}$, $\overline{QD}$, and $\overline{QE}$.

d. Use slopes to explain why ∠*PAQ*, ∠*PBQ*, ∠*PCQ*, ∠*PDQ*, and ∠*PEQ* are all right angles.

11. Write a coordinate proof of Theorem 3.8: An inscribed angle whose intercepted arc is a semicircle is a right angle.

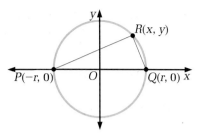

> **Given** $P(-r, 0)$, $Q(r, 0)$, and $R(x, y)$; $x^2 + y^2 = r^2$

> **Prove** $\angle PRQ$ is a right angle.

Plan Ahead

Show that the slope of $\overline{PR}$ is $\dfrac{y}{x + r}$ and the slope of $\overline{QR}$ is $\dfrac{y}{x - r}$.
Then show that the product of these slopes is -1, using the fact that $x^2 - r^2 = -y^2$.

12. Two chords, $\overline{AB}$ and $\overline{CD}$, intersect inside a circle at point E.

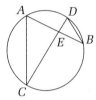

  a. **Using Manipulatives** Draw a large circle and any two chords that intersect inside it. Label the triangles formed as in the diagram. Fold your drawing once through point E so that the similarity of the triangles is clear.

  b. Prove that $\triangle ACE \sim \triangle DBE$.

Navigation Boat pilots have to be careful to avoid dangerous areas. Navigation charts often provide information about the "danger angle." Two landmarks on the shore at L and M are identified. A circle is drawn through L and M that encloses the danger area. $\angle LCM$ is called the danger angle.

13. Explain why any point C on major arc $\overparen{LNM}$ will give the same danger angle.

14. The pilot of the boat at B wants to stay away from the danger area. Should the pilot try to keep $m \angle LBM$ greater than or less than $m \angle LCM$? Explain.

15. **Open-ended** Find or draw a lake or ocean map with a danger area near the shore. Draw a circle that passes through two landmarks on the shore and that completely encloses the danger area. Measure the danger angle a boat pilot should use to avoid the danger area.

16. **Writing** Explain how the types of angles in a triangle are related to the types of arcs they intercept when the triangle is inscribed in a circle.

17. Draw a regular octagon inscribed in a circle. What is the measure of the arc intercepted by one side of the polygon? *(Section 3-5)*

For Exercises 18 and 19, what conclusion can you reach from each set of conditions? *(Toolbox Skill 35)*

18. Tanya eats either taco salad or pizza for lunch. She does not eat pizza.

19. Akio filled out an application with either a black pen, a blue pen, or a pencil. He did not use a pencil.

20. Show that if two integers are odd, then their sum is even. *(Toolbox Skills 13 and 17)*

Working on the Unit Project

21. In writing a proof, the order of the steps is important. In questioning a witness, the order in which questions are asked is important.

    Pick one of your witnesses and write four questions you plan to ask. Put them in order. Explain why you chose that order.

Unit 3	**CHECKPOINT 2**

1. **Writing** Which has larger interior angles, a regular 18-gon or a regular 19-gon? Which has larger exterior angles? Explain.   **3-4**

2. Describe how you can find the center of a circle that circumscribes a given triangle.   **3-5**

Find all the missing measures of angles and arcs.   **3-6**

3.
A 120° B 90° C

4.
G D E 90° F

5.
H 75° I 35° J

Section

3-7

Focus
Use indirect proof in
geometric, algebraic, and
everyday contexts. Examine
the properties of tangents
to circles.

Indirect Proof

Say It Isn't So

Here is a puzzle. Two opposite corners of a checkerboard have been removed. You have some dominoes, each of which covers two squares of the board. Can you cover the board with dominoes? No dominoes may overlap or spill over the edge of the checkerboard.

Talk it Over

1. How many squares are there on this checkerboard? How many are black and how many are red?

2. How many dominoes would it take to cover the checkerboard?

3. If one half of a domino covers a black square, what color must the other half cover?

4. If the correct number of dominoes covers the checkerboard, how many black squares will be covered? How many red squares?

5. Is it possible to solve the domino-checkerboard puzzle? Explain.

Assuming the Opposite

The domino-checkerboard puzzle illustrates *indirect proof.* In an **indirect proof,** you show that if you temporarily assume the opposite of what you want to prove, you are led to an impossible situation or a contradiction of a known fact.

You don't believe me? Suppose I *could* manage to cover all the squares. Each domino would cover one black square and one red square.

Sure, that's obvious.

Altogether I would have covered 31 red squares and 31 black squares. But I cut out two red squares so I have only 30 red squares left.

So what we just assumed could be done is impossible!

Right. And that's why we can be sure that we'll never be able to cover the board with 31 dominoes.

Sample 1

Prove that if two lines lie in the same plane and they are perpendicular to the same line, then they are parallel.

Sample Response

Given Line *j* is perpendicular to line *m* at *A*.
Line *k* is perpendicular to line *m* at *B*.
Lines *j*, *k*, and *m* lie in the same plane.

Prove *j* ∥ *k*

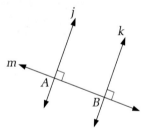

Plan Ahead

Use an indirect proof. Temporarily assume that *j* and *k* are not parallel. Show that this assumption leads to a contradiction.

Show Your Reasoning

Suppose that *j* and *k* are not parallel. Then since they lie in the same plane, they must intersect. Label as *C* the point at which they intersect.
  Then in △*ABC*, ∠*CAB* is a right angle and ∠*CBA* is a right angle, since perpendicular lines form right angles. The sum of the measures of the three angles in the triangle is 90° + 90° + m ∠*ACB*. This sum must be greater than 180°.
  This contradicts the Triangle Sum Theorem, so the assumption that *j* and *k* are not parallel must be false. Therefore *j* ∥ *k*.

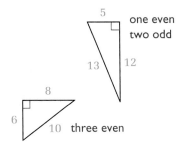

one even
two odd

three even

Three positive integers, a, b, and c, that satisfy the equation $a^2 + b^2 = c^2$ are called a *Pythagorean triple*. Prove that every Pythagorean triple contains at least one even number. Use an indirect proof.

Sample Response

Suppose there is a Pythagorean triple in which none of the numbers is even. That means a, b, and c are all odd numbers.

Then a^2 is an odd number, because $a^2 = a \cdot a$, and the product of two odd numbers is odd. For the same reason, b^2 and c^2 must be odd.

Then $a^2 + b^2$ is the sum of two odd numbers, which is even. But $a^2 + b^2 = c^2$, and c^2 is odd (Exercise 20, page 178).

This is a contradiction, because $a^2 + b^2$ cannot be even and odd at the same time, so the original assumption that there is a Pythagorean triple with three odd numbers must be false.

Therefore, every Pythagorean triple contains at least one even number.

▶ Now you are ready for:
Exs. 1–10 on pp. 183–185

Tangents and Secants

If a line intersects a circle, it does so in either one point or two points.

TANGENTS AND SECANTS

point of tangency

tangent: a line in the plane of a circle and intersecting the circle in exactly one point

secant: a line intersecting the circle in two points

6. Which point on a tangent line is closest to the center of the circle?

7. A city planner wants to build a bridge to cross the river from point A. To which point on the opposite shore should the planner build to make the shortest bridge?

SHORTEST PATH POSTULATE

A segment can be drawn perpendicular to a given line from a point not on the line. The length of this segment is the shortest distance from the point to the line.

PQ is the shortest distance from P to line l.

Sample 3

Prove that if a line is tangent to a circle, then the line is perpendicular to the radius drawn from the center to the point of tangency.

Sample Response

Given Line t is tangent to circle O at P.

Prove $\overline{OP}$ is perpendicular to t.

Plan Ahead

Use the Shortest Path Postulate in an indirect proof. Temporarily assume that $\overline{OP}$ is not perpendicular to t.

Show Your Reasoning

Suppose that $\overline{OP}$ is not perpendicular to t. Then there is another segment $\overline{OM}$ from O to line t which is perpendicular to t. By the Shortest Path Postulate, OM < OP. Because a tangent line intersects a circle in only one point, M lies outside the circle and OM > OP.

It is impossible for $\overline{OM}$ to be both shorter and longer than the radius $\overline{OP}$. So the assumption that $\overline{OP}$ is not perpendicular to t is false. Therefore, $\overline{OP}$ is perpendicular to t.

THEOREMS ABOUT TANGENTS

Theorem 3.10 If a line is tangent to a circle, then the line is perpendicular to the radius drawn from the center to the point of tangency.

Theorem 3.11 If a line in the plane of a circle is perpendicular to a radius at its outer endpoint, then the line is tangent to the circle.

Theorem 3.12 If two tangent segments are drawn from the same point to the same circle, then they are equal in measure.

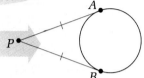

····▶ Now you are ready for:
Exs. 11–22 on pp. 185–186

Look Back ◄

Describe the technique of indirect proof.

3-7 Exercises and Problems

1. **Reading** There are four indirect proofs in this section. Complete this table to summarize them.

	To prove	**Temporarily assume the opposite**
Domino-Checkerboard Puzzle	The board cannot be covered.	It can be covered.
Sample 1	line $j \parallel$ line k	_?_
Sample 2	All three numbers in a Pythagorean triple cannot be odd.	_?_
Sample 3	_?_	$\overline{OP}$ is not perpendicular to line t.

2. Fill in the blanks to complete this proof of the fact that no triangle has two obtuse angles.

Suppose _?_. Let the two obtuse angles be $\angle A$ and $\angle B$.
Then $m \angle A > 90°$ and $m \angle B$ _?_.

The sum, $m \angle A + m \angle B + m \angle C >$ _?_.

This contradicts the _?_ theorem. Therefore _?_.

3. Use an indirect proof to show that no quadrilateral has four acute angles.

4. Elisa Rodriguez is a sales representative. She has scheduled a one-hour meeting with a customer in Indianapolis at 9:00 A.M. On the same day she must meet another customer in Evansville at noon. Her only transportation is her car. The distance between the cities is 168 mi. Elisa Rodriguez never drives above the 65 mi/h speed limit. Prove that she cannot attend both meetings.

5. At Sunnydale High School the following schedule of classes is available for seniors.

PERIOD	COURSES OFFERED
1	PHYSICS, ACCOUNTING, ADVANCED FRENCH
2	DISCRETE MATHEMATICS, ENGLISH, CALCULUS
3	AMERICAN GOVERNMENT, ENGLISH, PHYSICS
4	AMERICAN GOVERNMENT, ADVANCED SPANISH, BIOLOGY
5	INTERNATIONAL RELATIONS, MUSIC THEORY, COMPUTER SCIENCE
6	ACCOUNTING, STUDIO ART, DISCRETE MATHEMATICS

All seniors are required to take English and American Government. Prove that no senior can take both Calculus and Biology.

6. Prove that if two lines in the same plane are parallel to the same line, then they are parallel to each other. Use the postulate: Through a point not on a line there is exactly one line parallel to a given line.

7. Prove that there is no Pythagorean triple with two even numbers and one odd number.

8. **Open-ended** Describe a situation in everyday life where you use indirect reasoning.

9. **Map making** On a map, regions that share a border are not the same color.

Here is a section of a map, showing six European countries. Using this section of the map, write an indirect proof of this statement:

Some maps require at least four colors.

(*Hint:* Start by assuming this map can be colored with only three colors.)

10. Puzzles In a *magic square* the sum of the numbers in each row, column, and diagonal is the same. The classical 3-by-3 magic square uses the first nine positive integers.

Use an indirect proof to explain why there is no magic square using only the first nine prime numbers: 2, 3, 5, 7, 11, 13, 17, 19, and 23.

Detail from Albrecht Dürer's Melancholia

11. Copy and complete this indirect proof of Theorem 3.11: If a line in the plane of a circle is perpendicular to a radius at its outer endpoint, then the line is tangent to the circle.

Given $\overline{OA}$ is a radius of circle O.
Line m is in the plane of circle O and is perpendicular to $\overline{OA}$.

Prove Line m is a tangent to circle O.

Since line m intersects the circle at A, it is either a tangent or a secant. Suppose m is not a tangent to the circle. Then it is a secant and it intersects the circle at another point B.

Draw $\overline{OB}$. Then, since $\overline{OA}$ and $\overline{OB}$ are both radii, $OA = OB$ and $\triangle OAB$ is isosceles. (Continue the indirect proof from here.)

12. Copy and complete this proof of Theorem 3.12: If two tangent segments are drawn from the same point to the same circle, then they are equal in measure.

Given $\overline{PA}$ and $\overline{PB}$ are both tangents to circle O at A and B.

Prove $PA = PB$

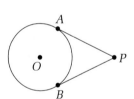

Plan Ahead

Draw $\overline{OA}$, $\overline{OB}$, and $\overline{OP}$. Use theorem 3.10 to show that $\triangle OAP$ and $\triangle OBP$ are both right triangles. Use the Pythagorean theorem to find PA and PB in terms of h and r.

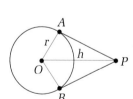

13. Research Find an indirect proof that $\sqrt{2}$ is an irrational number and present it to the class.

14. a. Solve the system of equations: $x + y = 4$
$x^2 + y^2 = 8$

   b. Show that this system represents a circle and a line tangent to the circle. Find the coordinates of the point of tangency.

   c. Use coordinate geometry to show that the radius to the point of tangency is perpendicular to the tangent line.

Global Communications Communications satellites are used to transmit radio and television signals around the world. They circle Earth in a stationary orbit at a height of 22,300 mi above the surface. At this height they travel just fast enough to keep up with Earth's rotation. The radius of Earth is about 4000 mi.

View from above North Pole

(Not drawn to scale)

BY THE WAY...

The Milstar satellite provides global communications. Systems director Dr. Wanda Austin provided engineering support to the Milstar. Her background includes degrees in mathematics and systems engineering.

15. A communications satellite is placed in orbit at point S. Use trigonometry to find the degree measure of $\overset{\frown}{ACB}$.

16. Use proportions to find the length of $\overset{\frown}{ACB}$, the number of miles along the equator that the satellite covers.

17. Suppose three satellites are placed in orbit around the equator, 120° apart. Would the range of these satellites include the entire equator? the entire surface of Earth? Explain.

Ongoing **ASSESSMENT**

18. **Writing** Explain to a friend who missed class how to write an indirect proof.

Review **PREVIEW**

19. Draw any quadrilateral with vertices on a circle. Draw its diagonals. Label your diagram and name *two* pairs of similar triangles. Explain how you can prove that the triangles are similar. *(Section 3-6)*

20. Use the function $f(x) = \dfrac{x^2 + 4x + 1}{x + 1}$.

   a. Find $f(-4)$.

   b. Find x when $f(x) = 3$.

21. Find the circumference and the area of a circle with radius 4.5 m. *(Toolbox Skill 29)*

Working on the Unit Project

22. What is an alibi defense? How can an alibi be used as an indirect proof? Give an example of a case you have read about in which an alibi played a significant role.

Circumscribed Polygons

At the right, a circle is inscribed in a square. The square is circumscribed about the circle. The sides of a circumscribed polygon are tangents to the inscribed circle.

A regular polygon with *n* sides may be circumscribed about a circle by drawing tangents at points on the circle that form *n* arcs of equal measure.

Pleasure wheel from about 1860

Talk it Over

1. In the diagrams above, *D, E, F, G, H, I, J,* and *K* are spaced equally around circle *O*. Find $m \overset{\frown}{EF}$. What other arcs have the same measure?

2. Tangents are drawn at the eight points on the circle to form octagon *PQRSTUVW*. Explain why $\triangle OER$ and $\triangle OFR$ are congruent.

3. Find $m \angle EOR$ and $m \angle FOR$. What other angles must have the same measures?

4. Explain why $\triangle SOR$ and $\triangle ROQ$ are congruent.

5. Explain why *PQRSTUVW* is a regular octagon.

Suppose the radius of circle O is 1 m. Find the area of regular octagon *PQRSTUVW*.

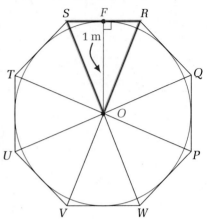

Sample Response

Since the octagon is made of 8 congruent triangles, you can find the area of one triangle and multiply it by 8.

To find the area of $\triangle SOR$, you need to find the length RS.

Step 1 Use the tangent ratio to find RF in right $\triangle FOR$.

$$m \angle SOR = \frac{360°}{8} = 45°; \; m \angle FOR = \frac{1}{2} \cdot m \angle SOR = 22.5°$$

In right $\triangle FOR$, $\dfrac{RF}{OF} = \dfrac{RF}{1} = \tan 22.5°$

$$RF \approx 0.414$$

$$RS = 2(RF) \approx 0.828 \text{ (m)}$$

Step 2 Use the formula $A = \frac{1}{2}bh$.

Area of $\triangle SOR = \frac{1}{2}(RS)(OF)$

$$\approx \frac{1}{2}(0.828)(1) = 0.414 \text{ (m}^2\text{)}$$

Step 3 Multiply the area of $\triangle SOR$ by 8: $8(0.414) \approx 3.31$

The area of octagon *PQRSTUVW* is about 3.31 m².

Talk it Over

6. The **semiperimeter** of a polygon is half the perimeter. Find the semiperimeter of octagon *PQRSTUVW*.

7. Show that the area of an octagon may be found by multiplying the radius of the inscribed circle and the semiperimeter.

8. Find the area of the circle. How does it compare to the area of the octagon?

The area of any circumscribed polygon may be found when the radius of the inscribed circle and the sides are known. This is true for nonregular as well as regular polygons.

AREA OF A CIRCUMSCRIBED POLYGON

The area of any circumscribed polygon is the product of the radius (r) of the inscribed circle and the semiperimeter (s).

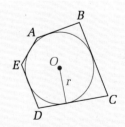

$$A = rs$$

$$\frac{AB + BC + CD + DE + AE}{2} = \text{semiperimeter}$$

As the number of sides of a regular polygon increases, its area approaches that of the inscribed circle.

   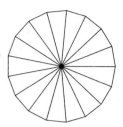

Talk it Over

9. **a.** The semiperimeter of a circle is half of its circumference. Write a formula for the semiperimeter *s* of a circle in terms of *r*.

b. Use your answer to part (a) to write a formula for the area of a circle in terms of *s*.

Look Back

What is the relationship between an inscribed circle and its circumscribed polygon?

3-8 Exercises and Problems

1. **Reading** What is a semiperimeter?

2. Circle *O* is inscribed in △*ABC*. Find the perimeter of the triangle.

3. Circle *O* is inscribed in a regular pentagon. Find *m* ∠*AOP* and *m* ∠*APO*.

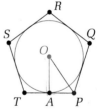

4. △*BCD* has an inscribed circle whose radius is $4\frac{1}{3}$ cm. Find the area of the triangle.

5. Circle *O* is inscribed in a triangle. *AB* = 25 ft, *AC* = 63 ft, and *BC* = 52 ft. The radius of the circle is 9 ft. Use two methods to find the area of the triangle.

6. **Using Manipulatives** You will need tracing paper or wax paper, a compass, and a straightedge.

   a. Draw a large scalene triangle on your paper.

   b. Fold each pair of sides together and crease to form the angle bisectors. Label the point of intersection of these bisectors *I*.

   c. Experiment with the compass opening to find the shortest distance from *I* to one of the sides of the triangle. Show that *I* is equidistant from the three sides.

   d. With *I* as the center, draw a circle tangent to the three sides of the triangle.

   e. **Writing** Write a short paragraph about what you learned from this activity.

7. **Open-ended** It is impossible to draw an inscribed circle inside some quadrilaterals. Make drawings or use geometric drawing software to determine which types of quadrilaterals may be circumscribed about circles.

8. A regular hexagon is circumscribed about a circle with radius 1 m.

   a. Find $m \angle AOQ$.

   b. Use trigonometry to find the length of one side of the hexagon.

   c. Find the perimeter of the hexagon.

   d. Find the area of the hexagon.

   e. Julie says the area and the perimeter of this hexagon are the same. Do you agree? Explain.

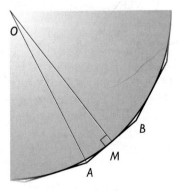

9. **Open-ended** Repeat Exercise 8 with a regular polygon with more than six sides that is circumscribed about a circle with radius 1 m.

10. $\overline{AB}$ is the side of a regular *n*-gon circumscribed about circle *O*. *M* is the midpoint of $\overline{AB}$.

   a. Find an expression in terms of *n* for $m \angle MOA$.

   b. Show that the expression you found in part (a) gives the correct value for a regular octagon (see Sample), a regular hexagon (see Exercise 8), and another regular polygon (see Exercise 9).

11 TECHNOLOGY Use spreadsheet software or a graphics calculator to find the semiperimeters and areas of regular n-gons circumscribed about a circle with radius 1 unit. Use the degree mode, or convert from degrees to radians, if necessary.

a. **Writing** Start with $n = 3$ and increase n by 1 each time. Extend the pattern to $n = 25$. Describe any patterns you see in your chart.

			Semiperimeters, areas			
n	**m ∠MOA**	**tan MOA**	**Length of side**	**Semiperimeter**	**Area**	
3	60°	1.7320499361	3.4640998722	5.1961498083	5.1961498083	
4	45°	1	2	4	4	
5	36°	0.7265423282	1.4530846566	3.6327116414	3.6327116414	

b. Change the spreadsheet so that n doubles each time. Extend this pattern until you get an area that is about 3.14159. What is n?

c. What happens to the ratio of the area of the circumscribed polygon to the area of the circle as the number of sides increases? What happens to the ratio of the perimeter to the circumference?

Ongoing **ASSESSMENT**

12. **Writing** Explain why the formula $A = rs$ can be used to find the area of any nonregular polygon that is circumscribed about a circle.

Review **PREVIEW**

13. Write an indirect proof to show that $m \angle MOA$ in the figure for Exercise 10 can never be 25° if the polygon is regular. *(Section 3-7)*

14. Identify these space figures by name. *(Toolbox Skill 29)*

15. Tell whether the function $f(x) = \frac{4}{5}x - 2$ is linear. Find $f(-5)$, $f(0)$, and $f(20)$. *(Section 2-2)*

 Working on the Unit Project

16. As an attorney you want to discredit your opponent's arguments.

a. List the arguments you think the opposing attorneys will make. List your counterarguments to their arguments.

b. Make a list of questions you intend to ask in cross-examining witnesses for the other side.

"A unique and stirring plea, counsellor."

Shanahan

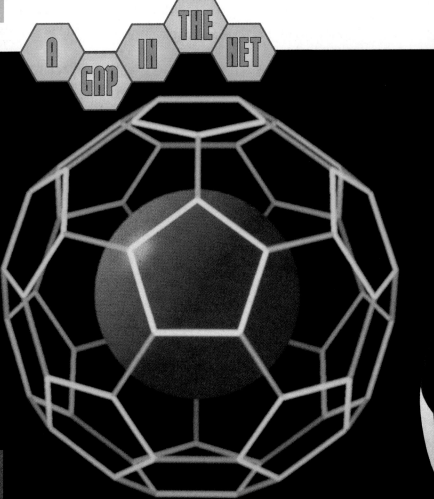

Focus

Recognize the five regular polyhedra and examine properties of regular and semiregular polyhedra.

This computer-generated model of a molecule is a *buckminster-fullerene,* or *buckyball* for short. It has 60 atoms of carbon joined as 12 regular pentagons and 20 regular hexagons. Crystallized buckyballs may form a substance harder than diamonds.

Buckyballs have the same structure as the pattern on soccer balls. You can visualize the structure of a buckyball by imagining an atom of carbon at each of the vertices on a soccer ball.

BY THE WAY...

The buckminsterfullerene molecule was discovered in 1985. It is named after R. Buckminster Fuller, the architect who invented geodesic domes.

Talk it Over

1. How many hexagons and how many pentagons meet at each vertex of a buckyball?

2. How many degrees are there in each angle at each vertex?

3. Find the sum of the measures of the angles at each vertex.

Regular and Semiregular Polyhedra

A space figure whose faces are all polygons is a **polyhedron** (plural: polyhedra). A buckyball is an example of a *semiregular polyhedron*. The faces of a **semiregular polyhedron** are all regular polygons, and at each vertex there is the same number of faces of each type.

Since the faces include both regular pentagons and regular hexagons, the buckyball is *not* a regular polyhedron. In a **regular polyhedron** only one type of regular polygon is used for the faces, and there is the same number of faces at each vertex.

Semiregular Polyhedra

2 squares and 2 equilateral triangles at each vertex

2 regular octagons and 1 equilateral triangle at each vertex

Regular Polyhedra

3 squares at each vertex

4 equilateral triangles at each vertex

The first model of the buckyball was made by cutting regular pentagons and regular hexagons out of paper and pasting them together. On the left is part of a **net** of polygons that can be used to make this model. The existence of a gap allows a net to "fold up" to make a polyhedron.

The sum of the measures of the angles is less than 360°.

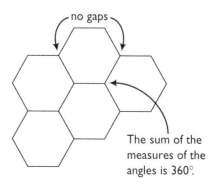

The sum of the measures of the angles is 360°.

4. The angle measure of the gap in a net for a polyhedron is called the **defect** for the vertex. Find the defect at vertex *A* in the net for the buckyball on page 193.

5. How is the tessellation of hexagons different from the net for the buckyball?

The polyhedra you study in this course are convex. Prisms and pyramids are convex polyhedra. All regular and semiregular polyhedra are convex.

CONVEX POLYHEDRON POSTULATE

In any convex polyhedron, the sum of the measures of the angles at each vertex is less than 360°.

By the way...

Grace Chisholm Young (1868–1944) was the first woman to receive an official doctorate in mathematics in Germany. In her *First Book of Geometry* she included nets, believing they would help students become familiar with three-dimensional figures.

Sample

Find the sum of the defects for all the vertices of a cube.

Sample Response

At each vertex there are three 90° angles, for a total of 270°.

The defect at each vertex is 360° − 270° = 90°.

Since a cube has eight vertices, the sum of the defects is 8(90°) = 720°.

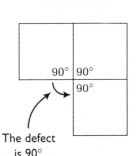

90° | 90°

90°

The defect is 90°.

The Five Regular Polyhedra

Starting with triangles, there are regular polygons with any number of sides. There are regular quadrilaterals, pentagons, hexagons, heptagons, and so on. You might conjecture that there are infinitely many types of regular polyhedra also.

Talk it Over

6. A regular tetrahedron has 3 equilateral triangles at each vertex. Is it possible to have a regular polyhedron with 4 equilateral triangles at each vertex? with 5? with 6? with more than 6?

7. Is it possible to have a regular polyhedron with more than 3 squares at each vertex? with more than 3 pentagons at each vertex?

8. Is it possible to make a regular polyhedron with hexagons? Why or why not?

The *Talk it Over* questions demonstrate that it is impossible to have more than five regular polyhedra.

REGULAR POLYHEDRA

Theorem 3.13 There are exactly five regular polyhedra.

Triangular Faces

Square Faces

Pentagonal Faces

| **Tetrahedron** 4 faces | **Octahedron** 8 faces | **Icosahedron** 20 faces | **Hexahedron** 6 faces | **Dodecahedron** 12 faces |

Look Back

Explain why a regular polyhedron cannot be made using polygons with seven or more sides.

3-9 Exercises and Problems

1. **Reading** What is a semiregular polyhedron?

2. **Using Manipulatives** Construct the five regular polyhedra. Use polyhedral nets provided by your teacher or use toothpicks and gum drops.

3. **Using Manipulatives** Construct three congruent regular hexagons and show that they will not "fold up" to make the corner of a polyhedron.

4. A *regular tessellation* is a tiling of the plane made up of only one type of regular polygon. Show that only three regular polygons can form regular tessellations.

5. For each of the regular polyhedra, find the number of faces, vertices, and edges. Complete the table to show that Euler's formula, $F + V = E + 2$, holds.

	Number of Faces (F)	Number of Vertices (V)	Number of Edges (E)
tetrahedron	?	?	?
hexahedron	?	?	?
octahedron	?	?	?
dodecahedron	?	?	?
icosahedron	?	?	?

6. A *prism* is a polyhedron formed when two congruent polygons in parallel planes, with corresponding sides parallel, are joined at corresponding vertices. Prisms are classified according to the shape of the base. Show that Euler's formula, $F + V = E + 2$, holds for each of the prisms below.

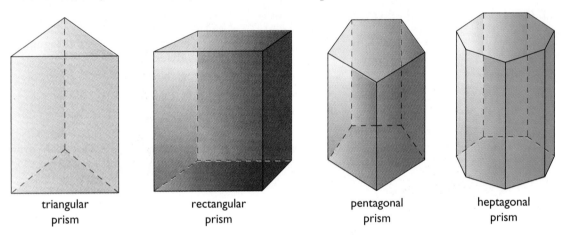

| triangular prism | rectangular prism | pentagonal prism | heptagonal prism |

7. Find the number of edges in a buckyball using three methods.

a. There are 60 vertices. Each vertex connects three edges. That gives a total of __?__ edges. But you have counted each edge how many times? Divide to find the answer.

b. Each edge is the side of a face. There are 12 pentagonal faces and 20 hexagonal faces. How many sides is that altogether? You have now counted each edge how many times? Divide to find the answer.

c. You know the number of faces (F) and the number of vertices (V). Use Euler's formula, $F + V = E + 2$, to find the number of edges.

Find the sum of the defects for all the vertices of each polyhedron.

8. regular tetrahedron

9. regular octahedron

10. buckyball

11. prism with regular pentagonal base

12. Make a conjecture based on your answers to Exercises 8–11 and the Sample. Test your conjecture for several other polyhedra.

13. Write an indirect proof to show that no regular polyhedron has faces with more than five sides.

14. **Open-ended** Make a chart similar to the quadrilateral chart to show relationships among polyhedra. Include these categories in your chart: regular polyhedron, semiregular polyhedron, prism, cube, buckyball, and others that you choose.

Tell whether *exactly* or *at least* fits best in each sentence.

15. Every polyhedron has (exactly/at least) three faces at each vertex.

16. Each edge of a polyhedron is shared by (exactly/at least) two faces.

17. A prism has (exactly/at least) one pair of parallel faces.

18. There are (exactly/at least) five regular polyhedra.

19. Each edge of the cube measures 2 m. One sphere is circumscribed about the cube. The other sphere is inscribed in the cube.

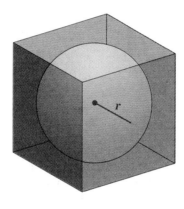

Remember:
Volume of sphere $= \frac{4}{3}\pi r^3$
Surface area $= 4\pi r^2$

a. Find the radii r and R of the two spheres. (*Hint:* A diameter of the circumscribed sphere is equal in length to a diagonal of the inscribed cube.)

b. Find the surface area of each sphere and compare it with the surface area of the cube.

c. Find the volume of each sphere and compare it with the volume of the cube.

20. This "globe" by R. Buckminster Fuller is made by circumscribing a regular icosahedron about Earth. Which is greater, the surface area of Earth or the surface area of the icosahedron?

21. **Research** Learn how the structures of different crystals are related to polyhedra.

22. **Group Activity** Work in a group of four students.

Using toothpicks as edges, and gumdrops, raisins, or miniature marshmallows as vertices, build as many different convex polyhedra as you can that use *only equilateral triangles* as faces. They do not have to be regular polyhedra.

a. These polyhedra are called *deltahedra*. Make a systematic list of the deltahedra you build, including the number of vertices, edges, and faces for each.

b. Check to see if Euler's formula, $F + V = E + 2$, holds for your deltahedra.

c. Choose one of your deltahedra. How many vertices join 3 edges? How many join 4 edges? How many join 5 edges? What are the defects at each of these different kinds of vertices?

d. Find the sum of the defects at the vertices of the deltahedron you chose in part (c). Compare your answer with others in your group. What do you notice?

Review **PREVIEW**

23. A prism whose base is a regular hexagon is circumscribed about a cylinder. The radius of the cylinder is 5 cm, the height of the cylinder is 10 cm, and the semiperimeter of the hexagon is $10\sqrt{3}$ cm.

a. Find the volume of both the prism and the cylinder.

b. Suppose a prism whose base is a regular 12-gon is circumscribed about the same cylinder. How does its volume compare with that of the cylinder? with that of the hexagonal prism? *(Section 3-8)*

Solve. *(Toolbox Skills 22 and 23)*

24. $\frac{x-5}{2} + 3 = 7$

25. $10 < -5(x + 2)$

26. $2x^2 + 6 = 7x$

27. a. Graph $y = 3x + 4$. *(Section 2-1)*

b. On a separate set of axes, plot the points $(-1, 1)$, $(0, 4)$, $(1, 7)$, $(2, 10)$.

c. Are both graphs examples of functions? Explain.

  Working on the Unit Project

28. As you finish preparing your brief, describe in what ways a legal brief is like a mathematical proof and in what ways it is different. Describe the most interesting part of preparing your brief.

Completing the Unit Project

Now you are ready to finish your brief.
Your finished project should include:

➤ an opening statement

➤ questions you plan to ask witnesses

➤ questions you plan to ask witnesses for
the opposing side during cross-examination

➤ the law as it applies to your case

➤ the reasoning you will use to convince others
that the evidence presented justifies your
position according to the law

➤ counterarguments you will make to your
opponent's case

➤ closing arguments

Sarah Wilkins
vs.
Springfield High School

Look Back ◄

How did you use reasoning
in constructing your brief?
Do you think your argu-
ments are convincing?

Alternative Projects

Project 1: Research a Famous Case

▼ Research a famous court case. Prepare a written or oral report about the case.
Describe the reasoning used by the attorneys during the trial, and tell the
outcome.

Project 2: Put on a Mock Trial

▼ Simulate a trial in your classroom. Have students act as judge, jurors, bailiff,
witnesses, defense, plaintiff, attorneys, and so forth. You may want to act out
the case of Wilkins vs. Springfield School System.

1. *ABCD* is a parallelogram; $\overline{AC} \perp \overline{BD}$.

   3-1

   a. Prove that $\triangle DEC \cong \triangle BEC$.

   b. Explain in a short paragraph how you can use the proof from part (a) to complete the proof of the following statement:

   If the diagonals of a parallelogram are perpendicular, then the parallelogram is a rhombus.

   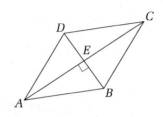

2. a. State the converse, inverse, and contrapositive of this implication:

   If a quadrilateral is a kite, then its diagonals are perpendicular.

   b. Tell whether each statement in part (a) is *True* or *False*. Give a counterexample for each false statement.

3. The *y*-axis is a line of symmetry for hexagon *QRSTUV*.

   3-2

   a. Find the coordinates of points *Q, S,* and *U*.

   b. Show that this hexagon can be formed by joining two isosceles trapezoids.

   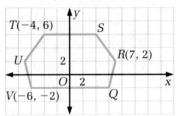

4. **Writing** Suppose you use an exclusive rather than an inclusive definition of trapezoid. How does the quadrilateral chart shown on page 155 change?

   3-3

5. **Open-ended** Identify at least four words or phrases that must be clearly defined in order to properly interpret these bylaws:

   > The treasurer shall be elected by majority vote of the executive board. To serve as treasurer, a person must be a member in good standing for three years. The treasurer is responsible for ensuring that all club funds are deposited in an appropriate account at a reliable financial institution.

For each polygon described in Questions 6 and 7, determine the number of sides.

3-4

6. Each interior angle of a regular polygon measures 135°.

7. Each exterior angle of a regular polygon measures 30°.

8. *Q* is the midpoint of $\overline{TS}$, and *R* lies on the perpendicular bisector of $\overline{TS}$. *RS* = 17 cm and *RQ* = 15 cm. Find *QS, TQ,* and *TR*.

   3-5

9. Find all the missing measures
   for angles and arcs.

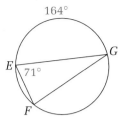

3-6

10. **Open-ended** Eight points, labeled *A* through *H*, are equally spaced
    around a circle. List all the measures of the inscribed angles you can
    make using just these points. Give an example of an inscribed angle for
    each angle measure.

11. Write an indirect proof to show that no regular polygon has an exterior
    angle measuring 150°.

3-7

12. An astronaut in a spacecraft at point *R* observes the horizon of
    Earth at point *H*.

    a. If the spacecraft is 100 mi above the surface of Earth, find the distance
       from *R* to *H*. Earth's radius is about 4000 mi.

    b. State any theorems you used to answer part (a).

    c. Find a formula for the distance from *R* to *H*
       when the spacecraft is *d* mi above the
       surface of Earth.

(Not drawn to scale)

13. A circle has a radius of 5 in. Find the area of a square inscribed in the
    circle and the area of a square circumscribed about the circle. Is the
    area of the circle closer to the area of the inscribed square or the
    circumscribed square?

3-8

14. A pyramid with a square base has equilateral triangles as its
    four other faces.

    a. Explain why the pyramid is not a regular polyhedron.

    b. Find the sum of the defects at each vertex.

3-9

15. **Self-evaluation** Which kind of proof do you prefer to
    write, a synthetic proof or a coordinate proof? Why?

16. **Group Activity** Work in a group of three students.

   a. Draw a circle and a circumscribed triangle.

   b. Pass your paper to the student on your right. Measure the radius of the circle and the sides of the triangle on your new paper. Find the area of the triangle using the formula $A = rs$.

   c. Again pass your paper to the student on your right. Use a different method to find the area of the triangle on your new paper.

   d. Compare your result from part (c) with the result found in part (b) by the student on your left.

IDEAS AND (FORMULAS) = X^2

$_5P_5$

GEOMETRY

➤ If the two diagonals of a quadrilateral bisect each other, then the quadrilateral is a parallelogram. *(p. 141)*

➤ In an isosceles triangle, the medians drawn to the legs are equal in measure. *(p. 150)*

➤ In an isosceles trapezoid, (1) the legs are equal in measure, (2) the diagonals are equal in measure, and (3) the two angles at each base are equal in measure. *(p. 150)*

➤ The sum of the interior angle measures of an n-gon is given by the formula $S(n) = (n - 2)180°$. *(p. 161)*

➤ The sum of the exterior angle measures of an n-gon, one at each vertex, is 360°. *(p. 161)*

➤ The perpendicular bisector of a chord of a circle passes through the center of the circle. *(p. 166)*

➤ The measure of an inscribed angle of a circle is equal to half the measure of its intercepted arc. *(p. 174)*

➤ An inscribed angle whose intercepted arc is a semicircle is a right angle. *(p. 174)*

➤ If two inscribed angles in the same circle intercept the same arc, then they are equal in measure. *(p. 174)*

➤ A segment can be drawn perpendicular to a given line from a point not on the line. The length of this segment is the shortest distance from the point to the line. *(p. 182)*

➤ If a line is tangent to a circle, then the line is perpendicular to the radius from the center to the point of tangency. *(p. 183)*

➤ If a line in the plane of a circle is perpendicular to a radius at its outer endpoint, then the line is tangent to the circle. *(p. 183)*

➤ If two tangent segments are drawn from the same point to the same circle, then they are equal in measure. *(p. 183)*

➤ The area of any circumscribed polygon may be found by multiplying the radius (*r*) of the inscribed circle and the semiperimeter (*s*). *(p. 188)*

➤ In any convex polyhedron, the sum of the measures of the angles at each vertex is less than 360°. *(p. 194)*

➤ There are exactly five regular polyhedra. *(p. 195)*

➤ The contrapositive of a true implication is always true. The converse and inverse of a true implication are not necessarily true. *(p. 142)*

➤ In mathematics, as well as in other aspects of life, precise definitions are often essential. *(p. 154)*

➤ The formula for the sum of the measures of the interior angles of an *n*-gon can be proved using mathematical induction. *(p. 160)*

➤ An indirect proof begins by temporarily assuming the opposite of what is to be proved and showing that this leads to an impossible situation or to a contradiction. *(p. 180)*

➤ Coordinate proofs can be used as well as synthetic proofs to demonstrate geometric theorems. *(p. 147)*

Sequences and Series

The incredible shrinking dollar . . . Sixty years ago, you could treat yourself and three friends to a movie for a dollar! Today, your own ticket may cost $7 or more. *. . . And how to stretch it.* Now imagine that sixty years ago you had invested a dollar at 5% annual interest compounded quarterly. By now your dollar would have grown to $20 — enough to buy tickets for you and three friends. (But you may have to go to the bargain matinee!)

Here's what you could get for about $25 at a ballgame in earlier days:

1976	1980	1989	1994
2 tickets	2 tickets	2 tickets	2 tickets
2 soft drinks	2 soft drinks	2 soft drinks	
2 hot dogs	2 hot dogs	2 hot dogs	
2 baseball caps	2 baseball caps		
1 program	1 program		
2 bags of peanuts			
2 boxes of popcorn			
2 ice cream bars			
1 pennant			
1 helmet			
1 autographed ball			

investments

What would you bid for a cheap lunch box with a picture of a cartoon character that was popular in your childhood? At an auction, a collector paid $2760 for one from 1972, setting a new world record!

Sometimes the most unlikely **collectibles** turn out to be an investment. Besides stamps, coins, and artwork, people collect everything from toy robots to butter molds!

Save for the Future

Your project is to learn how to make a small investment grow in order to pay for a college education, a down payment on a home, a trip around the world, or any other high-cost item 20–25 years in the future.

You will trace the effect of inflation by predicting the increase in the purchase price of the item you choose.

You will use computer spreadsheet software to explore the changes in both the value of your investment and the price of your purchase over many years. Spreadsheet software stores information in matrices, allowing you to quickly and easily see the effect of a change in the interest or inflation rate.

People around the world invest in stocks to try to offset inflation.

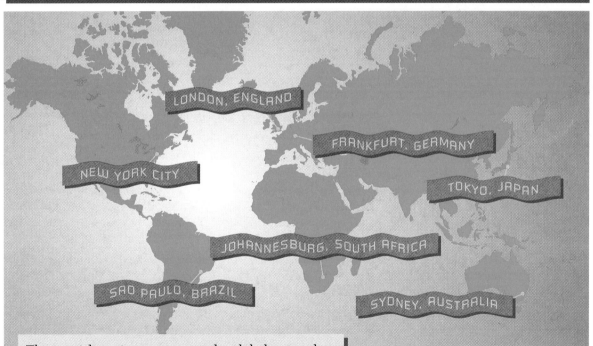

MAJOR WORLD STOCK MARKETS

LONDON, ENGLAND

FRANKFURT, GERMANY

NEW YORK CITY

TOKYO, JAPAN

JOHANNESBURG, SOUTH AFRICA

SAO PAULO, BRAZIL

SYDNEY, AUSTRALIA

The sun (almost) never sets on the global network of stock exchanges. Three hours after the New York Stock Exchange closes for the day, the one in Tokyo is just opening. Three hours after the Tokyo exchange closes, the one in London opens.

Getting Started

For this project you should work in a group of four students. Here are some ideas to help you get started.

☞ Decide what your group will plan to save for. Discuss how you can find out how much it costs today and how its price has changed over the past 20 years.

☞ Look through the business sections of newspapers. Examine the stock tables, mutual fund listings, and information about other investment opportunities.

☞ Have members of the group with experience using spreadsheets demonstrate their use.

☞ Plan to meet again later to schedule library research.

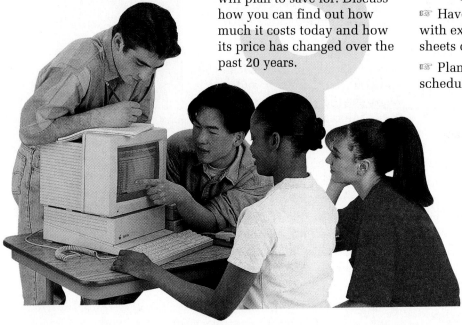

Can We Talk INVESTING

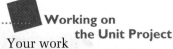

Working on the Unit Project

Your work in Unit 4 will help you save for the future.

Related Exercises:

Section 4-1, Exercise 32
Section 4-2, Exercise 22
Section 4-3, Exercises 23, 24
Section 4-4, Exercise 39
Section 4-5, Exercise 27
Section 4-6, Exercise 27
Section 4-7, Exercise 33

Alternative Projects p. 259

➤ In the last few years, have you noticed any changes in the prices of the things you buy? Have prices increased or decreased? Why do you think this has happened? Have price changes affected how you spend your money?

➤ Do you collect stamps, baseball cards, or something else, or do you know someone who does? Do you know the value of the collection?

➤ Can you think of anything that was once a good investment but is a poor one now? Can you think of something that was once a poor investment but is a good one now? What happened to bring about any changes?

➤ Economists sometimes use the term "purchasing power" when they talk about the value of a dollar. What do you think this term means and why is it useful?

Exploring Patterns

········Focus

Describe and continue
patterns. Graph sequences
and find apparent limits.

What's next?

Stage 1

Stage 2

Stage 3

EXPLORATION

How can you describe and extend patterns?

- **Materials:** graph paper
- **Work with another student.**

1 **a.** Use graph paper and draw the shapes shown in
Stages 1–4. Draw Stage 2 from Stage 1, Stage 3 from
Stage 2, and Stage 4 from Stage 3.

b. Describe any patterns you used to draw each stage from
the stage before it.

c. Continue the squares pattern by drawing a Stage 5 from
Stage 4.

d. Copy and complete this table.

Stage number	1	2	3	4	5
Number of squares	5	?	?	?	?

e. Suppose you continue drawing more stages of the
squares pattern. How many squares will be in Stage 10?
Explain how you found your answer.

2 Use the list of numbers $\frac{1}{2}, \frac{2}{3}, \frac{3}{4}, \frac{4}{5}, \ldots$

a. Describe any patterns you see in
the list.

b. Use the patterns you see to find
the next three numbers in the list.

c. Find the tenth number in the list.

3 Repeat Step 2 for each list of
numbers.

List A 96, 48, 24, 12, . . .

List B 2, 5, 8, 11, 14, . . .

List C 1, −1, 1, −1, . . .

Stage 4

The lists of numbers in the Exploration are called *sequences*. A **sequence** is an ordered list of numbers, called the **terms** of the sequence. A sequence with a last term is a **finite sequence**. A sequence with no last term is an **infinite sequence**. A counting number identifies each term's position in the sequence.

positions of terms →   1   2   3   4
terms of a sequence →   **2,   5,   8,   11, . . .**

11 is the *fourth term* of the sequence.

These three dots show that the sequence continues in the same pattern. This sequence is infinite.

Sample 1

Write the sequence of the number of cloth strips in each color used to make this square for a log cabin quilt. Do not count the middle square. Find the 10th term if the sequence continued.

Sample Response

There are 2 yellow strips, 6 blue strips, 12 pink strips, and 20 green strips shown. The sequence is 2, 6, 12, 20, ...

Method ❶

Look for a relationship between each term and its position number.

position	1	2	3	4	5	6	7	8	9	10
	(× 2)	(× 3)	(× 4)	(× 5)						(× 11)
term	2	6	12	20						110

To find a term, multiply the position number by the next larger integer.

The 10th term is → 10×11, or 110.

Method ❷

Look for a relationship between each term and the term before it.

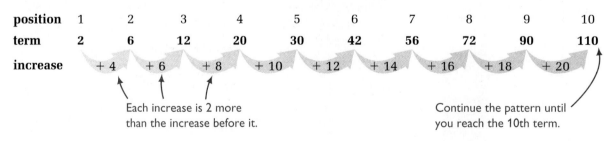

position	1	2	3	4	5	6	7	8	9	10
term	2	6	12	20	30	42	56	72	90	110
increase		+ 4	+ 6	+ 8	+ 10	+ 12	+ 14	+ 16	+ 18	+ 20

Each increase is 2 more than the increase before it.

Continue the pattern until you reach the 10th term.

1. a. Find a pattern in the sequence 1, 8, 27, 64, ...

   b. What is the 10th term of the sequence in part (a)?

   c. Which method shown in Sample 1 did you use to find the 10th term?

······► Now you are ready for:
Exs. 1–12 on pp. 211–214

Graphs and Limits of Sequences

Each term of a sequence is paired with the number that gives its position in the sequence. By plotting points with coordinates (*position*, *term*), you can graph a sequence on a coordinate plane.

Sample 2

Graph each sequence on a coordinate plane. Plot at least six points.

a. 2, 5, 8, 11, . . .

b. $1, \frac{1}{2}, \frac{1}{3}, \frac{1}{4}, \ldots$

Sample Response

a. Find the pattern.

Starting with the second term, each term is 3 more than the term before it. Continue the pattern for the 5th and 6th terms.

position	1	2	3	4	5	6
term	2	5	8	11	14	17

Plot the points (*position*, *term*).

b. Find the pattern.

Each term is the reciprocal of its position number. Continue the pattern for the 5th and 6th terms.

position	1	2	3	4	5	6
term	1	$\frac{1}{2}$	$\frac{1}{3}$	$\frac{1}{4}$	$\frac{1}{5}$	$\frac{1}{6}$

Plot the points (*position*, *term*).

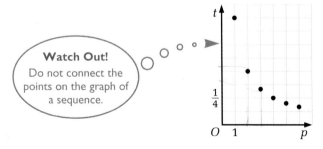

Watch Out!
Do not connect the points on the graph of a sequence.

2. Do the graphs in Sample 2 represent functions? Why or why not?

3. Will the graph of *every* sequence represent a function? If so, what is the domain of the function? What is the range?

4. Are the graphs of sequences *continuous* or *discrete*? Explain.

5. Use the sequences in Sample 2.

   a. Suppose you continue listing the terms of each sequence. What number, if any, will the terms get closer to the farther out you go in each sequence?

   b. Suppose you continue plotting more points of each sequence. Describe what the graph will look like the farther out you go in each sequence.

The terms of the sequence in part (b) of Sample 2 appear to approach 0. When the terms of an infinite sequence get closer and closer to a single fixed number L, then L is called the **limit of the sequence.**

Not all infinite sequences have limits. The terms of the sequence in part (a) of Sample 2 do not get close to a single fixed number. This sequence does not have a limit.

Sample 3

Decide whether each infinite sequence appears to have a limit. If it does, give its value.

a. $\dfrac{1}{2}, \dfrac{5}{4}, \dfrac{7}{8}, \dfrac{17}{16}, \dfrac{31}{32}, \dfrac{65}{64}, \ldots$

b. $1, 2, 3, 1, 2, 3, 1, 2, 3, \ldots$

Sample Response

a. **Step 1** Find a trend.

Look at the decimal value of each term   or   look at the graph of the sequence.

Even-numbered terms decrease toward 1.

position	1	2	3	4	5	6
term	0.5	1.25	0.875	1.0625	0.96875	1.015625

Odd-numbered terms increase toward 1.

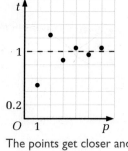

The points get closer and closer to the line $t = 1$.

Step 2 When possible, check a term farther out in the sequence to see if it follows the same trend.

Find the pattern of the sequence. Look at the 20th term.

The numerators in the even positions are one *more* than the denominators.

$$\frac{1}{2}, \frac{5}{4}, \frac{7}{8}, \frac{17}{16}, \frac{31}{32}, \frac{65}{64}, \ldots$$

The denominators are powers of two. The power matches the position number.

20th term $\rightarrow \dfrac{2^{20} + 1}{2^{20}} \approx 1.000000954$

The 20th term follows the trend from Step 1.

The sequence $\dfrac{1}{2}, \dfrac{5}{4}, \dfrac{7}{8}, \dfrac{17}{16}, \dfrac{31}{32}, \dfrac{65}{64}, \ldots$ appears to have a limit of 1.

b. Since the numbers 1, 2, and 3 will continue to repeat, there is no *single* fixed number that the terms of the sequence get close to. The sequence 1, 2, 3, 1, 2, 3, 1, 2, 3, . . . has no limit.

Talk it Over

6. Graph the sequence in part (b) of Sample 3. Explain how the graph shows that the sequence has no limit.

7. Explain how the limit of a sequence is different from a speed limit.

Look Back

Describe at least two methods you can use to look for a pattern in the terms of a sequence. Describe at least two methods you can use to decide whether an infinite sequence appears to have a limit.

▶ Now you are ready for:
Exs. 13–32 on pp. 214–215

4-1 Exercises and Problems

1. **Using Manipulatives** Use toothpicks.

a. Build each of these shapes. Use one toothpick for each side of the smallest square.

b. Describe any patterns you used to build each stage from the one before it.

c. How many toothpicks will be in Stage 10?

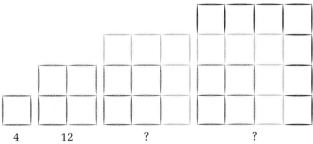

4   12   ?   ?

For each sequence in Exercises 2–8:

a. **Find the next three terms.**

b. **Find the 12th term.**

c. **Describe the method you used to find the 12th term.**

2. 3, 6, 9, 12, . . .   **3.** 3, 6, 12, 24, . . .   **4.** 3, 6, 10, 15, . . .   **5.** 3, 6, 18, 72, . . .

6. A, AB, ABC, ABCD, . . .   **7.** triangle, square, pentagon, hexagon, . . .

8. The sequence of the maximum number of pieces, not necessarily equal, a circle can be cut into with one cut, two cuts, three cuts, four cuts, and so on.

2   4   ?   ?

9. Skydiving A group of free-falling skydivers may join together to form a geometric-shaped formation before opening their parachutes. This is called *relative work skydiving*.

a. **Open-ended** Write the first three terms of a sequence that you see in the rings of skydivers. Explain the pattern in your sequence.

b. Find the 4th, 5th, and 10th terms of your sequence.

BY THE WAY...

The parachute that a skydiver wears today is made of nylon. In the 12th century, the Chinese experimented with rigid, umbrella-like devices.

The *visual magnitude* of a star, planet, or moon is a measure of how bright the object appears to an observer on Earth. The lower the magnitude, the brighter the object appears.

A difference of 5 visual magnitudes between two objects means that one object is 100 times as bright as the other. So, a difference of 1 magnitude is equivalent to a brightness factor of about 2.51 since $(2.51)^5 \approx 100$. For example, the star Vega, with visual magnitude 0, is about 2.51 times as bright as the star Spica, a star in the Virgo constellation, with visual magnitude 1.

Polaris
(Ursa Minor)

Sirius
(Canis Major)

Vega
(Lyra)

Gomeisa

(Canis Minor)

Procyon

(Not drawn from one viewpoint)

Spica
(Virgo)

10. a. Complete the table.

b. Describe the sequence that is formed.

c. What is the brightness factor for a difference of 6 magnitudes? 10 magnitudes?

difference in magnitude	1	2	3	4	5
brightness factor	2.51	?	?	?	100

11. a. Canis Minor (Little Dog) is a small constellation that has only two stars, Procyon, with visual magnitude 0, and Gomeisa, with visual magnitude 3. Which star is brighter? By how much?

b. The North Star, or Polaris, has visual magnitude 2. How does the brightness of Polaris compare to that of the two stars that make up Canis Minor?

c. The brightest star in the night sky is Sirius, which has visual magnitude −1. Sirius is how many times as bright as Polaris?

12. Reading Why are the points of a graph of a sequence not connected?

For Exercises 13–18:

a. Graph each sequence. Plot at least six points.

b. Decide whether each sequence appears to have a limit.

13. $3, 7, 11, 15, \ldots$ **14.** $-1, -3, -9, -27, \ldots$ **15.** $-2, 4, -8, 16, \ldots$

16. $-1, \dfrac{1}{2}, -\dfrac{1}{3}, \dfrac{1}{4}, \ldots$ **17.** $10, 8, 6, 4, \ldots$ **18.** $1, 8, 27, 64, \ldots$

For Exercises 19–22, tell whether each sequence appears to have a limit. Justify your answer.

19. $\dfrac{1}{3}, \dfrac{1}{9}, \dfrac{1}{27}, \dfrac{1}{81}, \ldots$ **20.** $3, 6, 9, 12, \ldots$

21. $-0.5, 0.25, -0.125, 0.0625, \ldots$ **22.** $-5, 25, -125, 625, \ldots$

23 a. TECHNOLOGY Use a calculator to evaluate the first 20 terms of the sequence

$$\sqrt{3},\ \sqrt{\sqrt{3}},\ \sqrt{\sqrt{\sqrt{3}}},\ \sqrt{\sqrt{\sqrt{\sqrt{3}}}},\ldots.$$

    b. What appears to be the limit of this sequence?

For Exercises 24 and 25, use the sequence $\dfrac{3}{4}, \dfrac{8}{9}, \dfrac{15}{16}, \dfrac{24}{25}, \dfrac{35}{36}, \ldots.$

24. Kimiko says that each of these numbers is a term of the sequence.

$$\frac{99}{100} \qquad \frac{399}{400} \qquad \frac{899}{900}$$

    a. Describe a pattern Kimiko may have used to find the three terms.

    b. Find the decimal value of each of Kimiko's terms.

    c. What number appears to be the limit of this sequence?

25. a. The 1st term is $\dfrac{1}{4}$ less than 1. How much less than 1 is the 2nd term? the 3rd term? the 4th term? the 5th term?

    b. What number appears to be the limit of the sequence of differences in part (a)?

    c. Writing Compare the method used in part (a) to find the terms of the sequence with the method described in Exercise 24. Do both methods give you the same answer? Which method do you prefer? Why?

Ongoing ASSESSMENT

26. Open-ended Write at least four sequences that start with $2, 4, \ldots.$ Describe a pattern in each sequence.

Review PREVIEW

27. Show that the sum of the defects at the vertices of a regular octahedron is $720°$. *(Section 3-9)*

Simplify. *(Toolbox Skill 14)*

28. 2^{-5} **29.** $(-4)^0$ **30.** 7^{-3}

31. Find $f(0)$, $f(-3)$, and $f(12)$ when $f(x) = 4x - 5$. *(Section 2-1)*

Working on the Unit Project

TECHNOLOGY NOTE

Technology Handbook
See p. 595.

32. a. **Research** Find the most recent edition of the *Digest of Educational Statistics*. Find and record the data on the total annual tuition, room, and board costs at four-year universities, both public and private, for the last 29 years.

b. Make a five-column spreadsheet as shown.

Digest for Educational Statistics

	A	B	C	D	E
1	Year	Public U. Cost	% increase	Private U. Cost	% increase
2	1964	1051		2202	
3	1965	1105	= (B3 − B2)/B2	2316	
4	1966	1171		2456	

Columns C and E show the percent of increase in cost from the previous year. Format them to display percents with two decimal places.

c. Below the last row of the percent of increase columns (C and E), find the average percent of increase for each type of university.

Digest for Educational Statistics

	A	B	C	D	E
29	1991	6051	8.34%	17779	7.73%
30	1992	6449	6.58%	18892	6.26%
31					
32		Average % inc.	= AVERAGE (C3:C30)	Average % inc.	
33					

= AVERAGE (E3:E30)

d. Use the rates from part (b) to continue your spreadsheet by predicting the total annual cost of each type of university for the next 25 years.

Digest for Educational Statistics

	A	B	C	D	E
30	1992	6449	6.58%	18892	6.26%
31					
32		Average % inc.	6.73%	Average % inc.	8.01%
33					
34	1993	= B30*1.0673			
35	1994				

Project into the future by multiplying the last year for which you have data by 1 + the average percent of increase (expressed as a decimal).

Format columns B and D to display whole numbers.

Digest for Educational Statistics

	A	B	C	D	E
30	1992	6449	6.58%	18892	6.26%
31					
32		Average % inc.	6.73%	Average % inc.	8.01%
33					
34	1993	6883			
35	1994	= B34*1.0673			
36	1995				

Since the data in column B skips a few lines, enter the formula again before you FILL DOWN.

e. How much do you predict it will cost to attend each type of university 25 years from now?

Sequences

Focus
Use subscripts and formulas for sequences.

n-FORMATION

The ancient Mayan pyramid in Chichén Itzá, Mexico, has nine terraces on each side, split by a stairway leading up to a temple. The diagram shows two of the many sequences hidden in the pyramid.

You can use *subscripts* to write the terms of a sequence. The subscript of each term matches the position of the term in the sequence. The symbol a_n (read "*a* sub *n*") represents the *n*th term, or term in position *n*, of the sequence $a_1, a_2, a_3, \ldots$.

MEXICO

Chichén Itzá

a_8 is the 8th term of the sequence of distances from the center of the pyramid to the edge of each terrace.

b_9 is the 9th term of the sequence of heights from the ground to each terrace.

Each terrace is about 7 ft deep.

The rise between terraces is about $8\frac{1}{3}$ ft.

a_9
a_8
a_7
a_6
a_5
$a_4 = 69$
$a_3 = 76$
$a_2 = 83$
$a_1 = 90$

$b_9 = 75$ b_8 b_7 b_6 b_5 b_4 b_3 b_2 b_1

180 ft

BY THE WAY...

This pyramid represents the Mayan year. The four 91-step stairways plus the top platform make 365 steps, one for each day of the year. Doubling the nine terraces on each side makes 18, the number of months in the Mayan year. Each side has 52 carved panels for the 52 weeks in the year.

Talk it Over

1. What is the value of b_2? b_3?

2. What is the value of a_7? How did you find a_7?

3. How many times do you have to subtract 7 from a_1 (or 90) to find a_9?

Find a formula for the sequence of distances from the center of the pyramid to the edge of each terrace.

Sample Response

Step 1 Find a pattern. The pattern is a repeated subtraction of 7.

Step 2 Write the first few terms. Show how you found each term.

$a_1 = 90$

$a_2 = 83 = 90 - 1(7)$ ⟵—— Subtract 7 from 90 once.

$a_3 = 76 = 90 - 2(7)$ ⟵—— Subtract 7 from 90 twice.

$a_4 = 69 = 90 - 3(7)$ ⟵—— Subtract 7 from 90 three times.

Step 3 Express the pattern in terms of n.

For each term, a_n, the number of times you subtract 7 from 90 is one less than the subscript, n. The formula for the sequence is:

$a_n = 90 - (n - 1)(7)$ ⟵—— Subtract 7 from 90 a total of $(n - 1)$ times.

The formula found in Sample 1 is an example of an **explicit formula** for a sequence because it gives the value of any term a_n in terms of n.

Talk it Over

4. Explain why the explicit formula $a_n = 90 - (n - 1)(7)$ is a rule for a function. What is the control variable? What is the dependent variable? What is the domain? What is the range?

5. Find an explicit formula for the sequence of heights from the ground to each terrace of the pyramid.

Write the first three terms and the 12th term of each sequence.

a. $a_n = 3n - 5$ b. $b_n = 2^{1 - n}$

Sample Response

Substitute 1, 2, 3, and 12 for n in each explicit formula.

a. $a_1 = 3(1) - 5 = -2$

$a_2 = 3(2) - 5 = 1$

$a_3 = 3(3) - 5 = 4$

$a_{12} = 3(12) - 5 = 31$

b. $b_1 = 2^{1 - 1} = 2^0 = 1$

$b_2 = 2^{1 - 2} = 2^{-1} = \dfrac{1}{2}$

$b_3 = 2^{1 - 3} = 2^{-2} = \dfrac{1}{4}$

$b_{12} = 2^{1 - 12} = 2^{-11} = \dfrac{1}{2048}$

Student Resources Toolbox
p. 637 *Algebraic Expressions*

When the first term of a sequence represents a starting value before any change occurs, the subscript 0 is often used. In a sequence of monthly bank account balances, the first term v_0 would be the initial deposit, the next term v_1 would be the balance after the *first* month's interest, and so on.

Sample 3

Samara Reese invests $1000 to open a savings account that earns 3% annual interest, compounded monthly.

a. Find a formula for the value of her account after n months.

b. Find the value of her account after one year.

Sample Response

a. **1** Find the monthly interest rate.

$\frac{1}{12}$ of 3% = $\frac{0.03}{12}$ = 0.0025

2 Look at what happens after one month to an account with starting value v.

new value = $v + 0.0025v$	⟵ The value of the account increases by 0.0025v.
= $v(1 + 0.0025)$	⟵ Factor out v.
= $v(1.0025)$	⟵ The value of the account is multiplied by 1.0025.

3 Write several terms of the sequence of values of the account. Look for a pattern. To see the pattern, leave each value unsimplified.

$v_0 = 1000$	⟵ starting value
$v_1 = 1000(1.0025)$	⟵ value at the end of one month
$v_2 = v_1(1.0025)$	⟵ Multiply the value at the end of one month by 1.0025.
$= 1000(1.0025)(1.0025)$	⟵ Substitute 1000(1.0025) for v_1.
$= 1000(1.0025)^2$	⟵ value at the end of two months
$v_3 = v_2(1.0025)$	⟵ Multiply the value at the end of two months by 1.0025.
$= 1000(1.0025)^2(1.0025)$	⟵ Substitute 1000(1.0025)^2 for v_2.
$= 1000(1.0025)^3$	⟵ value at the end of three months
$\vdots$	
$v_n = 1000(1.0025)^n$	⟵ value at the end of n months

b. Use the formula from part (a). One year is 12 months, so find v_{12}.

$v_{12} = 1000(1.0025)^{12}$	⟵ Substitute 12 for n.
≈ 1030.42	

After one year, the value of Samara's account will be $1030.42.

6. How does using 0 instead of 1 as the subscript for the first term of a sequence affect the domain of its explicit formula?

7. In Sample 3, find the value of Samara's investment after five years.

Look Back

Explain the role of subscripts when finding an explicit formula of a sequence.

4-2 Exercises and Problems

1. **Reading** When would you use the subscript 0 for the first term of a sequence?

Write the first four terms and the 24th term of each sequence.

2. $b_n = 5n + 12$

3. $a_n = \dfrac{n-1}{2}$

4. $t_n = \dfrac{n}{2n+3}$

5. $a_n = \dfrac{3^{2-n}}{n}$

For Exercises 6–9, write an explicit formula for each sequence.

6. 11, 17, 23, 29, . . .

7. 3, 9, 27, 81, . . .

8. $\dfrac{1}{2}, \dfrac{2}{3}, \dfrac{3}{4}, \dfrac{4}{5}, \ldots$

9. The number of diagonals from *one* vertex of a regular polygon.

| $d_1 = 0$ | $d_2 = 1$ | $d_3 = 2$ | $d_4 = ?$ |
| 0 diagonals | 1 diagonal | 2 diagonals | |

10. Use the formula $b_n = 2^{1-n}$ from part (b) of Sample 2.

   a. Find b_{100}, b_{250}, and b_{500}.

   b. Do you think this sequence has a limit? Explain.

   c. **Writing** Explain how you can use an explicit formula for an infinite sequence to decide if the sequence has a limit.

11. In Japan, a child is considered to be one year old at birth. Let y_n be the sequence of ages for a Japanese person, where y_0 = age at birth.

   a. Explain why the subscript 0 is used for the first term.

   b. The subscript does not match the position in this sequence. What does the subscript match?

   c. Find an explicit formula for this sequence.

12. Maxim Gutte invests $500 to open a money market account that earns 4.2% annual interest, compounded monthly.

   a. Find an explicit formula for the value of his account after n months.

   b. Find the value of his account after two years.

13. a. **Personal Finance** In Sample 3, Samara Reese's account increased from $1000 to $1030.42 after one year. By what percent did the account increase? This percent is called the *effective annual yield*.

   b. How does the effective annual yield compare to the annual interest rate compounded monthly for the problem in Sample 3?

   c. What is the value of Samara's savings account after one year when the 3% annual interest is compounded yearly? when it is compounded daily?

   d. **Writing** Find the effective annual yield of Samara's account when the interest is compounded yearly and daily. Discuss the effect different compounding periods have on the effective annual yield.

14. In the last unit, you used the perimeter of a regular polygon circumscribed about a circle to estimate the circumference of the circle. You can also use a regular polygon inscribed in a circle to estimate the circumference. The more sides the polygon has, the better the estimate will be.

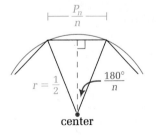

Let P_n = the perimeter of a regular n-gon inscribed in a circle of diameter 1. Use the diagram at the left.

   a. Explain why the measure of the labeled angle is $\dfrac{180°}{n}$.

   b. Complete this statement to find an explicit formula for the sequence of perimeters P_n:

   $$\sin\left(\frac{180°}{n}\right) = \frac{?}{?}$$

   c. What is the apparent limit of the sequence of perimeters? Why?

15. a. Open-ended Write the first five terms of a sequence with a pattern that involves repeated division by the same value.

  b. Write an explicit formula for your sequence in part (a).

16

16. a. Graph this sequence. *(Section 4-1)*

$$-1, 1, -\frac{1}{2}, \frac{1}{2}, -\frac{1}{3}, \frac{1}{3}, \ldots$$

1.0035

  b. Does the sequence in part (a) appear to have a limit?

17. Use Pascal's triangle to find the number of possible ways to choose two representatives from six students. *(Toolbox Skill 5)*

Simplify. *(Toolbox Skill 20)*

18. $(7 + 2i) + (4 + i)$ **19.** $(2i)(3i)$ **20.** $(5 + i)^2$ **21.** $4i(1 - 2i)$

Working on the Unit Project

22. One way of investing money is with long-term time deposit accounts for 2.5 years or more. The interest rates for these accounts tend to be higher because the bank has more time to put the money to work.

  a. Research Find out the current rate for a long-term deposit account at a local bank.

  b. Use your answers to part (d) of Exercise 32 on page 215. Choose a lump sum amount of money that, if you invest it for 25 years at the rate in part (a), it will be enough to pay the cost of a public university education in 25 years. Choose another lump sum for a private university. Set up a spreadsheet to test your choice.

  c. Continue to choose lump sums and repeat part (b) until the return on your investment is within a dollar of the university cost needed.

  d. Choose the highest rate from the table and repeat part (c). How does your new lump sum compare with the lump sum from part (c)?

  e. Choose the lowest rate from the table and repeat part (c). How does your new lump sum compare with the lump sum from part (c)?

This table shows average interest rates for long-term accounts in the period 1983–1993.

Year	Rate
1983	10.48
1984	10.80
1985	8.73
1986	6.61
1987	7.86
1988	8.39
1989	7.86
1990	7.52
1991	5.56
1992	4.77
1993	4.29

Using Recursive Formulas

Focus

Write and use formulas for sequences in which each term is found by using the preceding term(s).

BRANCHING OUT

Many irregular shapes found in the natural world can be modeled by geometric shapes called *fractals*. These diagrams show some of the early stages of the "growth" of a fractal tree.

Stage 1

A single branch grows.

Stage 2

A branch grows two new branches.

Stage 3

At each stage, each new branch from the previous stage grows two new branches.

Stage 6

This process continues without end. The appearance of any part of a fractal is similar to the whole fractal. This property of a fractal is called *self-similarity*.

BY THE WAY...

Computer fractal programs can generate images from nature that are almost identical to the real thing. These images are called *fractal forgeries*.

Talk it Over

1. How are a fractal tree and a real tree alike? How are they different?

2. Write a sequence whose first four terms are the number of branches on a fractal tree at stages 1–4.

3. For the sequence in question 2, describe how each term after the first is related to the term before it.

1   2   4   8

Look at the sequence of numbers of *new* branches that grow at each stage.

After the first term, each term is twice the term before it. You can use subscripts to express this relationship.

the *n*th term $\nearrow$ $a_n = 2a_{n-1}$ $\longleftarrow$ The term *before* the *n*th term is the $(n - 1)$st term.

You can use the equation above to write a *recursive formula* for the sequence. A **recursive formula** for a sequence tells you how to find the *n*th term from the term(s) before it. A recursive formula has two parts:

$$a_1 = 1 \qquad \longleftarrow \text{The value(s) of the first term(s) are given.}$$

$$a_n = 2a_{n-1} \qquad \longleftarrow \begin{array}{l}\text{A } \textit{recursion equation} \text{ shows how to find} \\ \text{each term from the term(s) before it.}\end{array}$$

Sample 1

Write a recursive formula for the sequence 1, 2, 6, 24, ...

Sample Response

Write several terms of the sequence using subscripts. Then look for the relationship between each term and the term before it.

$a_1 = 1$

$a_2 = 2 = 2 \cdot 1$ $\longrightarrow$ Write a_2 in terms of a_1. $\longrightarrow$ $a_2 = 2 \cdot a_1$

$a_3 = 6 = 3 \cdot 2$ $\longrightarrow$ Write a_3 in terms of a_2. $\longrightarrow$ $a_3 = 3 \cdot a_2$

$a_4 = 24 = 4 \cdot 6$ $\longrightarrow$ Write a_4 in terms of a_3. $\longrightarrow$ $a_4 = 4 \cdot a_3$

$\vdots$ $\qquad \vdots$

Write a recursion equation. $\longrightarrow$ $a_n = na_{n-1}$

These values are always equal.

Use the value of the first term and the recursion equation to write a recursive formula for the sequence.

$$a_1 = 1$$

$$a_n = na_{n-1}$$

Talk it Over

4. a. Write an explicit formula for the sequence 1, 2, 6, 24, . . . in Sample 1.

   b. Which formula was easier to find? Do you think this is always the case? Why or why not?

Write the first four terms of each sequence.

a. $a_1 = -1$
$a_n = 3a_{n-1} + 4$

b. $b_1 = 5$
$b_2 = 1$
$b_n = b_{n-1} - b_{n-2}$

Sample Response

a. $a_1 = -1$

Substitute 2 first, then 3, and then 4 for n in the recursion equation.

$a_2 = 3a_1 + 4 = 3(-1) + 4 = 1$

$a_3 = 3a_2 + 4 = 3(1) + 4 = 7$

$a_4 = 3a_3 + 4 = 3(7) + 4 = 25$

b. $b_1 = 5$

$b_2 = 1$

Substitute 3 first and then 4 for n in the recursion equation.

$b_3 = b_2 - b_1 = 1 - 5 = -4$

$b_4 = b_3 - b_2 = -4 - 1 = -5$

Robert Nuttall injured his shoulder. For the pain, his doctor prescribed 650 mg of aspirin to be taken every 6 h. Only 26% of the aspirin remains in his body by the time he takes a new dose. What will happen to the amount of aspirin in his body if he takes aspirin for several days?

Sample Response

You can write a recursion equation to model the amount of aspirin in Robert Nuttall's body after every dose.

amount of aspirin after nth dose	=	26% of the amount of aspirin after previous dose	+	new dose of 650 mg
a_n	=	$(0.26)(a_{n-1})$	+	650

Look at what happens to a_n the farther out you go in the sequence.

Method ❶ Use a graphics calculator.

ENTER a_1. ⟶

ENTER the ⟶
recursion equation
using ANS for a_{n-1}.

Keep pressing ENTER
to see the terms
of the sequence.

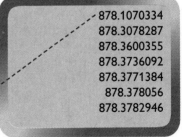

The sequence appears to approach a limit of about 878.

The amount of aspirin in his body will level off at about 878 mg.

Method ❷ Use a spreadsheet.

Enter 650 in cell A1.

Key in =0.26*A1+650 in cell A2 and use the FILL DOWN command.

The sequence appears to approach a limit of about 878.

A12			✗ ✓	= 0.26*A11 + 650
		A	**B**	**C**
1		650		
2		819	This is the recursion	
3		862.94	equation for the 12th	
4		874.3644	term.	
5		877.334744		
6		878.107033		
7		878.307829		
8		878.360035		
9		878.373609		
10		878.377138		
11		878.378056		
12		878.378295		

Aspirin Levels

The amount of aspirin in his body will level off at about 878 mg.

Talk it Over

5. After which dose does the amount of aspirin first reach a level of 878 mg in Robert Nuttall's body? After how many hours does this happen?

6. In Sample 3, what will you key in differently if Robert Nuttall's first dose is 1000 mg and each dose after that is 650 mg?

Look Back

How are explicit and recursive formulas alike? How are they different?

4-3 Exercises and Problems

1. **Reading** What are the two parts of a recursive formula?

Write a recursive formula for each sequence.

2. 9, 14, 19, 24, . . .

3. $-3, 9, -27, 81, . . .$

4. $9, 3, 1, \frac{1}{3}, . . .$

5. 8.32, 8.44, 8.56, 8.68, . . .

6. $2, \frac{1}{4}, 16, \frac{1}{256}, . . .$

7. $\frac{1}{2}, \frac{2}{3}, \frac{4}{4}, \frac{8}{5}, . . .$

Write the first six terms of each sequence.

8. $a_1 = 3$
   $a_n = a_{n-1} - 5$

9. $a_1 = 0.5$
   $a_n = (0.2)a_{n-1}$

10. $a_1 = 10$
    $a_n = (a_{n-1})^2$

11. $a_1 = 5$
    $a_n = \dfrac{a_{n-1}}{n}$

12. $a_1 = 5$
    $a_n = (i)(a_{n-1})$

13. $a_1 = 1$
    $a_2 = 2$
    $a_n = (a_{n-1})(a_{n-2})$

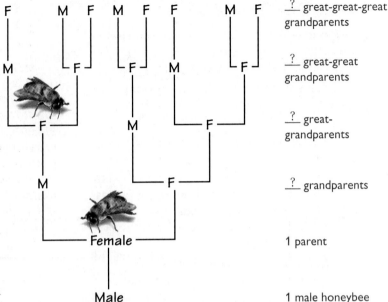

connection to BIOLOGY

14. Male honeybees hatch from unfertilized eggs and therefore have a female parent, but no male parent. Look at the family tree of a male bee.

  a. Starting with the male honeybee, write the sequence of the number of bees in each preceding generation. This sequence is known as the *Fibonacci sequence* and occurs in many aspects of nature.

  b. Write a recursive formula for the Fibonacci sequence. (*Hint:* The recursion equation involves *two* previous terms.)

15. **Medicine** Naomi Pedraza has bronchitis. She takes 250 mg of an antibiotic every four hours. Only 33% of the antibiotic is left in her body by the time she takes a new dose. What will the amount of antibiotic in her body level off to?

16. **State Lotteries** In some states a $1,000,000 lottery winner receives $50,000 per year for 20 years. The winner receives $50,000 right away. The state then puts just enough money into an account to pay the prize winner $50,000 per year for the next 19 years, leaving a zero balance in the account after the 19th payment from the account.

  Suppose an account has a fixed annual interest rate of 6.33%. Let a_0 be the amount of money the state puts into the account and let a_n be the amount of money left in the account after the nth payment.

  a. Write a recursion equation for a_n.

  b. What is the value of a_{19}?

  c. Find a_{19} when $a_0 = \$950,000$, when $a_0 = \$700,000$, and when $a_0 = \$500,000$. Do any of these values for a_0 come close to giving you the correct value for a_{19}?

  d. Solve your recursive formula in part (a) for a_{n-1}. Use this new equation as a recursive formula for the sequence that has a_{19} as the first term and a_0 as the last term. Will this method give you the correct value for a_0? Explain.

  e. What is the amount the state should put into the account?

  f. **Writing** Why do you think some states pay a lottery winner over many years rather than all at once?

17. **Writing** Explain how finding the 100th term of a sequence defined explicitly is different from finding the 100th term of the same sequence defined recursively.

18. **Group Activity** Work with another student.

This fractal is called a *Koch snowflake.* The first four stages in the formation of a Koch snowflake are shown. At each stage, the middle third of each side is replaced with an equilateral triangle.

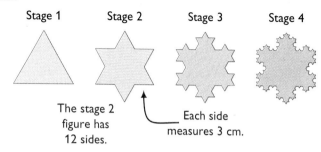

Stage 1   Stage 2   Stage 3   Stage 4

The stage 2 figure has 12 sides.

Each side measures 3 cm.

a. Suppose each side of the original equilateral triangle is 9 cm. Complete the table.

b. The table in part (a) shows the first three terms of three sequences. Write a recursive formula for each of the sequences.

c. Use your formulas from part (b) to find the 12th term of each sequence.

d. What appears to be the limit, if there is one, of each sequence?

	Number of segments	Length of each segment	Perimeter
Stage 1	3	9	27
Stage 2	?	?	?
Stage 3	?	?	?

19. Find the first four terms and the 9th term of the sequence $b_n = \dfrac{3n}{n+5}$. *(Section 4-2)*

20. Solve $x = \sqrt{1 - \dfrac{3}{2}x}$. *(Section 2-6)*

For each sequence: *(Section 4-1)*

a. **Write the next three terms.**   b. **Write the 10th term.**

c. **Describe the method you used to write the 10th term.**

21. 5, 10, 20, 40, . . .   22. 5, 10, 15, 20, . . .

 .... **Working on the Unit Project**

23. Repeat parts (a)–(e) of Exercise 22 on page 221, except, instead of choosing a lump sum, this time choose an amount of money to make equal annual deposits into a long-term deposit account for 25 years.

24. **Research** Read about the many different ways you can invest money. Here are some books that advise people how and where to invest their money.

Sylvia Porter's Money Book: How To Earn It, Spend It, Save It, Invest It, Borrow It, And — Use It To Better Your Life by Sylvia Field Porter

Susan Lee's ABZs of Money & Finance by Susan Lee

Everyone's Money Book by Jane Bryant Quinn

Arithmetic and Geometric Sequences

Focus

Identify sequences that have a common difference, a common ratio, or neither. Write explicit and recursive formulas.

What's the Difference

Sequences are found in many everyday situations—in fuel tank readings, in calendar dates, and in the heights of a bouncing ball. Although these situations seem to have nothing in common, they are sometimes described mathematically using the same kind of sequences.

Talk it Over

Use these two groups of sequences.

Group 1

a. 1, 8, 15, 22, 29

b. $1, \frac{3}{4}, \frac{1}{2}, \frac{1}{4}, 0$

c. 2, 4, 6, 8, . . .

Group 2

a. 32, 24, 18, 13.5, . . .

b. $1, \frac{1}{2}, \frac{1}{4}, \frac{1}{8}, \ldots$

c. 2, 4, 8, 16, . . .

1. Write a recursive formula for each sequence in Group 1.

2. Write a recursive formula for each sequence in Group 2.

3. Describe any similarities within each group. Describe any differences between the two groups.

A sequence in which the difference between any term and the term before is a constant is an **arithmetic sequence.**

$$2, 4, 6, 8, \ldots$$

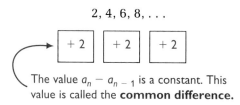

The value $a_n - a_{n-1}$ is a constant. This value is called the **common difference.**

A sequence in which the ratio of any term to the term before it is a constant is a **geometric sequence.**

$$2, 4, 8, 16, \ldots$$

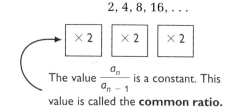

The value $\dfrac{a_n}{a_{n-1}}$ is a constant. This value is called the **common ratio.**

Sample 1

Tell whether each sequence is *arithmetic, geometric, or neither.*

a. $27, 9, 3, 1, \ldots$ b. $1, 3, 7, 15, \ldots$ c. $12, 9.5, 7, 4.5, \ldots$

Sample Response

Look for a common difference or a common ratio.

a. sequence   27,   9,   3,   1, . . .

difference → -18 -6 -2 There is no common difference.

ratio → $\dfrac{1}{3}$ $\dfrac{1}{3}$ $\dfrac{1}{3}$ The common ratio is $\dfrac{1}{3}$.

The sequence is geometric.

b. sequence   1,   3,   7,   15, . . .

difference → 2 4 8 There is no common difference.

ratio → 3 $\dfrac{7}{3}$ $\dfrac{15}{7}$ There is no common ratio.

The sequence is neither arithmetic nor geometric.

c. sequence   12,   9.5,   7,   4.5, . . .

difference → -2.5 -2.5 -2.5 The common difference is -2.5.

The sequence is arithmetic.

Talk it Over

4. a. Write an explicit formula for the arithmetic sequence in Sample 1.

   b. To find the *n*th term of an arithmetic sequence, how many times do you add the common difference to the first term?

5. a. Write an explicit formula for the geometric sequence in Sample 1.

   b. To find the *n*th term of a geometric sequence, how many times do you multiply the first term by the common ratio?

6. **a.** Graph five terms of each sequence and compare.

2, 4, 6, 8, . . .   2, 4, 8, 16, . . .

b. Graph five terms of each sequence and compare.

$1, \dfrac{3}{4}, \dfrac{1}{2}, \dfrac{1}{4}, 0$ $1, \dfrac{1}{2}, \dfrac{1}{4}, \dfrac{1}{8}, \ldots$

c. Use your answers to parts (a) and (b) to make a conjecture about the graphs of arithmetic and geometric sequences.

GENERAL FORMULAS FOR ARITHMETIC SEQUENCES

For the sequence $a_1, a_2, a_3, a_4, \ldots$

with $d = a_n - a_{n-1}$

Example

3, 5, 7, 9, . . .

Explicit formula

$$a_n = a_1 + (n - 1)d$$

*n*th term   1st term   common difference

$a_n = 3 + (n - 1)2$

Recursive formula

$$a_1 = \text{value of first term}$$

$$a_n = a_{n-1} + d$$

*n*th term   previous term   common difference

$a_1 = 3$

$a_n = a_{n-1} + 2$

Graph:

You can use an explicit formula to find out how many terms are in a finite sequence that is arithmetic or geometric.

Sample 2

Etenia is knitting a sweater with a repeating triangle pattern. The pattern repeat for each triangle is to knit 33 stitches, purl 29 stitches, knit 25 stitches, purl 21 stitches, and so on, ending with one knit stitch. How many rows are there in each triangle?

Step 1 Decide whether the sequence is arithmetic, geometric, or neither.

$$a_1, \quad a_2, \quad a_3, \quad a_4, \dots, a_n$$
$$\downarrow \quad \downarrow \quad \downarrow \quad \downarrow \qquad \downarrow$$
$$33, \quad 29, \quad 25, \quad 21, \dots, 1$$

$-4 \quad -4 \quad -4$ ← The sequence is arithmetic and $d = -4$.

Step 2 **Problem Solving Strategy:** Use a formula.

Write the general explicit formula for an arithmetic sequence.

Substitute **1** for a_n, 33 for a_1, and -4 for d. →

$$a_n = a_1 + (n - 1)d$$
$$1 = 33 + (n - 1)(-4)$$
$$1 = 33 - 4n + 4$$
$$-36 = -4n$$
$$9 = n$$

There are 9 rows in each triangle.

······► **Now you are ready for:**
⋮ **Exs. 1–24 on pp. 233–234**

GENERAL FORMULAS FOR GEOMETRIC SEQUENCES

For the sequence $a_1, a_2, a_3, a_4, \dots$
with $r = \dfrac{a_n}{a_{n-1}}$:

Example

$3, 6, 12, 24, \dots$

Explicit formula

$$a_n = a_1 r^{n-1}$$

nth term · 1st term · common ratio

$$a_n = 3 \cdot 2^{n-1}$$

Recursive formula

$$a_1 = \text{value of first term}$$
$$a_n = (a_{n-1})r$$

nth term · previous term · common ratio

$$a_1 = 3$$
$$a_n = (a_{n-1}) \cdot (2)$$

Graph:

**Find the ninth term of the geometric sequence
−2, 6, −18, 54, ...**

Sample Response

The common ratio is -3.

$a_n = a_1 r^{n-1}$ ◄——— Use the general explicit formula for a geometric sequence.

$a_9 = -2(-3)^{9-1}$ ◄——— Substitute **−2** for a_1, **−3** for r, and **9** for n.

$\quad = -2(-3)^8$

$\quad = -2(6561)$

$\quad = -13{,}122$

You can find an unknown term between any two known terms of an arithmetic or geometric sequence.

Find the value of x in the geometric sequence 3, x, 18, ...

Sample Response

In a geometric sequence, $\dfrac{a_n}{a_{n-1}}$ is a constant.

$\dfrac{x}{3} = \dfrac{18}{x}$ ◄——— $\dfrac{a_2}{a_1} = \dfrac{a_3}{a_2}$

$x^2 = 54$ ◄——— Use cross products.

$x = \pm\sqrt{54}$ ◄——— Take the square root of both sides. ◄ ○ ₀ ○ ◯

$\quad = \pm 3\sqrt{6}$ ◄——— Simplify.

x is $3\sqrt{6}$ or $-3\sqrt{6}$.

> **Watch Out!**
> A positive number has both a positive and a negative square root.

In Sample 4, the *positive* value of x is known as the *geometric mean* of 3 and 18. The **geometric mean** of any two positive numbers a and b is $\sqrt{ab}$ since the sequence a, $\sqrt{ab}$, b is geometric.

Talk it Over

7. **a.** How many different geometric sequences are possible from the sequence in Sample 4? List the first three terms of each possible sequence.

   b. Find the common ratio of each sequence in part (a).

   c. What is the next term of each sequence in part (a)?

8. **a.** Suppose 3, x, 18, . . . is an arithmetic sequence. Find x.

   b. How many different sequences are possible in part (a)? What is the common difference for each sequence?

   c. Find the mean of 3 and 18.

   d. The value of x in part (a) is the *arithmetic mean* of 3 and 18. How is the arithmetic mean of two numbers related to the mean of the numbers?

Look Back ←

······▶ Now you are ready for:
Exs. 25–39 on pp. 234–236

How are arithmetic and geometric sequences alike? How are they different?

4-4 Exercises and Problems

Tell whether each sequence is *arithmetic, geometric, or neither*.

1. 5, 8, 11, 14, . . .
2. 24, 11, −2, −15, . . .
3. 1, 11, 111, 1111, . . .
4. 1, 10, 100, 1000, . . .
5. 7, 8, 7, 8, . . .
6. $1, \dfrac{1}{5}, \dfrac{1}{25}, \dfrac{1}{125}, \ldots$

Tell whether the sequence defined by each explicit formula is *arithmetic, geometric, or neither*.

7. $a_n = 2n + 1$
8. $d_n = 3(2)^n$
9. $a_n = \dfrac{n + 1}{n + 2}$
10. $t_n = \dfrac{(-2)^n}{8}$
11. $a_n = 5 - 3n$
12. $d_n = 4n - \dfrac{1}{2}$

For each sequence in Exercises 13–18:

a. Decide whether the sequence is *arithmetic, geometric, or neither*.

b. Write a recursive formula.

13. 64, 16, 4, 1, . . .
14. 3, 5, 9, 17, . . .
15. 5, 3, 1, −1, . . .
16. −3, −12, −21, −30, . . .

17. the distance traveled after n hours by a jet flying at 550 mi/h, assuming there are no head or tail winds

18. the amount of money in a savings account after n months, if the initial amount is $500 and the annual interest rate is 3.6% compounded monthly

Find the number of terms in each sequence.

19. 15, 12, 9, 6, . . . , −36
20. −21, −9, 3, 15, . . . , 219
21. 72, 56, 40, 24, . . . , −440
22. 8, 15, 22, 29, . . . , 99

23. The *ywegale* is the smallest measure of weight in Myanmar and weighs about 0.026 g. Two ywegale equal one *ywegi*, two ywegi equal one *pai*, two pai equal one *moo*, two moo equal one *mat*, two mat equal one *ngamu*, and two ngamu equal one *tical*.

   a. Express every measure of weight in terms of ywegale.

   b. What type of sequence does the weight system in Myanmar form? What is the common difference or ratio?

   c. **Open-ended** Name another weight system that forms the same type of sequence as the one in Myanmar. What is the common difference or ratio?

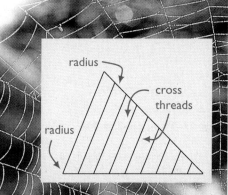

connection to **BIOLOGY**

Use this information for Exercises 24 and 25.

Scientists measure every part of a spider's web to understand the web's construction. When spinning a web, a spider makes several radii and then connects them with a spiral. The lengths of the cross threads between any two adjacent radii form an arithmetic sequence.

24. The shortest cross thread between two adjacent radii in a web measures 3.3 mm. The longest cross thread measures 46.5 mm. The difference in length between adjacent cross threads is 1.2 mm. How many cross threads are between the two radii?

25. The first cross thread between two radii in another web measures 3.0 mm. The last cross thread measures 42.6 mm. There are 13 cross threads in this section. What is the common difference in this sequence of cross threads?

26. **Reading** Why is $-3\sqrt{6}$ *not* a geometric mean of 3 and 18?

27. Use the geometric sequence 5, x, 7, ...

   a. Find the value of x.   b. Find the common ratio.   c. Find the next three terms.

28. Suppose $a_3 = 15$ and $a_5 = 2$ in a geometric sequence.

   a. Find the value of a_4.   b. Find the common ratio.   c. Find the value of a_1.

For each sequence in Exercises 29–31:

a. Find the value of x when the sequence is arithmetic.

b. Find the value of x when the sequence is geometric.

29. -20, x, -4, . . .   30. 21, x, 10, . . .   31. 4, x, 16, . . .

Use this theorem for Exercises 32 and 33.

If the altitude is drawn to the hypotenuse of a right triangle, then the measure of the altitude is the geometric mean between the measures of the parts of the hypotenuse.

Find the length of the altitude of each right triangle.

32.

33.

34. **Writing** Explain why there is no real number x for which $10, x, -20, \ldots$ is a geometric sequence.

Ongoing ASSESSMENT

35. **Group Activity** Work with another student.

Use these geometric sequences:

A. $6, -3, \dfrac{3}{2}, -\dfrac{3}{4}, \ldots$

B. $-5, 20, -80, 320, \ldots$

C. $\dfrac{1}{2}, -\dfrac{1}{8}, \dfrac{1}{32}, -\dfrac{1}{128}, \ldots$

D. $1, -3, 9, -27, \ldots$

a. What is the common ratio for each sequence?

b. Graph each sequence on a different set of axes.

c. What conjecture can you make about the graphs of geometric sequences with a negative common ratio?

d. Tell whether each sequence appears to have a limit.

e. What conjecture can you make about the limits of geometric sequences with a negative common ratio?

Review PREVIEW

36. Write the first six terms of this sequence. *(Section 4-3)*

$$b_1 = 15$$
$$b_n = b_{n-1} + (2n - 1)$$

37. Use the triangle. Find the value of x. *(Toolbox Skill 30)*

38. Find the value of A in the formula

$A = \dfrac{1}{2}(b_1 + b_2)h$, when $b_1 = 5$, $b_2 = 9$, and $h = 6$. *(Toolbox Skill 29)*

Working on the Unit Project

The Consumer Price Index (CPI) is a measure of the inflation rate in the United States or the change in the cost of goods and services from the previous year. "Cost of living" salary increases are based on the CPI.

39. a. **Research** Find the most recent edition of the *Statistical Abstract of the United States*. Find and record the data in the Annual Percent Changes in Consumer Prices table for the last 30 years or so. Find the mean and median of the data. Which do you think better represents the data? Why?

   b. **Research** Find the average annual entry-level salary for a career that interests you. Assume annual salary increases that match the more representative statistic in part (a).

   c. Choose a percent of salary from part (b) to save for a public university education. Choose another percent to save for a private university. Use the same interest rate that you found in part (a) of Exercise 22 on page 221. Use a spreadsheet to see how much is saved over 25 years.

   d. Repeat part (c), choosing different percents of salary to go to savings to find what percent of salary should be saved for a public education and for a private education.

Unit 4 **CHECKPOINT**

1. Kiyoshi is sewing a sunburst quilt made up of parallelograms.   **4-1**

   a. **Writing** Describe any pattern you see in the quilt.

   b. Use the pattern to find the number and color of parallelograms she will need for a fifth ring and a sixth ring.

For each sequence in Exercises 2 and 3:

a. Plot at least six points of the sequence.

b. Decide whether the sequence appears to have a limit.

2. $3, -4, 5, -6, \ldots$ 3. $\dfrac{1}{2}, \dfrac{1}{4}, \dfrac{1}{8}, \dfrac{1}{16}, \ldots$

Write an explicit formula for each sequence.   **4-2**

4. $1, \dfrac{4}{5}, \dfrac{7}{9}, \dfrac{10}{13}, \ldots$ 5. $-2, \dfrac{1}{2}, 1\dfrac{1}{3}, 1\dfrac{3}{4}, \ldots$

Write a recursive formula for each sequence.   **4-3**

6. $6, 13, 20, 27, \ldots$ 7. $1, 4, 9, 16, \ldots$

Tell whether each sequence is *arithmetic, geometric,* or *neither.*   **4-4**

8. $3, -6, 12, -24, \ldots$ 9. $1, 3, 7, 15, \ldots$

10. $\dfrac{7}{8}, \dfrac{3}{4}, \dfrac{5}{8}, \dfrac{1}{2}, \ldots$ 11. $2, 3, 5, 8, \ldots$

Arithmetic Series and Sigma Notation

THAT SPECIAL SUM-THING

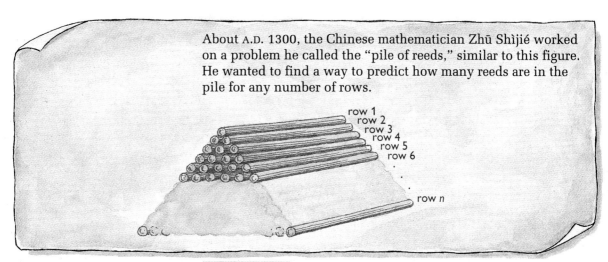

About A.D. 1300, the Chinese mathematician Zhū Shìjié worked on a problem he called the "pile of reeds," similar to this figure. He wanted to find a way to predict how many reeds are in the pile for any number of rows.

row 1
row 2
row 3
row 4
row 5
row 6

row *n*

Talk it Over

BY THE WAY...

Zhū Shìjié was a wandering teacher for more than 20 years. He also wrote two works. His second work, *Precious Mirror of the Four Elements*, began with what is now called Pascal's triangle. This scheme of numbers was considered an old one even then.

1. Write a sequence for the number of reeds in each row.

2. How many reeds are in the whole pile when there are six rows?

3. Explain how your answer to question 2 is related to the first six terms of your sequence in question 1.

4. Use your sequence in question 1 to write an expression for the number of reeds in the pile when there are *n* rows.

5. To find out how many reeds are in Zhū Shìjié's pile when there are 100 rows, you have to find this sum.

$$1 + 2 + 3 + 4 + \cdots + 97 + 98 + 99 + 100$$

   a. What is the sum of $1 + 100$? $2 + 99$? $3 + 98$? $4 + 97$?

   b. How many sums like the ones you found in part (a) are in $1 + 2 + 3 + 4 + \cdots + 97 + 98 + 99 + 100$? Explain.

   c. Use the information from parts (a) and (b) to find the number of reeds in 100 rows of Zhū Shìjié's pile.

6. Do you think the method described in question 5 will work if the difference between terms is not 1? if the first term is not 1? if the last term is not 100? if there is an odd number of terms being added?

When the terms of a sequence are added, the indicated sum of the terms is called a **series.** For example:

sequence → 1, 2, 3, 4, 5, 6

series → 1 + 2 + 3 + 4 + 5 + 6

A *finite series* has a last term, but an *infinite series* does not. The finite series above is an **arithmetic series** since the terms form an arithmetic sequence.

SUM OF A FINITE ARITHMETIC SERIES

The general formula for the sum S of a finite arithmetic series with n terms is

$$S = \frac{n(a_1 + a_n)}{2}.$$

Sample 1

**Find the sum of the finite arithmetic series
7 + 12 + 17 + 22 + · · · + 52. ,**

Sample Response

Step 1 Find the number of terms in the series.

$a_n = a_1 + (n - 1)d$ ←——— Use the general explicit formula for an arithmetic sequence.

$52 = 7 + (n - 1)5$ ←——— Substitute **52** for a_n, **7** for a_1, and **5** for d.

$52 = 7 + 5n - 5$ ←——— Solve for n.

$50 = 5n$

$10 = n$

Step 2 Use the formula for the sum of a finite arithmetic series.

$$S = \frac{n(a_1 + a_n)}{2}$$

$$= \frac{10(7 + 52)}{2}$$ ←——— Substitute **10** for n, **7** for a_1, and **52** for a_n.

······► **Now you are ready for:**
: **Exs. 1–12 on pp. 241–242**

$$= 295$$

Sigma Notation

A series can be written in a compact form using *sigma notation.* **Sigma notation** uses the *summation symbol* Σ, which is the Greek letter *sigma.*

In sigma notation, the series from Sample 1,
$7 + 12 + 17 + 22 + \cdots + 52$, looks like this.

Read: "The sum of $7 + (n - 1)5$ for integer values of n from 1 to 10."

last value of n

$$\sum_{n=1}^{10} [7 + (n - 1)5]$$

first value of n

explicit formula for the related sequence

When you substitute the values of n into the formula, you write the series in *expanded form*.

$$\sum_{n=1}^{10} [7 + (n - 1)5] = [7 + (1 - 1)5] + [7 + (2 - 1)5] + \cdots + [7 + (10 - 1)5]$$
$$= \quad 7 \quad + \quad 12 \quad + \cdots + \quad 52$$

Sample 2

Evaluate.

a. $\displaystyle\sum_{n=1}^{8} (5 - 2n)$

b. $\displaystyle\sum_{n=2}^{7} |4 - n|$

Sample Response

a. **Step 1** Write the series in expanded form.

$$\sum_{n=1}^{8} (5 - 2n) = [5 - 2 \cdot 1] + [5 - 2 \cdot 2] + [5 - 2 \cdot 3] + [5 - 2 \cdot 4] +$$
$$[5 - 2 \cdot 5] + [5 - 2 \cdot 6] + [5 - 2 \cdot 7] + [5 - 2 \cdot 8]$$
$$= 3 + 1 + (-1) + (-3) + (-5) + (-7) + (-9) + (-11)$$

Step 2 Find the sum of the series.

The series is arithmetic since there is a common difference of -2.

$$S = \frac{n(a_1 + a_n)}{2}$$ ◄——— Use the formula for the sum of a finite arithmetic series.

$$= \frac{8(3 + (-11))}{2}$$ ◄——— Substitute **8** for **n**, **3** for a_1, and **−11** for a_n.

$$= -32$$

b. **Step 1** Write the series in expanded form.

$$\sum_{n=2}^{7} |4 - n| = |4 - 2| + |4 - 3| + |4 - 4| + |4 - 5| + |4 - 6| + |4 - 7|$$

Step 2 Find the sum of the series.

$$S = 2 + 1 + 0 + 1 + 2 + 3$$
$$= 9$$

7. In part (a) of Sample 2, is using the sum formula easier than adding up the terms? Do you think the sum formula is always easier to use? Why or why not?

8. In part (b) of Sample 2, why can you not use the formula for the sum of a finite arithmetic series?

Sample 3

Write each series in sigma notation.

a. the total number of unit cubes needed to build these five models

b. $7 + 10 + 13 + 16 + \cdots + 64$

Sample Response

a. **Step 1** Find an explicit formula for the related sequence.

The total number of unit cubes in each model is equal to its volume. Write several terms of the sequence of the volumes of the models.

$$V_1 = 1^3$$
$$V_2 = 2^3$$
$$V_3 = 3^3 \quad \longleftarrow \quad \text{Each term is the third power of its position number.}$$

An explicit formula for the sequence is $V_n = n^3$.

Step 2 Find the first and last values of n.

There are five terms in the series. The first value of n is 1, and the last value is 5.

Step 3 Write the series in sigma notation.

$$\sum_{n=1}^{5} n^3$$

b. **Step 1** Find an explicit formula for the related sequence 7, 10, 13, 16, . . . , 64.

The series is arithmetic since there is a common difference of 3.

$$a_n = a_1 + (n - 1)d \quad \longleftarrow \quad \text{Use the explicit formula for an arithmetic sequence.}$$
$$= 7 + (n - 1)3 \quad \longleftarrow \quad \text{Substitute 7 for } a_1 \text{ and 3 for } d.$$

Step 2 Find the first and last values of n.

To find the last value of n, find out how many terms the series has.

$a_n = 7 + (n-1)3$ ←———— Use the explicit formula for the related sequence.

$64 = 7 + (n-1)3$ ←———— Substitute 64 for a_n.

$64 = 7 + 3n - 3$

$60 = 3n$

$20 = n$

The first value of n is 1, and the last value is 20.

Step 3 Write the series in sigma notation.

$$\sum_{n=1}^{20} [7 + (n-1)3]$$

·······▶ **Now you are ready for:**
Exs. 13–27 on pp. 242–243

Look Back ←————————————

Describe the relationship between a series and its related sequence.

···················

4-5   **Exercises and Problems**

1. **Reading** What three things must you know about a finite arithmetic series in order to use the sum formula?

For Exercises 2–6, find the sum of each finite arithmetic series.

2. $6 + 11 + 16 + 21 + \cdots + 116$

3. $98 + 94 + 90 + 86 + \cdots + 6$

4. $1 + 1.2 + 1.4 + 1.6 + \cdots + 5.0$

5. $13 + 12.25 + 11.5 + 10.75 + \cdots + 1$

6. the sum of all positive three-digit multiples of 5

7. **Festivals** *Kwanzaa* is an African-American festival. Each candle represents one of the seven principles associated with Kwanzaa. On the first night, one candle is lit and then blown out. Each night after that, one new candle is lit, and all candles from the previous nights are lit again and then blown out.

   a. Write the series for the sum of the candles that are lit *again* during the festival and find the sum.

   b. What is the total number of lightings and re-lightings of candles for the festival?

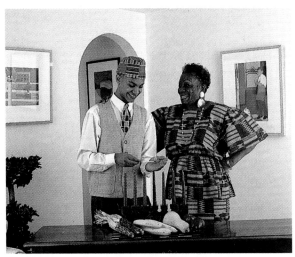

Open-ended For each number, write an arithmetic series that has the number as its sum. Each series should have at least four terms.

8. 25   **9.** 49   **10.** 15   **11.** 36

connection to **BIOLOGY**

QUADRANT

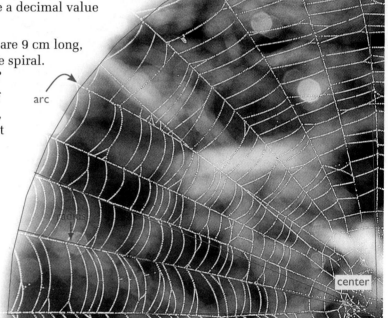

12. There are sequences hidden within a spider's web. The rings in the spiral of a spider's web are evenly spaced and can be approximated by circles. To estimate how much silk a spider uses for the spiral, scientists look at one section of the web. (Do not use a decimal value for π until part (d).)

  a. Suppose the radii in a web are 9 cm long, and there are 36 rings in the spiral. How far apart are the rings?

  b. Write the first four terms of the sequence of arc lengths, starting with the one closest to the center of the web. (*Hint:* What is the formula for circumference?)

  c. What is the length of the last arc?

  d. How much silk is used to make the spiral in one section of the web?

  e. How much silk is used to make the spiral for the whole web?

center

Evaluate.

13. $\displaystyle\sum_{k=1}^{8} 4k$ **14.** $\displaystyle\sum_{n=5}^{10} (2n-5)$ **15.** $\displaystyle\sum_{n=0}^{5} (-2)^n$ **16.** $\displaystyle\sum_{t=-2}^{4} (3+t)^2$

Write each series in sigma notation.

17. $28 + 23 + 18 + 13 + \cdots + (-7)$ **18.** $(-13) + (-2) + 9 + 20 + \cdots + 108$

19. $\dfrac{1}{2^3} + \dfrac{1}{2^4} + \dfrac{1}{2^5} + \cdots + \dfrac{1}{2^{10}}$ **20.** $\dfrac{1}{3} + \dfrac{2}{3} + 1 + \dfrac{4}{3} + \dfrac{5}{3} + \cdots + 33$

21. Shelley Tres wants to paint the side of a 16-step stairway. She needs to find the area in order to know how much paint to buy.

  a. **Writing** Explain how the side of the stairway can be divided into a series of rectangles.

  b. Write a series in sigma notation for the areas of the rectangles.

  c. A gallon of paint will cover about 300 square feet. Shelley Tres has about a half gallon of paint and wants to apply two coats. Should she buy more paint? Explain.

250 ft

support struts

10 ft

23 ft

22. Rosa Bonillas is designing a radio tower with four identical sides. One side is shown. The length of each leg is 250 ft. Each pair of adjacent legs is 23 ft apart on the ground. The tower needs a horizontal supporting *strut*, or steel beam, every 10 ft along the leg.

   a. Use similar triangles to find the lengths of the bottom four struts on one side.

   b. Write a sequence for the lengths of the struts. Is the sequence *arithmetic, geometric,* or *neither*?

   c. Write a series in sigma notation for the minimum length of steel beam Rosa will need for the struts on one side of the tower.

   d. Find the minimum length of steel beam Rosa needs for the struts for the whole tower.

Ongoing **ASSESSMENT**

23. **Open-ended** Without using a formula, write to a seventh-grader explaining how to use a shortcut to find the sum of the whole numbers from 1 to 50.

Review **PREVIEW**

24. Find the value of x in the geometric sequence 12, x, 1, ... *(Section 4-4)*

25. Find AB and BA. *(Toolbox Skill 11)*

$$A = \begin{bmatrix} 0 & 3 & -2 \\ 1 & 2 & 1 \end{bmatrix} \qquad B = \begin{bmatrix} \frac{1}{2} & -5 \\ 4 & 2 \\ -1 & 2 \end{bmatrix}$$

26. **a.** What type of sequence is 3, 6, 12, 24, 48, 96? *(Section 4-4)*

   b. Find the sum of the terms of the sequence in part (a).

Working on the Unit Project

27. **Group Activity** Work in a group of four students.

   a. **Research** Each student should research one of these types of investments: Certificates of Deposit (CDs), United States Savings Bonds, mutual funds, and zero-coupon bonds. Find out a typical rate of return, whether there are any tax advantages, and what kind of risk is involved with each investment type. Summarize your results with a chart and report.

   b. Set up a spreadsheet to calculate the results when your annual investment remains the same but is split between two different investment types.

Geometric Series

"SUM" M⊕RE

The NCAA Women's Basketball Tournament involves 64 teams. In each round, each team plays one other team and only the winners go on to the next round. The chart shows some results for the 1994 East-West regional games.

National Semifinals	Regional Finals	Regional Semifinals	2nd Round
			Purdue
		Purdue	Washington
	Purdue		San Diego State
		Texas A & M	Texas A & M
Purdue			Oregon
		Colorado	Colorado
	Stanford		Montana
		Stanford	Stanford
			Connecticut
		Connecticut	Auburn
	Connecticut		Western Ky.
		Southern Miss.	Southern Miss.
North Carolina			Old Dominion
		North Carolina	North Carolina
	North Carolina		Minnesota
		Vanderbilt	Vanderbilt

To National Championship

BY THE WAY...

Lynette Woodard, a University of Kansas All American, became the leading career scorer in the history of women's college basketball in 1981. After graduating, she captained the United States Olympic Basketball team that won a gold medal in 1984. Lynette was the first woman to play with the Harlem Globetrotters.

Talk it Over

1. a. Write the sequence for the number of games played in each round of a tournament involving 64 teams. What kind of sequence have you formed?

   b. Write the series related to your sequence in part (a).

   c. How many games are played in the tournament?

$$S = 3 + 6 + 12 + 24 + 48 + 96$$
$$2S = \quad 6 + 12 + 24 + 48 + 96 + 192$$
$$S - 2S = 3 - 192$$
$$S(1 - 2) = 3 - 192$$
$$S = \frac{3 - 192}{1 - 2}$$
$$S = 189$$

2. Elena used this method to find the sum of the series $3 + 6 + 12 + 24 + 48 + 96$.

   a. Explain her method. Is Elena's answer correct?

   b. Use Elena's method to find the sum of your series in part (b) of question 1. Did you get the same answer as before?

The series in question 2 and in part (b) of question 1 are finite *geometric series*. The terms of a **geometric series** form a geometric sequence. There is a formula for the sum of a finite geometric series.

Look closely at Elena's next-to-last step in question 2.

first term ⟶   ⟵ last term × common ratio
$$S = \frac{3 - 192}{1 - 2}$$
⟵ common ratio

SUM OF A FINITE GEOMETRIC SERIES

The general formula for the sum S of a finite geometric series with n terms and common ratio r is

$$S = \frac{a_1 - a_n r}{1 - r}.$$

Sample 1

Find the sum of the series $(-1) + 3 + (-9) + 27 + \cdots + 2187$.

Sample Response

Step 1 Decide whether the series is arithmetic, geometric, or neither.

There is a common ratio of -3, so the series is geometric.

Step 2 Use the formula for the sum of a finite geometric series.

$$S = \frac{a_1 - a_n r}{1 - r}$$

$$S = \frac{-1 - 2187(-3)}{1 - (-3)} \quad \longleftarrow \quad \text{Substitute } -1 \text{ for } a_1, 2187 \text{ for } a_n, \text{ and } -3 \text{ for } r.$$

$$= \frac{6560}{4}$$

$$= 1640$$

The sum of the series is 1640.

3. In Sample 1, why is the sum of the series less than the last term?

4. What three things do you need to know about a geometric series in order to find its sum using the formula?

5. a. Write a geometric series having six terms and a common ratio of 1.

   b. Explain why you cannot use the formula for the sum of a finite geometric series to find the sum of your series.

   c. Explain how to find the sum of your series without adding up the terms.

Using Σ

Geometric series can also be written in sigma notation. To write the geometric series for the number of games played in the NCAA Tournament in sigma notation, you must find an explicit formula for the related geometric sequence.

$$a_n = a_1 r^{n-1}$$ ⟵ Use the general explicit formula for a geometric sequence.

$$a_n = 32\left(\frac{1}{2}\right)^{n-1}$$ ⟵ Substitute **32** for a_1 and $\frac{1}{2}$ for r.

There are six terms in the series. In sigma notation, the series looks like this.

$$\sum_{n=1}^{6} 32\left(\frac{1}{2}\right)^{n-1}$$

Sample 2

Evaluate $\displaystyle\sum_{n=1}^{8} 13(2)^n.$

Sample Response

Step 1 Decide whether the series is arithmetic, geometric, or neither.

Write the series in expanded form.

$$\sum_{n=1}^{8} 13(2)^n = 13(2)^1 + 13(2)^2 + 13(2)^3 + 13(2)^4 + 13(2)^5 + 13(2)^6 + 13(2)^7 + 13(2)^8$$

The series is geometric with a common ratio of 2.

Step 2 Find the values of the first and last terms.

$$a_1 = 13(2)^1 \qquad a_8 = 13(2)^8$$
$$= 26 \qquad\qquad = 3328$$

Step 3 Use the formula for the sum of a finite geometric series.

$$S = \frac{a_1 - a_n r}{1 - r}$$

$$S = \frac{26 - 3328(2)}{1 - 2} \quad \longleftarrow \quad \text{Substitute } \mathbf{26} \text{ for } \boldsymbol{a_1}, \mathbf{3328} \text{ for } a_n, \text{ and } \mathbf{2} \text{ for } r.$$

$$= 6630$$

The sum of the series is 6630.

Look Back

Write the formula for the sum of a finite geometric series in words without using any symbols.

4-6 Exercises and Problems

1. **Reading** What values do you need to know to write a geometric series in sigma notation?

Find the sum of each series.

2. $3 + 15 + 75 + 375 + \cdots + 9375$

3. $4 + (-8) + 16 + (-32) + \cdots + 1024$

4. $5 + 1 + 0.2 + 0.04 + \cdots + 0.000064$

5. $10 + \dfrac{20}{3} + \dfrac{40}{9} + \dfrac{80}{27} + \cdots + \dfrac{640}{729}$

Evaluate.

6. $\displaystyle\sum_{n=1}^{17} 5(-1)^n$

7. $\displaystyle\sum_{t=0}^{7} \frac{2}{5}(2)^t$

8. $\displaystyle\sum_{n=1}^{8} (-1)\left(-\frac{2}{3}\right)^{n-1}$

9. $\displaystyle\sum_{s=1}^{10} 3(0.5)^{s-1}$

For each series in Exercises 10–15:

a. Decide whether the series is *arithmetic, geometric,* or *neither.*

b. Find the sum.

10. $0 + 2 + 6 + 12 + \cdots + 56$

11. $(-3) + 3 + 9 + 15 + \cdots + 33$

12. $\displaystyle\sum_{t=0}^{4} 7(0.1)^t$

13. $\dfrac{1}{5} + \left(-\dfrac{1}{10}\right) + \dfrac{1}{20} + \left(-\dfrac{1}{40}\right) + \cdots + \dfrac{1}{320}$

14. $\displaystyle\sum_{n=0}^{10} -\frac{1}{4}(n+1)$

15. $\displaystyle\sum_{n=1}^{6} \frac{1}{2}(3)^{n-1}$

In a Greek myth, Herakles performed twelve dangerous tasks to become immortal, or be allowed to live forever. The second task was to defeat the Hydra, a monster with nine heads.

Second Labour.– In the springs and swamps of Lerne dwelt a huge hydra which used to lay waste the lands round about, and to ensure his death Herakles was sent against this creature, from whose enormous body grew nine heads, the middle one being immortal. . . . finding the creature crouching sullenly in its lair, the hero forced it out by means of flaming missiles and grasped it at the same instant that it seized him. Stoutly swinging his club, he knocked off the hydra's heads . . . , but to his alarm two heads grew in the place of each one that he destroyed, ...

16. Suppose with one swing of his club, Herakles can knock off all the Hydra's heads, except the immortal one, before any new heads replace them.

   a. Write a series in sigma notation for the total number of heads that are knocked off after five swings.

   b. Is the series in part (a) *arithmetic, geometric,* or *neither?*

   c. Find the sum of your series.

17. Suppose Herakles can knock off only one head with each swing, and the head is replaced by two new heads before he can swing his club again.

   a. Write the first five terms of the sequence for the number of heads that the Hydra has after each swing.

   b. Is the sequence in part (a) *arithmetic, geometric,* or *neither?*

   c. **Writing** Explain why the sum of the series related to the sequence in part (a) has no meaning.

18. **Research** Find a copy of this myth. How did Herakles finally defeat the Hydra?

BY THE WAY...

The "Prosperity Club" chain letter is believed to have begun in Denver in April, 1935. As a result of its popularity, the volume of first class mail rose so high and so suddenly in Denver, there was talk of a breakdown in the postal system.

19. In 1935 the famous "Prosperity Club" chain letter caused quite a stir throughout the United States. The letter contained a list of six names and addresses and asked you to send a dime to the person at the top of the list and remove his or her name. You were then to add your name to the bottom of the list and pass the letter on to five friends. These five friends made up the second level in the chain.

a. Write several terms of the sequence of the number of people at each level of the chain.

b. The letter claimed that if you did not break the chain, you would receive a certain amount of money. How much was this?

c. The population of the United States in 1935 was about 127,250,000. Assuming no duplications, how many levels would it take for the entire population of the United States to receive the chain letter?

d. **Writing** Use your answer from part (c) to give a reason why it is illegal to send chain letters that request money.

e. **Research** Explain how events in the United States during the 1930s might account for the popularity of this chain letter.

20. A poem that is over 200 years old reads:

> As I was going to St. Ives,
>
> I met a man with seven wives,
>
> Each wife had seven sacks,
>
> Each sack had seven cats,
>
> Each cat had seven kits:
>
> Kits, cats, sacks, and wives,
>
> How many were there going to St. Ives?

a. Write a series for the number of people and objects the author met.

b. Find the sum of your series.

c. **Open-ended** There are several possible answers to the question in the last line. Find an answer and justify it.

21. **Open-ended** Suppose that your birthday is April 30, and that a wealthy relative gives you this choice of gifts.

    A. $1,000,000 on your birthday

    B. $.01 on April 1, $.02 on April 2, $.04 on April 3, $.08 on April 4, and so on with the last payment on your birthday

    Which gift would you choose? Justify your answer.

Review **PREVIEW**

22. Find the sum of the series $(-1) + 6 + 13 + 20 + \cdots + 111$. *(Section 4-5)*

Find the exact measure of each unknown side in each triangle. *(Toolbox Skill 30)*

23.

24.

Decide whether each sequence appears to have a limit. Justify your answer.
(Section 4-1)

25. 5, 11, 17, 23, . . .

26. 7, −3.5, 1.75, −0.875, . . .

 Working on the Unit Project

27. Suppose you have only six years to save for a university education. Select one or more investment types. Use a spreadsheet to find the annual amount, within a dollar, that you will need to invest.

    Assume you continue to invest during the four years it takes to earn a degree. Be sure to show the layout of your spreadsheet and the formulas used to make the calculations.

Infinite Series

Focus

Find the sum of an infinite geometric series.

TAKE IT TO THE LIMIT

$$A_1 = \frac{1}{2}$$

$$A_2 = \frac{1}{2} + \frac{1}{4} = \frac{3}{4}$$

$$A_3 = \frac{1}{2} + \frac{1}{4} + ? = ?$$

EXPLORATION

Can you find the sum of an infinite series?

- **Materials: large squares of paper, scissors**
- **Work with another student.**

Let the area of a square be one square unit.

(1) Fold a square in half and tear or cut along the fold line. Set aside one half. What is the area A_1 of this piece?

(2) Fold the leftover piece in half and tear or cut it along the fold line. Place one half next to the piece from step 1. What is the combined area A_2 of the pieces?

(3) Keep repeating step 2 until the leftover piece is too small to tear or cut. Be sure to find the combined area of the pieces you set aside at each step.

(4) Write several terms of the sequence $A_1, A_2, A_3, A_4, \ldots$. What limit does this sequence appear to have?

(5) a. Suppose you can continue halving the paper forever. Write a series that represents the combined area of the pieces that are being put aside.

b. Is your series *finite* or *infinite*? Is it *arithmetic* or *geometric*? What is the common difference or ratio?

c. Look at the area you are forming with the pieces that are being put aside. What must the sum of your series be? Why?

(6) Compare your answers to steps 4 and 5(c). What do you notice?

BY THE WAY...

Sonya Kovalevsky (1850–1891) was a Russian mathematician who worked with infinite series. In 1874 she became the first woman since the Renaissance to receive a doctorate in mathematics.

The sum of the first n terms of an infinite series is called a **partial sum** of the series. In the Exploration, the combined areas $\frac{1}{2}, \left(\frac{1}{2} + \frac{1}{4}\right), \left(\frac{1}{2} + \frac{1}{4} + \frac{1}{8}\right), \cdots$ form a sequence of partial sums for the infinite series $\frac{1}{2} + \frac{1}{4} + \frac{1}{8} + \cdots$ that represents the sum of the areas of the pieces put aside.

SUM OF AN INFINITE SERIES

If the sequence of partial sums of an infinite series has a limit, then that limit is the sum of the series.

Sample 1

Tell whether each series appears to have a sum. If it does, give its value.

a. $3 + (-1.5) + 0.75 + (-0.375) + \cdots$

b. $0.5 + (-1) + 2 + (-4) + \cdots$

c. $2 + 5 + 8 + 11 + \cdots$

Sample Response

Write several terms. Find the first few partial sums to see whether there is a trend.

a. This is a geometric series. The common ratio is -0.5.

$3 + (-1.5) + 0.75 + (-0.375) + 0.1875 + (-0.09375) + \cdots$

$S_1 = 3$

$S_2 = 3 + (-1.5) = 1.5$ ←   Each partial sum after the first

$S_3 = 1.5 + 0.75 = 2.25$ ←   is the sum of the previous partial sum and the next term in the series.

$S_4 = 2.25 + (-0.375) = 1.875$

$S_5 = 1.875 + 0.1875 = 2.0625$

$S_6 = 2.0625 + (-0.09375) = 1.96875$

Graph the partial sums.

The limit of the sequence of partial sums appears to be 2. →

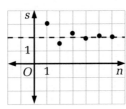

The sum of the series appears to be 2.

Unit 4 Sequences and Series

b. This is a geometric series. The common ratio is -2.

$0.5 + (-1) + 2 + (-4) + 8 + (-16) + \cdots$

$S_1 = 0.5$

$S_2 = 0.5 + (-1) = -0.5$

$S_3 = -0.5 + 2 = 1.5$

$S_4 = 1.5 + (-4) = -2.5$

$S_5 = -2.5 + 8 = 5.5$

$S_6 = 5.5 + (-16) = -10.5$

The series does not have a sum.

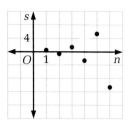

The partial sums do not get close to any number.

c. This is an arithmetic series. The common difference is 3.

$2 + 5 + 8 + 11 + 14 + 17 + \cdots$

$S_1 = 2$

$S_2 = 2 + 5 = 7$

$S_3 = 7 + 8 = 15$

$S_4 = 15 + 11 = 26$

$S_5 = 26 + 14 = 40$

$S_6 = 40 + 17 = 57$

The series does not have a sum.

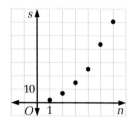

The partial sums increase and do not get close to any number.

Talk it Over

1. Does the method for finding the partial sums of the three series in Sample 1 involve recursion? Explain.

2. **a.** In part (c) of Sample 1, the arithmetic series with a positive common difference did not have a sum. Write any infinite arithmetic series with a negative common difference. Does it appear to have a sum?

   b. Do you think every infinite arithmetic series has a sum? Why or why not?

······▶ **Now you are ready for:**
Exs. 1–10 on pp. 255–256

Infinite Geometric Series

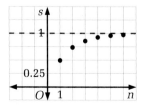

This graph shows that the series in the Exploration with $r = 0.5$ appears to have a sum.

The graph in part (a) of Sample 1 shows that a geometric series with $r = -0.5$ appears to have a sum.

In both of these cases, $|r| < 1$.

For any *infinite* geometric series with $|r| < 1$, the terms get closer and closer to zero. This suggests substituting zero for a_n in the formula for the sum of a finite geometric series.

$$S = \frac{a_1 - a_n r}{1 - r}$$

$$= \frac{a_1 - 0 \cdot r}{1 - r} \quad \longleftarrow \quad \text{Substitute 0 for } a_n.$$

$$= \frac{a_1}{1 - r}$$

SUM OF AN INFINITE GEOMETRIC SERIES

The general formula for the sum S of an infinite geometric series $a_1 + a_2 + \cdots$ with common ratio r where $|r| < 1$ is

$$S = \frac{a_1}{1 - r}.$$

Talk it Over

3. Find the sum of the series in part (a) of Sample 1 by using the formula. Did you get the same answer as before?

4. a. In part (b) of Sample 1, the infinite geometric series with $r < -1$ did not have a sum. Write any infinite geometric series with $r > 1$. Does your series appear to have a sum? Explain.

   b. Do you think every infinite geometric series with $|r| > 1$ has a sum?

Sample 2

Decide whether the series $4 + \frac{4}{5} + \frac{4}{25} + \frac{4}{125} + \cdots$ has a sum. If it does, give its value.

Sample Response

Step 1 The series is geometric with $r = \frac{1}{5}$. Since $\left|\frac{1}{5}\right| < 1$, the series has a sum.

Step 2 $S = \dfrac{a_1}{1 - r}$ $\quad \longleftarrow \quad$ Use the formula for the sum of an infinite geometric series.

$\quad = \dfrac{4}{1 - \frac{1}{5}}$ $\quad \longleftarrow \quad$ Substitute 4 for a_1 and $\frac{1}{5}$ for r.

$\quad = 5$ $\quad \longleftarrow \quad$ Simplify.

The sum of the series is 5.

To write an infinite series in sigma notation, use the symbol ∞ for "infinity." In sigma notation, the infinite series

$$\left(\frac{1}{2}\right)^1 + \left(\frac{1}{2}\right)^2 + \left(\frac{1}{2}\right)^3 + \left(\frac{1}{2}\right)^4 + \cdots$$

looks like this:

$$\sum_{n=1}^{\infty} \left(\frac{1}{2}\right)^n \quad \longleftarrow \quad \text{Read: "The sum of } \left(\frac{1}{2}\right)^n \text{ for integer values of } n \text{ from one to infinity."}$$

Sample 3

Evaluate $\displaystyle\sum_{n=1}^{\infty} (-0.25)^{n-1}$ if the sum exists.

Sample Response

Step 1 To see whether the sum exists, write the series in expanded form.

$$\sum_{n=1}^{\infty} (-0.25)^{n-1} = (-0.25)^0 + (-0.25)^1 + (-0.25)^2 + (-0.25)^3 + \cdots$$

The series is geometric with $r = -0.25$. Since $|-0.25| < 1$, the series has a sum.

Step 2 Find the sum.

$$S = \frac{a_1}{1-r} \quad \longleftarrow \quad \text{Use the formula for the sum of an infinite geometric series.}$$

$$= \frac{1}{1-(-0.25)} \quad \longleftarrow \quad \text{Substitute 1 for } a_1 \text{ and } -0.25 \text{ for } r.$$

$$= \frac{1}{1.25} = 0.8$$

$$\sum_{n=1}^{\infty} (-0.25)^{n-1} = 0.8.$$

Look Back

······▶ **Now you are ready for:**
Exs. 11–33 on pp. 257–258

How can you use partial sums to find the sum of an infinite series?

4-7 Exercises and Problems

For each series in Exercises 1–4:

a. Graph the first six partial sums.

b. Decide whether the series appears to have a sum. If it does, give its value.

1. $8 + 1 + (-6) + (-13) + \cdots$

2. $\dfrac{8}{5} + \dfrac{8}{25} + \dfrac{8}{125} + \dfrac{8}{625} + \cdots$

3. $5 + (-7.5) + 11.25 + (-16.875) + \cdots$

4. $(-6) + 3 + \left(-\dfrac{3}{2}\right) + \dfrac{3}{4} + \cdots$

Decide whether each series appears to have a sum. If it does, give its value.

5. $12 + (-6) + 3 + (-1.5) + \cdots$

6. $(-4) + 0 + 4 + 8 + \cdots$

7. $\dfrac{2}{3} + (-2) + 6 + (-18) + \cdots$

8. $9 + \dfrac{9}{4} + \dfrac{9}{16} + \dfrac{9}{64} + \cdots$

9. Suppose the branches in each stage of a fractal tree are half the length of the branches in the previous stage.

Stage 1   Stage 2   Stage 3   Stage 4

length = 1 unit

a. Write a sequence of partial sums for the total length of one path of the fractal tree.

b. Decide whether the sequence in part (a) appears to have a limit. If it does, give its value.

c. Write a sequence of partial sums for the total length of all the branches of a fractal tree, if the length of the first branch is 1.

d. Decide whether the sequence in part (c) appears to have a limit. If it does, give its value.

one path

e. **Writing** Explain how the length of a path of the tree can be finite, when the length of all branches of the tree is infinite.

10. Another example of a fractal is Sierpinski's triangle. Start with a triangle with area 1. In Stage 1, the triangle is divided into four congruent triangles by connecting the midpoints of the sides, and the center triangle is removed. In Stage 2, the three remaining triangles are divided as before and each center triangle is removed. At each successive stage, the remaining triangles are divided as before and each center triangle is removed.

Stage 1   Stage 2   Stage 3

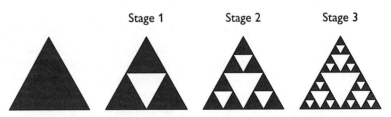

a. Write a sequence of partial sums for the area of the removed triangles.

b. What limit does the sequence appear to have, if any?

11. Reading Which geometric series have sums?

Tell whether each series has a sum. If it does, give its value.

12. $(-16) + 12 + (-9) + 6\frac{3}{4} + \cdots$

13. $13\frac{1}{2} + 9 + 6 + 4 + \cdots$

14. $0.5 + 3.5 + 6.5 + 9.5 + \cdots$

15. $(-1) + (-0.5) + (-0.25) + (-0.125) + \cdots$

16. $90 + 9 + 0.9 + 0.09 + \cdots$

17. $\sqrt{2} + 2 + 2\sqrt{2} + 4 + \cdots$

Evaluate each series, if the sum exists.

18. $\sum_{n=1}^{\infty} \left(\frac{1}{3}\right)^{n-1}$

19. $\sum_{t=0}^{\infty} 12\left(\frac{9}{11}\right)^{t}$

20. $\sum_{n=1}^{\infty} \left(\frac{1}{2} + 2n\right)$

21. $\sum_{n=1}^{\infty} 17\left(\frac{5}{4}\right)^{n-1}$

22. $\sum_{k=4}^{\infty} -(0.001)^{k}$

23. $\sum_{t=0}^{\infty} 10(0.2)^{t}$

24. The repeating decimal $0.3333\ldots$ can be expressed as the infinite geometric series: $0.333333\ldots = 0.3 + 0.03 + 0.003 + 0.0003 + \cdots$.

    a. Find the sum of the series. Give your answer as a fraction.

    b. What fraction is equal to $0.454545\ldots$?

    c. Show that $0.999999\ldots = 1$.

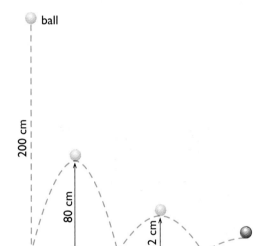
ball
200 cm
80 cm
32 cm

connection to **PHYSICS**

25. Use the diagram. Suppose a ball dropped from a height of 200 cm will bounce forever. Each bounce height is 0.4 of the height of the bounce before it.

    a. Write a series for the vertical distance the ball travels only when it is *falling*.

    b. Write a series for the vertical distance the ball travels only when it is *bouncing upward*.

    c. Find the total vertical distance the ball travels.

For Exercise 26, use these theorems and the diagram.

If a segment joins the midpoints of two sides of a triangle, then the segment is parallel to the third side and half as long. A median of an equilateral triangle is also an altitude.

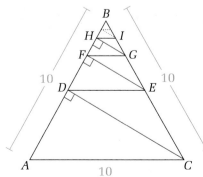

26. Point D is the midpoint of $\overline{AB}$, E is the midpoint of $\overline{BC}$, F is the midpoint of $\overline{DB}$, G is the midpoint of $\overline{BE}$, and so on.

    a. Find the sum of the lengths of the horizontal segments of the zigzag line from C to D to E to F to G to H, and so on.

    b. Find the sum of the lengths of the diagonal segments of the zigzag line.

    c. What is the length of the zigzag line?

    d. What is the length of the zigzag line for an equilateral triangle with sides of length 20 units? 30 units? n units?

27. Suppose the bob of a pendulum travels 90% as far on each swing as on the previous swing and will swing forever. When the bob travels 50 cm on the first swing, what is the total distance the bob will swing?

1st swing

50 cm

2nd swing

90% of 50 cm

Ongoing **ASSESSMENT**

28. Use this true statement: If an infinite sequence does not have a limit, then the related series does not have a sum.

  a. Does the infinite sequence $\frac{1}{2}, \frac{2}{3}, \frac{3}{4}, \frac{4}{5}, \cdots$ appear to have a limit? If so, what is the value?

  b. Does the series $\frac{1}{2} + \frac{2}{3} + \frac{3}{4} + \frac{4}{5} + \cdots$ appear to have a sum? Explain.

  c. **Writing** What is the inverse of the original statement? Is it also true? Explain.

Review **PREVIEW**

Find the sum of each series. *(Section 4-6)*

29. $500 + 50 + 5 + 0.5 + \cdots + 0.00005$ **30.** $0.2 + 0.4 + 0.8 + 1.6 + \cdots + 25.6$

31. A circle has radius 4 cm. Find the length of the longest chord of the circle. Explain your reasoning. *(Section 3-5)*

32. a. **Writing** Explain why this graph represents a function. *(Section 2-1)*

  b. Find the domain and range of the function.

Working on the Unit Project

33. a. **Research** Find these things: the current rate for student and personal loans, limitations on amounts borrowed, and the terms of the repayment agreements. Summarize your findings.

  b. Using the information from part (a), set up a spreadsheet showing how to finance the cost of a university education 25 years from now through both student and personal loans without any savings. Show a repayment plan spread out over ten years.

  c. **Writing** Discuss other options for making a four-year university education affordable in 25 years. Be as specific as you can about the amount of savings you are suggesting.

Completing the Unit Project

Now you are ready to complete your savings plan for the future.

Your completed plan should include these things:

➤ **printouts of your spreadsheet calculations**

➤ **data displays based your spreadsheets**

➤ **a written report summarizing your results and describing how you used sequences and series to develop them**

Look Back ◄

Did any of your results surprise you? Why or why not?

Alternative Projects

Project 1: Sequences and Series in Everyday Things

Look for sequences and series in the world around you. Include at least two examples each from architecture, science, music, art, and business. Include some progressions in time and some in space. Find some sequences and series that are visual and some that can only be heard. In each case, tell whether the progression is a *sequence* or a *series,* whether it is *arithmetic, geometric,* or *neither,* and whether it is *finite* or *infinite.* For infinite progressions, tell whether sequences appear to have limits and whether series have sums.

Project 2: Fractal Patterns

Research fractal shapes, such the simple fractal tree in Section 4-3, the Koch snowflake (see Exercise 18 of Section 4-3) and other Koch curves, the Sierpinski triangle (see Exercise 10 in Section 4-7), the Sierpinski carpet, and Peano curves. Describe how each fractal shape is generated and find as many related sequences and series as you can. Analyze the sequences and series you discover.

For each sequence in Questions 1–3: 4-1

a. Find the next three terms.

b. Find the 10th term.

c. **Writing** Describe the method you used to find the 10th term.

1. 1, 4, 13, 40, . . . **2.** 3, 8, 18, 38, . . . **3.** AA, AB, AC, AD, . . .

For each sequence in Questions 4–6:

a. Graph the sequence. Plot at least six points.

b. **Writing** Tell whether the sequence appears to have a limit. Justify your answer.

4. $\dfrac{1}{3}, \dfrac{3}{5}, \dfrac{5}{7}, \dfrac{7}{9}, \ldots$ **5.** 7, 14, 21, 28, . . .   **6.** $7, \left(-\dfrac{7}{2}\right), \dfrac{7}{4}, \left(-\dfrac{7}{8}\right), \ldots$

Write an explicit formula for each sequence. 4-2

7. $9, 3, 1, \dfrac{1}{3}, \ldots$ **8.** $\dfrac{1}{3}, \dfrac{1}{4}, \dfrac{1}{5}, \dfrac{1}{6}, \ldots$

Find the first four terms and the 17th term of each sequence.

9. $b_n = |n - 3|$ **10.** $d_n = \dfrac{18 - n}{n}$

11. Moira paid for a car stereo on an installment plan. She paid a $200 down payment, and then paid $30 per month for 12 months.

   a. Write an explicit formula for the sequence of the total amount she has paid at the end of n months.

   b. The stereo cost $500. How much extra did Moira pay in interest?

Write the first five terms. 4-3

12. $a_1 = 3$ **13.** $a_1 = 6$
   $a_n = -(a_{n-1} - 7)$ $a_n = (-0.6)a_{n-1}$

14. Write a recursive formula for the sequence 11, 24, 37, 50, ...

15. **Archery** An archery target has a center, or bull's-eye, with a radius of 4 cm, and nine rings that are each 4 cm wide.

   a. Find the sequence of the areas of the rings.

   b. Write a recursive formula and an explicit formula for this sequence.

   c. Find the area of the ninth ring.

For each sequence in Questions 16–18:

a. Tell whether the sequence is *arithmetic, geometric,* or *neither.*

b. Write a recursive formula.

16. $10, 21, 43, 87, \ldots$

17. $\dfrac{2}{3}, \dfrac{4}{9}, \dfrac{16}{81}, \dfrac{256}{6561}, \ldots$

18. $\dfrac{1}{8}, \dfrac{1}{2}, \dfrac{7}{8}, 1\dfrac{1}{4}, \ldots$

19. Find the sum of the series $8 + 11 + 14 + 17 + \cdots + 98$.

20. Evaluate $\displaystyle\sum_{n=1}^{7} 2n + 4$.

21. Write the series $95 + 90 + 85 + 80 + \cdots + 0$ in sigma notation.

22. Writing Draw a concept map that summarizes what you have learned in this unit. Your map should include the relationships among a series, its related sequence, the sequence of partial sums of the series, and the sum of the series.

23. Find the sum of the series $300 + 30 + 3 + 0.3 + \cdots + 0.00003$.

24. Evaluate $\displaystyle\sum_{k=0}^{8} 4\left(\dfrac{1}{4}\right)^{k}$.

For each series in Questions 25 and 26:

a. Graph the first six partial sums.

b. Tell whether each series appears to have a sum. If it does, give its value.

25. $500 + 100 + 20 + 4 + \cdots$

26. $0.003 + 0.03 + 0.3 + 3 + \cdots$

Evaluate each series, if the sum exists.

27. $\displaystyle\sum_{n=1}^{\infty} 11\left(\dfrac{3}{2}\right)^{n-1}$

28. $\displaystyle\sum_{t=0}^{\infty} -3\left(\dfrac{5}{8}\right)^{t}$

29. Open-ended Write two infinite geometric series, only one of which has a sum.

30. Self-evaluation Do you think it is easier to find an explicit formula or a recursive formula for a sequence? Do you find one type of formula more useful than the other? Explain.

31. Group Activity Work with another student.

   a. One of you should write four terms of an arithmetic sequence.

   b. The other should write an explicit formula for an arithmetic sequence.

   c. Trade papers. The student who wrote the terms should now write the first four terms of the sequence defined by the other student's formula. The student who wrote the formula should write a formula for the other student's sequence.

   d. Repeat parts (a)–(c) with a geometric sequence.

IDEAS AND (FORMULAS) $=\chi^2$

➤ Three dots ($\cdots$) show that some terms are not shown but the sequence or series continues in the same pattern. *(p. 208)*

➤ The general explicit formula for an arithmetic sequence where d is the common difference is

$$a_n = a_1 + (n - 1)d. \text{ (p. 230)}$$

➤ The general explicit formula for a geometric sequence with common ratio r is

$$a_n = a_1 r^{n-1}. \text{ (p. 230)}$$

➤ The formula for the sum S of a finite arithmetic series with n terms is

$$S = \frac{n(a_1 + a_n)}{2}. \text{ (p. 238)}$$

➤ The symbol Σ (sigma) can be used to express both finite and infinite series. *(pp. 238, 246, 255)*

➤ When you substitute the values of n into a series in sigma notation, you write the series in expanded form. *(p. 239)*

➤ The formula for the sum S of a finite geometric series with n terms and common ratio r is

$$S = \frac{a_1 - a_n r}{1 - r}. \text{ (p. 245)}$$

➤ When the sequence of partial sums of an infinite series has a limit, then that limit is the sum of the series. *(p. 252)*

➤ When $|r| < 1$, an infinite geometric series has a sum. *(p. 254)*

➤ The formula for the sum of an infinite geometric series with common ratio r where $|r| < 1$ is

$$S = \frac{a_1}{1 - r}. \text{ (p. 254)}$$

➤ The number identifying each term's position in a sequence is usually a counting number. *(p. 208)*

➤ You can graph a sequence on a coordinate plane by plotting points with the coordinates (*position, term*). The points on a graph of a sequence should not be connected. *(p. 209)*

➤ The graph of any sequence represents a function whose domain is the counting numbers only. *(p. 209)*

➤ The symbol a_n is used to represent the nth term of the sequence $a_1, a_2, a_3, \ldots$ *(p. 216)*

➤ Sometimes the first term of a sequence is called a_0, rather than a_1, to show the starting value before any change occurs. *(p. 218)*

➤ A graphics calculator or a spreadsheet can help you find the nth term of a sequence described by a recursive formula. *(pp. 224–225)*

➤ The recursive formula for an arithmetic sequence where d is the common difference is:

$$a_1 = \text{value of the first term}$$
$$a_n = a_{n-1} + d \ (p. \ 230)$$

➤ The graph of an arithmetic sequence is a discrete linear function. *(p. 230)*

➤ The recursive formula for a geometric sequence where r is the common ratio is:

$$a_1 = \text{value of the first term}$$
$$a_n = (a_{n-1})r \ (p. \ 231)$$

➤ The graph of a geometric sequence is a discrete curve. *(p. 231)*

LOGICAL
if - then REASONING

➤ There are two ways to describe the pattern of a sequence. You can look for a relationship between each term and its position number (that is, an explicit formula), or you can look for a relationship between each term and the term(s) before it (that is, a recursive formula). *(p. 208)*

➤ To determine whether a sequence appears to have a limit, look at the graph of the sequence or the decimal value of each term to see a trend. Verify your observation with a term farther out in the sequence. *(p. 210)*

If you wanted to write a song for the whole world to sing, what musical system would you use? In China most music is written in a five-note scale. Traditional European music is based on an eight-note octave. In India the raga is an important musical form. Ragas use scales with various sequences of five, six, or seven notes.

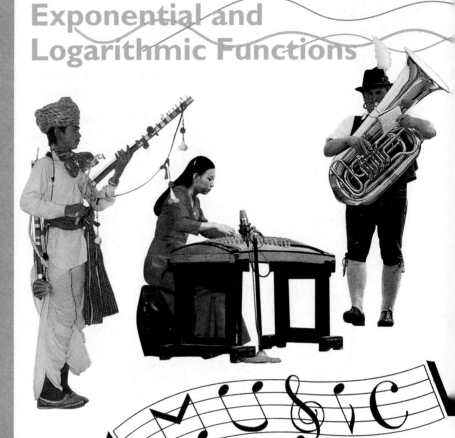

MUSIC

handcrafted

Different instruments sound different because of the blend of higher tones, or overtones, produced with each note. In 1965 the first **electronic** synthesizer to produce music with vibrating electric circuits was invented. Synthesizers can imitate all the instruments of the orchestra.

To uncover the secrets of the great **violin makers** of the past, scientist and violin maker Carleen M. Hutchins has handcrafted over 400 instruments in the last 40 years. When a violin is played, the vibrating strings cause both the wooden walls of the violin and the air inside to vibrate. By analyzing these vibrations, Carleen M. Hutchins has worked out basic rules for making violins.

digital

Unit Project 5

Making Music with Mathematics

Your project is to give a lecture/performance that demonstrates how mathematics and music are related. Following the guidelines in the Working on the Unit Project exercises, your group should make two sets of panpipes and two simple guitars. You should describe how you built your instruments, use them to play music, and explain how they produce musical notes.

Describe at least two examples of the relationship between mathematics and music.

This wooden harp is from Zaire. African harps like this traditionally played a vital role in the lives of millions of people. Many harp songs tell of historical events or legends.

On a **stringed instrument** like a violin or a guitar, one way to raise the pitch, or produce a higher note, is to shorten or tighten a string. Another way is to use a thinner string.

Shortening the column of air that vibrates when a musician blows into a **wind instrument** like a flute or panpipe raises the pitch.

265

Unit Project 5

For this project you should work in a group of four students. Here are some ideas to help you get started.

☞ Collect the materials and tools—plastic drinking straws, wood, strong nylon fishing line, several large screw eyes, a screwdriver, and pliers—that you will need to build your instruments.

☞ As a group, decide which instrument each member will make.

☞ Plan to meet to listen to recordings of many different kinds of music. Notice which instruments are used on the recordings and try to listen for them as the music plays.

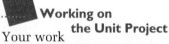

Working on the Unit Project

Your work in Unit 5 will help you to make your musical instruments and prepare your lecture/performance.

Related Exercises:

Section 5-1, Exercises 32, 33
Section 5-2, Exercise 22
Section 5-3, Exercises 48–52
Section 5-4, Exercise 34
Section 5-5, Exercise 34
Section 5-6, Exercises 46, 47
Section 5-7, Exercise 48
Section 5-8, Exercise 32

Alternative Projects p. 323

Can We Talk — MUSIC

➤ What kind of music do you like? What instruments do the members of your favorite band play?

➤ Have you ever attended a live performance by an orchestra or listened to a recording of an orchestra? If you did, were you able to hear the individual instruments when all the musicians were playing together?

➤ The ridges on the neck of a guitar are called *frets*. As they play, most guitarists will hold strings down by pressing at various frets. What effect do you think this has on the sound produced? Why?

➤ If you play an instrument, discuss what you like about it. Is it easy to learn? Does your music teacher ever talk about mathematics in relation to the music?

5-1

Exponential Growth and Decay

The Next Generation

The number of ancestors a person has in a past generation can be modeled by a *discrete* exponential growth function.

The population of the world over time can be modeled by a *continuous* exponential growth function.

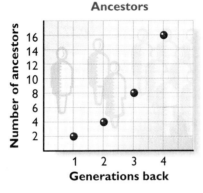

Ancestors

Number of ancestors / Generations back

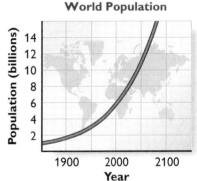

World Population

Population (billions) / Year

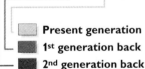

Present generation
1st generation back
2nd generation back

Mother Father   Mother Father

Mother   Father

Talk it Over

1. The function $y = 2^x$ can be used to model the number of ancestors a person has in a certain generation, where x represents the number of past generations.

   a. Find the number of ancestors a person has in the fifth generation back.

   b. What is the domain of the function? What is the range?

   c. Explain why it does not make sense to use a continuous graph to model this situation.

2. Use the continuous graph to estimate the world population in 1975.

Both discrete and continuous exponential growth can be modeled by an exponential function. The general form of an exponential function is $y = ab^x$.

growth factor

amount after x periods ⟶ $y = ab^x$ ⟵ time period

initial value

In 1980 Colorado's population was about 2.8 million. Since then, the population has increased by about 1.5% each year.

a. Write an exponential function to model the population growth of Colorado.

b. If the population continues to grow at this rate, when will the population of Colorado reach 4 million people?

Denver International Airport, on the world's largest airport site, was planned to accommodate predicted growth in the number of daily passengers.

Sample Response

a. **Step 1** Find the growth factor b.

$$\begin{array}{ccc} \text{population at end} \\ \text{of each year} \end{array} = \begin{array}{c} \text{100\% of population} \\ \text{at start of year} \end{array} + \begin{array}{c} \textbf{1.5\% of population} \\ \text{at start of year} \end{array}$$

$$= \text{101.5\% of population at start of year}$$

The growth factor b is 101.5%, or 1.015.

Step 2 Model the growth with an exponential function.

Let y = the population ⟶ $y = ab^x$ ⟵ Let x = the number of years after x years. since 1980.

$$= (2.8)(1.015)^x$$

Substitute **2.8** for the initial value a and **1.015** for the growth factor b.

b. **Method ① Use a graph.**

Graph the equation $y = (2.8)(1.015)^x$.

Since an x-value of zero represents 1980, an x-value of 24 represents the year 2004. The population of Colorado will be about 4 million in the year 2004.

Read the value of x when $y \approx 4$.

X = 24   Y = 4.0026079

Method ② Use recursion.

Enter the initial amount 2.8 and repeatedly multiply it by the growth factor 1.015.

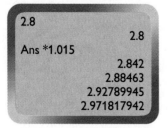

2.8
                2.8
Ans *1.015
                2.842
                2.88463
                2.92789945
                2.971817942

Count the number of times —24— that you press ENTER to reach 4 million.

3.715462087
3.771194018
3.827761929
3.885178358
3.943456033
4.002607873
4.062646992

24 years after 1980 represents the year 2004. The population of Colorado will be about 4 million in the year 2004.

3. What information does the model in Sample 1 assume? What may affect the accuracy of the model's estimate for Colorado's population?

4. Graph each function on the same calculator screen. How does changing the value of b in $y = ab^x$ affect the graph of an exponential function?

$$y = (6)(3.1)^x \qquad y = (6)(2.5)^x \qquad y = (6)(1.25)^x$$

······▶ **Now you are ready for:**
Exs. 1–16 on pp. 271–272

Toss	Number of objects remaining
0	50
1	?
2	?
3	?
⋮	?

E X P L O R A T I O N

Can an exponential model show a decreasing amount?

- **Materials: 50 objects with 2 differently marked sides (for example, pennies), a container large enough to hold your 50 objects, graphics calculators**

- **Work in a group of four students.**

(1) In this Exploration, you will remove objects that land "face up." Decide which side of your object will be the face.

(2) Shake the objects in a container and spill them onto a flat surface. Remove the ones that land face up. Record the number of objects that remain.

(3) Repeat Step 2 until there are no objects left.

(4) Consider each data value listed in the row of data labeled *Number of objects remaining* as a term a_n in a sequence.

For each data value less than 50, find the ratio $\dfrac{a_n}{a_{n-1}}$.

Then find the average of these ratios.

(5) What number represents the *initial value* in this situation? Use the initial value and the average ratio you found in Step 4 to write an exponential equation to model this situation. Graph your equation.

(6) Compare your equations and graphs with those of other groups. Describe any patterns you see.

(7) Besides representing the decay factor in the number of objects remaining after each toss, what do you think the value of b represents in this situation? Explain your reasoning.

EXPONENTIAL FUNCTIONS

Exponential Growth

$y = ab^x, b > 1$

Example: $y = (5)(1.2)^x$

Exponential Decay

$y = ab^x, 0 < b < 1$

Example: $y = (5)(0.5)^x$

Sample 2

The average amount of fuel used annually by each car in the United States has decreased by about 2% each year since 1980, when it was about 591 gallons.

a. Write an exponential function to model this situation.

b. Estimate the average number of gallons of gasoline used by a car in 1987.

Sample Response

a. $y = ab^x$ ⟵ Let x = the number of years since 1980.
Let y = the average number of gallons of gasoline used.

$= (591)b^x$ ⟵ Substitute 591 for the initial amount a.

$= (591)(0.98)^x$ ⟵ The expression $(1 - 0.02)$ represents a 2% decrease. Substitute 0.98 for b.

b. **Problem Solving Strategy:** Use a graph.

Graph the equation $y = (591)(0.98)^x$. The initial value occurs in 1980, so an x-value of zero represents 1980.

An x-value of 7 represents 1987. Read the value of y when $x = 7$.

In 1987, each car in the United States used an average of about 513 gallons of gasoline.

Look Back

Describe a function that models exponential decay. How is this function like an exponential growth function? How is it different?

┈┈► Now you are ready for:
Exs. 17–33 on pp. 272–274

1. **Reading** What does each part of the general form of an exponential function $y = ab^x$ represent?

Match each function with its graph. On each scale one unit is 5.

2. $y = 5(1.04)^x$

3. $y = 5(1.2)^x$

4. $y = 2(1.1)^x$

A.

X = 0   Y = 5

B.

X = 0   Y = 2

C.

X = 0   Y = 5

connection to **BUSINESS EDUCATION**

Madam C. J. Walker was one of the first business people to teach her employees effective sales techniques and provide information about the company's products. As a result, sales of Madam Walker's hair care products increased exponentially.

Use this information for Exercises 5–8.

Madam Walker's weekly sales revenues, in dollars, from 1906 to 1914 can be modeled by the function $R = (17.6)(1.88)^x$, where x represents the number of years since 1906.

For each year, estimate the weekly sales revenues.

5. 1906

6. 1909

7. 1912

8. In what year did the weekly revenues reach $2000?

9. Madam Walker opened Lelia College in 1908 to give her sales force formal training. About 100 people were sales agents in 1908. The number of sales agents increased exponentially by about 102% each year until about 1914.

   a. Find the growth factor b.

   b. Write an exponential equation to model the increase in the number of sales agents between 1908 and 1914.

   c. About how many sales agents were there in 1910? in 1912?

Madam C. J. Walker (right), the first American woman self-made millionaire, in the car she loved; (below) graduates of Lelia College

BY THE WAY...

At a 1912 convention of African-American business leaders, Sarah Walker described her success:

*I am a woman who came from the cotton fields of the South. I was promoted from there to the washtub. Then I was promoted to the cook kitchen, and from there **I promoted myself** into the business of manufacturing hair goods and preparations. I have built my own factory on my own ground. My object in life is not simply to make money for myself or to spend it on myself. I love to use a part of what I make in trying to help others.*

For each situation in Exercises 10 and 11:

a. Tell whether the situation is *discrete or continuous.*

b. Write an exponential function to model the situation.

c. Find the number asked for.

10. The amount of memory available on a computer circuit board doubles with each increase to the next larger size. The smallest size board holds 0.5 megabytes of memory. How many megabytes of memory are on the third smallest circuit board?

11. In 1964, a person invested $48,000. Suppose the investment grows at an average annual rate of 5% compounded yearly. When will the investment be worth one million dollars?

12. **a** TECHNOLOGY Graph each function on the same calculator screen.

$$y = 5(1.65)^x \qquad y = 9(1.65)^x \qquad y = 13(1.65)^x \qquad y = 15(1.65)^x$$

b. What is the *y*-intercept for each graph? How is the *y*-intercept represented in the equation?

c. Compare the graphs. How does changing the initial value of an exponential function affect its graph?

13. **Open-ended** Graph $y = (3)(1.5)^x$. Change one number in the equation to any number you wish. Graph the new equation. How are the graphs related? How are the functions alike? How are they different?

connection to **HISTORY**

During the Revolutionary War battle at Valley Forge, Pennsylvania, in 1777, George Washington's army received a loan of $450,000 from Jacob DeHaven. The Continental Congress agreed to pay back the loan at 6% interest, but DeHaven never received the money. In 1989, Jacob DeHaven's family filed a lawsuit to collect the money owed Jacob DeHaven, but no settlement was reached.

14. Suppose the interest was compounded yearly.

   a. How much was owed on the loan in 1783, when the Revolutionary War ended?

   b. When was five million dollars owed on the loan? 100 million dollars?

For Exercises 15 and 16, find how much was owed on the loan in 1989 using each type of interest calculation.

15. Suppose the 6% annual interest is compounded yearly.

16. Suppose the 6% annual interest is compounded daily.

17. **a** TECHNOLOGY Graph each function on the same calculator screen.

$$y = 5(0.9)^x \qquad\qquad y = 5(0.09)^x$$

   b. What effect does changing 5 to −5 have on each graph?

   c. What effect does adding 1 to each value of *b* have on each graph?

BY THE WAY...

Since the United States debt is already so large, the DeHaven family is willing to accept a "thank you" note and a statue built in Jacob DeHaven's honor.

Without the loan from Jacob DeHaven, Washington's troops may not have had enough food and supplies to survive the winter.

18. Suppose you repeat the Exploration using 30 dice and remove a die if a 6 lands face up.

    a. Write an equation to model the number of dice remaining after each toss.

    b. Write an equation to model the number of dice remaining after each toss if you remove a die if either a 1 or a 6 is face up.

    c. Graph each of the equations you wrote in parts (a) and (b) on the same axes. How are the graphs alike? How are they different?

19. a. **Writing** Compare the functions $y = (3)(1.25)^x$ and $y = (3)(0.75)^x$. How are the functions alike? How are they different?

    b. Graph each of the functions in part (a) on the same set of axes. Describe each graph. What point(s) do the graphs have in common?

Career After reaching a peak level, the concentration of a medication in a person's bloodstream decreases exponentially. Pharmacists can use an exponential model to determine the concentration level.

20. A medication for treating skin infections is available in three strengths. In each model, t represents the number of hours since the medication reached its peak concentration and y represents the concentration of the medication in the blood in micrograms per milliliter (μg/mL).

weakest strength	medium strength	greatest strength
$y = (0.8)(0.84)^t$	$y = (1.6)(0.84)^t$	$y = (3.2)(0.84)^t$

    a. Graph each equation on the same set of axes. What do the y-intercept values represent in this situation?

    b. How long does it take for each strength to reach a concentration of 0.1 μg/mL, the level at which the medication is considered cleared from a person's system?

21. The concentration of a stomach medication in a person's bloodstream in nanograms per milliliter (ng/mL) can be represented by the function $y = (492.5)(0.79)^t$, where t represents the number of hours since the medication reached its peak concentration.

    a. Graph the equation.

    b. Find the peak concentration.

    c. Find the time when half of the peak concentration remains. This is the medication's half-life.

    d. Use the information from the photo and your answer to part (c) to estimate when the stomach medication is cleared from a patient's blood stream.

Pharmacists multiply a medication's half-life by five to estimate when a medication is cleared from a patient's blood stream.

22. Repeat Exercise 21 for a hypertension medication whose concentration, in ng/mL, can be modeled by the equation $y = (115)(0.95)^t$.

23. Repeat Exercise 21 for an allergy medication whose concentration, in ng/mL, can be modeled by the equation $y = (263)(0.92)^t$.

24. **Open-ended** Describe a situation that can be modeled by each of the following: *discrete exponential growth, continuous exponential growth, discrete exponential decay, continuous exponential decay.* Sketch a graph for each example.

Evaluate each series, if the sum exists. *(Section 4-7)*

25. $\sum_{n=0}^{\infty} (1.03)^n$

26. $\sum_{t=1}^{\infty} \left(\frac{1}{2}\right)^t$

27. $\sum_{n=1}^{\infty} -5(0.003)^{n-1}$

28. Can the sum of the interior angle measures of a regular polygon be $655°$? Why or why not? *(Section 3-4)*

Simplify. Write answers with positive exponents. *(Toolbox Skill 14)*

29. $(3x^2)(5x^{-3})$

30. $5t(s^{-1}t^{-2})^{-2}$

31. $\dfrac{p^{-1}q^{-2}}{p^{-3}}$

Working on the Unit Project

The *pitch* of a note is how high or low the note sounds to a listener. Pitch depends on frequency. The frequencies of musical notes in a scale form a geometric sequence.

32. Suppose there were a musical instrument whose notes are related to one another by the function $f(n) = 20(2)^n$, where n is the number of the note in the sequence, and the frequency of the note is measured in hertz (Hz).

    a. Find $f(1)$, the frequency of the note with the lowest pitch.

    b. Find the frequency for the next seven notes in the instrument's sequence.

    c. Graph the function. How does the frequency of a note change as the pitch of a note gets higher?

    d. The human ear can hear sounds in the range 20–20,000 Hz. What problem can you foresee in terms of the instrument described above?

An electronic representation of a 440 Hz note produced by a vibrating violin string

This C note is one octave higher than middle C.

This note is middle C.

33. In the music of Europe and the United States, the frequency of a note is double the frequency of the same note one *octave* lower. One of the C notes on a piano has a frequency of 130.8 Hz. Find the frequency of the C note that is one octave higher.

Negative Exponents

NATIONAL PASTIME

Focus

Use exponential functions with negative *x*-values to model situations.

Talk it Over

The function $y = (283)(1.2)^x$ can be used to model the average salary for a professional baseball player in the United States, in thousands of dollars, since 1984.

1. What year is represented by an *x*-value of 0? of 3? of 8?

2. What *x*-value should you use to find the average salary in 1991?

3. Use the *x*-value you found in question 2 to estimate the average salary in 1991.

4. What *x*-value should you use to find the average salary in 1983?

Use the function $y = (283)(1.2)^x$ to estimate the average salary in each year.

5. 1979
6. 1973
7. 1967

Baseball Players' Salaries

Average salary (thousands of dollars)

Number of years since 1984

Mickey Cochrane, the best hitting, fastest running catcher up to that time, in action with the 1930 Philadelphia Athletics

Sometimes an exponential function models a change in a quantity over a certain period of time. To evaluate the function at an *earlier* time, you use negative *x*-values. In the model of baseball players' average salary, you use negative *x*-values to find the average salary in a year before 1984.

(How) does a negative exponent affect an
exponential function?

- **Materials: graphics calculators**
- **Work with another student.**

① Graph $f(x) = 3 \cdot 2^x$. Include both positive and negative
values for x. What are the domain and the range of $f(x)$?

② Write an equation for the image when $f(x) = 3 \cdot 2^x$ is
reflected over the y-axis.

③ Graph $g(x) = 3 \cdot 2^{-x}$ and $h(x) = (3)\left(\dfrac{1}{2}\right)^x$ on the same set of
axes. What do the graphs tell you about the relationship
between $g(x)$ and $h(x)$?

④ Show that $(2)\left(\dfrac{1}{4}\right)^x = (2)(4)^{-x}$.

Student Resources Toolbox
p. 637 *Algebraic Expressions*

Sample

In 1989 there were 24.1 students for each school computer
in the United States. By 1990 this number decreased to 20.7.

a. Write an exponential function to model the number of
students per computer over time.

b. Use the model you wrote in part (a) to estimate the
number of students for each computer in 1986.

Sample Response

a. **Step 1** Find the decay factor b.

$$\dfrac{\text{no. of students per computer in 1990}}{\text{no. of students per computer in 1989}} = \dfrac{20.7}{24.1} \approx 0.86 \quad \longleftarrow \quad \text{The value of } b \text{ must be less than 1 since the function is decreasing.}$$

Step 2 Model the situation with an exponential function.

$$y = ab^x \quad \longleftarrow \quad \text{Let } x = \text{the number of years since 1989.}$$

$$= (24.1)(0.86)^x \quad \longleftarrow \quad \text{Substitute } 24.1 \text{ for the initial value } a \text{ and } 0.86 \text{ for the decay factor } b.$$

b. Since the value $x = 0$ represents 1989, the value $x = -3$ represents 1986.

Method ❶ Use a graph.

Graph $y = (24.1)(0.86)^x$.

X = -3   Y = 37.889746

Read the value of y
when $x = -3$.

Method ❷ Use an equation.

$$y = (24.1)(0.86)^x$$

$$= (24.1)(0.86)^{-3} \quad \longleftarrow \quad \text{Substitute } -3 \text{ for } x.$$

$$\approx 37.9$$

There were about 38 students for each computer.

Look Back ←

Give an example of a situation that can be modeled by an equation of the form $y = ab^x$ where negative values of x have meaning. Describe a situation in which negative values of x would not have meaning.

5-2 Exercises and Problems

1. **Reading** What other value can you use for a in the equation $y = ab^x$ to model the situation in the Sample? What x-value represents 1986 in this model?

Rewrite each function in the form $y = ab^x$.

2. $y = (25)\left(\dfrac{5}{6}\right)^{-x}$

3. $y = (0.5)(8)^{-x}$

4. $y = (8)(0.125)^{-x}$

For each graph, answer parts (a)–(c).

5.

Percent of United States Population Completing Four or More Years of College

6.

Population of Alaskan Caribou

a. What year is represented by an x-value of 0? of -5? of 15?

b. What happens to the graph as the x-values become negative? positive?

c. **Writing** What happens to the y-values as the x-values increase? Do all y-values make sense in this situation? Why or why not?

7. **Cellular Phones** The first commercial cellular phone system in the United States began service in 1983. The function $y = (91.6)(1.77)^x$, where x represents the number of years since 1983, shows how many thousands of cellular phone subscribers there are in the United States.

a. Estimate the number of subscribers in 1984.

b. Without calculating, tell how many subscribers there were in 1982.

c. **Writing** The domain of the function is $x \geq 0$. Explain why it does not make sense to assign a negative value to x in this situation.

Although the population of the United States has increased, different areas have experienced various rates of growth at different times. These rates are often determined by economic events.

8. Use the equation $y = (46.6)(1.23)^x$ to model the population of the United States in millions, where x is the number of decades after 1890.

   a. Which year is represented by an x-value of 10? of 0? of -2?

   b. What was the approximate population of the United States in 1790? in 1840? in 1940?

9. The function $y = (2988)(1.132)^x$, where x represents the number of months since March of 1849, models the population of San Francisco between 1847 and 1849.

   a. Find the approximate population of San Francisco in January of 1848, when gold was discovered in the Sierra Nevada.

   b. Find the approximate population of San Francisco in January of 1849, after President James K. Polk addressed Congress and announced the discovery of gold.

10. In the 1960s and early 1970s, the silicon chip was developed in Santa Clara County, California. The function $y = (1.5)(1.026)^x$ can be used to model the population, in millions, of this region from 1960 to 1992, where x represents the number of years since 1990. Use this function to estimate the population of Santa Clara County during each year below.

   a. In 1969 a chip becomes the main component of a computer.

   b. In 1971 the world's first "computer on a chip" is developed.

   c. In 1974 the phrase "Silicon Valley" is used to describe this area where many electronics and computer corporations are located.

   d. **Research** Use the function to estimate the present population of Santa Clara County. Then look up the present population. Give a possible reason for any differences in the two numbers.

11. During the first half of the twentieth century, many people moved to Detroit to work on the assembly line at the Ford Motor Company. The company offered wages of $25 per week, about $12 more than the average salary of that time.

a. Use the populations of Detroit during 1920 and 1930 to write an exponential function that models the population of Detroit.

b. Estimate the population of Detroit in 1903, when the Ford Motor Company was founded. (*Hint:* Since 10 years is represented by 1 unit, 1 year is represented by 0.1 unit.)

Year	Population
1920	993,678
1930	1,568,662

c. Repeat part (b) for 1908, the year the Model T was invented.

12. Since 1970, manufacturing companies in Gary, Indiana, have become more modernized. Fewer workers are needed at these companies and people have left to take jobs in other cities.

a. **Writing** Describe a graph that could represent the change in Gary's population.

b. The population of Gary, Indiana, can be modeled by the function $y = (218{,}378)(0.82)^x$. Graph this function. How does the model compare with your graph from part (a)?

13. After the Industrial Revolution, people began moving out of rural areas and into cities. In 1890 only 64.9% of people in the United States lived in a rural area as opposed to 71.8% in 1880.

a. Write an exponential function to model the rural population as a percent of the total United States population.

b. Estimate the percent of people living in rural areas in 1870.

c. Estimate the percent of people living in rural areas in 1840. Tell whether you think this is a reasonable estimate and why.

14. Mark and Chandra's data from a chemistry lab shows that the amount of a material left after each experiment depends on the length of the experiment.

Length of experiment (min)	7	8	9	10	11
Amount of material left (mL)	187.5	75	30	12	4.8

a. Explain the method each person used to find an equation to model the data.

b. How long an experiment does an x-value of zero represent in each of the functions?

c. Use Chandra's function to estimate the amount of material that is left after each length of time.

3 min	5 min
12 min	15 min

d. Repeat part (c) using Mark's function. How do your answers compare with your answers from part (c)?

e. Use the rules of exponents to show that $g(x) = f(x + 3)$. What does this tell you about the relationship between the graphs of $g(x)$ and $f(x)$? Graph the functions to check your answer.

Ongoing ASSESSMENT

15. **Writing** Explain the relationship between the graphs of the functions $y = ab^x$ and $y = ab^{-x}$.

Student Resources Toolbox
p. 637 *Algebraic Expressions*

Review PREVIEW

16. In 1940 the population of the United States was about 132 million. Since then, it has increased at an average rate of 1.3% each year. Write an exponential function to model the population of the United States. (*Section 5-1*)

Simplify. (*Section 2-6*)

17. $\sqrt[3]{(-2)^3}$ **18.** $\sqrt[4]{(-1)^4}$ **19.** $\sqrt[3]{27d^9}$ **20.** $\sqrt[6]{64x^6}$

21. Use the geometric sequence 41, x, 369, ... (*Section 4-4*)

a. Find the value of x.

b. Find the common ratio.

c. Find the next three terms.

Working on the Unit Project

22. **Research** Find out how many of each instrument are included in a typical orchestra and where each is located in the orchestra. How do you think an instrument's position affects the performance?

5-3 Fractional Exponents

Focus

Use expressions involving fractional exponents or radicals. Model situations using exponential functions with fractional exponents.

$$\sqrt{\begin{array}{l} \text{Getting To The} \\ \text{Root Of It} \end{array}}$$

An average can of a soft drink may contain about 40 mg of caffeine. In an adult, the half-life of caffeine in the bloodstream is about 5 hours. This is how long it takes for half the amount of caffeine to be eliminated from the bloodstream.

about 50% carbonated water

about 50% corn syrup or sugar

other ingredients: caramel coloring, phosphoric acid, natural flavors, caffeine

Sample 1

a. Suppose an adult drinks a soft drink containing 40 mg of caffeine. The amount of caffeine in the bloodstream of an adult is a function of the number of 5-hour periods after the beverage is consumed. Write an equation to model this function.

b. How much caffeine is left in the bloodstream 1 hour after an adult drinks a soft drink with 40 mg of caffeine?

Sample Response

a. Find an equation to model the amount of caffeine in the bloodstream after x periods of 5 hours.

After one half-life (5 hours)

$$(40)\left(\frac{1}{2}\right) = 20 \text{ mg of caffeine remaining}$$

After two half-lives (2 · 5 hours)

$$(40)\left(\frac{1}{2}\right)\left(\frac{1}{2}\right) = 10 \text{ mg of caffeine remaining}$$

This pattern can be modeled by the function $f(x) = 40\left(\frac{1}{2}\right)^x$, where x represents the number of 5-hour periods after an adult consumes a soft drink.

b. One hour is $\frac{1}{5}$ of a 5-hour period.

$$f(x) = 40\left(\frac{1}{2}\right)^x$$

$$f(1) = (40)\left(\frac{1}{2}\right)^{1/5} \longleftarrow \text{Substitute } \frac{1}{5} \text{ for } x.$$

$$\approx 34.82$$

There are about 35 mg of caffeine left in the bloodstream.

TECHNOLOGY NOTE

Use parentheses to enter a fractional exponent on a calculator.

1. The half-life of caffeine in the bloodstream of a child is about 2 hours. Rewrite the function in Sample 1 to represent the amount of caffeine in the bloodstream of a child after *t* hours.

2. What does it mean to say that carbon 14 has a half-life of 5780 years?

EXPLORATION

(What) does a fractional exponent mean?

- **Work with another student.**

$y = 2^x$	
x	*y*
0	1
1	?
2	?
3	?

① Complete the first table. Notice that the *x*-values form an arithmetic sequence. What type of sequence do the *y*-values form?

② Choose a different arithmetic sequence of integers for the *x*-values. What type of sequence do the *y*-values form?

③ The *x*-values in the second table also form an arithmetic sequence. Assume that you can expect the *y*-values to form a geometric sequence. What number makes 1, __?__, 2 a geometric sequence? Copy and complete the table with exact *y*-values.

④ Use your results from step 3 to complete each equation.

$$2^{1/2} = \underline{\ ?\ } \qquad 2^{3/2} = \underline{\ ?\ }$$

Confirm these results by using a calculator to find decimal values for both sides of each equation.

⑤ What do you think is the value of $2^{1/3}$? of $2^{2/3}$?

(*Hint:* Complete the third table.)

Raising any nonnegative number a to the $\frac{1}{2}$ power is the same as finding its square root.

$$(a^{1/2})^2 = a^{(1/2)(2)} = a^1 = a \qquad\qquad (\sqrt{a})^2 = a$$

These are equal.

RULES FOR FRACTIONAL EXPONENTS

For integers m and n with $n > 0$, and any nonnegative real number a:

$a^{1/n} = \sqrt[n]{a}$ ◄——— Both expressions mean the nth root of a.

$a^{m/n} = (\sqrt[n]{a})^m = \sqrt[n]{a^m}$

Fractional exponents follow the same rules as integral exponents.

Examples

$4^{1/3} = \sqrt[3]{4}$

$5^{3/4} = (\sqrt[4]{5})^3 = \sqrt[4]{5^3}$

Student Resources Toolbox
p. 637 *Algebraic Expressions*

Sample 2

Simplify.

a. $9^{5/2}$

b. $4^{3/5}$

Sample Response

a. $9^{5/2} = (\sqrt{9})^5$ or $\sqrt{9^5}$ ◄——— Use the rule $a^{m/n} = (\sqrt[n]{a})^m = \sqrt[n]{a^m}$.

$\quad = 3^5$ ◄——— Use $(\sqrt{9})^5$, since $\sqrt{9} = 3$.

$\quad = 243$

b. $4^{3/5} = (\sqrt[5]{4})^3$ or $\sqrt[5]{4^3}$ ◄——— Use the rule $a^{m/n} = (\sqrt[n]{a})^m = \sqrt[n]{a^m}$.

$\quad = \sqrt[5]{64}$ ◄——— Use $\sqrt[5]{4^3}$, since $4^3 = 64$.

$\quad = \sqrt[5]{32 \cdot 2}$ ◄——— Factor 64 as $32 \cdot 2$, since $32 = 2^5$.

$\quad = \sqrt[5]{2^5 \cdot 2}$ ◄——— Write 32 as 2^5.

$\quad = \sqrt[5]{2^5} \cdot \sqrt[5]{2}$ ◄——— Use the rule $\sqrt[n]{a} \cdot \sqrt[n]{b} = \sqrt[n]{ab}$.

$\quad = 2\sqrt[5]{2}$ ◄——— $\sqrt[n]{b^n} = b$ when n is odd.

Talk it Over

······► **Now you are ready for:**
Exs. 1–22 on pp. 285–286

3. Write $\sqrt[5]{6^2}$ as a power with a fractional exponent.

4. Use the fact that $18 = 2 \cdot 3^2$ to simplify $18^{3/2}$.

You can use the rules of fractional exponents to simplify variable expressions.

Sample 3

Simplify.

a. $\sqrt[3]{x^7}$

b. $\sqrt[4]{81c^8d^6}$

Sample Response

a. $\sqrt[3]{x^7} = \sqrt[3]{x^6 \cdot x}$

$= \sqrt[3]{(x^2)^3} \cdot \sqrt[3]{x}$ ⟵ $x^6 = (x^2)^3$ and $\sqrt[n]{a} \cdot \sqrt[n]{b} = \sqrt[n]{ab}$

$= x^2 \sqrt[3]{x}$

b. $\sqrt[4]{81c^8d^6} = \sqrt[4]{81} \cdot \sqrt[4]{c^8} \cdot \sqrt[4]{d^6}$ ⟵ $\sqrt[n]{a} \cdot \sqrt[n]{b} = \sqrt[n]{ab}$

$= 3 \cdot c^2 \cdot \sqrt[4]{d^4 \cdot d^2}$ ⟵ $c^8 = (c^2)^4$

$= 3c^2 \cdot \sqrt[4]{d^4} \cdot \sqrt[4]{d^2}$ ⟵ $\sqrt[n]{a} \cdot \sqrt[n]{b} = \sqrt[n]{ab}$

$= 3c^2 |d| \sqrt[4]{d^2}$ ⟵ $\sqrt[n]{a^n} = |a|$ when n is even.

TECHNOLOGY NOTE

You can use fractional exponents to find nth roots on scientific calculators. However, you might get an error message if you use this method to find the nth root of a negative number. ⟵

You can solve equations like $x^3 = 1000$ by finding the cube root of both sides, which is the same as raising both sides to the reciprocal power $\frac{1}{3}$. This technique can be used with fractional exponents as well.

Sample 4

Find the value of b when $f(x) = 3b^x$ and $f\left(\dfrac{3}{2}\right) = 24$.

Sample Response

$f(x) = 3b^x$

$24 = 3b^{3/2}$ ⟵ Substitute **24** for $f(x)$ and $\dfrac{3}{2}$ for x.

$8 = b^{3/2}$ ⟵ Divide both sides by 3.

$8^{2/3} = (b^{3/2})^{2/3}$ ⟵ Raise each side to the reciprocal of the exponent 3/2.

$\left(\sqrt[3]{8}\right)^2 = b^1$

$4 = b$

······▶ **Now you are ready for:**
Exs. 23–52 on pp. 286–287

Look Back ⟵

Explain how fractional exponents and radicals are related.

5-3   Exercises and Problems

1. **Reading** State the rules for fractional exponents. Give your own examples.

Write each expression in radical form.

2. $33^{1/2}$

3. $13^{1/5}$

4. $5^{2/3}$

5. $15^{5/3}$

Write each expression as a power with a fractional exponent.

6. $\sqrt[3]{10}$

7. $\sqrt[4]{12}$

8. $\sqrt{7^3}$

9. $\sqrt[3]{21^4}$

10. In Sample 2, one method is shown in part (a) and another in part (b). Which method would you use to simplify $16^{4/3}$? Explain.

Simplify.

11. $8^{3/4}$

12. $81^{3/4}$

13. $3^{1/2} \cdot 3^{1/3}$

14. $100^{5/2} \cdot 10^{1/4}$

15. $\left(\dfrac{64}{25}\right)^{3/2}$

16. $\dfrac{7^{4/5}}{7^{2/5}}$

17. $20^{5/2}$

18. $250^{2/3}$

connection to **BIOLOGY**

Biologists sometimes grow bacteria in a liquid medium. A reasonable range for the mass of a bacteria culture in 1 L of a liquid is 0.1 g to 10 g. For Exercises 19 and 20, suppose a biologist plans to start with 0.1 g of a bacteria in 1 L of a liquid.

19. **a.** Write an exponential function to represent the mass of the bacteria after t hours when the growth rate of the bacteria is 35% per hour.

   b. What will be the mass of the bacteria after 20 min? after 75 min?

   c. What is the domain of the function you wrote in part (a)? Are the function values in part (b) reasonable?

   d. When will the mass of the population have doubled?

20. Suppose the doubling period of another type of bacteria is 2 h. Use an exponential function to find the mass of the bacteria after 5 h and after 10 h. Are these values reasonable? Why or why not?

BY THE WAY...

Biologists, like Lynn Margulis, often use a liquid medium instead of a solid medium to grow bacteria because the bacteria grow more quickly. Dr. Margulis's research has led her to the theory that parts of animal and plant cells originated as free-living bacteria.

21 TECHNOLOGY Use a calculator to find $\sqrt[3]{64}$ and $\sqrt[3]{-64}$. Tell which keys or menu items you used. If you get an error message, does it mean that there is no answer or that your calculator will not perform that operation?

22. Writing Explain in words or in symbols why $\left(\sqrt[n]{a}\right)^m$ is the same as $\sqrt[n]{a^m}$. Give specific examples.

Simplify.

23. $\sqrt{x^3}$ **24.** $\sqrt{x^9y^8}$ **25.** $\sqrt{49v^5}$ **26.** $\sqrt[3]{24c^3}$

27. $\sqrt{36z^{-4}}$ **28.** $\sqrt[4]{16p^6q^2}$ **29.** $\sqrt[3]{d^6} \cdot \sqrt[3]{d^{-6}}$ **30.** $\sqrt[3]{x^3} \cdot \sqrt[3]{x}$

Real Estate The exponential curves in the diagram below approximate the median sales prices of new one-family houses from 1970 to 1992.

Median Sales Prices of New One-Family Houses, 1970 to 1992

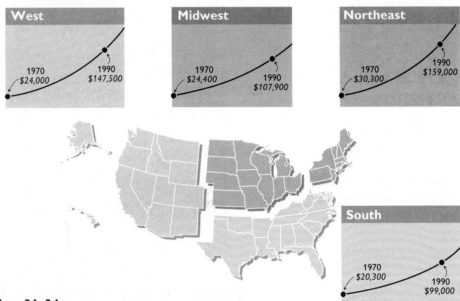

For Exercises 31–34:

a. Find the growth factor for the prices for each region.

b. Write the function represented by each exponential curve.
   (**Hint:** Use number of years since 1970 as the control variable.)

31. West   **32.** Midwest   **33.** Northeast   **34.** South

35. a. Which of the regions in Exercises 31–34 had the greatest median sales price in 1970? in 1990?

   b. Which had the greatest growth factor from 1970 to 1992?

36. a. Research Find the most recent figure available for the median sales price of new one-family houses in the West.

   b. Suppose housing prices continued to grow at the same rate after 1992. Use the function you wrote in Exercise 31 to estimate the median sales price in the year from part (a).

   c. Open-ended Compare the results of parts (a) and (b). Is the actual number close to your estimate? If not, suggest some ways that you could improve the model.

Solve each function for b.

37. $f(x) = \frac{1}{5}b^x$, $f\left(\frac{1}{3}\right) = 200$ **38.** $g(x) = 9b^x$, $g\left(\frac{2}{3}\right) = 27$ **39.** $h(x) = 64b^x$, $h\left(-\frac{3}{2}\right) = 125$

40. a. Writing Describe Kerri's method for simplifying $\sqrt[3]{x^7}$.

    b. Use Kerri's method to simplify $\sqrt{x^5}$.

Kerri Riley

$\sqrt[3]{x^7} = x^{7/3}$

$= x^{2 + 1/3}$

$= x^2 \cdot x^{1/3}$

$= x^2 \sqrt[3]{x}$

Ongoing **ASSESSMENT**

41. Writing Write an algorithm to find the growth factor of an exponential function given the initial value and one other value of the function.

Review **PREVIEW**

42. Show two different ways to write $\left(\frac{1}{b}\right)^x$. Use the rules of exponents to show that the expressions you wrote are equal. *(Section 5-2)*

43. Write an algorithm for multiplying two binomials. *(Section 1-1, Toolbox Skill 15)*

Tell whether each function is an example of *exponential growth* or *exponential decay*. *(Section 5-1)*

44. $y = (3.2)(3.5)^{-2x}$ **45.** $y = (0.5)(1.8)^x$ **46.** $y = (1.8)(0.5)^x$ **47.** $y = (1.8)(0.5)^{-x}$

Working on the Unit Project

An octave spans the notes from any note to a note with the same name that is eight full tones above or below the original note. The frequency of the last note in an octave is double that of the first note. The frequencies of the notes of the white and black keys of a piano form a geometric sequence.

octave

If you number the 88 keys of a piano from left to right beginning with 1, then the function

$$f(n) = (27.5)(2)^{(n-1)/12}$$

represents the frequency of the *n*th key.

For Exercises 48–50, find the frequency of each given note.

48. the 5th lowest note   **49.** the 20th lowest note   **50.** the 28th highest note

51. Graph the function for the frequency of the notes on a piano. What is the domain and range of this function? Explain your reasoning.

52. Use the rules for exponents to rewrite $f(n)$ in two different ways.

5-4

The Number e

In Your Be$t Intere$t

Focus
Model situations using
exponential functions with
base e.

EXPLORATION

Does compounding interest more often give
you unlimited returns?

- **Materials: graphics calculators**
- **Work with a partner.**

(1) In your group, decide which of the following investments
would give you more for your dollar.

**Invest \$1 at an annual
interest rate of 100%
for 1 year**

**Invest \$1 at a semiannual
interest rate of 50%
for 1 year**

$$1 + 100\% \text{ of } 1 = 1 + 1$$

$$(1 + 50\% \text{ of } 1) + 50\%(1 + 50\% \text{ of } 1) = \left(1 + \frac{1}{2}\right)^2$$

Frequency of compounding	Number of times interest is calculated in a year (n)	$\left(1 + \frac{1}{n}\right)^n$	Dollar value (A)
annual	$n = 1$	$\left(1 + \frac{1}{1}\right)^1$	2.00
semiannual	$n = 2$	$\left(1 + \frac{1}{2}\right)^2$	2.25
quarterly	$n = 4$	$\left(1 + \frac{1}{4}\right)^4$	2.44141
monthly	$n = ?$	?	?
weekly	$n = ?$	?	?
daily	$n = ?$	?	?
hourly	$n = ?$	?	?
every minute	$n = 525,600$	?	?
every second	$n = 31,536,000$	?	?

(2) Complete the table to see
whether compounding
interest more often can
give you a million dollars
for your dollar in one year.

(3) What happens to the
dollar value as you
compound the interest
more often? What do you
think is the maximum
amount you can earn in
one year?

Continued on next page.

④ Use your calculator to find the value of e^1. How does the value of e compare to the maximum dollar value in the table in step 1?

⑤ Graph the function $y = e^x$. What is the y-intercept of the graph? What type of function is $y = e^x$?

The number **e** is an irrational number that is approximately equal to 2.718281828. It is the limit of the sequence:

$$\left(1 + \frac{1}{1}\right)^1, \left(1 + \frac{1}{2}\right)^2, \left(1 + \frac{1}{3}\right)^3, \dots$$

Sample 1

In 1980 the average cost of a movie ticket was $2.62. The function $y = 2.62e^{0.058x}$, where x represents the number of years since 1980, can be used to model the average cost, in dollars, of a movie ticket. Find the average cost of a movie ticket for each year.

a. 1990   **b.** 1953

Sample Response

a. $y = 2.62e^{0.058x}$ ←—— Write the given equation.

$= 2.62e^{(0.058)(10)}$ ←—— Since 1990 is 10 years *after* 1980, substitute 10 for x.

≈ 4.68

The average cost of a movie ticket in 1990 was about $4.68.

b. $y = 2.62e^{0.058x}$

$= 2.62e^{(0.058)(-27)}$ ←—— Since 1953 is 27 years *before* 1980, substitute −27 for x.

≈ 0.55

The average cost of a movie ticket in 1953 was about $.55.

Admit 1 = ?

Admit

Talk it Over

1. Use the model from Sample 1 to estimate the cost of a ticket in the year 2025.

2. Use your knowledge of exponential functions and the value of e to describe the graph of $y = 2.62e^{0.058x}$. Graph the function to check your description.

·····► Now you are ready for:
Exs. 1–21 on pp. 291–293

Logistic Growth

The rate of growth of a quantity may slow down after initially increasing or decreasing exponentially. A function that behaves in this way is a **logistic growth function.**

increasing logistic growth function

decreasing logistic growth function

Sample 2

The spread of a flu virus in a school with about 1000 people can be modeled by the logistic growth function $y = \dfrac{1000}{1 + 990e^{-0.7x}}$ where y is the number of people infected after x days.

a. About how many people will be infected after nine days?

b. What are the horizontal asymptotes of the function?

c. Estimate the maximum number of people who will be infected.

Sample Response

a. **Problem Solving Strategy:** Use a graph.

Graph the function $y = \dfrac{1000}{1 + 990e^{-0.7x}}$.

About 355 people will be infected with the virus after nine days.

Read the value of y when $x = 9$.

$X = 9 \qquad Y = 354.86894$

b. Trace along the graph of the function.

The minimum y-value of the function gets closer and closer to zero but does not reach 0.

There is a horizontal asymptote at $y = 0$.

$X = 21 \qquad Y = 999.58137$

The maximum y-value of the function gets closer and closer to 1000 but does not reach 1000.

There is a horizontal asymptote at $y = 1000$.

c. About 1000 people will be infected with the virus.

····► **Now you are ready for:**
: **Exs. 22–34 on pp. 294–295**

Look Back ◄——————————

How is a logistic growth function like an exponential function? How is it different?

5-4 Exercises and Problems

1. **Reading** What kind of number is e? What is the approximate value of e?

Without using a calculator, choose the letter that represents the best estimate for each expression.

2. e^{-1} 3. $2e$ 4. $e - 1$ 5. e^2

A. 7
B. 1.7
C. 5.5
D. $\dfrac{1}{3}$

6. How is the number e like π? Which number is larger?

7. Find $f(3.6)$ when $f(x) = 5.3e^{-4x}$.

8. Find $f(14.5)$ when $f(x) = \dfrac{125{,}000}{(1 + 124e^{-1.5x})}$.

connection to SCIENCE

The percent of available surface light, L, that filters down through bodies of water can be modeled by the exponential function $L(x) = 100e^{kx}$, where k is a measure of the murkiness of the water, and x is the depth below the surface in meters.

clear water   murky water   muddy water

50% light   50% light   50% light

9. In clear water, the value of k in $L(x) = 100e^{kx}$ is about -0.2.

   a TECHNOLOGY Use a graphics calculator or graphing software. Graph an equation that models the percent of available light in clear water. What percent of available surface light does a diver have 4 m below the surface?

   b. How far below the surface can a diver swim in clear water before only 50% of the surface light is available?

10. Repeat Exercise 9 for murky water. Use the function $L(x) = 100e^{-0.3x}$.

11. Repeat Exercise 9 for muddy water. Use the function $L(x) = 100e^{-0.5x}$.

Banking The formula $A = P\left(1 + \dfrac{r}{n}\right)^{nt}$ can be used to find the dollar value of an investment when interest is compounded n times a year for t years at a rate of r percent on a beginning balance of P dollars.

Becky Quezada invests \$100 at 6% interest. Find the value of her investment after one year with each type of compound interest.

12. yearly   **13.** monthly   **14.** daily

15. Bob Drake sold an antique stuffed bear for \$2000. He decides to invest the money in a bank account until he retires in 25 years.

a. The formula $A = Pe^{rt}$ can be used to find the dollar value of an investment of P dollars when interest is compounded continuously for t years at a rate of r percent. Find the amount that he will earn in a bank that pays 5.25% interest compounded continuously.

b. Find the amount that he will earn in a bank that adds \$10 to the initial deposit as a bonus for new accounts, and pays 5.25% interest compounded quarterly.

c. Should he invest in the account with *continuous compounding* or the one with *quarterly compounding*? Why?

16. **a** TECHNOLOGY Graph the functions $y = 2^x$, $y = e^x$, and $y = 3^x$ on the same screen. How are the graphs alike? How are they different?

b. For which values of x is e^x greater than 2^x? For which values of x is e^x greater than 3^x?

17 TECHNOLOGY Repeat Exercise 16 using the functions $y = 2^{-x}$, $y = e^{-x}$, and $y = 3^{-x}$.

18. **a** TECHNOLOGY Graph the functions $y = e^x$ and $y = e^x + 4$ on the same screen. Describe how the functions are alike and how they are different.

b. **Open-ended** Think of a situation that can be modeled by each function in part (a). Explain how the situations are different.

c. Use your answer from part (a) to sketch the graph $y = e^x - 2$.

19. Between 1888 and 1988, the United States Post Office issued new stamps at an exponential rate. The number of new stamps issued, S, can be modeled by the function $S = 83e^{0.024t}$, where t is the number of years since 1888.

a. About how many new stamps were issued in 1900?

b. When will the number of new United States stamps issued reach 2000?

c. According to the model, what is the growth rate?

Architecture The Eiffel Tower was built between 1887 and 1889 for the 100th anniversary of the French Revolution. The tower starts with a wide base and narrows as it rises. This shape can be modeled by the equation $y = 327.4e^{-0.05x}$, where x represents the distance, in meters, from the center of the tower and y represents the height in meters.

20. a. **TECHNOLOGY** Graph $y = 327.4e^{-0.05x}$. Use $-188 \leq x \leq 188$ and $0 \leq y \leq 350$ for your viewing window.

    b. Write an equation for the reflection of the graph of $y = 327.4e^{-0.05x}$ over the y-axis. Graph this equation on the same calculator screen as your graph from part (a).

    c. Estimate the height of the Eiffel tower.

    d. The first platform of the tower is 57 meters from the ground. About how wide is this platform?

    e. The lantern of the tower has a platform that is 5 m in diameter. Estimate the height of the lantern.

x = the distance from the center to the edge

y = the height

21. The height, in feet, of the Gateway Arch in St. Louis, Missouri, can be modeled by the function $y = 757.7 - 63.85(e^{x/127.7} + e^{-x/127.7})$, where x represents the horizontal distance, in feet, from the center of the arch.

    a. Graph the function. Estimate the height of the vertex of the arch.

    b. About how far apart are the ends of the arch?

    c. **Research** The Gateway Arch forms a *catenary curve*. Find out how a catenary curve is different from a parabola. What other structures are built with catenary curves?

For Exercises 22 and 23, graph each function on a graphics calculator. Sketch the screen. Identify the horizontal asymptotes.

22. $f(x) = \dfrac{43}{(1 + 2e^{-x})}$ **23.** $f(x) = \dfrac{1}{(1 + 0.7e^{-2x})}$

24. Higher Education The number of medical degrees awarded to women each year between 1960 and 1990 can be modeled by the logistic function $f(x) = \dfrac{5300}{(1 + 100e^{-0.27x})}$, where x is the number of years since 1960.

  a. Graph the function. About how many women earned a medical degree in 1960? in 1976?

  b. Between what years did the number of women earning medical degrees appear to increase exponentially? What may have been a cause?

  c. In what year did the number of women earning medical degrees begin to level off?

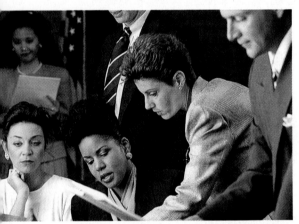

  d. The number of law degrees awarded to women each year between 1960 and 1990 can be modeled by the logistic function $f(x) = \dfrac{15{,}000}{(1 + 403e^{-0.33x})}$. Repeat parts (a)–(c) for the number of women obtaining law degrees.

  e. Graph each function on the same calculator screen. When was the number of women awarded medical degrees greater than the number awarded law degrees? When were these numbers equal?

  f. By 1990, about how many more law degrees than medical degrees were awarded to women?

Ongoing **ASSESSMENT**

25. **Writing** Explain why it does not make sense for banks to offer an account in which interest is compounded hourly.

Review **PREVIEW**

Simplify. *(Section 5-3)*

26. $125^{1/3}$ **27.** $1000^{4/3}$ **28.** $\sqrt{98x^3}$ **29.** $\sqrt[4]{256b^{12}c^{10}}$

30. Graph the feasible region for this system of inequalities. Label each vertex with its coordinates. *(Section 1-8)*

$$\begin{array}{l} x \geq 0 \\ y \geq x \\ y \leq 6 \end{array}$$

For each function, graph the function and its reflection over the line y = x. *(Toolbox Skill 38)*

31. $y = 3x + 2$ **32.** $y = x^2 + 4x - 5$ **33.** $y = 2^x$

Working on the Unit Project

34. To make a panpipe, you will need 8 plastic straws, scissors, masking tape, a centimeter ruler, a calculator, and an instrument to produce a middle C note, such as a piano.

    a. Blow across the opening of one of the straws and compare the note with middle C. Cut off short segments of the straw to raise the pitch until the note of the straw sounds like middle C. Measure the length of the straw to the nearest 0.1 cm. Record this length as l_1.

    b. Use your value for l_1 from part (a) and the equation $l_n = l_1 e^{-0.057(n - 1)}$, where n is the number of the note, to find the lengths of the straws, in centimeters, needed to produce the remaining notes for your panpipe.

    c. Use your measurements from part (b) to cut the straws for the remaining notes. Compare each note to the note produced by the musical instrument. Label each straw with the name of the note it plays.

    d. Place the straws on a flat surface in order from largest to smallest. Align the top edges. Put masking tape across the set. Pick up the set and wrap the rest of the tape around it.

Unit 5   CHECKPOINT

1. **Writing** How is an exponential growth function like an exponential decay function? How are they different?   5-1

2. The number of golfers in the United States has grown exponentially since 1970.   5-2

Year	Number of golfers
1980	15,112,000
1985	17,520,000

    a. Write a function to model the number of golfers in the United States.

    b. Estimate the number of golfers in the year 2025.

    c. Estimate the number of golfers in the year 1970.

Simplify.   5-3

3. $27^{2/3}$ 4. $81^{5/4}$ 5. $32^{3/5}$

Sona Doshi invested \$250 at 7% interest. Find the value of her investment after two years with each type of compounding.   5-4

6. yearly   7. monthly   8. daily

5-4 The Number e   **295**

5-5 Inverse Functions

Focus
Find and graph inverse functions.

Switching Lanes

10,000 m
5000 m
3000 m
3.75 laps
2.5 laps
1.25 laps

Bonnie Blair won the 500-meter and 1000-meter speed skating races at the 1994 Olympics in Lillehammer, Norway. Her two gold medals gave her a career total of five gold medals and one bronze—the most medals awarded to any United States Winter Olympian.

The official track for speed skating is 0.4 km long. The number of laps a skater needs to skate depends on the distance of the race.

Speed Skating Races	
Distance (km)	Number of laps
10	?
5	?
3	?
?	3.75
?	2.5
?	1.25

Talk it Over

1. Complete the table.

2. Write a rule for $L(D)$, the number of laps skated as a function of the distance of the race.

3. Write a rule for $D(L)$, the distance of a race as a function of the number of laps skated.

4. For each function in questions 2 and 3, state the domain and range. Consider only the six races given. What do you notice?

5. Graph each function from questions 2 and 3 on the same set of axes. What transformation describes the relationship between the two graphs?

Two functions f and g are **inverse functions** if $g(b) = a$ whenever $f(a) = b$.

The graph of the inverse is the reflection of the graph of the function over the line $y = x$.

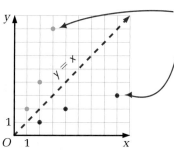

When (a, b) is on the graph of a function, (b, a) is on the graph of the inverse.

The inverse of a function $f(x)$ can be written $f^{-1}(x)$ or f^{-1}.

An inverse is a function. If the reflection of a function over the line $y = x$ is not a function, then the inverse does not exist.

Watch Out!

Although the exponent -1 usually means the reciprocal, $f^{-1}(x)$ is *not* equal to $\dfrac{1}{f(x)}$.

Sample 1

Graph each function and its reflection over the line $y = x$. Is the reflection the graph of a function?

a. $y = 2^x$

b. $y = x^2$

Sample Response

Step 1 Plot points to graph each function. Then interchange the coordinates of the ordered pairs and plot these points. Draw smooth curves through each set of points.

a. $(1, 2) \rightarrow (2, 1)$
$\left(-1, \dfrac{1}{2}\right) \rightarrow \left(\dfrac{1}{2}, -1\right)$

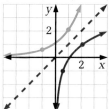

b. $(2, 4) \rightarrow (4, 2)$
$(-2, 4) \rightarrow (4, -2)$

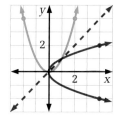

Step 2 Use the vertical line test to decide whether the reflection is the graph of a function.

The reflection of the graph of $y = 2^x$ represents a function.

The reflection of the graph of $y = x^2$ does *not* represent a function. The function $y = x^2$ does *not* have an inverse.

Just as you use the vertical line test to tell whether a graph is a function, you can use the horizontal line test to tell whether a function has an inverse.

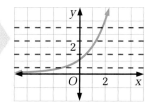

No two points lie on the same horizontal line. The function has an inverse.

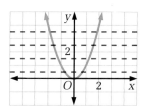

Two points lie on the same horizontal line. The function does not have an inverse.

5-5 Inverse Functions

Tell whether each graph represents a function. If so, does it have an inverse? Explain.

6.

7.

8.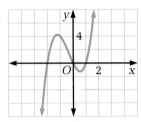

9. Suppose the function $y = x^2$ represents the area (y) of a square as a function of the length (x) of one side.

 a. What are the domain and the range of this area function?

 b. What part of the graph in Sample 1(b) is the graph of this area function?

 c. Does the function have an inverse? Explain.

Sample 2

Write an equation of the inverse function of $f(x) = \frac{2}{3}x - 4$.

Sample Response

$$f(x) = \frac{2}{3}x - 4 \quad \longleftarrow \text{Write the original equation.}$$

$$y = \frac{2}{3}x - 4 \quad \longleftarrow \text{Write } y \text{ for } f(x).$$

$$x = \frac{2}{3}y - 4 \quad \longleftarrow \text{Interchange the positions of } x \text{ and } y.$$

$$x + 4 = \frac{2}{3}y \quad \longleftarrow \text{Solve for } y.$$

$$\frac{3}{2}x + 6 = y \quad \longleftarrow y \text{ represents } f^{-1}(x).$$

$$f^{-1}(x) = \frac{3}{2}x + 6$$

Look Back

In Sample 2 the third step was to interchange the variables x and y. Explain why this method works.

Exercises and Problems

1. **Reading** How are the domain and the range of a function related to the domain and the range of its inverse?

2. Suppose $(-1, 3)$ is a solution of $f(x)$. Find a solution of $f^{-1}(x)$.

For each function, tell whether the inverse exists. If it does, graph the inverse. If it does not exist, give a domain so that the function has an inverse.

3.

4.

5.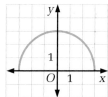

Graph each function and its reflection over the line y = x. Is the reflection the graph of a function?

6. $y = x^{1/3}$

7. $y = e^x$

8. $y = x^4 + \dfrac{1}{2}$

9. The traditional Japanese calendar is 660 years ahead of the calendar developed in Europe and used today in the United States. For example, when the European year was 1000, the Japanese year was 1660.

   a. Write an equation for the function that converts the European year to the Japanese year.

   b. Write an equation for the inverse function that converts the Japanese year to the European year.

   c. What is the slope of each equation?

   d. **Writing** Will the graphs of the equations in parts (a) and (b) intersect? Give both a mathematical reason and a practical reason for your answer.

Write an equation of the inverse of each function.

10. $y = \dfrac{1}{3}x - 5$

11. $y = -x + 6$

12. $y = x - 3\dfrac{1}{2}$

13. $y = x$

14. $y = -2x^2, x \geq 0$

15. $y = 2x^5 - 3$

16. $y = x^{2/5}$

17. $y = 2|x|, x \leq -1$

18. $y = mx + b$

19. $y = x + b$

20. $y = ax^b$

21. $y = x^{a/b}$

BY THE WAY...

According to legend, Jimmu Tenno became the first emperor of Japan in 660 B.C. The Japanese calendar is based on the start of Jimmu's reign—placing the Japanese year 660 years ahead of the European calendar.

22. **Travel** Leanne used this equation to exchange her United States dollars for Indian rupees: $r = 31.15d$, where r is the number of rupees with the same value as d dollars.

   a. Write an equation for the inverse of the function. Can you use the inverse function to exchange rupees for dollars? Explain.

   b. What are the domain and the range of the function? of the inverse function?

In Exercises 23–25, tell whether each function has an inverse.

23. $f(x)$ is not one-to-one.   **24.** $f(x)$ is linear with slope -1.   **25.** $f(x) = k$

26. **a** TECHNOLOGY Use a graphics calculator or graphing software. Find where the graphs of $f(x)$ and $f^{-1}(x)$ intersect.

➤ $f(x) = 4x - 12$ ➤ $f(x) = \dfrac{1}{x}$ ➤ $f(x) = x^3$

$f^{-1}(x) = 0.25x + 3$ $f^{-1}(x) = \dfrac{1}{x}$ $f^{-1}(x) = \sqrt[3]{x}$

  b. **Writing** Make a conjecture about where the graph of a function intersects the graph of its inverse. Why do you think this is true?

27 TECHNOLOGY Use a graphics calculator or graphing software.

  a. Set $x_1 = t$ and $y_1 = 2t - 7$. How should you set x_2 and y_2 in order to graph the reflection of the graph over the line $y = x$?

  b. Set $x_1 = t$ and $y_1 = 2e^t$ to graph $y = 2e^x$. Then use the method from part (a) to graph its reflection over the line $y = x$.

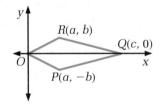

TECHNOLOGY NOTE

Work in parametric mode.
Use the range key to set the t, x, and y values between -10 and 10.

Ongoing ASSESSMENT

28. **Group Activity** Work in a group of four students. After completing each part, give your paper to the person on your right.

  a. Each student should write an equation for a function that has an inverse. Do not write an exponential function.

  b. Write the equation for the inverse of the function you receive.

  c. On the same set of axes, graph the original function and the inverse function you receive.

  d. Check the equation and the graphs you receive. Discuss any errors.

Review PREVIEW

29. The equation $y = 3.4e^{0.12x}$ can be used to model the number of ATM transactions, in billions, where x represents the number of years since 1985. Find the number of transactions in 1990. *(Section 5-4)*

30. Write a coordinate proof to show that $OPQR$ is a kite. *(Section 3-2 and Toolbox Skill 31)*

Write each number in scientific notation. *(Toolbox Skill 14)*

31. 0.00000291   **32.** 47,000,000   **33.** 482,900

Working on the Unit Project

34. **Research** Find a book of music for beginners that you can use to play songs on your instruments.

Logarithmic Functions

Section

Recording of a 5.1 quake

Focus
Focus
Recognize and evaluate logarithmic functions. Use logarithmic functions to solve problems.

Richter scale number	Relative size	
6	1,000,000	10^6
5	100,000	10^5
2	100	10^2
1	10	10^1

On January 19, 1994, an earthquake measuring 5.1 on the Richter scale struck California. A one-point increase in the Richter scale number indicates a ten-fold increase in the relative size of the earthquake.

Talk it Over

1. What relationship do you notice between a Richter number and the relative size of the earthquake?

2. What is the relative size of the California earthquake that measured 5.1 on the Richter scale?

3. Is an earthquake that measures 8 on the Richter scale four times the size of an earthquake that measures 2 on the scale? Explain.

4. Does the sequence of Richter scale numbers represent an *arithmetic sequence* or a *geometric sequence*? Does the sequence of relative size numbers represent an *arithmetic sequence* or a *geometric sequence*?

5. The relative size of an earthquake is a function of its Richter scale number x: $f(x) = 10^x$. Look at the graphs below. Does $f(x)$ have an inverse function? Why or why not?

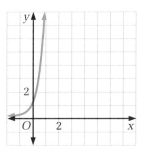

Epicenter of 1989 earthquake at Los Gatos, California

$y = 10^x$ Interchange x and y. $x = 10^y$

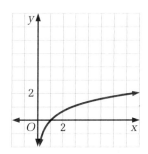

The exponential function $f(x) = 10^x$ has an inverse function called a **logarithmic function** that is written as $f^{-1}(x) = \log_{10} x$. A **logarithm** of any positive real number x is the exponent a when you write x as a power of a base b.

Read as "the base-b logarithm of x" or "log base b of x."

$$\log_b x = a \text{ when } x = b^a$$

The base of a logarithm can be any positive number except 1. A logarithm with base 10 is called a **common logarithm.** You write the common logarithm of x as log x. A logarithm with base e is called a **natural logarithm.** It is usually written as ln x.

Logarithmic and Exponential Form

An exponential function and a logarithmic function are related in the following way:

$$x = b^y \qquad y = \log_b x$$

TECHNOLOGY NOTE

You can use LOG or LN to find a common logarithm or a natural logarithm on your calculator.

Exponential Form: $x = b^y$	Logarithmic Form: $y = \log_b x$
$1000 = 10^3$	$3 = \log 1000$
$16 = 4^2$	$2 = \log_4 16$
$\dfrac{1}{2} = 2^{-1}$	$-1 = \log_2 \dfrac{1}{2}$
$5 \approx e^{1.6}$	$1.6 \approx \ln 5$

Talk it Over

6. The base of a logarithm can be any positive number except 1. Why do you think 1 cannot be a base of a logarithm?

7. Write each equation in exponential form.

    a. $\log_5 25 = 2$ b. $\log_4 4 = 1$ c. $\log (0.01) = -2$

8. Write each equation in logarithmic form.

    a. $10^5 = 100{,}000$ b. $4^{3/2} = 8$ c. $7^0 = 1$

$X \overset{\triangle}{\underset{\bullet}{\cdot}}ab$

LOGARITHMS

When x and b are positive numbers ($b \neq 1$):   Examples

    $\log_b x = a$ if and only if $x = b^a$ $\log_2 16 = \log_2 2^4 = 4$

    common logarithm: **$\log x = a$ when $10^a = x$** $\log 100{,}000 = \log_{10} 10^5 = 5$

    natural logarithm: **$\ln x = a$ when $e^a = x$** $\ln 8 \approx \log_e e^{2.08} \approx 2.08$

Sample 1

Evaluate each logarithm. Round decimal answers to the nearest hundredth.

a. $\log_4 64$ b. $\log \dfrac{1}{10,000}$ c. $\ln 5.3$ d. $\log 145$

Sample Response

a. $\log_4 64 = \log_4 4^3$ ⟵ Write 64 as a power of the base 4.

         $= 3$

b. $\log \dfrac{1}{10,000} = \log 10^{-4}$ ⟵ Rewrite $\dfrac{1}{10,000}$ as a power of the base 10.

         $= -4$

c. $\ln 5.3 \approx 1.67$ ⟵ Use a calculator to find the natural logarithm.

d. $\log 145 \approx 2.16$ ⟵ Use a calculator to find the common logarithm.

⋯▶ Now you are ready for:
Exs. 1–25 on p. 305

Sample 2

Solve $\log_x 81 = 2$.

Sample Response

$\log_x 81 = 2$

     $x^2 = 81$ ⟵ Rewrite as an exponential equation.

       $x = 9$ ⟵ Find the positive square root of both sides, since the base of a logarithm is positive.

Sample 3

Solve. Round decimal answers to the nearest hundredth.

a. $10^x = 15$ b. $e^x = 29$

Sample Response

a. $10^x = 15$

      $x = \log 15$ ⟵ Rewrite as a logarithmic equation.

        ≈ 1.18 ⟵ Use a calculator to find the common logarithm.

b. $e^x = 29$

      $x = \ln 29$ ⟵ Rewrite as a logarithmic equation.

        ≈ 3.37 ⟵ Use a calculator to find the natural logarithm.

pH Values of Some Common Substances

Substance	pH
lemon juice	2.1–2.3
tomato juice	4.1
milk	6.6
pure water	7.0
eggs	7.6–8.0
baking soda	8.5
ammonia	11.9

Applying Logarithms

Acidity is a measure of the concentration of hydrogen ions, $[H^+]$, measured in moles/L. Since $[H^+]$ is usually a very large or very small number, it is converted to a pH number between 0 and 14 that shows relative acidity. A solution that has a pH less than 7 is acidic and a solution that has a pH greater than 7 is basic. A solution with a pH of 7 is neutral. The conversion formula is $pH = -\log [H^+]$.

Talk it Over

9. Normal drinking water has a pH between 6.3 and 6.6. Is this water more acidic or less acidic than pure water?

10. Coffee has a pH of 5.0. When milk is added, does the pH level of the mixture become more acidic or less acidic than the coffee alone?

Sample 4

Piki bread is a Native American food that is made with blue corn flour and water. To release the B-vitamin niacin from the flour mixture, limewater or ash water needs to be added to the batter.

The batter changes color from a deep blue to a grayish blue when limewater or ash water is added. The Hopi and Zuni people use the color of the batter to determine when the bread will taste the best and be the most nutritious.

a. Suppose the color of the batter changes to a grayish blue when $[H^+] = 10^{-8}$. Find the pH level of the grayish blue batter.

b. Suppose the concentration of hydrogen ions in blue corn flour is about 1.6×10^{-7}. What is the pH level of blue corn flour? Is the flour *acidic* or *basic*?

Sample Response

a. **Problem Solving Strategy:** Use a formula.

$pH = -\log [H^+]$ ← Write the conversion formula.

$pH = -\log 10^{-8}$ ← Substitute for $[H^+]$.

$\quad = -(-8)$ Use a calculator to find the common logarithm.

$\quad = 8$

The grayish blue batter has a pH of 8.

b. **Problem Solving Strategy:** Use a formula.

→ $pH = -\log [H^+]$

→ $pH = -\log (1.6 \times 10^{-7})$

→ $\quad \approx -(-6.8)$

$\quad \approx 6.8$

The blue corn flour has a pH of about 6.8. The flour is acidic.

······▶ Now you are ready for:
Exs. 26–47 on pp. 305–308

Look Back ◀
How are common logarithms and natural logarithms alike? How are they different?

5-6 Exercises and Problems

1. **Reading** How is the inverse of an exponential function related to a logarithmic function?

2. a. **Geology** On July 11, 1993, an earthquake that registered 6.1 on the Richter scale struck the coast of northern Chile. This earthquake is how many times greater in size than an earthquake that registers 5.1 on the Richter scale?

   b. On January 15, 1993, an earthquake that registered 7.1 on the Richter scale struck the Hokkaido region in Japan. This earthquake is how many times greater in size than an earthquake that registers 5.1 on the Richter scale?

About 80% of all earthquakes occur along the borders of the Pacific Ocean. This zone is called the Ring of Fire because of its earthquakes (red areas) and volcanoes (black triangles).

Write each equation in logarithmic form.

3. $y = 7^x$

4. $a = \left(\dfrac{1}{2}\right)^b$

5. $e^1 = e$

6. $3^3 = 27$

7. $2^{-3} = \dfrac{1}{8}$

8. $10^2 = 100$

9. $8^0 = 1$

10. $\sqrt{36} = 6$

Write each equation in exponential form.

11. $\log_6 1 = 0$

12. $\log_4 64 = 3$

13. $\log 10{,}000 = 4$

14. $\log_3 \sqrt{81} = 2$

15. $\ln 2.718 \approx 1$

16. $\ln 8 \approx 2.08$

Evaluate each logarithm. Round decimal answers to the nearest hundredth.

17. $\log 100$

18. $\log_5 625$

19. $\log 10$

20. $\log \dfrac{1}{1000}$

21. $\ln 10$

22. $\ln 100$

23. $\ln 1$

24. $\log 625$

25. a. $\log_2 8 = 3$ and $\log_2 16 = 4$. Estimate the value of $\log_2 10$.

    b. **Writing** Explain your reasoning in part (a).

Solve. Round decimal answers to the nearest hundredth.

26. $\log_x 9 = 2$

27. $\log_x 8 = -3$

28. $e^x = \dfrac{1}{e^2}$

29. $10^x = 21$

30. $\log 1 = x$

31. $e^x = 10$

32. Acid rain is rain that has a pH below 5.6. Suppose the rain's concentration of hydrogen ions, $[H^+]$, is 10^{-4}. Is this acid rain? (Use the formula on page 304.)

Photographers Ansel Adams and Fred Archer developed the *Zone System*, a system photographers can use to adjust the exposure to lighten or darken selected portions of the images in a black-and-white photograph.

To make an image whose color matches Zone III look like it is in Zone V, the photographer adjusts the exposure time by two settings.

Zone	O	I	II	III	IV	V	VI	VII	VIII	IX
Gray scale										
Exposure time (seconds)	2	1	$\frac{1}{2}$	$\frac{1}{4}$	$\frac{1}{8}$	$\frac{1}{16}$	$\frac{1}{32}$	$\frac{1}{64}$	$\frac{1}{128}$	$\frac{1}{256}$

33. a. To produce an image in Zone VI, do you expose the film to light for a *longer* or a *shorter* time than you would to produce an image in Zone II?

b. What type of sequence is formed by the exposure times listed in the table? Write an equation to find the exposure time given the Zone number.

34. Film is made of tiny crystals of light-sensitive silver. When light reaches the film in a camera and the film is developed, the density of silver on the film changes—more silver is left where the scene was bright and less silver is left where it was dark.

a. Would an image exposed in Zone II leave *more* or *less* silver on the film than an image exposed in Zone VII?

b. The formula $d = \log \frac{1}{t}$ can be used to find the density of silver, d, on the film after an exposure time, t. Find the density of silver remaining on the film after each exposure time shown in the Zone System table. Round your answers to the nearest tenth. What type of sequence do these values form?

Moon and Half Dome, Yosemite National Park, California, 1960, by Ansel Adams. How many zones can you see in this photograph?

35. **Earthquakes** Many scientists prefer to use a scale that measures the total amount of energy released by an earthquake. A formula that relates the number on the Richter scale to the energy of an earthquake is

$$r = 0.67 \log E - 7.6,$$

where r is the number on the Richter scale and E is the energy in ergs.

a. What is the Richter number of an earthquake that releases 3.9×10^{15} ergs of energy?

b. What is the Richter number of an earthquake that releases 2.5×10^{20} ergs of energy?

Marine Biology Rain can deposit acidic pollutants in lakes, rivers, and streams. This causes the water chemistry to change.

36. Fresh-water clams require a pH level that is above 6.0. Can a lake where the concentration of hydrogen ions is 10^{-7} support clams? Why or why not?

37. When the pH level in a lake drops below 4.5, fish cannot survive. Can a lake where the concentration of hydrogen ions is 10^{-5} support fish? Why or why not?

38. a. **Writing** The pH value for a fresh-water aquarium with tropical fish should be between 6.0 and 6.8, and should never drop below 5.5. Would it be safe for the fish to be put in water where the concentration of hydrogen ions is 1.2×10^{-7}? Explain.

b. What is the greatest concentration of hydrogen ions that is safe for fish? Is this *acidic* or *basic*?

BY THE WAY...

Some fish are very sensitive to the pH of the water they live in. For instance, a Scleropages requires water with a pH between 5.5 and 6. A bumblebee goby can survive in water with a more varied pH, between 7 and 9.

Ongoing ASSESSMENT

39. **Group Activity** Work with another student.

a. Each student should write two equations in exponential form on a sheet of paper. On the back of your paper, write each equation in logarithmic form.

b. Trade papers with your partner and write each equation in the alternate form.

c. Return each paper to its owner. Check the equations and discuss any differences between the equations on the reverse side of the paper and the equations written by your partner.

Review PREVIEW

40. Find the equation of the inverse function of $y = 4x + 1$. *(Section 5-5)*

Simplify. Write each answer without negative exponents. *(Toolbox Skill 14)*

41. $(8x^3)(2xy)(y^{-2})$

42. $(15t^3)(3t^2)^{-1}$

43. $\left(\dfrac{6a^2}{4a^5b^6} \right)^2$

44. $\left(\dfrac{mn^{-5}}{n^{-7}} \right)^{-3}$

45. Describe the graph of $f(x) = -16x^2 + 20$. *(Section 2-4)*

Working on the Unit Project

To make a stringed instrument, you will need a piece of wood about 30 in. × 3 in. × $\frac{3}{4}$ in., nylon fishing line cut into four equal lengths (about 85 cm each), 8 large screw eyes, a screwdriver, pliers, and a marking pen.

46. a. Position the screw eyes so that all four strings will be the same length. Tighten the first string. Pluck the string and tighten it until the pitch of the string matches the pitch of the middle C on your group's panpipes.

b. Repeat the tightening and tuning procedure for the remaining three strings for the notes E, G, and upper C.

47. You can use the equation $l_n = l_1(0.9439)^{n-1}$ to find the distance, in centimeters, from one end of the strings to the position of the *frets* that will allow you to play other notes.

a. Substitute the length of your string for l_1. Substitute whole number values of n from 1 to 13 into the equation to find the position of the fret to produce the nth note. Record each distance.

b. Use the distances you recorded in part (a) to find the position of each fret. For each fret, measure the distance from one end of the strings to the position on the wood representing the shortened length. Mark this position with the marking pen.

Properties of Logarithms

SPLITTING LOGS

Focus

Learn about the properties of logarithms. Use these properties to solve problems.

A. $y = 4 \log x$

B. $y = (\log 4)(\log x)$

C. $y = \log 4 + \log x$

EXPLORATION

How can you rewrite the logarithm of a product, a quotient, or a power?

- **Materials: graphics calculators**
- **Work with another student.**

(1) **a.** Graph $y = \log 4x$. Choose the function at the left that appears to have the same graph.

b. Check your answer to part (a) by graphing the function you chose and $y = \log 4x$ on the same screen. Are the two graphs the same?

c. Complete this statement: When $x > 0$, $\log 4x = \underline{\ ?\ }$.

(2) For parts (a)–(c), graph the two functions on the same screen, and tell whether the graphs are the same. Be sure to enter $\log \frac{x}{2}$ as $\log \left(\frac{x}{2} \right)$.

a. $y = \log \frac{x}{2}$

$y = \dfrac{\log x}{\log 2}$

b. $y = \log \frac{x}{2}$

$y = \log x - \log 2$

c. $y = \log \frac{x}{2}$

$y = \frac{1}{2} \log x$

(3) Use your results from step 2 to complete this statement: When $x > 0$, $\log \frac{x}{2} = \underline{\ ?\ }$.

(4) For parts (a)–(c), graph the two functions on the same screen, and tell whether the graphs are the same.

a. $y = \log x^3$
$y = \log 3x$

b. $y = \log x^3$
$y = (\log x)^3$

c. $y = \log x^3$
$y = 3 \log x$

(5) Use your results from step 4 to complete this statement: When $x > 0$, $\log x^3 = \underline{\ ?\ }$.

PROPERTIES OF LOGARITHMS

M, N, and b are positive numbers with $b \neq 1$, and k is any real number.

Product of Logarithms Property $\log_b MN = \log_b M + \log_b N$

Quotient of Logarithms Property $\log_b \dfrac{M}{N} = \log_b M - \log_b N$

Power of Logarithms Property $\log_b M^k = k \log_b M$

Watch Out!
There are no properties that let you simplify
$\log_b (M + N)$ or $\log_b (M - N)$.

Sample 1

Write each expression in terms of log M and log N.

a. $\log M^2 N^3$

b. $\log \dfrac{\sqrt[3]{M}}{N^4}$

Sample Response

a. $\log M^2 N^3 = \log M^2 + \log N^3$ ⟵——— Use the product property.

         $= 2 \log M + 3 \log N$ ⟵——— Use the power property.

b. $\log \dfrac{\sqrt[3]{M}}{N^4} = \log \sqrt[3]{M} - \log N^4$ ⟵——— Use the quotient property.

         $= \log M^{1/3} - \log N^4$ ⟵——— Write the radical in exponential form.

         $= \dfrac{1}{3} \log M - 4 \log N$ ⟵——— Use the power property.

Sample 2

Write as a single logarithm:

ln 18 − 2 ln 3 + ln 4

Sample Response

$\ln 18 - 2 \ln 3 + \ln 4 = \ln 18 - \ln 3^2 + \ln 4$ ⟵——— Use the power property.

         $= \ln 18 - \ln 9 + \ln 4$

         $= \ln \dfrac{18}{9} + \ln 4$ ⟵——— Use the quotient property.

         $= \ln 2 + \ln 4$

         $= \ln (2 \cdot 4)$ ⟵——— Use the product property.

         $= \ln 8$

······▶ **Now you are ready for:**
: **Exs. 1–20 on p. 313**

The *loudness L* of a sound is related to the sound's *intensity I* by the equation

$$L = 10 \log \frac{I}{I_0}$$

where L is measured in decibels, I is measured in watts per square meter, and I_0 is the intensity of a barely audible sound. Suppose the intensity of the sound from a tuning fork is doubled. By how many decibels does the loudness increase?

An oscilloscope screen shows an electronic representation of the sound waves produced when the prongs of a tuning fork vibrate. The harder a tuning fork is struck, the more intense the sound will be. This is shown on an oscilloscope as an increase in the height of the graph.

Sample Response

Let L_1 = the original loudness, and let L_2 = the loudness after the intensity is doubled.

increase in loudness $= L_2 - L_1$

$$= 10 \log \frac{2I}{I_0} - 10 \log \frac{I}{I_0}$$

$$= 10 \log \left(2 \cdot \frac{I}{I_0} \right) - 10 \log \frac{I}{I_0} \qquad \longleftarrow \text{Rewrite } \frac{2I}{I_0}.$$

$$= 10 \left(\log 2 + \log \frac{I}{I_0} \right) - 10 \log \frac{I}{I_0} \qquad \longleftarrow \text{Use the product property.}$$

$$= 10 \log 2 + 10 \log \frac{I}{I_0} - 10 \log \frac{I}{I_0} \qquad \longleftarrow \text{Use the distributive property.}$$

$$= 10 \log 2 \qquad \longleftarrow \text{Simplify.}$$

$$\approx 3$$

The loudness increases by about 3 decibels.

BY THE WAY...

The decibel is named after Alexander Graham Bell, the inventor of the telephone.

Talk it Over

1. In general, does doubling the intensity of a sound cause the loudness to double? Explain.

2. Explain how to use the quotient property to solve the problem in Sample 3 by using this as the third step:

$$\text{increase in loudness} = 10 \left(\log \frac{2I}{I_0} - \log \frac{I}{I_0} \right)$$

Changing the Base of a Logarithm

Most calculators have keys for evaluating common and natural logarithms like log 7 and ln 7. You can use the following property to evaluate a logarithm whose base is not 10 or e. You will prove this property in Exercise 35.

CHANGE-OF-BASE PROPERTY OF LOGARITHMS

For all positive numbers with $b \neq 1$ and $c \neq 1$,

$$\log_b M = \frac{\log_c M}{\log_c b}.$$

Sample 4

Evaluate $\log_3 8$ to three decimal places.

Sample Response

$$\log_3 8 = \frac{\log 8}{\log 3} \quad \longleftarrow \quad \text{Use the change-of-base property to write } \log_3 8 \text{ in terms of common logarithms.}$$

$$\approx 1.893 \quad \longleftarrow \quad \text{Simplify.}$$

Sample 5

Use a graphics calculator to graph $y = \log_6 x$.

Sample Response

1 Use the change-of-base property to write $y = \log_6 x$ in terms of common logarithms:

$$y = \frac{\log x}{\log 6}$$

2
Graph $y = \frac{\log x}{\log 6}$.

X = 5.9893617   Y = .99900956

3 Check
You know that $\log_6 6 = 1$. Using TRACE confirms this.

3. How can you use the power key on a calculator to check the answer to Sample 4?

4. Use natural logarithms to evaluate the logarithm in Sample 4.

5. Use natural logarithms to graph the function in Sample 5.

Look Back

······▶ Now you are ready for: Exs. 21–48 on pp. 313–316

Look back at the properties of logarithms on pages 310 and 312. Explain why M and N must be positive numbers.

5-7 Exercises and Problems

1. **Reading** In part (b) of Sample 1, why was it necessary to write the radical in exponential form?

2. Complete each statement.

   a. The logarithm of the product of two numbers equals the __?__ of the logarithms of the numbers.

   b. The logarithm of the __?__ of two numbers equals the difference of the logarithms of the numbers.

Write each expression in terms of log M and log N.

3. $\log M^3$

4. $\log MN^2$

5. $\log \dfrac{M^7}{N^5}$

6. $\log \dfrac{1}{N^2}$

7. $\log \sqrt[5]{M^4}$

8. $\log M\sqrt{N}$

Write each expression as a single logarithm.

9. $\ln 2 - 3 \ln 7$

10. $\ln 16 + 2 \ln 5 - \ln 4$

11. $\log_4 7 + \log_4 5$

12. $7 \log x + \dfrac{1}{4} \log x^8$

13. $3 \ln 2 + \dfrac{1}{2} \ln 49 - \ln 14$

14. $4 \log_6 t - 8 \log_6 u + 5 \log_6 v$

Evaluate.

15. $\log 5 + \log 2$

16. $2 \log_6 12 - \log_6 4$

17. $\log_5 6 - \log_5 150$

Let x = log₃ 2 and y = log₃ 10. Write each expression in terms of x and y.

18. $\log_3 20$

19. $\log_3 \dfrac{1}{8}$

20. $\log_3 250$

21. **Acoustics** Use the information in Sample 3 on page 311.

   a. Suppose the intensity of the sound from the tuning fork is tripled. By how many decibels does the loudness increase?

   b. Suppose the intensity of the sound from the tuning fork is increased by a factor of n. By how many decibels does the loudness increase? (Your answer will involve n.)

22. Aviation A *pressure altimeter* is an instrument that finds the height of an airplane above sea level based on the pressure of the surrounding air. The height h and pressure p are related by the equation

$$h = -26{,}400 \ln\left(\frac{p}{2120}\right)$$

where h is measured in feet and p is measured in pounds per square foot.

a TECHNOLOGY Graph the equation above on a graphics calculator. Does an increase in air pressure indicate an increase or decrease in altitude?

b. Suppose that an airplane's altimeter measures a 20% drop in air pressure. How has the altitude of the airplane changed?

c. Writing Look at the photograph of the airplane. Why would the reading on a pressure altimeter *not* equal the airplane's height above the ground?

Evaluate to three decimal places.

23. $\log_2 11$

24. $\log_5 8$

25. $\log_7 6$

26. $\log_6 7$

27. $\log_9 \frac{4}{5}$

28. $\log_{1/4} 0.92$

TECHNOLOGY **Graph each function on a graphics calculator.**

29. $y = \log_2 x$

30. $y = \log_5 x$

31. $y = \log_{1/3} x$

32. Show that $\log_b MN = \log_b M + \log_b N$. (*Hint:* Let $\log_b M = x$ and $\log_b N = y$. Then $M = b^x$ and $N = b^y$.)

33. Show that $\log_b M^k = k \log_b M$. (*Hint:* Let $\log_b M = x$. Then $M = b^x$.)

34. Use the product and power properties to show that $\log_b \frac{M}{N} = \log_b M - \log_b N$. (*Hint:* Write $\frac{M}{N}$ as MN^{-1}.)

35. Show that $\log_b M = \frac{\log_c M}{\log_c b}$. (*Hint:* Let $\log_b M = x$. Then $M = b^x$.)

Cuckoo
0.23 lb
1.90 ft

The pictures show some typical weights and wingspans for different types of birds. Let x = the weight and y = the wingspan.

36. a. Make a scatter plot of the data pairs (x, y). Draw a smooth curve that passes as close as possible to each plotted point.

   b. **Writing** Use the data or the graph to answer these questions: Does wingspan appear to be a linear function of weight? an exponential function of weight? Give a reason for your answer.

37. a. Copy and complete the table below. Give each logarithm to two decimal places.

   b. Make a scatter plot of the data pairs (u, v). What do you notice about the plotted points?

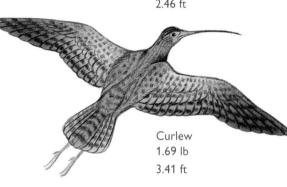

Sparrow hawk
0.49 lb
2.46 ft

   c. Draw a fitted line for your scatter plot. Write an equation of your fitted line in terms of u and v.

   d. Write the equation you wrote in part (c) in terms of x and y. (*Hint*: Replace u with $\ln x$ and v with $\ln y$.)

   e. Show that your equation from part (d) can be written in the form $y = ax^b$, where a and b are constants. A function of this form is called a *power function*.

Curlew
1.69 lb
3.41 ft

   f. Use the power function you wrote in part (e) to estimate the wingspan of a golden eagle weighing 8.2 lb.

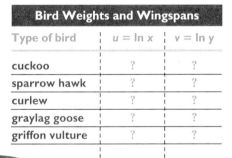

Bird Weights and Wingspans		
Type of bird	$u = \ln x$	$v = \ln y$
cuckoo	?	?
sparrow hawk	?	?
curlew	?	?
graylag goose	?	?
griffon vulture	?	?

Graylag goose
6.76 lb
5.35 ft

Griffon vulture
16.03 lb
8.40 ft

38. **Writing** Suppose $f(x) = \log \sqrt{x}$ and $g(x) = \frac{1}{2} \log x$. Explain how to convince someone that $f(x) = g(x)$ for $x > 0$ using the properties of logarithms and using graphs.

Review **PREVIEW**

Write each equation in exponential form. *(Section 5-6)*

39. $\log_3 81 = 4$ **40.** $\ln 5 \approx 1.61$ **41.** $\log_2 64 = 6$

Evaluate each series. *(Sections 4-5, 4-7)*

42. $\displaystyle\sum_{k=1}^{10} (3k - 2)$ **43.** $\displaystyle\sum_{n=0}^{\infty} 4\left(\frac{5}{7}\right)^n$ **44.** $\displaystyle\sum_{m=1}^{5} \frac{1}{4}(2^{m-1})$

Solve. *(Section 2-6)*

45. $\sqrt{x} = 3x$ **46.** $z = \sqrt{z + 8} - 2$ **47.** $x = x\sqrt{x - 2}$

Working on the Unit Project

When a musician plays an instrument in a concert hall, the sound *reverberates*, or echoes, off the walls of the hall even after the musician has stopped playing. The time it takes for the sound to fade away is called the *reverberation time*.

48. At the Royal Albert Hall in London, England, the approximate reverberation time T (in seconds) is given by the function

$$T = 5.24 - 0.408 \ln f$$

where f is the frequency of the sound in hertz (Hz).

 a. Suppose a violinist plays a middle C in the Royal Albert Hall. Estimate the reverberation time. Use 261.6 Hz as the frequency of middle C.

 b. Suppose the violinist in part (a) plays two notes. The frequency of the second note is half the frequency of the first note. Which note has the longer reverberation time? By how many seconds do the reverberation times differ?

5-8 Solving Exponential and Logarithmic Equations

Focus
Use exponential and logarithmic equations to solve real-life problems.

OUTDATED MATERIAL

Some of the carbon in the air we breathe and in the food we eat is a harmless radioactive form called *carbon 14.* Over time, carbon 14 breaks down due to *radioactive decay.*

When a plant or animal dies, the amount of carbon 14 in the cells begins to decrease exponentially.

amount of carbon 14 present t thousand years after death

amount of time since death (in thousands of years)

$$A(t) = A_0(0.883)^t$$

amount of carbon 14 present at time of death

In 1968 a bison bone was found in Calgary, Canada. Scientists measured its carbon 14 content using the equation above. They estimated that the bison died 8000 years ago. This process is called *carbon-14 dating.*

The bison bone found in 1968 contained about 37% of the carbon 14 present when the bison died. Estimate the age of the bone.

Sample Response

Problem Solving Strategy: Use a formula.

$$A_0(0.883)^t = A(t)$$

$$A_0(0.883)^t \approx 0.37A_0 \quad \longleftarrow \text{Substitute } 0.37A_0 \text{ for } A(t).$$

$$(0.883)^t \approx 0.37 \quad \longleftarrow \text{Divide both sides by } A_0.$$

$$\log (0.883)^t \approx \log 0.37 \quad \longleftarrow \text{Take the common logarithm of both sides.}$$

$$t \log 0.883 \approx \log 0.37 \quad \longleftarrow \text{Use the power property of logarithms.}$$

$$t \approx \frac{\log 0.37}{\log 0.883} \quad \longleftarrow \text{Divide both sides by } \log 0.883.$$

$$t \approx 8$$

The bone is about 8000 years old.

Chemical analysis proved this ax to be copper, making the Iceman (see below) the only mummy found from the Copper Age.

Talk it Over

1. Describe the method used in Sample 1 to solve the exponential equation $(0.883)^t = 0.37$.

2. To solve the equation $(0.883)^t = 0.37$, can you take the natural logarithm of both sides instead of the common logarithm? Explain.

3. Explain how to solve $5^x = 27$ using the method shown in Sample 1.

4. How can you solve the problem in Sample 1 with a graph?

BY THE WAY...

On September 19, 1991, the mummified body of a man buried in a glacier was discovered in the Tyrolean Alps. Scientists used carbon-14 dating to determine that he lived around 3000 B.C. Known as the Iceman, he was five feet two inches tall, had wavy, medium length hair and a beard, and was between 25 and 40 years old.

Unit 5 Exponential and Logarithmic Functions

In Sample 1, the power property of logarithms was used to solve an exponential equation. You can also use properties of logarithms to solve logarithmic equations.

Sample 2

Solve $\log_2 x + \log_2 (x - 2) = 3$.

Sample Response

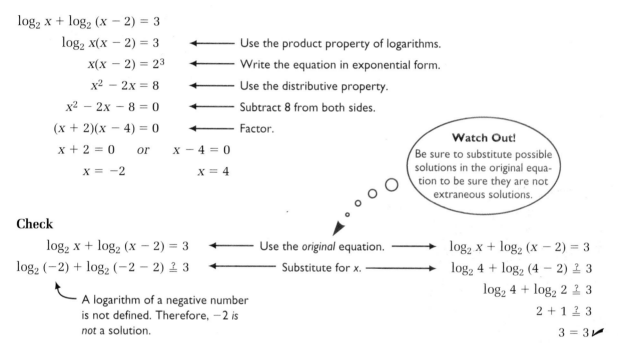

$$\log_2 x + \log_2 (x - 2) = 3$$
$$\log_2 x(x - 2) = 3 \qquad \longleftarrow \text{Use the product property of logarithms.}$$
$$x(x - 2) = 2^3 \qquad \longleftarrow \text{Write the equation in exponential form.}$$
$$x^2 - 2x = 8 \qquad \longleftarrow \text{Use the distributive property.}$$
$$x^2 - 2x - 8 = 0 \qquad \longleftarrow \text{Subtract 8 from both sides.}$$
$$(x + 2)(x - 4) = 0 \qquad \longleftarrow \text{Factor.}$$
$$x + 2 = 0 \quad \textit{or} \quad x - 4 = 0$$
$$x = -2 \qquad\qquad x = 4$$

Watch Out!
Be sure to substitute possible solutions in the original equation to be sure they are not extraneous solutions.

Check

$$\log_2 x + \log_2 (x - 2) = 3 \qquad \longleftarrow \text{Use the } \textit{original} \text{ equation.} \longrightarrow \qquad \log_2 x + \log_2 (x - 2) = 3$$
$$\log_2 (-2) + \log_2 (-2 - 2) \overset{?}{=} 3 \qquad \longleftarrow \text{Substitute for } x. \longrightarrow \qquad \log_2 4 + \log_2 (4 - 2) \overset{?}{=} 3$$
$$\log_2 4 + \log_2 2 \overset{?}{=} 3$$
$$2 + 1 \overset{?}{=} 3$$
$$3 = 3 \; \checkmark$$

A logarithm of a negative number is not defined. Therefore, -2 *is not* a solution.

The solution is 4.

Talk it Over

5. Solve the equation in Sample 2 by using a graphics calculator to graph $y = \log_2 x + \log_2 (x - 2)$ and $y = 3$ on the same screen. (*Hint:* Use the change-of-base property to write the first function in terms of common logarithms.)

6. Explain how to solve this system of equations by using a graphics calculator.
$$y = 4(1.14)^x$$
$$y = 2(1.65)^x$$

Look Back

Explain how you can use the properties of logarithms to solve exponential and logarithmic equations.

Exercises and Problems

1. **Reading** Why is it not possible for -2 to be a solution of the logarithmic equation in Sample 2?

Solve.

2. $2^x = 3$

3. $12^y = 4$

4. $100(1.05)^t = 350$

5. $8(0.32)^t = 1$

6. $5^{3n} = 9$

7. $e^{-2x} = 6$

Archaeology For Exercises 8–10, use the function $A(t) = A_0(0.883)^t$ described on page 317.

8. In 1950 some wood in Zoser's Step Pyramid in Saqqara, Egypt, contained about 59% of its original carbon 14. Estimate the age of the wood in 1950.

9. In the summer of 1993, scientists were exploring a burial mound of the ancient Pazyryk culture in southern Siberia. In one of the tombs they found a mummified woman. Research showed that the mummy contained 75% of the body's original carbon. Estimate the age of the mummy.

10. Find the half-life of carbon 14. (*Hint:* You want the value of t for which $A(t) = \dfrac{A_0}{2}$.)

Solve.

11. $\log_2 x + \log_2 (x - 4) = 5$

12. $\log_7 (x - 2) + \log_7 (x - 8) = 1$

13. $\log_3 (2y - 1) + \log_3 (y + 7) = 3$

14. $\log_5 m = 1 - \log_5 (m + 2)$

15. $\log_2 5x - \log_2 (x + 6) = 3$

16. $2 \log_3 z - \log_3 (z - 2) = 2$

TECHNOLOGY Use a graphics calculator or graphing software to solve each system of equations. Write the coordinates of each solution (x, y) to the nearest hundredth.

17. $y = 4(1.15)^x$
    $y = 2(1.65)^x$

18. $y = 3 \ln x$
    $y = \ln 3x$

19. $y = 10 \cdot 2^x$
    $4x + 2y = 160$

Use the diagram at the right. Assume that the rate of population growth remains constant in both countries.

20. **a.** Write an equation to predict Peru's population, in millions, x years after 1990.

    1990 population: 21.9 million
    Annual rate of increase: 2.4%

   b. Write an equation to predict Argentina's population, in millions, x years after 1990.

   c. TECHNOLOGY Use a graphics calculator or graphing software to graph the equations from parts (a) and (b) on the same screen. Find the point where the graphs intersect. Estimate when Peru's population will be greater than Argentina's population.

   1990 population: 32.3 million
   Annual rate of increase: 1.3%

In Michael Crichton's *The Andromeda Strain*, a group of scientists tries to stop the spread of deadly bacteria from outer space. At one point, the scientists discuss how quickly bacteria can multiply.

> The mathematics of uncontrolled growth are frightening.
> A single cell of the bacterium *E. coli* would, under ideal
> circumstances, divide every twenty minutes. That is not
> particularly disturbing until you think about it, but the
> fact is that bacteria multiply geometrically: one becomes two,
> two become four, four become eight, and so on. In this way,
> it can be shown that in a single day, one cell of *E. coli* could
> produce a supercolony equal in size and weight to the entire
> planet earth.

E. coli dividing, viewed through an electron microscope.

21. Suppose a single cell of *E. coli* exists under ideal circumstances.

    a. Write an equation that gives the number *N* of cells after *t* twenty-minute periods.

    b. How long does it take to produce one million cells of *E. coli*?

22. a. How many cells can a single cell of *E. coli* produce in one day?

    b. The radius of Earth is about 2×10^7 ft. Find Earth's volume.

       (*Hint:* Use the formula $V = \frac{4}{3}\pi r^3$ for the volume of a sphere.)

    c. Based on the excerpt from *The Andromeda Strain* and your answers to parts (a) and (b), what is the volume of a single cell of *E. coli*? Does this volume seem reasonable? Explain.

23. **Personal Finance** When you take out a loan to buy a car, you must repay a portion of the loan with interest each month. The amount *A(x)* you still owe after making *x* monthly payments is given by the formula

$$A(x) = \left(A_0 - \frac{P}{r}\right)(1 + r)^x + \frac{P}{r}$$

    where A_0 is the original amount of the loan, *P* is the monthly payment, and *r* is the monthly interest rate expressed as a decimal. (*Hint*: The monthly rate is the annual rate divided by 12.)

    a. Alvin Thompson borrows $10,800 at 12% annual interest to buy a new car. His monthly payment is $240.24. Write a function that gives the amount Alvin still owes after making *x* monthly payments.

    b. As soon as Alvin drives his car off the dealership lot, the car's resale value drops to about $8600. The resale value continues to decrease by about 1.1% each month. Write a function that gives the resale value *R(x)* after *x* months.

    c. **TECHNOLOGY** Use a graphics calculator or graphing software to graph the functions from parts (a) and (b) on the same screen. When should Alvin sell his car?

24. **Writing** List the steps needed to solve an exponential equation of the form $ab^x = c$ where a, b, and c are positive numbers. What is the solution in terms of a, b, and c?

....
Review **PREVIEW**

Write each expression as a single logarithm. *(Section 5-7)*

25. $2 \log_5 6 - \log_5 4$ 26. $3 \log_b p + 7 \log_b p^2 - \log_b q$

Simplify. *(Toolbox Skill 15)*

27. $w(w + 1)(w - 1)$ 28. $7(2a^2 - 3) - 2(5a^2 - a + 1)$ 29. $\dfrac{x^3 - 2x^2 + x}{x - 1}$

$x^2 \ 2x + 1$

Find the mean and the median of each set of numbers. *(Toolbox Skill 1)*

30. 85, 100, 58, 77, 92, 81, 39   31. 2.22, 0.98, 5.74, 3.48, 1.53, 4.35

Working on the Unit Project

32. Notice the long crest on top of the dinosaur's head. This *Parasaurolophus* made hooting sounds by forcing air through nasal passages inside the crest.

    a. The sound made by air blowing through a tube open at both ends has frequency f given by

    $$f = \frac{170}{l}$$

    where f is measured in hertz and l is the length of the tube in meters. Use this formula to find the frequency of the sound made by *Parasaurolophus*. The total length of its nasal passages was about 2 m.

    b. You can estimate the pitch of a sound made by *Parasaurolophus* by playing the note on a piano having about the same frequency. The frequency of the note made by the nth piano key is given by

    $$f = (27.5)(2)^{(n - 1)/12}$$

    where $n = 1$ corresponds to the leftmost key. Find the number of the piano key whose sound is closest in pitch to a sound made by *Parasaurolophus*.

A recorder is also a tube open at both ends.
Sound is made by blowing air through the tube.

Unit Project 5

Completing the Unit Project

Now you are ready to complete your musical instruments and plan your lecture/performance.

Your completed project should include these things:

➤ two handmade panpipes and two hand-made simple guitars

➤ drawings of your panpipes and guitars with descriptions of how you built them and how they are played

➤ a written report describing two examples of how mathematics is related to music

➤ a musical performance involving all four of your handmade instruments

Look Back ◄

Was the panpipe or the guitar easier to make? to play? to understand in terms of mathematics? Why?

Alternative Projects

Project 1: Mathematics and My Musical Instrument

If you play a musical instrument, prepare a lecture/performance in which you demonstrate and discuss how mathematical models are used in making and playing it.

Project 2: Applying Exponential and Logarithmic Functions

Choose one of the applications you saw in this unit, such as the Richter scale or carbon dating. Find out more about the topic and the mathematics involved. Prepare a presentation for your class.

1. **Writing** Describe how you can use the equation $y = ab^x$ to model a 5% annual growth in population. Describe how you can model a 5% annual decrease in population.

5-1

2. The equation $y = (1.06)(1.1)^x$ can be used to model the United States' debt, in billions of dollars, since 1978. Assume the United States' debt continues to follow this model. Use this model to estimate the United States' debt in 2010.

3. **Open-ended** Describe a situation that can be modeled by exponential growth. Describe a situation that can be modeled by exponential decay.

Match each function with its graph.

5-2

4. $y = (3.8)(0.75)^x$ 5. $y = (3.8)(1.15)^x$ 6. $y = (3.8)(0.75)^{-x}$

A.

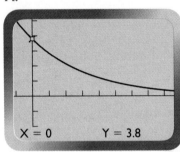

X = 0   Y = 3.8

B.

X = 0   Y = 3.8

C.

X = 0   Y = 3.8

7. In 1950 the population of California was about 10,586,000. In 1960 the population was about 15,717,000.

   a. Write an exponential function to model the population of California.

   b. Use your function to estimate the population in 1900.

8. Rewrite $y = (20)\left(\dfrac{1}{5}\right)^{-x}$ in the form $y = ab^x$.

Simplify.

5-3

9. $25^{3/2}$ 10. $2000^{1/3}$ 11. $\sqrt[4]{64x^{16}}$

12. Find b when $f(x) = 2b^x$ and $f\left(\dfrac{4}{3}\right) = 162$.

13. The breathing rate of a cyclist in liters of oxygen per minute can be modeled by the equation $y = 0.25e^{0.11x}$, where x represents the speed of the bicycle in miles per hour.

5-4

   a. Find the breathing rate for a cyclist riding at 12 mi/h.

   b. Suppose the cyclist in part (a) wants to double the breathing rate. How fast does the cyclist have to ride?

14 **TECHNOLOGY** Graph the function $f(x) = \dfrac{5}{1 + 0.5e^{-2x}}$. What are the horizontal asymptotes of the graph?

Graph each function and its reflection over the line y = x.
Determine whether each function has an inverse.

5-5

15. $y = 3^x$

16. $y = 4x^2 + 1$

17. Tell whether the inverse of $y = \frac{1}{4}x + 2$ exists. If it exists, write its equation.

Evaluate each logarithm. Round decimal answers to the nearest hundredth.

5-6

18. $\log \dfrac{1}{100,000}$

19. $\ln 6$

20. $\log_6 216$

Solve. Round decimal answers to the nearest hundredth.

21. $\log_x 121 = 2$

22. $e^x = \dfrac{1}{e^4}$

23. $10^x = 35$

For Questions 24–26, write each expression in terms of log M and log N.

5-7

24. $\log N^7$

25. $\log MN^5$

26. $\log \dfrac{\sqrt{M}}{N^6}$

27. Simplify $\log_3 4 + \log_3 20 - \log_3 6$.

28. Find the value of $\log_3 17$ to three decimal places.

29. Solve $\log_2 x + \log_2 (x - 4) = 5$.

5-8

For Questions 30 and 31, use the formula $A = Pe^{rt}$ and the information below.

5-4, 5-8

In 1983 the United States government agreed to pay the Native American Pequot people for land they owned in 1856. The Pequots asked for $900,000. A government official suggested that the Pequots be paid the value of the land in 1856 ($8091.17) plus interest.

30. How much did the government official offer the Pequots in 1983, considering the average 1983 interest rate of 10% compounded continuously?

31. Find the interest rate, compounded continuously, requested by the Pequots.

32. **Self-evaluation** Do you prefer to solve problems like *Question 7* or like *Question 26*? Why?

33. **Group Activity** Work in a group of four students. After completing each part, pass your paper to the person on your right.

a. Write an equation for an exponential function.

b. Write the equation for the inverse of the function you receive.

c. Graph the original function and the inverse function you receive on the same set of axes.

d. Check the equation and graphs you receive. Discuss any errors you find.

The region of greatest expansion of the Pequot people in the 1600s is shown in orange. The small purple region is all the land they owned in 1856.

IDEAS AND (FORMULAS) = X^2

➤ **Problem Solving** Discrete exponential growth can be modeled by an exponential function in the form $y = ab^x$ where $b > 1$. *(p. 267)*

➤ Discrete exponential decay can be modeled by an exponential function in the form $y = ab^x$ where $0 < b < 1$. *(p. 267)*

➤ The general form of an exponential function is $y = ab^x$, where a represents the initial value and b represents the growth factor. *(p. 267)*

➤ **Problem Solving** Continuous exponential growth can be modeled by an exponential function in the form $y = ab^x$ where $b > 1$. *(pp. 267, 269)*

➤ **Problem Solving** Continuous exponential decay can be modeled by an exponential function in the form $y = ab^x$ where $0 < b < 1$. *(pp. 267, 269)*

Exponential Growth
$y = ab^x$, $b > 1$
Example: $y = (5)(1.2)^x$

Exponential Decay
$y = ab^x$, $0 < b < 1$
Example: $y = (5)(0.5)^x$

➤ Changing the value of a in an exponential function in the form $y = ab^x$ changes the y-intercept of the graph of the function. *(p. 271)*

➤ $y = ab^{-x}$ is the same function as $y = a\left(\dfrac{1}{b}\right)^x$. *(p. 276)*

➤ For integers m and n with $n > 0$, and any nonnegative real number a:

$$a^{1/n} = \sqrt[n]{a} \qquad a^{m/n} = \left(\sqrt[n]{a}\right)^m = \sqrt[n]{a^m} \text{ (p. 283)}$$

➤ You can use the rules of fractional exponents to simplify variable expressions. *(p. 284)*

➤ The number e is an irrational number that is approximately equal to 2.718281828. *(p. 289)*

➤ A logistic growth function increases or decreases exponentially at first. Then the rate of growth slows down as the function approaches an upper or lower boundary. *(p. 290)*

➤ Two functions f and g are inverse functions if $g(b) = a$ whenever $f(a) = b$. *(p. 297)*

➤ The inverse of a function can be written $f^{-1}(x)$ or f^{-1}. *(p. 297)*

➤ If the reflection of the graph of a function over the line $y = x$ is not a function, then the function does not have an inverse. *(p. 297)*

➤ You can use the horizontal line test to tell whether a function has an inverse. *(p. 297)*

➤ The base b logarithm of any positive real number x is the exponent a when you write x as a power of a base b. *(p. 302)*

$$\log_b x = a \text{ when } x = b^a$$

➤ A natural logarithm of any positive real number x is the exponent a when you write x as a power of e. *(p. 302)*

$$\ln x = a \text{ when } e^a = x$$

➤ Let M, N, b, and c be positive numbers with $b \neq 1$ and $c \neq 1$. *(pp. 310, 312)*

$\log_b MN = \log_b M + \log_b N$ (product of logarithms property)

$\log_b \dfrac{M}{N} = \log_b M - \log_b N$ (quotient of logarithms property)

$\log_b M^k = k \log_b M$ (power of logarithms property)

$\log_b M = \dfrac{\log_c M}{\log_c b}$ (change-of-base property of logarithms)

➤ You can use properties of logarithms to solve exponential and logarithmic equations. Some solutions may be extraneous. *(p. 319)*

GEOMETRY

➤ The graph of $y = ab^x$ is a reflection over the y-axis of the graph of $y = ab^{-x}$. *(p. 276)*

➤ The graph of the inverse of a function is the reflection of the graph of the function over the line $y = x$. *(p. 297)*

.........Key Terms

- **logistic growth function** (p. 290)
- **common logarithm** (p. 302)
- **inverse functions** (p. 297)
- **natural logarithm** (p. 302)
- **logarithm** (p. 302)
- **logarithmic function** (p. 302)

6

Modeling and Analyzing Data

September brings an end to summer, the beginning of a new school year — and the unveiling of next year's new car models. Every year for the past decade, there have been over 500 models to choose from. For a couple of years in the late 1980s, there were more than 600!

Color is so important to new-car buyers that some car makers use computer-aided design (CAD) systems for designing color as well as shape and construction. Color designers use the systems to create colors that people associate with "feeling" words like elegant and dynamic. The software even adjusts the color display to show how a color looks under different weather conditions.

protective

Airbags, seat belts, and reinforced frames help prevent injury.

preventive

Antilock braking systems (ABS) and all-wheel drive (AWD) help stop skidding and increase traction.

There are two types of car **safety features**; those that help prevent accidents and those that protect passengers in case an accident happens.

The Mean Machine

Your project is to create a pro-file of a typical car, one that has all the features that people typically choose. To collect information about preferences, you should survey at least 30 people. Ask them to sup-pose they are planning to buy a new car that suits their present lifestyle and is priced within their present budget. Using the concepts and skills you learn in this unit, you should ana-lyze the data collected and assemble the features that make up the typical car. Present your conclusions in a visual display combined with a written report.

environment

To reduce air pollution, engines will burn **cleaner** and cars made of lighter materials will burn less fuel.

In Brazil some cars use ethanol made from sugar cane as an alternative to gasoline.

Intelligent Vehicle Highway Systems (IVHS) will make the car of the future safer and cleaner, automatically:

➤ electronic linkage of steering and braking

new technology

➤ radar for avoiding collisions and changing lanes

➤ infrared imaging for night driving

➤ sensors that monitor weather conditions

Getting Started

Unit Project 6

For this project you should work in a group of four students. Here are some ideas to help you get started.

☞ Discuss what kind of sampling method you should use for selecting a sample for your survey.

☞ Look at advertisements for cars in magazines and newspapers. Make a list of some of the major built-in features and options of the cars advertised.

☞ Plan to visit a car dealership. Try to interview some of the salespeople and some of the customers. Find out what features new-car buyers want.

Can We Talk

Working on the Unit Project

Your work in Unit 6 will help you create a profile of a typical car.

Related Exercises:

Section 6-1, Exercise 18
Section 6-2, Exercise 14
Section 6-3, Exercise 17
Section 6-4, Exercise 18
Section 6-5, Exercise 17

Alternative Projects p. 365

➤ Suppose you are planning to buy a new car tomorrow. What color will you choose? Why? What colors appear to be popular this year? What colors were popular last year? the year before?

➤ How do you think factors besides personal taste affect color choice in a new car? Consider security, visibility, weather (temperature, rain, snow, amount of sun), frequency of cleaning, and so on.

➤ Which of the safety features named on page 328 do you think are the most effective? Why?

➤ Suppose you ask a random sample of 10,000 people how much money they are willing to spend on a new car. Describe what you think the shape of a histogram that displays the data will be. What prices do you think are typical for the sample—very high, very low, or in-between? How did you decide?

Distributions of Data

How Does It SHAPE Up?

EXPLORATION

What do survey results "look" like?

- **Materials: clock with a second hand**
- **Work in a group of four students.**

Student Resources Toolbox
p. 627 *Making a Histogram*

You take a pulse by placing your fingers on the inside of the wrist above the thumb. Count the number of beats in 15 seconds, then multiply by 4.

① The whole class should answer these questions with the results shown on the board.

➤ In what month were you born?

➤ What is the last digit of your telephone number?

➤ How many letters are in your full first name?

➤ How many times does your heart beat per minute while you are sitting at your desk?

② A **histogram** shows how many data values are in each interval. Your group should make histograms showing the results of each survey question.

③ Compare the shapes of your histograms. Does the shape of each histogram look the way you expected?

④ How many students were born during the summer? How many have a telephone number with a last digit less than 4? How many have first names with three to five letters? How many have heart rates of over 70 beats per minute?

The horizontal axis shows the *intervals*.

⑤ Discuss what you think is the "average" answer to each survey question. Write down your group's reasons.

A histogram is a graph of a **frequency distribution.** A frequency distribution can be categorized by the general shape of its histogram. Notice where the mean and median fall on each histogram.

mean → ▲ ← median

In a **uniform distribution,** all the intervals have approximately equal frequencies.

mean → ▲ ← median

A **mound-shaped distribution** is approximately symmetrical about a line passing through the interval or between the intervals with the greatest frequency.

mean → ▲ ▲ ← median

In a **skewed distribution,** the interval or group of intervals that contains the greatest frequencies is near one end.

mean → ▲ ▲ ← median

A **bimodal distribution** has two distinct intervals or groups of intervals that contain the greatest frequencies.

Student Resources Toolbox
p. 626 *Mean, Median, and Mode*

mean ▲

·······▶ Now you are ready for:
Exs. 1–9 on pp. 335–336

Talk it Over

1. Tell whether the shape of each of your survey histograms is most like a *uniform, mound-shaped, skewed,* or *bimodal* distribution or a combination of these.

2. The mean of a data set would fall at the "balance point" of its histogram if the bars had weight. This is not true for the median. How you can estimate where a median will be on a histogram?

3. The mean and median are called *measures of central tendency* of a data set. Why do you think this is so?

4. In a data set, an **outlier** is a value whose distance from the center of the data is much greater than the distances for other data values.

   a. How do you think an outlier appears on a histogram? Does a histogram always show outliers?

   b. Will outliers have a greater effect on the *mean* or on the *median* of a data set? Why?

Blood sugar readings: July

before breakfast

129	78	161	150	102	167	132
90	113	218	63	170	124	193
216	68	93	134	163	240	209
101	190	196	78	104	122	224
140	106	120				

before lunch

56	190	191	213	41	57	49
119	71	96	41	51	40	40
57	44	114	47	44	83	157
64	100	78	51	54	138	61
66	39	133				

Tricia Barry has diabetes. She tries to keep her blood glucose (sugar) level at 80 to 120 mg of glucose per deciliter of blood, which is the normal level. Her diabetes is considered in poor control if her glucose level consistently goes below 40 or above 240.

a. Draw a histogram for each data set and identify the type of distribution.

b. Compare where the mean and median of the data fall on each histogram.

c. **Writing** Make a conclusion based on the histograms.

Sample Response

a. Tricia needs to know how often her readings are below 40 or above 240. The lowest possible reading is zero, so let the intervals be 0–39, 40–79, 80–119, and so on until the last interval includes the highest reading. Count the frequencies of the readings for each interval.

There are 4 readings in the 200–239 interval.

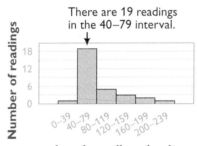

There are 19 readings in the 40–79 interval.

The breakfast distribution is basically mound-shaped. The lunch distribution is skewed.

b.

median = 132 — mean ≈ 142

The mean and median of the breakfast data are close together and fall within the same interval.

median = 61 — mean ≈ 83

The mean and median of the lunch data are farther apart and fall in separate intervals.

c. Tricia's blood glucose readings tend to be higher than normal at breakfast and lower than normal at lunch. However, since she has gone below 40 only once and above 240 only once at either meal time, her diabetes seems in good control.

BY THE WAY...

The structure of insulin, the drug used to control diabetes, was discovered in 1969 by Dorothy Crowfoot Hodgkin. She won the Nobel Prize in 1964 for discovering the structure of vitamin B$_{12}$.

The scale on the vertical axis of each histogram in Sample 1 tells you how many data values are in each interval. In a **relative frequency histogram,** the scale on the vertical axis tells you what fraction or what percent of the data values are in each interval.

Sample 2

Draw a relative frequency histogram for each data set in Sample 1.

Sample Response

There are 31 readings for each meal time. Divide the number of readings in the interval by the total number of readings, then multiply by 100 to find the relative frequency as a percent.

	BREAKFAST		LUNCH	
INTERVAL	Number of readings	Percent of total readings	Number of readings	Percent of total readings
0–39	0	0	1	3.2
40–79	4	12.9	19	61.3
80–119	7	22.6	5	16.1
120–159	8	25.8	3	9.7
160–199	7	22.6	2	6.5
200–239	4	12.9	1	3.2
240–279	1	3.2	0	0
Total	31	100	31	100

$4 \div 31 \times 100 \approx 12.9$

12.9% of the readings are in the 40–79 interval.

Breakfast readings (mg)

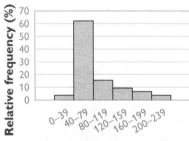

Lunch readings (mg)

Talk it Over

5. Compare the histograms in Sample 2 with those in Sample 1. How are they alike? How are they different?

6. What percent of breakfast readings were 160 or higher? What percent of lunch readings were 159 or lower?

▶ **Now you are ready for:**
Exs. 10–18 on pp. 336–337

Look Back ◀

Explain how to make a relative frequency histogram.

Exercises and Problems

1. **Reading** How is a skewed distribution different from a mound-shaped distribution?

2. **Writing** Explain how you chose the intervals for the histograms in the Exploration on page 331.

3. Use the data in Sample 1. Change the size of the intervals and draw a new histogram for the breakfast or the lunch data. What do you notice about the shape of the new histogram?

For Exercises 4–7, use these histograms based on a survey given to a high school junior class.

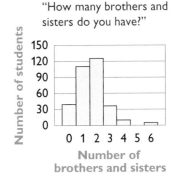

4. About how many students were surveyed?

5. **a.** About how many students were born on each weekday? on each weekend day?

   b. Does the histogram for birthdays look the way you expected? Why or why not?

6. Do most of these students have many brothers and sisters? Explain.

7. **Writing** What do you think is the average number of minutes it takes these students to get to school? What do you think is the average number of brothers and sisters? Explain your reasoning.

8. **a.** **Ornithology** Draw a histogram of the bird nest temperature data.

   b. Identify the type of distribution. Justify your answer.

The air temperature in the nest of a common tern is 36.0°C.

Air Temperature in Birds' Nests	
Temperature (°C)	Number of species
30.0–30.9	1
31.0–31.9	2
32.0–32.9	3
33.0–33.9	7
34.0–34.9	7
35.0–35.9	9
36.0–36.9	3
37.0–37.9	1

9. a. Draw a histogram for the lengths of words in English. Draw a histogram for the lengths of words in Italian.

b. Identify the type of distribution for each histogram. Justify your answers.

c. Find the mean and median for each data set and show them on the histograms.

d. Open-ended What can you say about the lengths of words used in English and Italian?

10. Reading How is a histogram different from a relative frequency histogram?

11. a. Make a relative frequency histogram for the data in Exercise 8.

b. What percent of bird species have nests with air temperatures of 35.0°C or greater?

Lengths of words in the first paragraph of *At Bertram's Hotel* by Agatha Christie		
Number of letters	Number of words English	Italian
1	1	3
2	5	4
3	6	8
4	7	4
5	4	6
6	6	4
7	4	4
8	2	3
9	1	0
10	0	2
11	0	0
12	1	1
13	0	1

1993 Average Annual Baseball Players' Salaries by Team			
National League	1,453,538	1,371,692	1,584,302
	327,926	653,484	1,072,981
	1,448,200	543,401	1,431,099
	1,039,897	850,580	877,048
	1,264,315	935,501	
American League	1,078,359	1,329,414	923,511
	1,304,747	548,156	1,331,414
	1,503,247	811,852	978,462
	1,578,192	1,430,493	1,052,694
	1,046,661	1,708,000	

12. a. Salaries Make a histogram for the data for each league.

b. Identify each type of distribution.

c. Estimate the mean and median of each data set and compare where they fall on the histograms.

d. Writing Use the histograms to compare the salaries in the two leagues. What conclusion(s) can you make? Explain your reasoning.

13. a. Salaries Make a relative frequency histogram for each data set.

b. Identify the type of distribution for each histogram.

c. What percent of doctors in each group had an annual salary between $100,000 and $299,999 in 1992?

d. Writing What conclusion(s) can you make based on the histograms? Explain your reasoning.

1992 United States Annual Doctors' Salaries		
Salary ($)	Female (%)	Male (%)
0–99,999	52	25
100,000–199,999	36	43
200,000–299,999	10	21
300,000–399,999	1	6
400,000 +	1	5

14. **Open-ended** Make at least five conclusions based on these voting and registration histograms. Justify your conclusions.

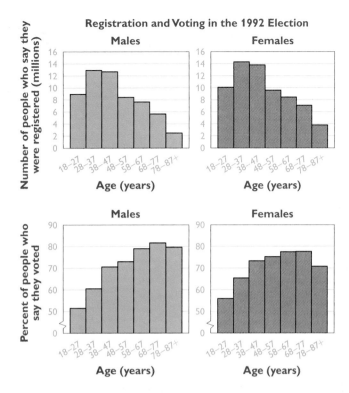

Registration and Voting in the 1992 Election

15. Solve $4^x = 20$. *(Section 5-8)*

16. Tell whether the inverse of $y = -\frac{1}{2}x^2$ exists when $x \geq 0$. If it exists, write an equation of the inverse function. *(Section 5-5)*

17. Evaluate $\displaystyle\sum_{n=0}^{6} (3 - 4n)$. *(Section 4-5)*

Working on the Unit Project

18. **a.** Create a survey to give to 30 people. Ask them to suppose they plan to buy a new car that suits their present lifestyle and is priced within their present budget. Here are some questions you can ask.

➤ How much money will you pay for the car?

➤ How many miles per gallon of gasoline will it average?

➤ About how many miles per year will you drive it?

➤ What color will it be?

➤ How many doors will it have?

➤ How many options and safety features will it have? What are they?

➤ How long do you plan to keep the car?

b. Make a histogram for the responses to as many survey questions as you can. Can you make a histogram for every set of responses? Explain.

c. Identify the type of distribution for each histogram in part (b). Show where the mean and median fall on your histograms.

Standard Deviation

············Focus

Use mean, range, and standard deviation to compare data sets with technology.

How Far Off?

San Francisco

Kansas City, MO

Monthly Mean Temperatures (°F)												
	J	**F**	**M**	**A**	**M**	**J**	**J**	**A**	**S**	**O**	**N**	**D**
San Francisco	50.7	53.0	54.7	55.7	57.4	59.1	58.8	59.4	62.0	61.4	57.4	52.5
Kansas City, MO	31.7	35.8	43.3	55.7	65.6	75.9	81.5	79.8	71.3	60.2	44.6	35.8

Talk it Over

1. What do the graphs show about the temperature pattern in each city?

2. Find the mean annual temperature for each city. Is the mean alone a good way to compare the temperatures in these cities? Explain.

3. The **range** of a data set is the difference between the greatest and least data values. What is the range of temperatures for each city?

4. Are the mean and the range a good way to compare the temperatures in these cities? Explain.

5. When you subtract the mean from a data value, you find the value's *deviation from the mean.* For both cities, find the deviation from the mean for each temperature. What is the average of these deviations?

For example, in the San Francisco data, the deviation from the mean for February is $53.0 - 56.8 = -3.8$.

The mean is one statistic you can use to describe a data set, but it describes only the center. The range is an example of a *measure of variability* because it measures how variable or spread out the data are. Another measure of variability uses the square of the deviation of each data value from the mean.

STANDARD DEVIATION

Read as "x bar." → For a data set $x_1, x_2, x_3, \ldots, x_n$, where $\bar{x}$ = the mean of the data values and n = the number of data values, the **standard deviation** σ is

Read as "sigma." → $\sigma = \sqrt{\dfrac{(x_1 - \bar{x})^2 + (x_2 - \bar{x})^2 + \cdots + (x_n - \bar{x})^2}{n}}$

$= \sqrt{\dfrac{\sum\limits_{i=1}^{n} (x_i - \bar{x})^2}{n}}$

To find the standard deviation:
1. Find the mean, $\bar{x}$.
2. Find the deviations from the mean, $x_i - \bar{x}$.
3. Find the squares of the deviations, $(x_i - \bar{x})^2$.
4. Find the sum of the squares, then divide by the number of data values, n.
5. Take the positive square root.

Sample 1

Find the standard deviation of the monthly mean temperatures in San Francisco.

Sample Response

Method ❶ Use a formula.

standard deviation → $\sigma = \sqrt{\dfrac{\sum\limits_{i=1}^{12} (x_i - 56.8)^2}{12}}$ mean: $\bar{x} = \dfrac{50.7 + 53.0 + \cdots + 52.5}{12} \approx 56.8$

$= \sqrt{\dfrac{(50.7 - 56.8)^2 + (53.0 - 56.8)^2 + \cdots + (52.5 - 56.8)^2}{12}}$

≈ 3.4

Method ❷ Use a calculator.

Put your calculator in statistics mode or select the statistics menu. Enter the data. Have the calculator compute and display the mean, usually shown as $\bar{x}$, and the standard deviation, usually σ_x or σ_n.

```
1–Var Stats
  x̄ = 56.84166667
  Σx = 682.1
  Σx² = 38912.41
  Sx = 3.576554547
  σx = 3.424290275
↓n = 12
```

Calculations for Kansas City Temperatures

```
1–Var Stats
  x̄ = 56.76666667
  Σx = 681.2
  Σx² = 42316.9
  Sx = 18.20950468
  σx = 17.4342734
↓n = 12
```

Talk it Over

6. Which city has more variability in temperature? Explain.

7. For both cities, find $\bar{x} + \sigma$ and $\bar{x} - \sigma$. What *percent* of temperatures in each city were between these values? These values are within one standard deviation of the mean.

Standard deviation is used in business for quality control. Machines that manufacture products are designed to minimize error, but their performance must be tested often.

Sample 2

Writing Puff Pop Company produces microwave popcorn and has two machines that package the kernels. Sample packages are collected from each machine 20 times per day. The popcorn from each package is popped. If there are more than 15 unpopped kernels, the package is considered not salable. How is each machine performing this day?

Number of unpopped kernels	
Machine 1	9, 8, 10, 12, 12, 10, 11, 16, 11, 13, 11, 9, 10, 14, 11, 14, 12, 15, 11, 15
Machine 2	8, 9, 9, 14, 15, 9, 8, 10, 18, 9, 10, 16, 18, 10, 8, 17, 20, 10, 8, 12

Sample Response

Machine 1

```
1–Var Stats
  x̄ = 11.7
  Σx = 234
  Σx² = 2830
  Sx = 2.202868943
  σx = 2.147091055
↓n = 20
```

I found the mean and standard deviation for the number of unpopped kernels from each machine.

	Mean	S.D.
Machine 1	11.7	2.1
Machine 2	11.9	3.9

The means for both machines are about equal and both are less than 15. The standard deviation for Machine 1 is smaller than that for Machine 2. On average, Machine 1 produces fewer unpopped kernels.

For Machine 2, the value of the mean plus the standard deviation (11.9 + 3.9 = 15.8) is very close to the allowable limit. 25% of the sample packages from Machine 2 are not salable. Perhaps Machine 2 should be stopped until it can be adjusted.

Machine 2

```
1–Var Stats
  x̄ = 11.9
  Σx = 238
  Σx² = 3138
  Sx = 4.011824628
  σx = 3.910242959
↓n = 20
```

Look Back
Why might you want to use other statistical measures besides
the mean to compare data sets?

6-2 Exercises and Problems

1. **Reading** How many data items do you use to find the range? How many data items do you use to find the standard deviation?

2. **a.** Find the mean of the credit card interest rates in each state.

Interest Rates of Credit Cards Issued by New Hampshire and Iowa Banks												
NH	10.9,	13.9,	14.4,	14.4,	14.4,	14.5,	14.9,	14.9,	14.9,	14.9,	17.9,	17.9
IA	13.4,	13.4,	13.4,	13.4,	13.4,	13.4,	13.4,	15.0,	15.0,	15.0,	15.0,	15.0, 15.0, 15.0

b. Find the range of the credit card interest rates in each state.

c. **Writing** Suppose you know only the mean and the range of the data. In which state would you expect to find the bank offering the lowest interest rate? Explain.

For Exercises 3–5:

a. Find the mean.   **b. Find the range.**   **c. Find the standard deviation.**

d. Find the percent of the data within one standard deviation of the mean.

3. 1984–1993 U.S. Women's Open winning golf scores
290, 280, 287, 285, 277, 278, 284, 283, 280, 280

4. 1984–1993 U.S. Men's Open winning golf scores
276, 279, 279, 277, 278, 278, 280, 282, 285, 272

5. Length of 1991 and 1992 Space Shuttle flights (days)
8, 6, 9, 9, 7, 8, 8, 8, 13, 7, 7, 9, 7

6. **Writing** Compare the means and ranges of the data sets in Exercises 3 and 4. What conclusion(s) can you make?

7. **a.** **Demographics** Find the mean and the standard deviation of these two data sets. What conclusion(s) can you make?

b. Find the mean and the standard deviation of the South Atlantic data set *without* the outlier. Compare these new values to the mean and the standard deviation of the New England data set. What conclusion(s) can you make? Are they the same conclusion(s) you made in part (a)?

c. **Writing** Discuss the effects of an outlier on the mean and the standard deviation of a data set.

Number of Physicians per 10,000 People in 1992			
South Atlantic Region		New England Region	
Delaware	22.3	Maine	20.9
Maryland	34.0	New Hampshire	20.8
Washington, D.C.	64.5	Vermont	26.4
Virginia	21.7	Massachusetts	34.1
West Virginia	19.1	Rhode Island	27.5
N. Carolina	19.8	Connecticut	31.2
S. Carolina	17.3		
Georgia	18.4		
Florida	22.2		

8. **Quality Control** Many companies test a sample of their product several times a day in order to detect a problem as soon as possible. The companies may use a tool called a *quality control chart*. The diameter of a penny must be between 18.95 and 19.15 mm. The inspector at a United States Mint measures the diameters of four pennies to the nearest 0.0001 mm about three times a day to see on average how much the diameters vary.

Newly minted pennies being checked for size at the United States Mint

a. Complete the table by finding the mean diameter of these samples to the nearest 0.0001 mm.

Batch	1	2	3	4	5	6	7	8
Penny 1	19.0627	19.0398	19.0639	19.0703	19.0500	19.0538	19.0525	19.0639
Penny 2	19.0639	19.0296	19.0512	19.0512	19.0525	19.0627	19.0449	19.0525
Penny 3	19.0449	19.0284	19.0639	19.0601	19.0474	19.0487	19.0195	19.0461
Penny 4	19.0703	19.0220	19.0474	19.0703	19.0639	19.0512	19.0538	19.0703
Sample mean	19.0605	?	?	?	?	?	?	?

$(19.0627 + 19.0639 + 19.0449 + 19.0703) \div 4 = 19.0605$

b. Find the mean and the standard deviation of the sample means in the table. The mean of the sample means is called the *grand mean*.

c. The machine's performance is allowed to vary as much as three standard deviations from the grand mean. The *upper control limit* is the measurement that is three standard deviations above the grand mean. The *lower control limit* is the measurement that is three standard deviations below the grand mean. Find the upper and lower control limits.

d. Copy the Penny Control Chart. Find the value of the grand mean in the left column. Draw a heavy horizontal line across the chart at this value. Draw heavy horizontal lines across the chart at the upper control limit and the lower control limit.

Penny Control Chart

| | 1 | 2 | 3 | 4 | 5 | 6 | 7 | 8 |

19.08
19.07
19.06
19.05
19.04
19.03

e. **Writing** Below are some sample means of penny diameters measured a week later. Plot each sample mean as a point on your control chart and connect the points. What conclusion(s) can you make? Explain your reasoning.

Batch	1	2	3	4	5	6	7	8
Sample mean	19.0521	19.0491	19.0544	19.0532	19.0500	19.0528	19.0535	19.0497

Unit 6 Modeling and Analyzing Data

9. For any distribution, the fraction of the data that lies within k standard deviations of the mean is always at least $1 - \frac{1}{k^2}$, where $k > 1$.

    a. Show that for any distribution at least 75% of the data lie within two standard deviations of the mean.

    b. For a distribution with $\overline{x} = 80$ and $\sigma = 7$, at least what percent of the data lies between 59 and 101?

Ongoing **ASSESSMENT**

10. a. Open-ended Write a ten-number data set without any outliers. Find the mean, range, and standard deviation of your data set.

    b. Add 4 to each data value in your data set. Find the mean, range, and standard deviation of your new data set.

    c. Multiply each data value in your original data set by 4. Find the mean, range, and standard deviation of this new data set.

    d. Writing What conclusion(s) can you make based on the results of parts (a)–(c)? Explain.

Review **PREVIEW**

11. Make a relative frequency histogram for the data set given for machine 1 in Sample 2 on page 340. *(Section 6-1)*

12. Solve $\sqrt{2x + 10} - 5 = x$. *(Section 2-6)*

13. a. What type of distribution is shown? *(Section 6-1)*

    b. About what percent of students received a score between 70 and 79?

 Working on the Unit Project

Use the results of your survey from Exercise 18 on page 337.

14. a. Find the range and the standard deviation of the responses to as many survey questions as you can. How variable are the responses?

    b. Is there greater or less variety in the answers than you expected?

    c. Writing Would the mean of a set of responses with greater variability or less variability tend to be on the list of features for the typical car? Explain.

6-3 Normal Distributions

DOES THIS RING A BELL?

EXPLORATION

(How) would you describe the distribution of heights of you and your classmates?

- **Materials: tape measures**
- **Work in a group of four students.**

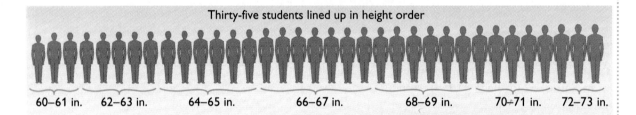

Thirty-five students lined up in height order

60–61 in.   62–63 in.   64–65 in.   66–67 in.   68–69 in.   70–71 in.   72–73 in.

60–61 in.   62–63 in.   64–65 in.   66–67 in.   68–69 in.   70–71 in.   72–73 in.

(1) List the height of everyone in the class to the nearest inch. Measure students who do not know their heights. Make separate lists for males and females.

(2) In your group, decide on a reasonable interval width and draw a relative frequency histogram for the heights of everyone in the class. What type of distribution have you drawn? Where does the mean fall? the median fall?

(3) Draw two new relative frequency histograms, one for the male students only and one for the female students only. What type of distribution is shown in each histogram? How do the histograms compare with the histogram for the whole class? Where do the means and medians fall?

(4) Suppose you drew a histogram for the heights of all the males or all the females in your school. What shape would you expect the new distribution to have?

Heights of Adult Males in the United States

When you draw a smooth curve close to or through the tops of the rectangles of a histogram, you get a bell-shaped curve like the one shown. This bell curve is called a *normal curve*. A distribution with a histogram that follows a normal curve is called a **normal distribution.** In a normal distribution, the mean and median of the data are equal and fall at the line of symmetry for the curve.

Talk it Over

1. What do you think is the average height of men in the United States?

2. About what percent of men in the United States are between 66 in. and 71 in. tall?

3. What kind of distribution would you get if you made a histogram of the heights of all adults in the United States? Explain.

4. Normal distributions are always bell-shaped, but the shape of the bell can vary. Make a statement about the mean and standard deviation of these two normal distributions.

·······► **Now you are ready for:**
Exs. 1–5 on p. 347

In a normal distribution, a known percent of the data falls within one, two, or three standard deviations of the mean.

X Lab

68-95-99.7 RULE FOR NORMAL DISTRIBUTIONS

For a normal distribution:

- about 68% of the data are within one standard deviation of the mean.

- about 95% of the data are within two standard deviations of the mean.

- about 99.7% of the data are within three standard deviations of the mean.

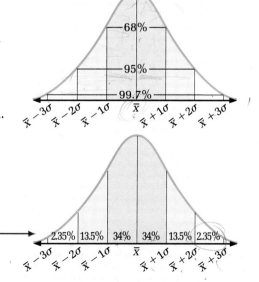

Since a normal distribution is symmetric, the 68-95-99.7 rule can be broken down in this way: ──────►

6-3 Normal Distributions

5. Why must you know that data have a normal distribution before you can apply the 68-95-99.7 rule to the data?

6. If 95% of the data are within two standard deviations of the mean, what percent are outside two standard deviations?

Sample

The 1992–1993 annual salaries of the 43 state lieutenant governors in the United States have a normal distribution with $\bar{x} = \$57,000$ and $\sigma = \$22,000$.

a. Within what range do about 95% of the lieutenant governors' salaries fall?

b. About what percent of the lieutenant governors have an annual salary between \$13,000 and \$79,000?

Sample Response

a. The data have a normal distribution, so 95% of the salaries will fall within two standard deviations of the mean.

$$\bar{x} + 2\sigma = 57,000 + 2(22,000)$$
$$= 101,000$$
$$\bar{x} - 2\sigma = 57,000 - 44,000$$
$$= 13,000$$

About 95% of the lieutenant governors have an annual salary between \$13,000 and \$101,000.

b. Draw a normal curve for the lieutenant governors' salaries and label what is known.

You know 13,000 is two standard deviations below the mean. Since 57,000 + 22,000 = 79,000, \$79,000 is one standard deviation above the mean.

So about 13.5% + 34% + 34% = 81.5% of the lieutenant governors have an annual salary between \$13,000 and \$79,000.

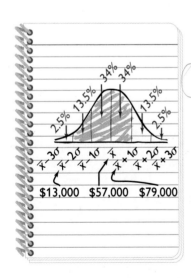

$13,000 $57,000 $79,000

······► Now you are ready for:
Exs. 6–16 on pp. 347–349

Look Back ◄

What is a normal distribution?

Exercises and Problems

For each data set in Exercises 1–3:

a. Make a histogram.

b. Show the mean and median on the histogram.

c. Tell whether the data appear to have a normal distribution.

1. Time 50 people took to complete the same test (minutes)

30, 29, 24, 28, 27,
40, 38, 23, 39, 33,
27, 32, 19, 40, 35,
25, 28, 30, 28, 27,
36, 25, 26, 30, 34,
34, 37, 37, 24, 24,
25, 34, 34, 26, 27,
33, 30, 26, 32, 38,
24, 29, 29, 31, 33,
38, 33, 33, 24, 34

2. Weights of 25 men given pre-employment physical exams (pounds)

188, 188, 168, 200,
185, 185, 175, 175,
185, 190, 192, 183,
180, 205, 195, 195,
170, 170, 190, 180,
185, 180, 190, 182,
190

3. Lifetime of 30 100-watt light bulbs (hours)

1013, 1000, 914,
910, 947, 1075,
1044, 1000, 1122,
1029, 982, 940, 994,
1038, 1036, 950,
950, 1044, 1081,
872, 900, 973, 1097,
1025, 970, 1022,
979, 1050, 984, 1000

4. a. Make a new data set of the last digit of each weight in Exercise 2. Draw a histogram for this data set. Give each digit its own interval.

  b. **Writing** Explain why the histogram in part (a) might convince someone that the men were not actually weighed.

5. a. **Open-ended** Sketch two normal distributions where the standard deviations are equal but the means are not equal.

  b. **Open-ended** Sketch two normal distributions where the standard deviations are not equal and the means are not equal.

6. Reading What is the 68-95-99.7 rule?

7. Health The blood cholesterol readings of a group of women have a normal distribution with $\bar{x} = 172$ and $\sigma = 14$.

  a. Within what range do about 95% of the readings fall?

  b. About what percent of the women have readings between 158 and 172?

  c. Readings higher than 200 are considered undesirable. About what percent of the readings are undesirable?

8. The amount of juice dispensed from a machine is normally distributed with a mean of 10.50 oz and a standard deviation of 0.75 oz.

  a. About 68% of the amounts dispensed fall within what range?

  b. About what percent of the time will the machine overfill a 12 oz cup?

9. Manufacturing The ICY Company offers a ten-year warranty for free repair of the major parts of a refrigerator. The life span of an ICY refrigerator shows a normal distribution with a mean of 17 years and a standard deviation of 3.3 years. About what percent of ICY refrigerators should the company expect to have to repair free of charge?

In *Jurassic Park* by Michael Crichton, Dr. Henry Wu uses dinosaur DNA to create dinosaurs for a zoo-like park. A mathematician, Dr. Ian Malcolm, claims that there are more dinosaurs in the park than there should be.

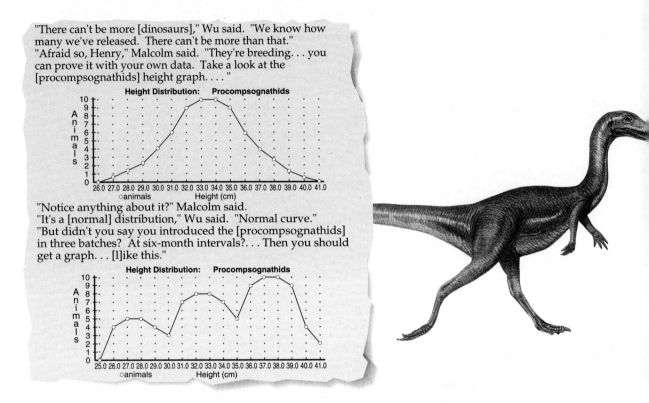

"There can't be more [dinosaurs]," Wu said. "We know how many we've released. There can't be more than that."

"Afraid so, Henry," Malcolm said. "They're breeding. . . you can prove it with your own data. Take a look at the [procompsognathids] height graph. . . . "

"Notice anything about it?" Malcolm said.

"It's a [normal] distribution," Wu said. "Normal curve."

"But didn't you say you introduced the [procompsognathids] in three batches? At six-month intervals?. . . Then you should get a graph. . . [l]ike this."

10. **a.** Suppose the only procompsognathids in the park are the ones that Dr. Wu introduced. For the second graph to be accurate, what must be true about the procompsognathids in each batch that was introduced?

b. Suppose the procompsognathids were all introduced as adults. What would be the expected height distribution?

11. **a.** Why does a normal height distribution convince Dr. Malcolm that the dinosaurs are breeding?

b. What is the approximate mean of the procompsognathids' heights?

c. The normal distribution graph above shows the heights of 65 procompsognathids. About how many have a height within one standard deviation of the mean? within two standard deviations of the mean?

Ongoing **ASSESSMENT**

12. **Writing** There is a rule of thumb that says that in a normal distribution $\sigma \approx \dfrac{\text{range}}{6}$. Do you think this formula gives a good estimate of σ? Explain.

13. Find the mean and the standard deviation of these temperatures (°F) taken at 6 A.M. on ten consecutive days in January. *(Section 6-2)*

$$-2, -1, 10, 15, 12, 16, 10, 12, 32, 30$$

Write an equation for each function in the form y = mx + b. *(Section 2-2)*

14. $f(4) = 1, m = 0.5$　　　　　　　　　　**15.** $f(0) = 3, f(2) = 11$

16. Solve $\begin{bmatrix} 3 & 0 \\ 1 & -2 \end{bmatrix} \begin{bmatrix} x \\ y \end{bmatrix} = \begin{bmatrix} 8 \\ 14 \end{bmatrix}$. *(Section 1-5)*

Working on the Unit Project

Use the histograms from Exercise 18 on page 337.

17. a. Do any of your survey histograms appear to show a normal distribution? How can you decide?

b. Open-ended Do you think more of the data would show a normal distribution if your survey involved more than 30 people? Explain.

c. For all normally distributed survey responses, within what range do 68% of the responses fall? Within what range do 95% fall?

Unit 6 CHECKPOINT

CEO Salaries at Major U.S. Corporations in 1992 (thousands of dollars)	
Financial institutions	Communications companies
2010	1434
1381	2258
2250	908
2185	1573
1164	1851
2433	1349
776	1547
1782	1086
1227	1705
1039	
1318	
2752	

1. Writing How is a normal distribution different from the other types of distributions presented in this unit?

2. a. Salaries Make a relative frequency histogram for each data set in the table of salaries of chief executive officers (CEOs). **6-1**

b. Identify each type of distribution.

c. What percent of executives in each group made between $750,000 and $1,500,000 in 1992? between $1,500,000 and $2,500,000?

d. Make a comparison based on the histograms.

3. The main span length of ten notable suspension bridges is given in feet. Find the mean, the range, and the standard deviation of the lengths. **6-2**

4626; 4260; 4200; 3800; 3609; 3576; 3524; 3500; 3323; 1595

4. Suppose the test scores on a Spanish exam show a normal distribution with $\overline{x} = 75$ and $\sigma = 8$. Within what range do about 68% of the scores fall? **6-3**

Fitting Linear Models to Data

Along These Lines

Focus

Identify data as fitting a linear model. Use technology to find the equations of fitted lines.

A scatter plot shows the relationship between two sets of data. Each point on a scatter plot shows a pairing of two data values. The scatter plots below show information about the cities on the world map below.

Latitude (°N of Equator)	56
January low temperature (°F)	9

January low temperature (°F)	42
Estimated Population in 1995	23,913,000

Air distance from New York City (miles)	5602
Roundtrip airfare from New York City (dollars)	750

Latitude vs. Jan. Low Temp.

Jan. Low Temp. vs. Population

Distance from NYC vs. Airfare

Talk it Over

Use the three scatter plots above in questions 1 and 2.

1. Which of the scatter plots looks the most linear? the least?

2. Of the scatter plots that look linear, which has a downward trend (or negative slope)? which has an upward trend (or positive slope)?

The least-squares line minimizes the sum of the squares of the vertical distances shown in red.

Least-Squares Line

The process of fitting a curve to a set of data is called *regression*. Although several linear regression models may be used, the *least-squares line* is most common. You can use technology to find an equation of the least-squares line for a set of data and use the equation to predict unknown values.

Sample 1

BY THE WAY...

The Pilgrims found pumpkins easy to grow, as is shown by this verse from a song.

> For pottage, and puddings, and custards, and pies,
> Our pumpkins, and parsnips, are common supplies;
> We have pumpkin at morning, and pumpkin at noon,
> If it was not for pumpkin we should soon be undoon.

Over a number of years the weights of prize-winning pumpkins at the annual Topsfield Fair in Topsfield, Massachusetts, have tended to increase. Predict the winning pumpkin weight for the year 2005.

Winning Pumpkin Weights — Topsfield Fair

Year	1984	1985	1986	1987	1988	1989	1990	1991	1992	1993
Weight (lb)	433	515.5	530.5	604.5	490	614	470	617.5	718	698

Sample Response

Step 1 Make a scatter plot of the ten data points. Let x represent the number of years after 1983 and y represent the winning pumpkin weight that year. Use technology to perform a linear regression.

Record the regression model for the data. It should be about the same as this equation: $y = 23.99x + 437.2$.

LinReg
$y = ax + b$
$a = 23.98787879$
$b = 437.1666667$
$r = .7546316529$

slope of least-squares line
y-intercept of least-squares line
correlation coefficient

Step 2 Use the equation of the least-squares line to predict the unknown value.

$y = 23.99x + 437.2$

$= 23.99(22) + 437.2$ ← 2005 is 22 years after 1983.
Substitute 22 for x.

$= 964.98$

According to this model, the winning pumpkin weight for the year 2005 will be about 965 lb.

The **correlation coefficient** for a data set describes how well the data points can be modeled by a line. The correlation is a number r between -1 and 1, inclusive. The closer $|r|$ is to 1, the more linear a graph of the data looks. A random distribution of data has a correlation close to 0.

For the data in Sample 1, $r \approx 0.75$. This positive correlation is due to the fact that the weights have tended to increase over time. The scattering of points around the least-squares line is why the correlation is not closer to 1.

·····▶ **Now you are ready for:**
Exs. 1–10 on pp. 354–356

Median-median Line

A graphics calculator uses every data point, even outliers, in performing a least-squares linear regression. The red point in the scatter plot represents the winning pumpkin weight of 914 lb at the 1994 Topsfield Fair. Another linear model, called the **median-median line,** is less influenced by outliers such as (11, 914). This line uses *summary points* calculated using medians.

Sample 2

Student Resources Toolbox
p. 626 *Discrete Mathematics*

Find an equation of the median-median line for the winning pumpkin weights at the Topsfield Fair for 1984–1994.

Sample Response

Step 1 Make a scatter plot of the data.

Step 2 On the scatter plot, draw two vertical lines that divide the points into three equal or nearly equal groups. In this case, the eleven data points are divided into groups of four, three, and four.

Watch Out!
For data sets where the number of points is not a multiple of three, divide the points so that the outer two groups have the same number of points.

Step 3 Find a summary point for each of the three groups. The summary point for each of the three groups has these coordinates:

(median *x*-value, median *y*-value)

For the three groups, the summary points are (2.5, 523), (6, 490), and (9.5, 708).

The median *y*-value is 708.

The median *x*-value is 9.5.

Step 4 Calculate the slope of the line through the outermost summary points.

$$m = \frac{708 - 523}{9.5 - 2.5} \approx 26.43$$

Step 5 Find the point whose coordinates are the means of the x- and y-coordinates of all three summary points.

$$\left(\frac{2.5 + 6 + 9.5}{3}, \frac{523 + 490 + 708}{3} \right), \text{ or about } (6, 573.7)$$

Step 6 The median-median line has the slope found in step 4 and passes through the point found in step 5.

$$y = mx + b$$
$$y = 26.43x + b \quad \longleftarrow \text{ Substitute 26.43 for } m \text{ from step 4.}$$
$$573.7 = (26.43)(6) + b \quad \longleftarrow \text{ Substitute 6 for } x \text{ and 573.7 for } y \text{ from step 5.}$$
$$573.7 = 158.58 + b$$
$$415.1 \approx b$$

An equation of the median-median line is $y = 26.43x + 415.1$.

TECHNOLOGY NOTE

Some graphics calculators will find equations of median-median lines.

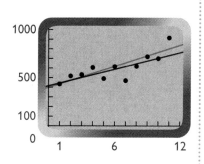

least-squares line:
$y = 33.67x + 398.4$

median-median line:
$y = 26.43x + 415.1$

Talk it Over

The graph shows both the least-squares line and the median-median line for the Topsfield Fair pumpkin data for 1984–1994 (from Exercise 6 and Sample 2).

3. Explain why the point (11, 914) may be an outlier.

4. Which of the lines has a greater slope? Give a reason why the lines have different slopes.

5. Would you expect the data point for the year 1995, (12, ?), to be closer to the median-median line or to the least-squares line? Why?

6. For a data set that includes outliers, which line is better for making predictions, the *least-squares line* or the *median-median line*?

Look Back

How do you determine whether to use the least-squares line or the median-median line for a given data set?

Now you are ready for:
Exs. 11–18 on pp. 357–358

TECHNOLOGY **For the technology exercises in this section, you can use a graphics calculator or statistical software.**

1. **Reading** Would you fit a linear model to data with a correlation coefficient that is close to zero? Why or why not?

2. Which of the scatter plots on page 350 do you think has each correlation coefficient? Why?

   a. $r = 0.89$ **b.** $r = -0.04$ **c.** $r = -0.77$

3. **Demographics** Suppose you have a scatter plot with the population of some cities along the horizontal axis and the area of the same cities along the vertical axis.

   a. In which range do you expect the correlation coefficient r for the data set to be: $-1 \le r < -\frac{1}{2}$, $-\frac{1}{2} \le r \le \frac{1}{2}$, or $\frac{1}{2} < r \le 1$?

   b. Make a scatter plot of the data below. Look at the distribution of the data points. Does your scatter plot support your prediction in part (a)? Explain.

Cities Around the World							
	Mexico City	Cairo	London	Tokyo	Calcutta	Moscow	Rome
Estimated population in 1995 (thousands)	23,913	11,155	8,897	28,447	12,885	10,769	3,079
Area (square miles)	522	104	874	1089	209	379	69

4. You can calculate the correlation coefficient r for a set of data points $(x_1, y_1), (x_2, y_2), \ldots$ by using the following formula:

   mean of the products of the x- and y-values

   product of the mean x-value and the mean y-value

   $$r = \frac{\overline{xy} - \overline{x} \cdot \overline{y}}{\sigma_x \sigma_y}$$

   product of the standard deviation of the x-values and the standard deviation of the y-values

   a. Make a scatter plot of these points:

   $$(-2, -3), (0, 1.5), (1, 2), (3, 3)$$

   b. Do the data points appear close to some line? Estimate the correlation coefficient.

   c. Find $\overline{xy}$, $\overline{x}$, $\overline{y}$, σ_x, and σ_y.

   d. Use the formula above to calculate the correlation coefficient.

   e. How close was your estimate in part (b)?

5 TECHNOLOGY The table at the right shows some information about canned soups prepared with an equal volume of water. The portions are each 100 g.

TYPE OF SOUP	Water (percent)	Food energy (Calories)
Beef noodle	93.2	28
Celery, cream of	92.3	26
Chicken, cream of	91.9	39
Minestrone	89.5	43
Mushroom, cream of	89.6	56
Tomato	90.5	36
Vegetable beef	91.9	32
Vegetable with beef broth	91.7	32

a. Make a scatter plot of the data. Let x = the percent of water (including the water content of the ingredients) and y = the number of Calories.

b. Find an equation of the least-squares line. Graph the line.

c. **Writing** Explain what a negative correlation coefficient means in this case.

d. Split pea soup is 85.4% water. What would you expect to be the number of Calories in 100 g of split pea soup?

6 TECHNOLOGY The record pumpkin weight in 1994 at the Topsfield Fair was 914 lb. Use this fact and the data from Sample 1 on page 351.

a. Find an equation of the least-squares line for the pumpkin weight data for 1984–1994.

b. Make a scatter plot and graph the least-squares line.

c. **Writing** Compare the line in parts (a) and (b) with the line in Sample 1. Explain why the slope of the line for 1984–1994 is greater than the slope of the line for 1984–1993.

> **BY THE WAY...**
>
> Pumpkins are eaten for good fortune in Japan for *Tōji* (the Winter Solstice), especially in rural areas.

7 TECHNOLOGY Japan joined the International Pumpkin Association's World Championship in 1987, competing against the United States, Great Britain, and Canada. The top weights in Japan for the years 1987–1994 are shown below.

Top Pumpkin Weights — Japan

Year	1987	1988	1989	1990	1991	1992	1993	1994
Weight (lb)	326.5	313	473	439	606.5	587.3	556.7	690

a. Make a scatter plot of the data.

b. Find an equation of the least-squares line. (*Hint:* You may want to use "Years since 1986" for the x-values.)

c. Use the equation of the least-squares line to predict the top pumpkin weight in Japan for the year 2000. How does this compare to the prediction for Topsfield in Sample 1?

8 TECHNOLOGY The table shows the number of Calories you might use while in-line skating at a comfortable pace for different periods of time.

In-Line Skating						
Time (minutes)	3	7	12	18	25	33
Energy used (Calories)	29	67	115	172	238	314

a. Make a scatter plot of the data points. Find an equation of the least-squares line and find the correlation coefficient.

b. **Writing** State a conjecture suggested by the graph.

c. Find the mean for the skating time, $\bar{x}$, and the mean for the energy used, $\bar{y}$.

d. Show that $(\bar{x}, \bar{y})$ is a point on the least-squares line.

9. The National Youth Physical Fitness Program establishes qualifying standards for the Presidential Physical Fitness Awards. The table below shows the standards for boys ages 9–17 on the one-mile run test.

One-mile Run Test									
Age (years)	9	10	11	12	13	14	15	16	17
Time (seconds)	511	477	452	431	410	386	380	368	366

a TECHNOLOGY Find an equation of the least-squares line.

b. What is the meaning of the slope and the *y*-intercept of the equation of the least-squares line in this situation?

c. **Writing** When a model is used to predict results beyond the given data, you *extrapolate* from the model. Tell whether you think this model would be useful for extrapolating the one-mile run time for a 25-year-old man.

10. **Group Activity** Work with another student.

a. **Open-ended** Collect data about your classmates or friends. Some suggested topics are given below, or you may decide to gather information on some other topic.

➤ heights of students and heights of same-sex adults in the family

➤ the number of hours spent on homework each week and the number of hours spent watching TV each week

b TECHNOLOGY Make a scatter plot of student height versus same-sex adult height, or of hours of homework versus hours of TV, or of the other information you gathered.

c. **Writing** Make a conjecture about the relationship between the two sets of data in your scatter plot.

d TECHNOLOGY Does your scatter plot look linear? If so, find an equation of the least-squares line.

11. **Health Care** The table shows that health care spending on a per person basis is higher in the United States than in many other countries.

Health Care Spending in 1991		
COUNTRY	GDP (dollars per person)	Spending on Health Care (dollars per person)
Greece	7,775	450
Portugal	9,191	624
Spain	12,719	848
New Zealand	13,883	1047
Netherlands	16,530	1360
France	18,227	1650
Canada	19,178	1915
United States	22,204	2867

The gross domestic product (GDP) is the total value of goods and services produced entirely within a country in one year.

a. Make a scatter plot of the data with GDP on the horizontal axis.

b. Draw vertical lines to divide the points into three equal or nearly equal groups.

c. Plot or circle the summary points.

d. Use the method from Sample 2 to find an equation of the median-median line. Graph the line.

e. **Writing** Tell whether or not you think the median-median line is a good fit for the health care spending data. Would the least-squares line be a better fit? Give a reason for your answer.

12. **Demographics** Use the information about population and area for the metropolitan regions in the table.

Cities Around the World							
	Mexico City	Cairo	London	Tokyo	Calcutta	Moscow	Rome
Estimated population in 1995 (thousands)	23,913	11,155	8,897	28,447	12,885	10,769	3,079
Area (square miles)	522	104	874	1089	209	379	69

a. **Writing** Which linear model would you expect to be a better fit for the data, the *least-squares line* or the *median-median line*? Explain your choice.

b. Find an equation of the model you chose and draw the line.

c. The estimated mid-year population in 1995 for the city of Chicago is 6,541,000. Use your model from part (b) to predict the area of Chicago.

d. **Research** Find the actual area of the Chicago metropolitan region from an almanac or encyclopedia. How do the actual value and your prediction compare?

13. In finding the median-median line, the first step is to find the three summary points. If these three points do not lie on the same line, they are the vertices of a triangle. The median-median line passes through a special point called the *centroid* of this triangle.

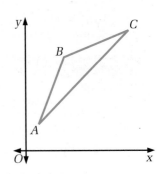

   a. On graph paper, locate these three summary points: $A(2, 4)$, $B(6, 14)$, and $C(16, 18)$. Draw $\triangle ABC$.

   b. Find the midpoints of each side of $\triangle ABC$.

   c. Draw the medians of $\triangle ABC$ by joining each vertex to the midpoint of the opposite side. Find the coordinates of the point where the three medians meet. This is the centroid of the triangle.

   d. Show that the coordinates of the centroid can be found by averaging the x-coordinates and averaging the y-coordinates of the summary points.

Ongoing ASSESSMENT

14. **Writing** Compare the median-median line and the least-squares line. How are they alike? How are they different?

Review PREVIEW

15. The weight of fish in Central Pond have a normal distribution with $\bar{x} = 28$ lb and $\sigma = 9$ lb. About what percent of the fish in the pond weigh between 10 lb and 37 lb? *(Section 6-3)*

16. Write the first five terms of the sequence: $a_1 = -3$ *(Section 4-3)*
$$a_n = 2a_{n-1} + 5$$

17. Write a matrix equation for the system: $2x + 3y - z = 16$ *(Section 1-5)*
$$-x + 5y + 8z = 16$$
$$5x - y = -7$$

 Working on the Unit Project

Use the results of your survey from Exercise 18 on page 337.

18 TECHNOLOGY

   a. Make several scatter plots comparing two sets of responses from your survey. Do any of the scatter plots suggest a linear model?

   b. Are you surprised at the number of scatter plots that are linear? Explain.

   c. Choose the scatter plot that looks most linear and find an equation of the least-squares line.

Fitting Quadratic Models to Data

········Focus

Decide whether a quadratic model fits data. Use technology and matrices to find quadratic models.

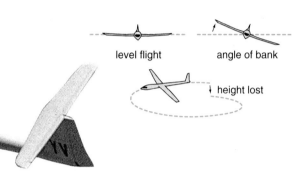

level flight   angle of bank

height lost

Talk it Over

The table below shows the height loss in feet for a glider completing a circle at the given angle of bank.

Angle of bank (degrees)	20	25	30	35	40	45	50
Height loss in 360° turn (feet)	108	91	81	74	71	70	71

	y-values		Devi-ation	
x	Actual	Model	d	d^2
20	108	?	?	?
25	91	?	?	?
30	81	?	?	?
35	74	?	?	?
40	71	?	?	?
45	70	?	?	?
50	71	?	?	?
				$\Sigma d^2 = ?$

1. Copy and complete the table at the left, using parts (a)–(e).

   a. Use a graphics calculator to find an equation of the least-squares line for the data. Let x represent the angle of bank and y represent the height loss in feet.

   b. Substitute the x-values from the data points to find the y-values of corresponding points on the least-squares line.

   c. Find the vertical deviation d between each data point and the least-squares line. Use the formula

   $$d = \text{actual } y\text{-value} - \text{model's } y\text{-value}.$$

   The deviation may be positive, negative, or zero.

   d. Find the square of each of the deviations, d^2.

   e. Find the sum of the squares of the deviations, Σd^2. Statisticians use this value to measure how well a model fits a data set.

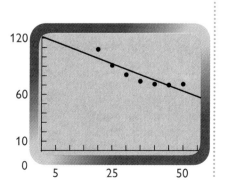

2. Look at the scatter plot shown. The data points at each end are above the least-squares line, and those in the middle are below the line. Do the points seem to lie on a curve rather than on a line? If so, what type of curve? Explain.

The points in the scatter plot on page 359 seem to lie closer to a parabola than to a line. In this case it is better to model the glider data by a **least-squares parabola,** which you can obtain by performing a quadratic regression using technology.

Sample 1

Find the least-squares parabola for the glider data and compare it to the least-squares line.

Sample Response

Step 1 Recall that the general equation for a parabola is
$y = ax^2 + bx + c.$

Use technology to perform a quadratic regression and find a, b, and c. A parabola that fits the data is
$y = 0.068x^2 - 5.9x + 198.$

With technology, graph this quadratic model along with the scatter plot and the linear model.

Step 2 To decide whether a quadratic model or a linear model fits the data better, compare the sums of the squares of the vertical deviations from the data points to each model. Find which model has the smaller *sum of squares*.

x	Actual y-value	$y = 0.068x^2 - 5.9x + 198$	Deviation d	d^2
20	108	107.2	0.8	0.64
25	91	93	−2	4
30	81	82.2	−1.2	1.44
35	74	74.8	−0.8	0.64
40	71	70.8	0.2	0.04
45	70	70.2	−0.2	0.04
50	71	73	−2	4
				$\Sigma d^2 = 10.8$

The sum of the squares of the deviations from the data points to the quadratic model is 10.8. From *Talk it Over* question 1, you should have found that the sum of the squares of the deviations for the linear model is about 300.

The quadratic model has a smaller sum of squares, so the parabola is a better fit for the data set than the line.

The glider data in Sample 1 was modeled using quadratic regression. You can also use a system of equations to fit a quadratic model to data. For this method, you need only three data points.

Unit 6 Modeling and Analyzing Data

Use a system of equations to find a quadratic model to fit the data points (20, 108), (35, 74), and (50, 71).

Sample Response

1 To fit a quadratic model to the data, you need to find a, b, and c in the equation $y = ax^2 + bx + c$. Substitute the three data points.

$400a + 20b + c = 108$ ⟵⟶ Substitute **20** for x and **108** for y.

$1225a + 35b + c = 74$ ⟵⟶ Substitute **35** for x and **74** for y.

$2500a + 50b + c = 71$ ⟵⟶ Substitute **50** for x and **71** for y.

2 This is a system of three equations with three variables. The matrix equation representing this system is:

$$\begin{bmatrix} 400 & 20 & 1 \\ 1225 & 35 & 1 \\ 2500 & 50 & 1 \end{bmatrix} \begin{bmatrix} a \\ b \\ c \end{bmatrix} = \begin{bmatrix} 108 \\ 74 \\ 71 \end{bmatrix}$$

⟵ coefficient · variable = constant
matrix   matrix   matrix

3 Use a graphics calculator to multiply both sides by the inverse of the coefficient matrix to find the solution matrix.

$$\begin{bmatrix} a \\ b \\ c \end{bmatrix} = \begin{bmatrix} 0.06889 \\ -6.0556 \\ 201.556 \end{bmatrix}$$

⟵ solution matrix

A quadratic model for the given data is $y = 0.069x^2 - 6.1x + 200$.

Talk it Over

3. Why are three linear equations needed to fit a quadratic model to data?

4. Why is the quadratic model found in Sample 1 slightly different from the model found in Sample 2?

5. Would choosing a different group of three data points from the data set result in the same quadratic model as in Sample 2? Explain.

6. How could you decide which quadratic model fits a data set better?

Look Back ⟵

Describe which types of data sets may be best modeled by a linear least-squares equation, by a median-median equation, or by a quadratic least-squares equation.

6-5 Exercises and Problems

TECHNOLOGY **For the technology exercises in this section, you can use a graphics calculator or statistical software.**

1. **Reading** How would you determine whether a linear model or a quadratic model fits a set of data better?

2. **a.** Use the least-squares quadratic equation from Sample 1 to predict the height loss for an angle of bank of 60°.

   b. The actual height loss is 80 feet. Explain why this value and the value in part (a) might be different.

   c. At about what angle of bank is there least height loss?

3. **Automobiles** An advertisement for a sports car states that the car reaches its maximum power, measured in horsepower (hp), at a lower engine speed, measured in revolutions per minute (rpm), than other cars. Some estimated values on which this claim was made are shown here.

Engine speed (rpm)	1000	2000	3000	4000	5000	6000
Engine power (hp)	16	35	55	72	77	68

   a. Make a scatter plot of the data.

   b. Find a quadratic model for the data.

   c. At about what engine speed does the maximum engine power occur?

4 TECHNOLOGY Look at the scatter plot on page 350 of Section 6-4 that shows distance and roundtrip airfare. The data are shown below.

WORLD TRAVEL	Mexico City	Cairo	London	Tokyo	Calcutta	Moscow	Rome
Air distance from New York City (miles)	2094	5602	3458	6740	7918	4665	4281
Roundtrip airfare from New York City (dollars)	250	750	375	1200	1500	624	520

   a. Perform a linear regression and graph the least-squares line for the data.

   b. Find a quadratic model for the data points.

   c. Graph the parabola on the same scatter plot as the least-squares line.

   d. **Writing** Which model seems to fit the data better, the *linear* model or the *quadratic* model? Explain.

In Exercises 5–8, the data points lie on a parabola.

a. **Write a system of three linear equations with three variables.**

b. **Write a matrix equation for the system.**

c. **Solve the system for *a*, *b*, and *c*, and write an equation for the parabola.**

5. $(2, 20), (5, 56), (-3, 0)$

6. $(0, -4), (0.6, -2.2), (-0.8, -0.8)$

7. $(1, 16), (-1, 16), (-2, -32)$

8. $(0, 9), (1, 4), (3, 0)$

9. a. Trace this scatter plot.

   b. Sketch a parabola that you think fits the data points well.

   c. TECHNOLOGY Find a quadratic regression equation using technology or choose three points and use a matrix equation to find a quadratic model.

   d. Graph your equation from part (c) on the same set of axes as your sketch in part (b).

   e. **Writing** How do the graphs in part (d) compare?

Salaries The table gives the average annual salaries of engineers with master's degrees in the United States. Use the table for Exercises 10–12.

Average Annual Salaries	
Experience (years)	Salary (dollars)
1	35,000
3	40,000
5	44,000
7	48,000
9	52,000
11	55,000
13	58,000
15	60,000
17	63,000
19	65,000
21	67,000
23	68,500
25	70,000
27	71,000
29	72,000

10. a. Make a scatter plot of the data.

    b. **Writing** How does the appearance of the scatter plot suggest a quadratic model?

11. TECHNOLOGY

    a. Find a quadratic model for the data.

    b. Graph the quadratic model on the same set of axes as the scatter plot.

    c. What is the meaning of the *y*-intercept in this situation?

12. TECHNOLOGY

    a. What is the approximate maximum salary for an engineer with a master's degree according to the model from Exercise 11?

    b. After how many years of employment does an engineer with a master's degree reach the maximum salary?

    c. According to the model, what happens after the maximum salary is reached?

BY THE WAY...

Engineering is a profession that puts scientific knowledge to practical use. Some of the branches of engineering are aerospace, biomedical, chemical, civil, electrical, environmental, industrial, mechanical, and nuclear.

13. **Group Activity** Work with another student. You will need small beans or other counters, and three jar lids of different sizes.

    a. **Using Manipulatives** Use three different-sized jar lids. Using small beans, collect two types of data from each lid—the number of beans needed to fill the lid one layer deep and the number of beans, laid end-to-end, needed to surround the lid.

    b. Combine your data with the data of one other group and make a scatter plot of the six points.

    c. TECHNOLOGY Find a model that you can use to predict the number of beans needed to fill a lid if you know the number it takes to surround the lid.

    d. Compare your model with those of other groups. Discuss similarities and differences in the models.

Review **PREVIEW**

14. Use the table. *(Section 6-4)*

Tuition at Selected Universities in Illinois						
Resident (dollars)	3025	2533	2455	3006	2590	2937
Nonresident (dollars)	7381	6228	6135	7506	6042	7425

    a. Draw a scatter plot of the data.

    b. Which kind of function appears to model the data? Why?

    c. TECHNOLOGY Find an equation to model this situation.

15. In $\triangle ABC$, $m \angle A = 100°$. Use an indirect proof to show that $\angle B$ is not a right angle. *(Section 3-7)*

16. Suppose you roll a die. What is the probability that you get an odd number? *(Toolbox Skill 6)*

 Working on the Unit Project

Use your scatter plots from Exercise 18 on page 358.

17. a. Do any of your scatter plots suggest a quadratic model? Are you surprised at the number of scatter plots that are quadratic? Explain.

    b. Choose the scatter plot that looks most quadratic and find a quadratic model for it.

Completing the Unit Project

Now you are ready to complete your profile of a typical car.

Your completed project should include these things:

➤ **a data table containing your survey results**

➤ **histograms of your survey results**

➤ **a visual display showing the features of your typical car**

➤ **a written analysis of your survey data, including a description of each distribution and its mean and standard deviation, as well as an explanation of how you selected the features of your typical car**

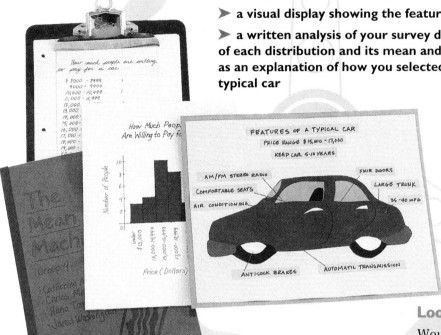

Look Back ◄

Would you recommend that a car maker design a car model based on your profile of the typical car? Why or why not?

Alternative Projects

Project 1: **TV Ratings**

Find out how television rating services such as the A.C. Nielsen Company collect data. Also find out how television networks analyze these data in order to make decisions about programming. Write a report describing what you have learned. Include a discussion of the reliability of the data and of the decisions based on it.

Project 2: **Is It Normal?**

List at least three kinds of data sets that you think are normally distributed and three kinds that you think are not normally distributed. Obtain samples of all six types of data sets. For each data set, find the mean(s) and, if possible, the standard deviation. Describe each distribution and determine which, if any, of the data sets are normally distributed.

1. These histograms show the distribution of the ages of students in three
   swimming classes.

   6-1

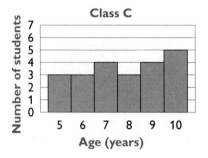

   a. Tell whether each distribution is *uniform, mound-shaped, skewed,*
      or *bimodal.*

   b. What are the mean age and the median age in each class?

   c. **Writing** Which class probably has the best swimmers?
      Justify your answer.

2. a. Make a relative frequency histogram of this data.

Number of Counties in Each State of the United States
67, 12, 15, 75, 58, 63, 8, 3, 67, 159, 4, 44, 102, 92, 99, 105, 120,   64, 16, 23, 14, 83, 87, 82, 114, 56, 93, 16, 10, 21, 33, 62, 100,   53, 88, 77, 36, 67, 5, 46, 67, 95, 254, 29, 14, 95, 39, 55, 72, 23

   b. Identify any outliers in the data set.

   c. Find the mean and the median of the data and show them on your
      histogram.

   d. What percent of states have between 20 and 49 counties?

3. a. Find the mean and the range of the number of sons and of the number
      of daughters of Presidents of the United States.

   6-2

Children of Presidents of the United States															
n	0	1	2	3	4	5	6	7	8	9	10	11	12	13	14
No. of Presidents with *n* sons	13	4	8	7	4	2	1	1	1	0	0	0	0	0	0
No. of Presidents with *n* daughters	12	12	11	2	1	2	1	0	0	0	0	0	0	0	0
No. of Presidents with *n* children	6	2	8	6	7	3	5	1	1	0	1	0	0	0	1

Thirteen Presidents
had no sons.

Eleven Presidents
had two daughters.

President John Tyler had 14 children:
8 sons and 6 daughters.

b. Find the standard deviation of the number of sons and of the number of daughters.

c. **Writing** The mean of the number of total children is about 3.6 with a standard deviation of about 2.8. Compare this to the values you found for sons and for daughters. What do you notice? Explain why you think the differences exist.

4. The age at inauguration for Presidents of the United States shows a normal distribution with a mean of 55 years and a standard deviation of 6 years.

6-3

a. About 95% of the Presidents were within what age range?

b. What percent of the Presidents were between the ages of 55 and 67 at inauguration? between the ages of 49 and 55?

5. **a.** Copy the sketch of a normal curve. Show the mean of the distribution.

b. **Open-ended** On the copy, sketch another normal curve with the same mean but a different standard deviation.

c. **Open-ended** On the same drawing, sketch another normal curve with a different mean but the same standard deviation as the given curve.

d. **Writing** Explain how a normal curve changes when the mean and the standard deviation change.

6. The price of a pizza depends upon both the size (area) of the pizza and the fixed cost of making the pizza.

6-4

The area of a circle is
$A = \pi \cdot (\text{radius})^2$.
Use $\pi \approx 3.14$.

Plain Cheese Pizzas at Central Pizza					
Size (diameter)	Personal (7 in.)	Small (10 in.)	Medium (12 in.)	Large (14 in.)	X-Large (16 in.)
Area (in.²)	38.48	78.54	113.10	153.94	201.06
Price ($)	2.49	6.49	8.49	11.49	14.49

a. Find a linear equation that models the price of a pizza as a function of its area.

b. Find the area of a pizza that is 20 in. in diameter and predict its price.

Median Household Income	
Years since 1986	**Income (dollars)**
1	26,061
2	27,225
3	28,906
4	29,943
5	30,126

7. **Household Income** The median household income for all households in the United States for the years 1987–1991 is shown in the table.

   a. Use quadratic least-squares regression or a system of equations to find a quadratic model for the situation.

   b. According to the model, what was the median household income in 1986?

8. **Self-evaluation** You see statistics every day in newspapers and magazines. Do you feel you understand the statistics quoted in the media better now that you have completed this unit? Explain.

9. **Group Activity** Work with another student.

   a. Make a scatter plot of the data.

   b. One student should find an equation of the least-squares line for the data while the other student finds a quadratic model to fit the data.

   c. Discuss and decide which model seems to fit the data better. Justify your answer.

Average Years of Life Left (1990)			
Age (years)	**Life left (years)**	**Age (years)**	**Life Left (years)**
0	75.4	45	33.4
5	71.2	50	29.0
10	66.3	55	24.8
15	61.3	60	20.8
20	56.6	65	17.2
25	51.9	70	13.9
30	47.2	75	10.9
35	42.6	80	8.3
40	38.0	85	6.1

IDEAS AND (FORMULAS)$=x^2$

➤ Making a scatter plot of paired data helps you to see if the data have a linear relationship, a quadratic relationship, or neither. *(pp. 350, 360)*

➤ Technology allows you to find a linear or quadratic model of a scatter plot easily. *(pp. 351, 360)*

➤ You can use linear or quadratic models to make predictions about a data set. *(pp. 351, 360)*

➤ You can use matrices to solve a system of three linear equations with three variables to find a quadratic model for data. *(p. 361)*

➤ Comparing the shapes of histograms allows you to make decisions regarding data sets. *(p. 333)*

➤ Range and standard deviation can help you make decisions when comparing data sets. *(pp. 338, 339)*

➤ A frequency distribution can be categorized by the shape of its histogram. *(p. 332)*

➤ You can estimate where the mean and median of a data set will fall on a histogram. *(p. 332)*

➤ Histograms can show you how many data values are in each interval or what percent of data values are in each interval. *(pp. 333, 334)*

➤ Measures of variability tell you how spread out the data are. *(p. 339)*

➤ Technology allows you to find the mean and standard deviation of a data set easily. *(p. 339)*

➤ In a normal distribution, about 68% of the data are within one standard deviation of the mean, about 95% of the data are within two standard deviations of the mean, and about 99.7% of the data are within three standard deviations of the mean. *(p. 345)*

➤ You can find linear or quadratic models to fit data using technology and other methods. *(pp. 351, 360)*

➤ A correlation coefficient that is close to 1 or −1 shows that a set of data points lies close to the least-squares line. A coefficient that is close to 0 shows that a line is not a good model for the data set. *(p. 352)*

➤ The median-median line may be a better fit than the least-squares line when the data set has outliers. *(p. 353)*

Key Terms

- **histogram** (p. 331)
- **mound-shaped distribution** (p. 332)
- **outlier** (p. 332)

- **$\bar{x}$** (p. 339)
- **normal distribution** (p. 345)
- **median-median line** (p. 352)

- **frequency distribution** (p. 332)
- **skewed distribution** (p. 332)

- **relative frequency histogram** (p. 334)

- **σ** (p. 339)
- **least-squares line** (p. 351)
- **least-squares parabola** (p. 360)

- **uniform distribution** (p. 332)
- **bimodal distribution** (p. 332)

- **range** (p. 338)

- **standard deviation** (p. 339)
- **correlation coefficient** (p. 352)

Applying Probability Models

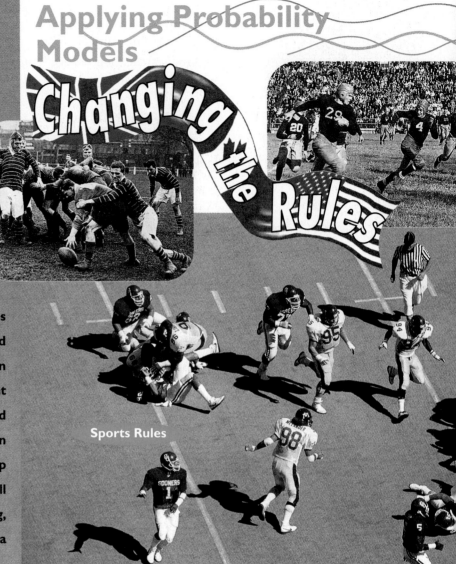

Changing the Rules

About 100 years ago, football emerged as a distinct game in the United States and Canada. It was the result of decades of rules changes in the English game of rugby.

Ongoing rules changes in each country have turned American and Canadian football into quite different games. With a larger field and fewer chances to gain 10 yards before giving up the ball, Canadian football features more passing, more touchdowns, and a faster pace.

Sports Rules

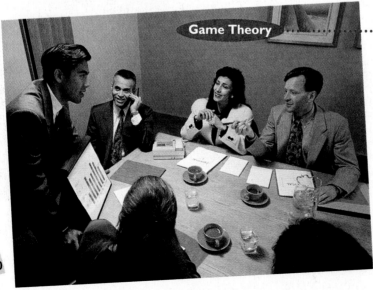

Game Theory ....

Competition among businesses is a "game" or rivalry in which each company tries to develop a winning strategy. Some economists use a strategy called *game theory* to help businesses predict how their competitors will react to a decision like an increase in prices. The theory assigns probabilities to the other companies' responses and counter-responses.

Rules of the Game

Your project is to create a new game by changing at least one of the rules of the Native American game *da-un-dah-qua*. You will then use the ideas of probability presented in this unit to study your new game.

Da-un-dah-qua is a traditional game played at midwinter and fall festivals by the Cayuga, a Native American people from western New York State and the Lake Ontario region of Canada. The rules of da-un-dah-qua appear with the "Working on the Unit Project" exercises in Section 7-1.

As you complete the "Working on the Unit Project" exercises, you will apply the ideas of probability to analyze da-un-dah-qua. A written set of rules for your new game, a probability analysis of both games, and a demonstration of your new game will complete your project.

The unwritten rules that govern social customs change as you move across national borders. Cultural tips from travel books and **cultural consultants** guide business people in their dealings around the globe.

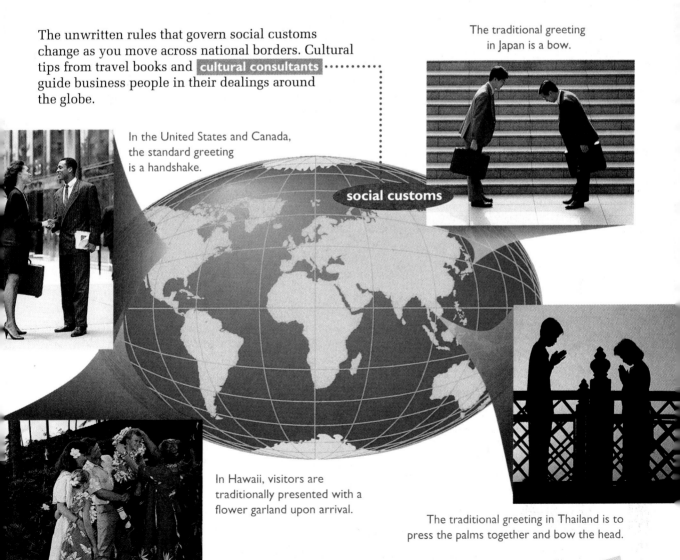

The traditional greeting in Japan is a bow.

In the United States and Canada, the standard greeting is a handshake.

social customs

In Hawaii, visitors are traditionally presented with a flower garland upon arrival.

The traditional greeting in Thailand is to press the palms together and bow the head.

For this project you should work in a group of four students. Here are some ideas to help you get started.

☞ Obtain or make the flat-bottomed bowl and the six two-sided pieces used to play da-un-dah-qua. For a detailed description of the materials needed, see the "Working on the Unit Project" exercises on page 381.

☞ Plan to go to the library to do research on the Cayuga and other groups of the Iroquois Confederacy. Learn more about the role of da-un-dah-qua in those cultures.

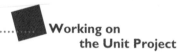

Can We Talk — Changing the Rules

When rules are changed, the results of those rules also change.

➤ Imagine changing one of the postulates listed in Unit 3. Predict the effect this has on the theorems in that unit.

➤ Your school has rules. Choose one and discuss the possible effects of a change in that rule.

➤ What changes in rules have occurred in a sport that you follow? How have the changes affected the sport?

➤ Do you think it is good that the United States constitution can be amended? Why or why not?

➤ Scientists develop theories and laws that model how the world works. Think of a law from a science course. Discuss what would happen if you made a change in the law.

➤ Some years ago a state passed a law declaring that the value of pi is exactly 3. Do you think this kind of rule change makes sense? Why or why not?

Working on the Unit Project

Your work in Unit 7 will help you to create a new game based on da-un-dah-qua and to analyze your new game.

Related Exercises:
Section 7-1, Exercises 25–27
Section 7-2, Exercises 27, 28
Section 7-3, Exercise 17
Section 7-4, Exercises 33–36
Section 7-5, Exercise 22
Section 7-6, Exercise 30

Alternative Projects p. 418

Simulation and Random Numbers

PICK A LETTER

International Artists Series

presents

Indonesian Dance Ensemble

September
23

—SATURDAY—
Doors 7:00 PM - Show 8:00 PM

University
Auditorium

GENERAL ADMISSION
TKT. NO. 557
NO REFUNDS • NO EXCHANGES
$11.50 ADVANCE
$13.50 DAY OF SHOW

There is a scratch-off circle on each ticket for an event in a series of concerts by international artists. One of the letters M, U, S, I, and C is hidden behind the circle. Anyone who holds tickets that spell "MUSIC" wins a free T-shirt. The letters are all equally likely to appear and their order is random.

Talk it Over

1. What is the probability of getting an "I" on the first ticket you buy?

2. What is the minimum number of tickets a person needs in order to win a T-shirt? Do you think there is a maximum number of tickets a person needs in order to win a T-shirt?

3. What do you think is the average number of tickets a person needs in order to win a T-shirt?

You can investigate the T-shirt problem from page 373 with a *simulation*. A **simulation** is an experiment that is enough like a real event that the event can be studied without the cost, time, materials, or risk of the real event. Scientists, business people, engineers, and others use simulation to test new materials and procedures.

Producing Random Numbers

Simulations sometimes involve *randomness*. Just as raindrops fall on a sidewalk in no apparent pattern and each point on the sidewalk has an equally likely chance of being hit, a sequence of **random numbers** has no pattern and each number has an equally likely chance of appearing in the sequence.

You can generate random numbers with a spinner. If conditions are perfect, you cannot predict the results from one spin to the next.

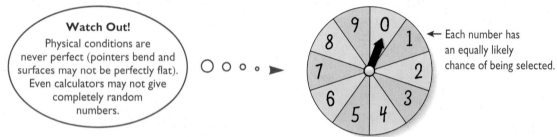

Watch Out!
Physical conditions are never perfect (pointers bend and surfaces may not be perfectly flat). Even calculators may not give completely random numbers.

← Each number has an equally likely chance of being selected.

Calculators can also be used to generate random numbers. Many calculators have a random number function that gives a number between 0 and 1.

MATH NUM HYP **PRB**
1: rand
2: nPr
3: nCr
4: !

Press **ENTER** *repeatedly to produce a sequence of random numbers.*

rand
    .7455607728
    .8559005971
    .2253600617
    .469229188
    .6866902136
    .0849241336

TECHNOLOGY NOTE

The random number function on your calculator may be a key or a menu option. On some calculators it is called "RND."

To produce a random number in any interval, you can use a formula to change the calculator's output.

Sample 1

Use a random number function on a calculator to simulate the outcomes of a roll of one die.

Sample Response

There are six equally likely outcomes. The digits 1, 2, 3, 4, 5, 6 are the six possible numbers.

		Formula		Example
Step 1	Use the "rand" function to get a random number between 0 and 1.	rand		0.3714226
Step 2	Multiply by 6 to get a random number between 0 and 6.	$6 \cdot \text{rand}$		2.2285356
Step 3	Use the greatest integer function to get a random integer between 0 and 5.	$\text{int}(6 \cdot \text{rand})$		2
Step 4	Add 1 to get a random integer between 1 and 6.	$\text{int}(6 \cdot \text{rand}) + 1$		3

The calculator screen shows a random sequence produced by the formula in Step 4.

int (6 * rand) + 1

6
2
5
6
2
3

Talk it Over

4. Suppose you change the coefficient in the formula in Step 2 of Sample 1 from 6 to 9. How does this change the results?

5. Suppose you change the coefficient to 9 and the number added in Step 4 from 1 to 3. How does this change the results?

6. Design and test a formula for a calculator to produce random integers from 10 to 29.

7. Design and test a formula to simulate tossing a coin.

······► Now you are ready for:
Exs. 1–10 on p. 378

(How) *many tickets do you need in order to win a T-shirt?*

• **Materials: calculators with a random number function**

• **Work in a group of five students.**

You will investigate the T-shirt problem on page 373.

(1) Use the numbers 1 through 5 to represent the letters on the tickets. Design a calculator formula to generate random numbers from 1 to 5.

(2) For each random number, record the letter. Continue until you have all five letters. This is one trial of the experiment. How many tickets (numbers) did you need to get all five letters? Record this value.

Example

Random numbers: 5 3 2 3 5 4 3 1

Letters represented: C S U S C I S M

Number of tickets needed: 8

1 → M
2 → U
3 → S
4 → I
5 → C

(3) Repeat step 2 nine times.

(4) Compare your results with the results of other groups. Make a line plot of all the results.

(5) **a.** How many trials did your class do?

b. What is the range of the number of tickets needed?

c. What is the mode of the number of tickets needed? What is the median? What is the mean?

d. Suppose the class repeats this experiment. How do you think the results will be different? How will they be the same?

(6) Make a relative frequency histogram to show the distribution of results from the ticket simulation for the class. You can think of the relative frequencies on the vertical axis as experimental probabilities, so the histogram represents a **probability distribution.**

(7) Is the distribution for your class *skewed, uniform, mound-shaped,* or *bimodal?*

Number of Tickets Needed to Win a T-shirt

Unit 7 Applying Probability Models

A Simulation Algorithm

In experiments involving chance, the results of specific trials are not predictable, but patterns may appear after many repeated trials. A simulation model can help you find these patterns.

Sample 2

Design a simulation for this situation.

Suppose a commuter plane holds 12 people. People buy tickets in advance. On average, 15% of the people who buy tickets do not take the flight. The airline sells 14 tickets for each flight. How often are flights overbooked because more than 12 people with tickets show up for a flight?

Sample Response

Use this algorithm.

1 State the problem clearly.

Find out how often 13 or 14 people show up for a flight.

2 Define the key question.

Select a passenger. Does the passenger show up for the flight?

3 State the underlying assumptions.

The probability that a person does not show up is 0.15. Each person's arrival has no effect on any other person's arrival.

4 Choose a model to answer the key question.

Generate random numbers from 00 to 99. A number from 01 to 15 inclusive means that the person does not show up. In all other cases, the person shows up.

5 Define and conduct a trial.

Pick 14 two-digit random numbers.

6 Record the observation of interest.

How many people showed up for the flight? Is it overbooked?

7 Repeat the last two steps several times.

Pick 14 two-digit random numbers repeatedly.

8 Summarize the information and draw conclusions.

Make a table or graph. Analyze and interpret the results.

····▶ **Now you are ready for:**
Exs. 11–27 on pp. 378–381

Talk it Over

8. For Sample 2, Sally used the numbers from 85 to 99 to represent passengers who did not show up for a flight, and numbers from 00 to 84 to represent passengers who did. Is this model the same as the model used in the Sample Response? Why or why not?

9. What are the eight steps of the simulation algorithm for the T-shirt experiment on page 376?

Look Back ◀──────────

Think of a real event that you can simulate by doing an experiment with random numbers. Describe how to use random numbers to simulate the event.

7-1 Exercises and Problems

1. **Reading** What are some benefits of simulating experiments?

2. Which of these numbers has a greater chance of appearing in a set of three-digit random numbers: *888*, *567*, or *351*? Why?

Tell whether each situation appears to produce a sequence of random numbers. Give a reason for your answer.

3. You ask each person in your class to think of a number and then to say it out loud to you.

4. You ask ten people for the last digit of their phone number.

5. You remove the face cards from a deck of cards, shuffle well, and use the number on the top card.

For Exercises 6–9, design and test a formula for a calculator to produce each set of random numbers.

6. integers from 0 to 9

7. integers from 1 to 100

8. integers from 5 to 8

9. integers from 11 to 29

10. **Writing** Give three advantages of using simulation instead of actually buying tickets to investigate the T-shirt problem.

11. In the Exploration, suppose that the probability that a ticket contains an "M" is $\frac{1}{25}$, and the probability for each of the other letters is $\frac{6}{25}$.

   a. How do you think this will affect the number of tickets needed to spell "MUSIC"?

   b. **Writing** Describe how to simulate the experiment with the new probabilities.

BY THE WAY...

To protect the privacy of people who use automatic teller machines, banks use random numbers to code transactions. A computer decodes the transaction using a mathematical procedure called the Data Encryption Standard.

Silvana's government project is about the population of the United States. She made this graph to show the distribution of ages.

12. If you select a person at random, what age group is he or she most likely to be in?

13. Suppose you select a person at random. Estimate the probability that he or she is younger than 30.

14. Suppose the distribution of ages were uniform. What would the graph look like?

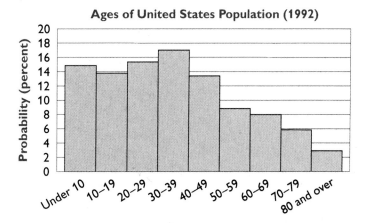

Ages of United States Population (1992)

Design and carry out a simulation to investigate each situation.

15. Suppose you randomly stop students in the hall and ask them what month they were born in. On average, how many people do you have to ask before you find someone born in the same month as you? (Assume that birth months are equally likely.)

16. Mina Parekh has a stack of résumés for a position she wants to fill. All the résumés are from qualified candidates. Suppose the probability that an applicant is an excellent candidate is $\frac{1}{5}$ and the probability that an applicant is an outstanding candidate is $\frac{1}{10}$. On average, how many applicants must Mina Parekh interview before she finds an excellent or outstanding candidate?

BY THE WAY...

The United States is expected to experience *population aging* over the next 50 years. The Census Bureau predicts that in 2050, almost 30% of the United States population will be 60 or older.

Design a simulation to investigate each situation.

17. A group of equally qualified candidates for a job contains 30 men and 20 women. Five people are hired. What is the probability that four or five of the people hired are women?

18. Change the airplane simulation in Sample 2 so that the plane holds the number of people shown in the diagram, the airline sells 14 tickets, and there is a 25% chance that a person does not take the flight. Then how often is the plane overbooked?

19. Design a simulation to investigate this situation: Suppose a water system has five pumps that work independently of each other.

At any time, the probability that a pump does not work is $\frac{1}{4}$. For water to flow from A to B, both pumps along at least one path must be working. How often can water flow from A to B?

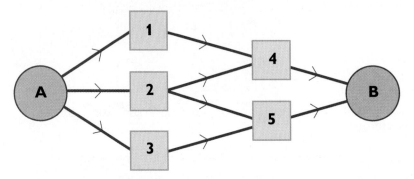

20. The tickets for a school fundraiser are numbered from 1 to n, the number of tickets sold. They will be used in a drawing for a door prize. Three friends arrive at the fundraiser separately (and randomly). Their ticket numbers are 43, 67, and 105. The friends estimate the number of tickets sold by using this algorithm:

> ➤ Find the mean of the differences between any two of their numbers.

> ➤ Add the mean to the greatest of their numbers.

a. What is their estimate of the total number of people at the fundraiser?

b. Estimate the probability that one of the friends wins the prize.

c. Suppose another friend joins the group and has ticket number 148. How does this change their estimate of n?

d. Choose three random numbers between 1 and 100. Use the process described above to estimate n (which in this case is 100). Do this several times. Is the mean of the estimates close to 100?

Ongoing **ASSESSMENT**

21. **Group Activity** Work with another student.

Suppose you can get to school by two different routes. You have collected this data over a period of several weeks:

Route A: 70% of the time it takes 5 minutes.
           30% of the time it takes 8 minutes.

Route B: 20% of the time it takes 3 minutes.
           80% of the time it takes 6 minutes.

Design and carry out a simulation in which one of you simulates using Route A for five weeks and the other simulates using Route B for five weeks (25 school days). Find the average time in each case. On average, which route is faster?

22. A parabola passes through the points $(-4, 0)$, $(-2, -8)$, and $(1, -5)$. Find an equation for the parabola. *(Section 6-5)*

23. Find the measures of each interior and each exterior angle of a regular 18-gon. *(Section 3-4)*

24. Suppose you toss three coins. What is the probability of getting all heads? *(Toolbox Skill 6)*

Working on the Unit Project

Da-un-dah-qua is a game for two players.

➤ Place six disks in a dish.

➤ Mark the disks so that the two faces are different from each other. For example, one side can be black and the other side green.

➤ One player shakes or rattles the dish so that the disks jump and resettle.

> **Rules of DA-UN-DAH-QUA**
>
> ➤ If the disks land with all the same color showing, the player scores 5 points and gets another turn.
>
> ➤ If five of the disks land with the same color showing, the player scores 1 point and gets another turn.
>
> ➤ For all other results, the player scores no points and the other player gets a turn.
>
> ➤ The first player who scores 40 points wins the game.

The Iroquois people used this decorated wooden bowl to play da-un-dah-qua at the Midwinter Ceremonial. The bowl is decorated with four clan symbols. The disks are peach pits burned black on one side.

Mohawk

Oneida

Onondaga

Cayuga

Seneca

25. a. Do you think that the events "6 disks land same color side up" and "5 disks land same color side up" are equally likely? Why or why not?

b. Make a list of all the possible outcomes. Which event is most likely?

26. How can you simulate the toss of one disk? of six disks?

27. Group Activity Work with another student.

Play two or three rounds of da-un-dah-qua. Record the outcome of each turn.

This maple cane was used to call the roll of the chiefs at meetings of the Iroquois League of Peace. The cane has five sections, one for each of the five nations that made up the league.

7-2 Probability of Either of Two Events

Find probabilities in situations with continuous outcomes and with discrete outcomes. Find the probability that either of two events occurs.

TO BE or NOT TO BE

Talk it Over

1. Answer each question for rolling the die and for spinning the pointer on the dial shown.

Each face of a die contains one of the *integers* 1–6.

All the positive *real numbers* less than 6 are around the dial.

The pointer spins freely.

a. What are all the possible outcomes?

b. Are the outcomes *discrete* or *continuous?* Explain your choice.

2. Suppose you roll the die. What is the probability of the event "a number less than or equal to 5"? Explain how you found the answer.

3. Charlene found the probability that the pointer on the dial will stop at a number less than or equal to 5 this way:

The length of the arc from 0 to 5 is $\frac{5}{6}$ of the circumference of the entire circle, so $P(\text{number} \leq 5) = \frac{5}{6}$.

Explain why her method works.

Student Resources Toolbox
p. 631 *Probability*

Student Resources Toolbox
p. 628 *Using Counting Techniques*

To find the probability of an event with discrete outcomes, you can find the number of outcomes by direct counting or by using the multiplication counting principle or permutations. To find the probability of an event with continuous outcomes, you can measure lengths, areas, and so on.

$$P(\text{event}) = \frac{\text{size of favorable outcomes}}{\text{size of possible outcomes}}$$

"Size" can be a count or a measurement.

Sample 1

For each situation, find the probability of the event "the sum of both outcomes is less than or equal to 5."

a. Suppose you roll two dice.

b. Suppose you spin the pointers on two dials like the one on page 382.

Sample Response

a. When you roll two dice, the outcomes are discrete. There are $6 \cdot 6 = 36$ possible outcomes.

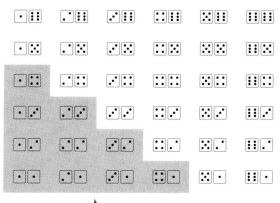

There are 10 outcomes for which sum ≤ 5.

$$P(\text{sum} \le 5) = \frac{\text{number of favorable outcomes}}{\text{number of possible outcomes}}$$

$$= \frac{10}{36} \approx 0.28$$

b. When you spin the pointers on two dials, the outcomes are continuous.
Let x = all possible outcomes on one dial.
Let y = all possible outcomes on the other dial.

Points (x, y) in the square represent all the possible outcomes for two dials.

Points in the shaded region represent outcomes for which $x + y \le 5$.

$$P(\text{sum} \le 5) = \frac{\text{area of shaded triangle}}{\text{area of 6-by-6 square}}$$

$$= \frac{12.5}{36} \approx 0.35$$

▶ Now you are ready for:
Exs. 1–8 on p. 387

Probability with or

outcomes from rolling a die

○ A   ○ B

Recall that logical statements in mathematics use the inclusive *or*. The statement "either event *A* occurs or event *B* occurs" is true when *at least one* of the events occurs. It is true:

➤ when *only* event *A* occurs,

➤ when *only* event *B* occurs,

➤ when *both* events *A* and *B* occur.

Talk it Over

4. Use the Venn diagram. Event *A* is "odd number." Event *B* is "number greater than 4." Find each probability.

   a. $P(A)$

   b. $P(B)$

   c. $P(A \text{ and } B)$

5. How can you use your answers to question 4 to find $P(A \text{ or } B)$?

Sample 2

Renata Baines rides the bus to work. She can take either the T-184 bus or the T-172 bus. During the morning and afternoon rush hours, the T-184 bus runs every 20 min, while the T-172 bus runs every 15 min. What is the probability that she will wait no more than 5 min for a bus during rush hour?

Sample Response

Find the probability that she waits no more than 5 min for the T-184 bus or no more than 5 min for the T-172 bus.

Problem Solving Strategy: Use a diagram.

Step 1 Find all the possible waiting times for both buses.

➤ Let x = the waiting time for the T-184 bus.

➤ Let y = the waiting time for the T-172 bus.

The points inside the rectangle formed by $0 \le x \le 20$ and $0 \le y \le 15$ represent all possible waiting times for the buses.

The area of this rectangle is $15 \cdot 20 = 300$.

The point (12, 7) means the T-184 bus arrives 12 min after she does and the T-172 bus arrives 7 min after she does.

Waiting time for T-172 bus

Waiting time for T-184 bus

Step 2 Find all waiting times in which a bus arrives within 5 min.

Graph the inequalities $0 \le x \le 5$ and $0 \le y \le 5$.

$$\begin{array}{c} \text{area of the} \\ \text{shaded region} \end{array} = \begin{array}{c} \text{sum of the areas of the} \\ \text{two shaded rectangles} \end{array} - \begin{array}{c} \text{area of the} \\ \text{doubly shaded region} \end{array}$$

$$= \qquad (5 \cdot 15 + 5 \cdot 20) \qquad - \qquad 5 \cdot 5$$

$$= 150$$

Step 3 Find the ratio of the areas you found in steps 1 and 2.

$$P(0 \le x \le 5 \text{ or } 0 \le y \le 5) = \frac{\text{area of the shaded region}}{\text{area of 15-by-20 rectangle}}$$

$$= \frac{150}{300} = 0.5$$

The probability that Renata Baines will wait no more than 5 min is 0.5.

PROBABILITY OF EITHER OF TWO EVENTS

To find the probability that either of two events occurs, you can add the probabilities of the events and subtract the probability that both events occur.

For any two events A and B:

$$\boldsymbol{P(A \text{ or } B) = P(A) + P(B) - P(A \text{ and } B)}$$

Talk it Over

6. Describe the region in Sample 2 that contains the points that represent this event:

   The waiting time for the T-184 bus is no more than 5 min *and* the waiting time for the T-172 bus is no more than 5 min.

7. Suppose you roll a die. Find each probability.

   a. $P(4)$ b. $P(\text{odd number})$

   c. $P(4 \text{ or odd number})$ d. $P(4 \text{ and odd number})$

8. Suppose you replace "odd number" with "not 4" in question 7. How do your answers to parts (b)–(d) change?

Mutually Exclusive Events

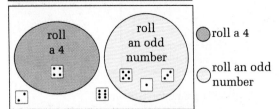

○ roll a 4

○ roll an odd number

Complementary Events

○ roll a 4

○ do not roll a 4

All the outcomes not in "roll a 4" are in its complement.

In Sample 2, both buses can arrive at the bus stop in 5 min or less from the time Renata Baines begins to wait. However, some events *cannot* occur at the same time. Events like these are called **mutually exclusive events.** When you roll a die, the events "roll a 4" and "roll an odd number" are mutually exclusive.

Two mutually exclusive events that account for all possibilities are called **complementary events.** When you roll a die, the events "roll a 4" and "do not roll a 4" are complementary events.

PROBABILITY OF MUTUALLY EXCLUSIVE EVENTS

When two events are mutually exclusive, you can add to find the probability that either one occurs. For any two mutually exclusive events A and B:

$$P(A \text{ or } B) = P(A) + P(B)$$

Complementary Events

The sum of the probabilities of complementary events is 1. For any event A:

$$P(\text{not } A) = 1 - P(A)$$

> **Talk it Over**
>
> 9. Explain how to use the general formula for $P(A \text{ or } B)$ to derive the formula for the probability of mutually exclusive events.
>
> 10. Explain how to use the general formula for $P(A \text{ or } B)$ to derive the formula for the probability of complementary events.

Look Back

Compare finding the probability of either of two events when the outcomes of both events are continuous and when the outcomes of both events are discrete.

····▶ **Now you are ready for:**
Exs. 9–28 on pp. 387–389

Exercises and Problems

1. **Reading** How can you find the probability of an event with continuous outcomes?

For each event in Exercises 2–8:

a. **Tell whether the outcomes are *discrete* or *continuous*.**

b. **Find the probability of the event.**

2. The freely spinning pointer on a dial numbered 0–8 stops at a value between 1 and 4.

3. You roll a 9 on a 12-sided die that has the numbers 1 through 12 on its faces.

4. You choose an ace at random from a well-shuffled standard deck of cards.

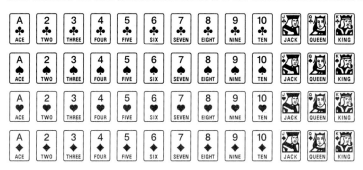

Each suit has 3 face cards — jack, queen, and king.

5. When you look at a clock, the second hand is between 6 and 7.

6. Suppose every board in a pile of 8-foot pine boards has a knot in it somewhere. A board is chosen at random and the knot is within 1 ft of one end of the board.

7. When you spin the pointers on the dial for Exercise 2 and the dial on page 382, the sum of the numbers where the pointers stop is greater than 10.

8. When you spin the pointers on the dial for Exercise 2 and the dial on page 382, the sum of the numbers where the pointers stop is between 2 and 4.

Find the probability of each event.

9. When you spin the pointers on two dials like the one on page 382, the sum of the numbers is less than 2 or greater than 3.

10. You choose an ace or a heart at random from a well-shuffled standard deck of playing cards.

11. You choose a face card or a red card at random from a well-shuffled standard deck of playing cards.

12. When you roll two dice, the sum of the outcomes is greater than 6 or you get a 4 on one of the dice.

13. **Writing** You use probability to solve the problem in Sample 2 because the outcomes in this situation are random. What is the source of randomness in this situation? Explain.

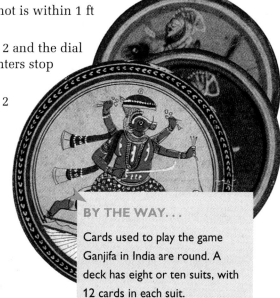

BY THE WAY...

Cards used to play the game Ganjifa in India are round. A deck has eight or ten suits, with 12 cards in each suit.

Use the Venn diagram for Exercise 14.

Suppose you select a planet at random. Find each probability.

14. **a.** P(at least two moons)

   b. P(gravity at least as strong as on Earth)

   c. P(at least two moons or gravity at least as strong as on Earth)

   d. P(at least two moons and gravity at least as strong as on Earth)

15. **Astronomy** The best time to view a planet is when its orbit around the sun brings it closest to Earth. When one of the planets farther from the sun is closest to Earth, it is said to be *in opposition*, since it appears directly opposite from the sun. What is the probability that either Mars or Jupiter will be in opposition during a six-month period?

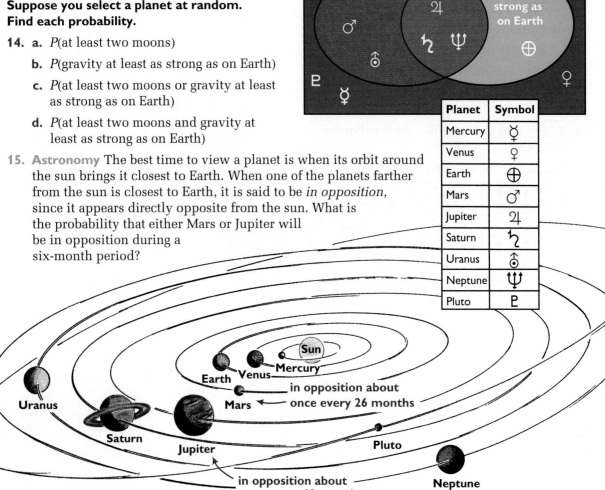

Planet	Symbol
Mercury	☿
Venus	♀
Earth	⊕
Mars	♂
Jupiter	♃
Saturn	♄
Uranus	♅
Neptune	♆
Pluto	♇

16. Suppose some students meet in the student center between classes. They take off their almost-identical denim jackets and pile them on a chair. Suppose they grab their jackets without looking when the bell rings for their next class.

   a. Without computing the probability, tell whether you think

   P(at least one student picks up the correct jacket)

   is greater when *three* students meet or when *two* students meet. Explain your reasoning.

   b. Find P(at least one student picks up the right jacket) in each situation described in part (a).

   c. Does your answer to part (b) surprise you? Why or why not?

   d. What do you think the probability is in this situation when four students meet? Check your answer by computing the probability.

17. **Open-ended** Describe a real-life situation in which two events are mutually exclusive but are not complementary.

18. Amir drew this diagram to model the situation in Sample 2.

    a. Write a system of inequalities for each shaded trapezoid.

    b. What event does each trapezoid represent?

    c. Are the events represented by the two shaded trapezoids mutually exclusive? Are the events represented by the two shaded rectangles in Step 2 of Sample 2 mutually exclusive?

    d. Use Amir's diagram to solve Sample 2.

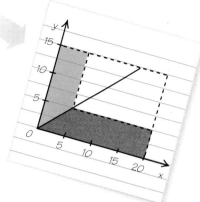

19. **Group Activity** Work with another student.

    a. Each of you should describe a possible event when three dice are rolled.

    b. Together, you should perform a simulation to find the experimental probability of either of the two events.

    c. Separately, you should calculate the theoretical probability of either of the two events.

    d. Compare your answers in part (c) to your results in part (b).

Review **PREVIEW**

Design and test a formula for a calculator to produce each set of random numbers. *(Section 7-1)*

20. integers from 0 to 12   21. integers from 1 to 35   22. integers from 47 to 62

For Exercises 23–25, graph each absolute value function. *(Section 2-3)*

23. $y = |x|$ 24. $y = |x + 2|$ 25. $y = 3|x| - 1$

26. Suppose a data set has a normal distribution with $\bar{x} = 384$ and $\sigma = 29$. *(Section 6-3)*

    a. Within what range do about 95% of the data items fall?

    b. About what percent of the data values are between 384 and 413?

Working on the Unit Project

Use the rules for the Cayuga game of da-un-dah-qua, which are given in the "Working on the Unit Project" exercises in Section 7-1.

27. Are the outcomes of the game *discrete* or *continuous*? Explain your choice.

28. Find the probability of each possible combination of two different colors.

Geometric Models for Probability

WAITING AREA

EXPLORATION

(What) is the probability that two friends will meet?

- **Materials: calculators with a random number function**
- **Work with another student.**

Suppose two friends take part in a fundraiser walk. They agree to arrive for registration between 8:00 A.M. and 8:30 A.M. They decide that they will wait for each other for 10 minutes, but no longer. What is the probability that they will meet?

Use simulation to find out.

① Use random numbers to represent the friends' times in minutes after 8:00. Generate numbers from 0 to 29. Each trial is represented by two random numbers (one for each person).

② Decide whether the times are within 10 minutes of each other. If so, the friends will meet. Record whether or not they will meet.

Example:

TRIAL	One friend's arrival time	The other friend's arrival time	Did they meet?
1	23	5	no (18 min apart)
2	6	13	yes (7 min apart)

③ Repeat the trial several times and record your results.

④ Combine your data with the data collected by the rest of the class. Using all the trials from the entire class, what is the experimental probability that the friends will meet?

⑤ What assumptions did you make in this simulation?

BY THE WAY...

About eighteen thousand people participated in an AIDS Walk through Golden Gate Park in San Francisco on July 17, 1994. The walk raised $2.8 million, a record for a single fundraising event in the Bay Area.

In the Exploration, you used simulation to find out whether the friends will meet. Another way to find out is to use coordinates. Then you can compare the areas of two regions, as you did in Section 7-2.

Sample

Use coordinates to find the theoretical probability of the event described in the Exploration.

Sample Response

Step 1 Find all the times when either friend can arrive.

Let x and y be the two arrival times in minutes after 8:00.

Either friend can arrive any time during a 30-minute period, so $0 \leq x \leq 30$ and $0 \leq y \leq 30$.

The area of this square is $30 \cdot 30 = 900$.

This square represents all the possible times when both people might arrive.

Step 2 Find out when both friends will be there.

One friend arrives x minutes after 8:00.

The number of minutes after 8:00 that the other friend arrives, y, must be less than $x + 10$ and greater than $x - 10$.

Graph the region that the inequalities $y < x + 10$ and $y > x - 10$ represent.

This region represents the times when the friends meet.

The area of the shaded region is

(the area of the square) − (the area of the two triangles in the corners).

Area of each triangle = $\frac{1}{2}(20)(20) = 200$ ⟵ $A = \frac{1}{2}bh$

Area of shaded region = $900 - 2(200) = 500$

Step 3 Find the ratio of the two areas.

$$P(\text{friends meet}) = \frac{\text{area of shaded region}}{\text{area of square}}$$

$$= \frac{500}{900} \approx 0.56$$

The theoretical probability is about 0.56.

Talk it Over

1. How close is the probability you found in step 4 of the Exploration to the result in the Sample?

2. May says that the shaded region in the Sample represents the friends' arriving at the same time ($y = x$) and all times within ten minutes before or after that. Do you agree with this statement? Why or why not?

3. Describe another way to find the area of the shaded region in the Sample.

4. Suppose the friends agree to wait 20 min for each other. How does this change the graph in the Sample? How does it change the probability?

Look Back ◄─────────────────────

In the Sample, where did you use probability? Where did you use algebra? Where did you use geometry?

7-3 Exercises and Problems

1. **Reading** Suppose the friends decide to meet between 8 A.M. and 9 A.M. How would you change the simulation in the Exploration?

2. **Writing** What does the expression $x - 10 < y < x + 10$ mean? Why does it model the situation in the Exploration?

3. Find the probability that the friends meet if they agree to wait just five minutes.

4. Suppose you and your mother open a joint checking account. You each deposit $50 and agree that no one will write a check over $60. You each write one check.

   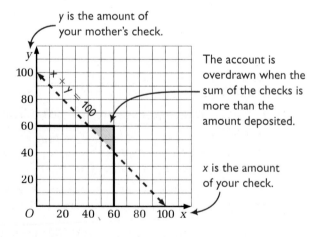

   y is the amount of your mother's check.

   The account is overdrawn when the sum of the checks is more than the amount deposited.

   x is the amount of your check.

   a. What does the square region represent?

   b. What does the line $x + y = 100$ represent?

   c. What are the coordinates of the vertices of the shaded region? What is the area of the shaded region?

   d. What is the probability that the account is overdrawn?

5. Suppose two sisters open a joint checking account. One sister deposits $30 and the other deposits $20. They agree that neither of them will write a check over $40. They each write one check. Use coordinates to find the probability that they overdraw the account.

6. Suppose two friends both say that they will call you tonight between 7:00 and 7:30. You plan to talk to each friend for 15 minutes. Use coordinates to find the probability that their calls will overlap.

7. Janelle and Abby work in a clothing store that has only one cash register. It takes two minutes to ring up a sale. Suppose they each ring up a sale at some time in a ten-minute period. Use coordinates to find the probability that one of them will have to wait to use the register.

8. You can estimate the area of an irregularly shaped region with a geometric probability model. Use this algorithm with tracing paper and graph paper:

1 Trace the outline of the irregularly shaped region on tracing paper.

2 Place the tracing over graph paper on which you have drawn x- and y-axes. Draw a rectangle that encloses the shape. Find the dimensions of the rectangle in terms of the coordinate system.

Use any conveniently sized grid.

Put the origin at a corner.

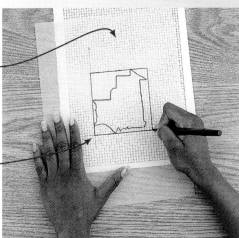

3 Produce random ordered pairs with coordinates (x, y), where x is a positive number less than or equal to the length of the rectangle and y is a positive number less than or equal to the width of the rectangle.

4 For each ordered pair, score 1 point if it is in the region and 0 points if it is not.

5 After at least 100 trials, find the ratio of the sum of the points in the region to the total number of trials.

6 Use the map scale to find the area that the rectangle represents. Multiply the ratio by the area of the rectangle to estimate the area.

a. Use this method to estimate the area of Mauritania.

b. Explain why this algorithm works.

c. **Research** Find the area of Mauritania in an atlas or an almanac. How close is the estimate you made in part (a) to the actual area? Describe two ways to make a better estimate.

9. **Open-ended** Think of a problem that you can solve with a geometric probability model. Sketch a model that represents the problem and solve it.

Review **PREVIEW**

Two dice are thrown. Find the probability of each event. *(Section 7-2)*

10. The sum is 7 or 5.

11. The sum is less than 4 or greater than 8.

12. The sum is greater than 9 or equal to 3.

13. The sum is less than 6 or equal to 2.

Write an equation for each function in the form $f(x) = mx + b$. *(Section 2-2)*

14. $f(4) = 3, f(-1) = 13$

15. $f(7) = 0, f(11) = 0$

16. A person chooses a bill at random from a wallet that contains four $1 bills, five $5 bills, two $10 bills, and one $20 bill. *(Toolbox Skill 7)*

   a. Find P($1 bill).

   b. Find P(bill worth less than $10).

Working on the Unit Project

17. **Research** Other Native American groups have different names and rules for the game of da-un-dah-qua. The first Europeans to see the game called it "Dish." Find out about the different ways people play this game and what its role is in Native American society.

Unit 7 CHECKPOINT

1. **Writing** Name two places in this unit where you used a formula. How are the formulas used? How are they related to probability?

For Exercises 2 and 3, design and test a formula for a calculator to produce each set of random numbers.   7-1

2. integers from 0 to 19   3. integers from 6 to 12

4. Design a simulation for this situation: Suppose a florist receives 60 orders for bouquets each weekend. Since, on average, 5% of the orders are cancelled later, the florist prepares 58 bouquets. How often does the florist have at least one extra bouquet?

For Exercises 5 and 6, suppose you draw a card from a well-shuffled standard deck. Find each probability.   7-2

5. P(diamond or club)   6. P(diamond or jack)

7. It takes 30 seconds to be served at a pretzel stand. Two people arrive randomly within a two-minute period. Use coordinates to find the probability that one of them will have to wait to be served.   7-3

Conditional Probability and Independent Events

·····Focus

Find conditional probabilities. Recognize independent and dependent events.

Healthy Conditions?

	Allergic	Not allergic	Total
Male students	12	7	19
Female students	9	8	17
Total	21	15	36

Simone noticed that in the fall and spring, many of her class-mates frequently sneezed or coughed. She wondered whether their symptoms were due to allergies. The school nurse surveyed Simone's class for allergies to airborne sub-stances. The results are shown in the table.

Sample 1

Find the probability that a student selected at random in Simone's class is not allergic, given that the student is a male.

Sample Response ·····

Problem Solving Strategy: Use a diagram.

Make a tree diagram to represent the allergy data for Simone's class.

Look at the part of the diagram that is shown in color. There are 19 male students. Of the 19 males, 7 are not allergic, so the probability that a male selected at random from the class is not allergic is $\frac{7}{19}$, or about 0.37.

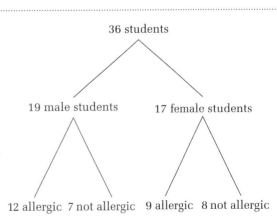

36 students

19 male students   17 female students

12 allergic 7 not allergic   9 allergic 8 not allergic

1. In Sample 1, why is the probability $\frac{7}{19}$, not $\frac{7}{36}$?

2. What is the probability that a student is allergic, given that the student is a female?

In situations like that in Sample 1, you need to find a probability under restricted conditions. In Sample 1, the condition is that the student is a male. This is called a **conditional probability.** In these cases the number of possible outcomes is reduced to reflect the restrictions.

You write the conditional probability in Sample 1 as

$$P(\text{not allergic} \mid \text{male}),$$

which is read, "the probability that a student is not allergic given that the student is a male."

You can use a *probability tree diagram* to show the probabilities that events will occur. These two partially completed diagrams are based on the allergy data from Simone's class.

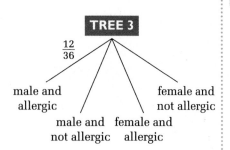

3. Compare Tree 1 and Tree 2. Describe any differences.

4. Tree 3 shows the probabilities that a randomly chosen student is a male or a female *and* is or is not allergic.

   a. Look at the branches of Trees 1, 2, and 3 that have been completed. Do you see any relationship among the probabilities in Tree 1 and Tree 3? among the probabilities in Tree 2 and Tree 3?

   b. Choose corresponding branches from Trees 1–3 and find the probabilities. Does the relationship from part (a) still hold?

CONDITIONAL PROBABILITY

For any events A and B:

$$P(A \text{ and } B) = P(A) \cdot P(B \mid A) \quad \text{and} \quad P(B \mid A) = \frac{P(A \text{ and } B)}{P(A)}$$

You read this as "the probability of B given A."

······► **Now you are ready for:**
Exs. 1–15 on pp. 399–400

Dependent and Independent Events

In some situations, the outcome of one event changes the probability of the outcome of another event.

Sample 2

Two green balls and three orange balls are placed in a jar. One ball is randomly chosen and its color is recorded. Then a second ball is chosen and its color is recorded. What is the probability of getting a green ball on the first draw and an orange ball on the second draw in each situation?

a. The first ball is replaced before the second is drawn.

b. The first ball is not replaced before the second is drawn.

Sample Response

Problem Solving Strategy: Use a diagram.

a. The first ball is replaced, so the probabilities are the same for each draw.

b. The first ball is not replaced, so the probabilities change for the second draw.

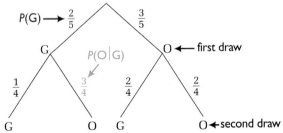

$$P(G \text{ and } O) = P(G) \cdot P(O \mid G)$$
$$= \frac{2}{5} \cdot \frac{3}{5}$$
$$= \frac{6}{25} = 0.24$$

$$P(G \text{ and } O) = P(G) \cdot P(O \mid G)$$
$$= \frac{2}{5} \cdot \frac{3}{4}$$
$$= \frac{6}{20} = 0.3$$

5. For each of the two cases in Sample 2, find the probability that the two balls drawn are *both* green.

6. In which situation in Sample 2 can you say that the probability of the event "the second ball is orange" depends on the probability of the event "the first ball is green"?

Two events are **independent** if and only if the occurrence of one does not affect the probability of the occurrence of the other.

INDEPENDENT EVENTS

Events A and B are independent if and only if $P(B \mid A) = P(B)$.

Sample 3

Use the allergy data on page 395. Are the events "female student" and "allergic" independent?

Sample Response

Use the definition of independent events.

If $P(\text{allergic} \mid \text{female}) = P(\text{allergic})$, then "female" and "allergic" are independent events.

$P(\text{allergic}) = \dfrac{21}{36} \approx 0.58$

$P(\text{allergic} \mid \text{female}) = \dfrac{9}{17} \approx 0.53$

The values are not equal. The events are not independent.

Slightly more than half of the female students (about 0.53) in Simone's class have allergies, yet females make up slightly less than half of the class (about 0.47). If "allergic" were independent of "female," then you could expect allergies to be distributed among male and female students in proportion to the sizes of these two groups. That does not happen here, so the events are *dependent*.

Look Back

Now you are ready for: Exs. 16–36 on pp. 400–402

Give examples of events you think are independent. How can you test mathematically whether they are independent?

Exercises and Problems

1. **Reading** Suppose you are tutoring another student. Explain the meaning of *conditional probability*.

This table gives majors of students at a small technical college. Use the data for Exercises 2–9.

	Freshmen	Sophomores	Juniors	Seniors	Total
Architecture	50	40	45	25	160
Engineering	30	25	35	40	130
Business	20	25	20	45	110
Total	100	90	100	110	400

Suppose a student is selected at random. Find each probability.

2. P(freshman)

3. P(architecture major)

4. P(freshman and architecture major)

5. P(sophomore | business major)

6. P(business major | sophomore)

7. P(sophomore or business major)

8. Show that these expressions are equal:

P(senior | engineering major) and $\dfrac{P(\text{senior and engineering major })}{P(\text{engineering major})}$

9. **Open-ended** Create a conditional probability question based on the table above. Answer the question.

10. **Reading** How is the second formula in the box at the top of page 397 related to the first formula?

11. A person is chosen at random from shoppers at a mall. Suppose the probability that the person has red hair and freckles, P(red hair and freckles), is $\dfrac{3}{25}$, and P(freckles) $= \dfrac{9}{25}$. What is P(red hair | freckles)?

12. **Research** Speak to your principal or to a person in the school administration office.

   a. Find out how many students are in your school. Find out how many students are in one grade.

   b. Find out how many students in that grade have last names that begin with a certain letter.

   c. What is the probability that a student chosen at random from that grade at your school has a last name beginning with that letter?

13. A road has stop lights at two consecutive intersections.

   ➤ The probability of passing through the first intersection without stopping is 0.5.

   ➤ The probability of passing through the second intersection without stopping, given that you made it through the first without stopping, is 0.8.

   What is the probability of passing through both intersections without stopping?

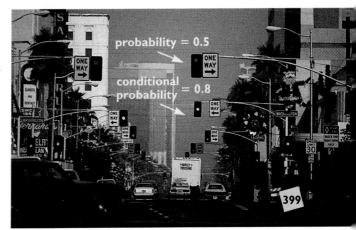

probability = 0.5

conditional probability = 0.8

399

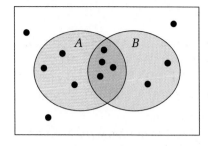

14. **Writing** Samuel drew this diagram to represent $P(B \mid A)$. He said, "We know that A has occurred, so look inside A. The probability of B given A is the ratio of the overlap of A and B to all of A. So we have $P(B \mid A) = \dfrac{\text{number in both } A \text{ and } B}{\text{number in } A}$."

Do you agree with Samuel's argument? Why or why not?

15. **Group Activity** Work with another student. You will need a spinner with ten equal sectors or a calculator with a random number function.

Have one student try to guess which random digit from 0 to 9 has been produced by the other student with a spinner or a calculator. The student producing the random number should give hints like, "It is odd," or "It is prime," or "It is less than 5."

a. Play the game 30 times with a partner. Take turns generating the random digit. The player with the most correct guesses wins.

b. **Writing** Which hints give more information than others? Give examples.

c. **Writing** How does conditional probability play a role in this game?

Market Research A movie studio conducted a test screening to get audience reactions to a new film. Some results are shown.

The researchers used a random sample of 50 people so that predictions can be made from the data.

Use the test screening results for Exercises 16–25.

16. a. Make a table to summarize the results.

b. Use the table to complete each tree diagram.

> 40% of the people surveyed were males.
> 60% of the males liked the film.
> 70% of the females liked the film.

```
        ?     ?              ?      ?
      male  female         likes  dislikes
     ? / \ ?  ? / \ ?      ? / \ ?  ? / \ ?
  likes dislikes likes dislikes  male female male female
```

BY THE WAY...

Movie studios usually begin screening a movie three to four months before it is released. The test screenings, along with other market research, are used to determine whether there is enough awareness of the movie and how strongly the audience wants to see it.

Suppose a person is chosen at random from the market research study. Find each probability.

17. $P(\text{female})$

18. $P(\text{female} \mid \text{person likes the film})$

19. $P(\text{person likes the film} \mid \text{male})$

20. $P(\text{male} \mid \text{person who likes the film})$

21. $P(\text{female likes the film})$

22. $P(\text{male likes the film})$

Unit 7 Applying Probability Models

Check one

Male   Female

☐   ☐

Did you like the film?

yes   no

☐   ☐

Why?_____

_____

23. **Writing** To answer Exercises 17–22, did you use a formula or a tree diagram from Exercise 16, part (b)? Explain why you prefer one method more than the other.

24. **Writing** Are the events "likes the film" and "male" independent? Explain.

25. **Open-ended** Make a table of possible outcomes of a survey where "likes the film" and "female" are independent.

26. Four boys and five girls are on a committee to organize a school dance. They are having trouble scheduling a time to meet. At each meeting, a random member of the committee is absent.

   a. Find the probability that a boy is absent at one meeting and then a girl is absent at the next meeting.

   b. Suppose students are removed from the committee if they miss a meeting. Find the probability that a boy is absent at one meeting and then a girl is absent at the next meeting.

   c. **Writing** In which case, part (a) or part (b), are the events "boy is absent" and "girl is absent" independent? Explain.

27. Use the formulas for conditional probability and independent events to show that if events A and B are independent, then $P(A \text{ and } B) = P(A) \cdot P(B)$.

28. **Weather** Before the development of radar, weather satellites, computers, and all the other technology used by today's forecasters, people used the behavior of animals and plants to predict the weather.

The reliability of these natural weather predictors varies greatly. In England, people used a plant called the scarlet pimpernel to predict whether it would rain.

   a. When the pimpernel's flowers open, the chance that it will not rain that day is 92%. Express this probability as a conditional probability.

   b. When the flowers do not open, the chance of rain is 17%. Express this probability as a conditional probability.

29. **Writing** Mutually exclusive events are always dependent. Explain why or give an example.

30. Suppose you go to a mall with a friend. You agree to shop on your own and then meet at the fountain between 7:00 P.M. and 8:30 P.M. You agree to wait for each other for 15 min before going home. What is the probability that you and your friend meet? *(Section 7-3)*

31. Write the expression log M^2N^3 in terms of log M and log N. *(Section 5-7)*

32. How many different groups of three class representatives can be chosen from a class of 22 students? *(Toolbox Skill 4)*

Working on the Unit Project

Use the description of da-un-dah-qua on page 381.

33. **a.** Complete the tree diagram for what can happen when a player has two consecutive tosses in the game of da-un-dah-qua.

    b. What property did you use to complete the diagram?

Key

C — all six same color

B — five same color, one different

A — other results

The Cayuga lived in longhouses made of bark over a frame of bent trees. They grew corn and other vegetables. To celebrate the first corn of the season, the Cayuga held a festival at which they played da-un-dah-qua.

34. Find each probability for two tosses.

    a. P(all six same color | five same color, one different)

    b. P(all green | all green)

35. Find the probability of getting all six of the same color on each of two consecutive tosses.

36. Suppose you have two consecutive tosses. What is the probability of getting all six the same color on one toss and getting exactly five the same color on the other toss?

Expected Value

What's a Fair Price?

How do insurance companies decide what is a fair rate to charge? They use data from past experience. For example, suppose insurance companies have found that, on average, in 10,000 homeowners' policies the following claims have occurred in the past.

Average value of claim	Number of claims per 10,000 policies
$200,000	1
$20,000	10
$2,000	200
$0	9789

BY THE WAY...

According to legend, merchants along the Yangtze River in ancient China "insured" their cargo by dividing it equally among all the boats. If a boat overturned in the rapids, each merchant shared equally in the loss.

How much does an insurance company expect to pay in one year on 10,000 policies in this situation?

$200,000 \cdot 1 + \$20,000 \cdot 10 + \$2000 \cdot 200 + \$0 \cdot 9789 = \$800,000$

Suppose the cost of these claims is shared evenly among the 10,000 policyholders. Then each policy-holder would contribute

$$\frac{\$800,000}{10,000} = \$80$$

This is a fair price to pay for the insurance. Usually the price is greater because the insurance company has additional costs and wants to make a profit.

You can calculate a fair price to pay for insurance in the situation on page 403 another way. You can find the probability of each claim by dividing each number of claims by 10,000.

Average value of claim	Probability
$200,000	0.0001
$20,000	0.001
$2,000	0.02
$0	0.9789

$$\frac{1}{10,000} = 0.0001$$

$$\frac{10}{10,000} = 0.001$$

$$\frac{200}{10,000} = 0.02$$

$$\frac{9789}{10,000} = 0.9789$$

Then you can find a fair price to pay for a policy this way:

$$(\$200,000)(0.0001) + (\$20,000)(0.001) + (\$2000)(0.02) + (\$0)(0.9789) = \$80$$

Talk it Over

1. Compare the two methods for finding a fair price.
   a. How are they alike? How are they different?
   b. Which do you prefer? Why?
   c. Use the distributive property to explain why the two methods are equivalent.
2. Does it make sense for an insurance company's policyholders to share the cost of everyone's insurance evenly? Why or why not?

The second method for finding a fair price can be used in many situations involving probabilities and gains or losses. The result is called **expected value**, which is the average gain or loss in repeated occurrences of a situation.

EXPECTED VALUE

To find an expected value, multiply the value of each outcome, x_i, by its probability, $P(x_i)$, and then add all the products.

Expected value $= x_1 \cdot P(x_1) + x_2 \cdot P(x_2) + x_3 \cdot P(x_3) + \cdots + x_n \cdot P(x_n)$

Sample 1

A nonprofit organization is selling lottery tickets for $1 each. There is one $500 prize, two $100 prizes, and ten $5 prizes. Two thousand tickets are sold. On average, how much can a person who buys a ticket expect to win or lose?

Problem Solving Strategy: Use a formula.

Step 1 Find the probability of winning each prize.

$$P(\$500) = \frac{1}{2000} = 0.0005 \qquad P(\$100) = \frac{2}{2000} = 0.001$$

$$P(\$5) = \frac{10}{2000} = 0.005 \qquad P(\$0) = \frac{1987}{2000} = 0.9935$$

Step 2 Find the expected value if the game were free.

$$(\$500)(0.0005) + (\$100)(0.001) + (\$5)(0.005) + (\$0)(0.9935) = \$.375$$

Step 3 Find the expected value including the cost of the ticket.

$$\$.375 - \$1 = -\$.625 \quad \longleftarrow \text{ Subtract the cost of a ticket.}$$

A person who buys this lottery ticket for $1 can expect to lose $.625. When a person plays the lottery repeatedly, or when a number of people each play the lottery once, the *average* of all the gains and losses is a loss of 62.5 cents for every ticket bought.

In Sample 1, if each person paid $.375 instead of $1 to play the lottery, the expected value would be $0. In that case the lottery would be considered a *fair game*. Any game or situation with an expected value of 0 is considered **fair**. Lotteries are fundraisers, so they are designed to have a negative expected value.

Sample 2

What price makes the following a fair game?

Roll three dice. You win as many dollars as there are "aces" (single dots) showing.

Problem Solving Strategy: Use a diagram.

Step 1 Make a probability tree diagram to show all the possible outcomes.

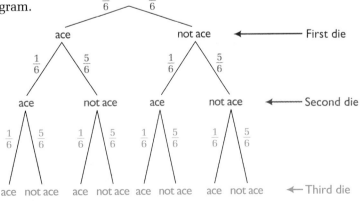

Continued on next page.

Step 2 Make a table to represent the events "exactly 3 aces," "exactly 2 aces," "exactly 1 ace," and "no aces."

Outcome	You win	Probability
exactly 3 aces	$3	$\frac{1}{6} \cdot \frac{1}{6} \cdot \frac{1}{6} = \frac{1}{216}$
exactly 2 aces	$2	$\frac{1}{6} \cdot \frac{1}{6} \cdot \frac{5}{6} \cdot 3 = \frac{15}{216}$
exactly 1 ace	$1	$\frac{1}{6} \cdot \frac{5}{6} \cdot \frac{5}{6} \cdot 3 = \frac{75}{216}$
no aces	$0	$\frac{5}{6} \cdot \frac{5}{6} \cdot \frac{5}{6} = \frac{125}{216}$

In these two cases, there are three ways that the outcome can occur.

Step 3 Find the expected value if the game were free.

$$\frac{1}{216} \cdot \$3 + \frac{15}{216} \cdot \$2 + \frac{75}{216} \cdot \$1 + \frac{125}{216} \cdot \$0 = \frac{\$3 + \$30 + \$75 + \$0}{216} = \$.50$$

A price of $.50 makes the game fair. Then the expected value is zero.

Look Back

What makes a game fair?

7-5 Exercises and Problems

Suppose the insurance company described on page 403 finds that the numbers of claims change to the ones in this table.

1. What does the company expect to pay in this situation?

2. What is a fair price when each of the 10,000 customers shares the cost evenly?

3. **Reading** Is the answer to Exercise 2 the amount the insurance company charges its customers? Why or why not?

Average value of claim	Number of claims per 10,000 policies
$200,000	1
$20,000	20
$2,000	300
$0	9679

A fair die is rolled. You win a dollar for every dot showing on the top when the die lands.

4. What is the expected value for the game?

5. Suppose you are the operator of the game. What should you charge to make the game fair?

For Exercises 6 and 7, suppose you roll a fair die. You win $1 for every dot showing on the top if the result is a prime number. You pay $1 per dot for any other result.

6. **a.** For which number(s) from 1 to 6 do you add to your winnings? For which number(s) do you subtract from your winnings?

   b. What is the expected value for this game?

7. Is this a fair game? If not, who is favored, the player or the person running the game?

8. A club is selling lottery tickets for $1 each. There is one $400 prize, two $50 prizes, and ten $2 prizes. Two thousand tickets are sold. On average, what can a person who buys a ticket expect to win or lose?

9. **Writing** In Sample 1, the expected value (−$.625) is not one of the possible outcomes ($500, $100, $5, or $0). Explain.

10. A food service company wants to make a bid for all the cafeterias in a large school district. The research and planning needed to make the bid costs $3000. If the bid is accepted, the company makes $23,000 over the life of the contract. Suppose the bid has a 25% chance of being accepted. Should the company make the bid? Why or why not?

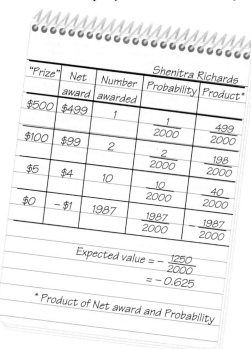

11. **Reading** Shenitra has another way to do Sample 1. Here is her work.

    a. Explain Shenitra's method.

    b. Compare it with the one in Sample 1.

    c. Why do both methods give the same answer?

    d. Which do you prefer? Why?

12. **Discount Shopping** As customers enter a store one day, they receive discount coupons for their purchases that day. The amount of the discount on the coupon is not known until the cashier scratches the coupon. The store claims that for every 100 coupons, one reads "50% off," ten read "30% off," twenty read "20% off," and the rest read "10% off." On average, what discount can a customer expect to receive?

13. **Game Shows** A contestant on a game show has won $1000 and a chance to spin the wheel. The wheel has the values shown. (Hitting the "bankrupt" sector means that the contestant loses the $1000 winnings.)

   a. Design a simulation in which 20 people are each in the same situation as this contestant. Keep track of the results.

   b. On average, what is a contestant's gain (or loss) in part (a)?

   c. Calculate the expected value from spinning the wheel. Compare this result to your answer from part (b).

connection to **LITERATURE**

In *The Promise*, by Chaim Potok, a pitchman at a fair interests three friends in a carnival game in the early 1950s.

   The counter that fronted the booth was painted gold. Upon it lay a white wooden board and a brown-leather dice cup. The board contained ten rows of holes, ten holes in each row, one hundred holes in all. A number ranging from one to ten had been painted in black beneath each hole. The numbers appeared to be in random sequence and stood out sharp and black beneath the holes, the insides of which were bright red. . . .

   . . .The dice cup contained eight silver balls. The balls were tossed onto the board. The numbers below the holes into which they fell were added together. A card, which (the pitchman) now brought out and placed on the counter next to the board, was then consulted to determine the value of the total. As soon as the player's separate throws added up to ten, he was given a (prize).

   "Can't be any simpler than that," the pitchman said. . . .

   "How much is it to play?" I heard Michael ask.

   "Twenty-five cents a toss."

Score card

18	42	38	15	19
9	28	48		

The pitchman in the story keeps changing the rules of the game as people play. Suppose, however, that a number of people play the game as described. The histogram shows the distribution of the number of tosses each player needs in order to score 10 points and win the prize.

14. What is the expected number of tosses needed?

15. What is the expected cost of the game?

16. What is the expected value for the game when the prize is worth $2?

17. Is the game fair? Why or why not?

18. **Group Activity** Work with another student.

    A basketball player is in a *one-and-one situation.* This means the player has a chance to shoot a free throw for one point. If she makes a basket, she has a chance to shoot a second free throw. The player's free-throw record is 40%.

    a. Make a tree diagram with labels to represent the possible outcomes of the free throw(s).

    b. What is the probability that the player makes a basket on a free throw? What is the probability that she does not make a basket? Fill in the probabilities along the branches of your tree diagram.

    c. How many points will the player score if she makes a basket on both free throws? if she makes a basket on the first free throw only? if she does not make a basket on the first free throw?

    d. What is the expected value for this situation?

19. Find $P(B\,|\,A)$ when $P(A \text{ and } B) = \frac{2}{5}$ and $P(A) = \frac{3}{5}$. *(Section 7-4)*

20. What is the measure of an inscribed angle of a circle whose intercepted arc is a semicircle? *(Section 3-6)*

21. a. Complete this chart of the first five powers of $(a + b)$. *(Toolbox Skill 16)*

    b. Describe any patterns you see.

    $$(a + b)^1 = 1a + 1b$$
    $$(a + b)^2 = 1a^2 + 2ab + b^2$$
    $$(a + b)^3 = ?$$
    $$(a + b)^4 = ?$$
    $$(a + b)^5 = 1a^5 + 5a^4b + 10a^3b^2 + 10a^2b^3 + 5ab^4 + 1b^5$$

 Working on the Unit Project

The table shows the point values that the Cayuga use in the game of da-un-dah-qua.

22. a. Complete the table.

    b. Find the expected value (points) for one toss.

    c. How are the points the Cayuga use related to the probabilities of the various outcomes?

    d. **Open-ended** Design a scoring system that is more closely related to the probabilities of different outcomes.

Outcomes	Probability	Points
6 Blue	?	5
5B and 1G	?	1
4B and 2G	?	0
3B and 3G	?	0
2B and 4G	?	0
1B and 5G	?	1
6 Green	?	5

Binomial Experiments and Decision-Making

Most *Likely* To SUCCEED

To determine whether the outcome in a real-life situation can be due to chance alone, you can use a simulation.

Pool of applicants

45% Women   55% Men

EXPLORATION

Is the outcome due to chance alone?

- **Materials: calculators with a random number function**
- **Work in a group of four students.**

In a very large pool of equally qualified candidates for a job, 55% are men and 45% are women. Ten people are hired. Eight of them are men. Assume that people are hired at random and that the selection of one person does not affect the ratio of men and women in the pool.

① Design a simulation to investigate this problem. For each trial, record the number of men hired.

② Combine your results with those of the other groups. Make a probability distribution of all the results.

③ Use the results from your class to estimate the probability of each event.

a. Eight of the people hired are men.

b. Nine of the people hired are men.

c. Ten of the people hired are men.

d. Eight or more of the people hired are men.

The experiment in the Exploration has several important characteristics. These are the characteristics of a **binomial experiment.** You can analyze a binomial experiment with a simulation, as you did in the Exploration, or with probability theory.

CHARACTERISTICS OF BINOMIAL EXPERIMENTS

Examples

➤ There are exactly two outcomes for each trial.　Either a man or a woman is hired.

➤ The trials are independent.　The ratio of men and women in a very large pool of candidates does not change.

➤ Each trial has the same probability of success.　P(man is hired) = 0.55 for each trial.

The "success" of a trial is defined arbitrarily. Here, "man is hired" is considered a "success."

➤ The experiment has a fixed number of trials.　Ten people are hired.

Sample 1

In the hiring situation in the Exploration, what is the theoretical probability that exactly 8 of the 10 people hired are men?

Sample Response

Step 1 Find the number of favorable outcomes.

When a person is hired, there are two possible outcomes: a man (M) is hired or a woman (W) is hired. When 10 people are hired, outcomes such as MMWWMMMMMM and MWMMMMMMWM are considered favorable.

The number of favorable outcomes is the number of combinations of 10 items taken 8 at a time.

$$_{10}C_8 = \frac{10!}{8!2!} = \frac{10 \cdot 9}{2 \cdot 1} = 45$$

Step 2 Find the probability of each outcome.

The trials are independent, so you can multiply to find the probability of each outcome.

P(man is hired) ⟶　　　⟵ P(woman is hired)

$$P(\text{one combination of 8 men and 2 women}) = (0.55)^8(0.45)^2$$

Step 3 Find the sum of the probabilities of the 45 mutually exclusive outcomes.

$$P(\text{exactly 8 men are hired}) = 45(0.55)^8(0.45)^2$$

⟵ Since each outcome has the same probability, you can multiply.

$$\approx 0.076$$

The probability that exactly 8 men are hired is about 7.6%.

1. Compare the experimental probability that you found in the Exploration with the result in Sample 1. How close was your estimate to the theoretical probability?

2. Describe how to find $_{10}C_8$ without using a formula.

3. Suppose all 10 of the people hired are men. What is the probability of that happening by chance?

4. Suppose that 30% of the candidates are men and 70% are women.

   a. Which step(s) of Sample 1 change? How?

   b. Find the probability that exactly 8 men are hired in this situation. How does this probability compare with the one in Sample 1?

PROBABILITY IN A BINOMIAL EXPERIMENT

In a binomial experiment with n trials, the probability of exactly r successes is:

$$P(r) = {}_nC_r \cdot p^r q^{n-r}$$

number of possible outcomes ⎯⎯⎯

probability of success in each trial

$1 - p$, or probability of failure

▶ Now you are ready for:
Exs. 1–13 on p. 415

This probability distribution shows the probabilities of all the possible outcomes in the hiring problem in the Exploration, using the formula above.

Probabilities when 10 People Are Hired

(graph: Probability vs. Number of men hired, 0 to 10)

Use the histogram on page 412.

5. What is the most likely outcome of the experiment in the Exploration?

6. Describe the shape of the probability distribution.

7. Use the histogram to estimate the probability of each event.

   a. Exactly seven men are hired.

   b. Seven or more men are hired.

   c. Explain why you can add probabilities to answer part (b).

Decision-Making with Probability

One of the important uses of probability is to make decisions like, "Can an outcome be due to chance alone?" To make a decision like this, researchers complete these steps.

Probabilities often used are 0.10, 0.05, and 0.01, each of which is called a **significance level.**

```
Create a probability model
based on chance alone.
        ↓
Decide which probabilities
to consider unusual if the
results were due to chance.
        ↓
Compare the model with the
actual results.
        ↓
Is the probability that a result is
due to chance less than 0.05?
   YES            NO
```

In situations like the hiring problem, researchers often use a 0.05 or 5% significance level.

YES	NO
Another factor, such as bias, may be involved.	The outcome can be due to chance alone.

8. Use the results of the Exploration. Is there reason to suspect bias if eight or more men are hired?

9. Use the probability distribution on page 412. For which outcome(s) is it reasonable to suspect bias?

   a. No men are hired.

   b. One man is hired or no men are hired.

   c. Two or fewer men are hired.

   d. Three or fewer men are hired.

Use the hiring situation on page 410.

a. Suppose that 8 or more men are hired. At the 0.05 significance level, can the outcome be due to chance alone?

b. Suppose that 9 or more men are hired. At the 0.05 significance level, can the outcome be due to chance alone?

Sample Response

a. The outcome "8 or more men are hired" means that exactly 8 men are hired, exactly 9 men are hired, or exactly 10 men are hired.

P(8 or more men are hired) = P(exactly 8 men are hired) + P(exactly 9 men are hired)

$\qquad$ + P(exactly 10 men are hired)

$\qquad = 45(0.55)^8(0.45)^2 + 10(0.55)^9(0.45)^1 + (0.55)^{10}$

$\qquad \approx 0.076 + 0.021 + 0.003$

$\qquad \approx 0.1$

This probability is greater than 0.05, so the outcome can be due to chance alone.

b. P(9 or more men are hired) = P(exactly 9 men are hired) + P(exactly 10 men are hired)

$\qquad = 10(0.55)^9(0.45)^1 + (0.55)^{10}$

$\qquad \approx 0.021 + 0.003$

$\qquad \approx 0.023$

This probability is less than 0.05, so there may have been bias.

Statistical decision-making *never proves or disproves* a claim. It does not have the certainty of deductive reasoning. Statistical analysis uses inferences that give reason to *support or deny* a claim.

······► **Now you are ready for:**
Exs. 14–30 on pp. 416–417

Look Back ◄

Explain how to use significance levels in statistical decision-making.

Exercises and Problems

For Exercises 1–6, suppose 25% of the people are male and 75% are female in the hiring situation on page 410.

1. What changes would you make to the simulation in the Exploration?

Find the probability of each event.

2. Exactly 8 men are hired.

3. Exactly 9 men are hired.

4. Exactly 10 men are hired.

5. At least 8 men are hired.

6. What is the probability that all ten of the people hired are women?

7. **Reading** What are the characteristics of a binomial experiment?

8. **Reading** Tell what each variable represents in this formula for an exact number of successes, r, in a binomial experiment:

$$P(r) = {}_nC_r \cdot p^r q^{n-r}$$

9. Suppose a group of job candidates contains exactly 11 men and 9 women.

 a. What is the probability that the first person hired is a man?

 b. What is the probability that the second person hired is a man?

 c. Why is the situation *not* a binomial experiment?

10. Perform an experiment by tossing a coin until it lands "heads." Explain why the binomial experiment formula does *not* apply in this case.

11. There are five true-false questions on a quiz. A student guesses randomly. Find the probability of each event.

 a. Exactly three answers are correct.

 b. Exactly four answers are correct.

 c. Exactly five answers are correct.

 d. At least three answers are correct.

12. In a school community-service club, 58% of the students are female and 42% are male. Twenty students are selected to attend a conference. What is the probability that exactly 12 of them are female?

13. **Gardening** Suppose that in a package of pepper seeds, the probability that a given seed will sprout is 0.9. Find the probability of each event when five pepper seeds are planted.

 a. Exactly four seeds sprout.

 b. Five seeds sprout.

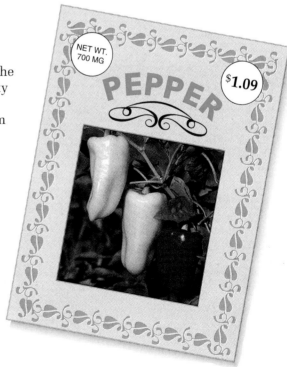

NET WT. 700 MG

PEPPER

$1.09

The principal of a school randomly selects six juniors and six seniors to answer a survey about after-school jobs. In their school, P(junior has a job) = 0.5 and P(senior has a job) = 0.75. These graphs show the probabilities of the possible outcomes.

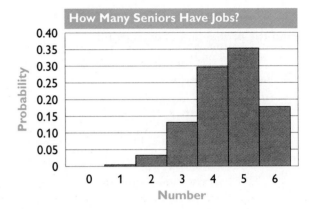

Use the graphs for Exercises 14–20.

14. Compare the shapes of the graphs. In each case, what is the most likely outcome?

15. Estimate P(exactly four seniors selected have jobs) and P(exactly four juniors selected have jobs). Explain why the probabilities are different.

Estimate the probability of each event.

16. Exactly two juniors have jobs.

17. Two or fewer juniors have jobs.

18. Exactly three seniors have jobs.

19. Three or more seniors have jobs.

20. Explain how to use the graph to find the expected value for the number of seniors selected who have jobs.

21. **Writing** What does a 0.01 significance level mean?

22. **Genetics** Children inherit genes independently from each parent. In order to have type O blood, a child must inherit two O genes, one from each parent. When both parents carry one O gene and one A gene, each child has a 0.25 probability of having blood type O.

Find the probability that in this situation, three or more children have blood type O when there are five children in the family.

Genetics researcher analyzing human chromosomes, the carriers of the genes

23. Five cars are in a parking lot on a very cold day. Suppose the probability of any one of them not starting is 0.05. What is the probability that at least two of the cars do not start?

Ongoing **ASSESSMENT**

24. **Group Activity** Work with another student. You will test your mind-reading skills. Use twelve playing cards, three of each of the four suits, or make four sets of three cards each using four different symbols (for example, circle, star, and so on).

a. One of you should shuffle and hold the cards. He or she should look at the top card. The other student should guess what suit (or symbol) it is. The first student should record whether the guess is correct but keep the answer secret until after the trial is completed. Continue until all the cards are used. Let r = the number of cards correctly identified.

b. Trade roles and repeat the experiment.

c. For this experiment, give the value of each variable in the formula $P(r) = {_nC_r} \cdot p^r q^{n-r}$.

d. For each value of r, find the probability that r cards were correctly identified by chance alone. At the 0.05 significance level, do your answers support the idea that either of you can read minds?

Cards like these were used in early experiments to test for the existence of extrasensory perception (ESP).

Review **PREVIEW**

25. Two hundred raffle tickets are sold to raise money for the library. The grand prize is a quilt worth $500, and the second prize is a $50 gift certificate from a book store. Each ticket costs $3. Find the expected value for the raffle. *(Section 7-5)*

26. Find the mean and the standard deviation of the number of Calories in six different flavors of instant soup: 150, 210, 180, 120, 140, 225. *(Section 6-2)*

Find the distance between each pair of points. *(Toolbox Skill 31)*

27. (0, 0) and (8, −6)   **28.** (0, 0) and (−5, −12)   **29.** (0, 0) and (−5, 5)

Working on the Unit Project

30. Suppose two people are playing da-un-dah-qua. Find the probability that one person scored exactly 6 points on each of 3 of her first 8 plays.

Completing the Unit Project

Now you are ready to demonstrate your new game based on da-un-dah-qua.

Your completed project should include these things:

➤ a probability analysis of the game of da-un-dah-qua based on your answers to the "Working on the Unit Project" exercises throughout the unit

➤ a written set of rules for your new game

➤ a probability analysis of your new game, including discussion of these questions — Is the game fair? Will playing the game take more or less time than playing da-un-dah-qua? Is the game easier than da-un-dah-qua? more difficult?

➤ a demonstration of how your new game is played

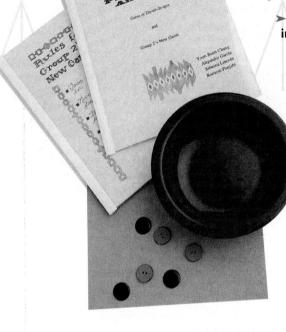

Look Back ◄

How has your study of the rules of a game changed the way you think about games?

Alternative Projects

Project 1: Consumer Economics and Maintenance Agreements

Consumers can buy maintenance agreements for many electronics items and home appliances. Use the ideas of probability to determine whether maintenance agreements are a good buy. You will need to find out the terms of manufacturers' warranties, as well as the probabilities that the items fail after the warranty expires or that the failures are not covered by the warranty. Estimate probabilities that are unavailable and describe any assumptions you made.

Project 2: Analyzing Advertising Claims

Advertisements on television, radio, and in newspapers and magazines are full of claims based on statistics — for example, taste tests. Select at least three claims of this type. Obtain the statistical data that are the basis of each claim. Using the ideas of probability, analyze each claim to determine whether it is justified by the data.

1. Suppose you give each student at your school a number from 1 to   **7-1**
786. You write down the numbers of the first 25 people who enter
the auditorium for a pep rally. Will this produce a random
sequence? Explain.

**For Questions 2 and 3, design and test a formula for a calculator
to produce each set of random numbers.**

2. integers from 0 to 99   3. integers from 1 to 10

4. a. **Writing** Describe how to
change this frequency distribution
to a probability distribution.

Incoming Calls at a Taxi Company in One Day	
Time period	**Number of calls**
midnight–4 A.M.	0
4 A.M.–8 A.M.	28
8 A.M.–noon	126
noon–4 P.M.	97
4 P.M.–8 P.M.	148
8 P.M.–midnight	153

   b. **Open-ended** Make two
conclusions about the
probability distribution.

5. In a very large pool of job applicants,
60% have previous experience for the
job and 40% do not. Of the 10 people
hired, 7 have no experience. Design a
simulation to investigate the situation.

For each event in Questions 6–8, find the probability.   **7-2**

6. Two dice are tossed. The sum of the numbers is 9 or greater.

7. You look at a clock at a random moment. The minute hand is
between 1 and 3.

8. You look at a clock at a random moment. The minute hand is
between 12 and 4 or it is between 2 and 5.

9. **Writing** Give an example of events that are mutually exclusive
but not complementary. Justify your response.

10. Arnie, Bettina, Cal, Dave, and Ellen are on a work crew. One crew
member is selected for a special job. Tell whether each statement
is *True* or *False*.

   a. Selecting Arnie and selecting Bettina are mutually exclusive
events.

   b. Selecting Arnie and selecting Bettina are complementary
events.

11. You agree with a friend that you will begin an on-line conversa-   **7-3**
tion by electronic mail some time between 7 P.M. and 9 P.M. You
each agree to be on the computer for half an hour some time in
that interval. What is the probability that you connect?

12. a. **Writing** What does it mean in everyday words for events to be   **7-4**
independent?

   b. What does it mean mathematically for events to be
independent?

For Questions 13–15, use this table. A student is selected at random. Find each probability.

	Male	Female	Total
In the band	8	7	15
Not in the band	12	5	17
Total	20	12	32

13. P(in the band | female)   14. P(female | in the band)

15. Are the events "in the band" and "female" independent? Explain.

16. A survey of households in a small community showed that 26% have three or more television sets, 42% of those with three or more television sets reported watching over 100 hours per week, and 35% of those with fewer than three television sets reported watching over 100 hours per week.

    a. Make a tree diagram or a table for this data.

    b. Is owning three or more television sets independent of watching over 100 hours per week? Explain.

17. In a state lottery, players buy cards for $1 each. Players mark any three   **7-5**
    digits (for example, 004 or 029) on a card. Players who select the winning number win $600. Find the expected value for this lottery.

18. The table shows the distribution of the Calories in 100 low-Calorie frozen dinners.

    a. What is the mean of this probability distribution?

    b. Suppose you choose one of the 100 dinners at random. What is the expected value of the number of Calories?

Number of Calories	Percent of dinners
250	10
260	20
270	20
280	30
300	0
310	10
320	10

Nutrition Facts

Serving Size 1 Package (297 g)
Servings Per Container 1

Amount Per Serving

Calories 250 Calories from Fat 45

% Daily Value*

Total Fat 5g   7%

Saturated Fat 1g

Polyunsaturated Fat 1g   5%

Monounsaturated Fat 1.5g

Cholesterol 35mg   12%

19. **Market Research** An ad for cat food claims that "4 out of 5 cats pre-   **7-6**
    fer Kitty Nibbles." Suppose that each cat was offered two bowls of food, Kitty Nibbles and Brand X, and chose randomly between them. Find the probability that 4 out of 5 cats chose Kitty Nibbles.

20. Twenty students are chosen at random for a crowd scene in a school play. Twenty percent of the students in the school are seniors. What is the probability that the crowd has 75% or more seniors?

21. **Self-evaluation** After completing this unit, do you think you will be better able to understand and think critically about claims involving probability and chance? Why or why not?

22. **Group Activity** Work with another student.
    A pool of citizens for a jury has 5 men and 15 women. The pool was chosen at random.

    a. Is selecting 12 people at random from this pool an example of a binomial experiment? Why or why not?

    b. Design and carry out a simulation to estimate the probability that of the 12 people selected, 8 are women.

IDEAS AND (FORMULAS)=

STATISTICS & PROBABILITY

➤ You can use simulation to study a real event without the time, cost, risk, or materials needed for the real event. (*p. 374*)

➤ A sequence of random numbers has no pattern, and each number has an equal chance of appearing in the sequence. (*p. 374*)

➤ The probability of any event is $\dfrac{\text{size of favorable outcomes}}{\text{size of possible outcomes}}$.

"Size" can be a count or a measurement. (*p. 383*)

➤ For any two events A and B:
$P(A \text{ or } B) = P(A) + P(B) - P(A \text{ and } B)$ (*p. 385*)

➤ You can use tree diagrams to investigate conditional probabilities. (*p. 396*)

➤ The probability that event B occurs given that event A occurred is written $P(B \mid A)$. For any two events A and B,

$$P(A \text{ and } B) = P(A) \cdot P(B \mid A) \text{ and } P(B \mid A) = \frac{P(A \text{ and } B)}{P(A)}.$$

(*p. 397*)

➤ Two events A and B are independent if and only if $P(B \mid A) = P(B)$. (*p. 398*)

➤ To find the expected value of an event, multiply the value of each outcome, x_i, by its probability, $P(x_i)$, and then add all the products. (*p. 404*)

Expected value $= x_1 \cdot P(x_1) + x_2 \cdot P(x_2) + \cdots + x_n \cdot P(x_n)$

➤ In a binomial experiment with n trials, where the probability of success in each trial is p, and the probability of failure is $q = 1 - p$, the probability of exactly r successes is: (*p. 412*)

$$P(r) = {}_nC_r \cdot p^r q^{n-r}$$

GEOMETRY

➤ You can use area models with coordinates to find probabilities. (*p. 391*)

········**Key Terms**

- **simulation** (p. 374)

- **mutually exclusive events** (p. 386)
- **independent events** (p. 398)
- **binomial experiment** (p. 411)

- **random numbers** (p. 374)

- **complementary events** (p. 386)
- **expected value** (p. 404)
- **significance level** (p. 413)

- **probability distribution** (p. 376)
- **conditional probability** (p. 396)
- **fair (game)** (p. 405)

Angles, Trigonometry, and Vectors

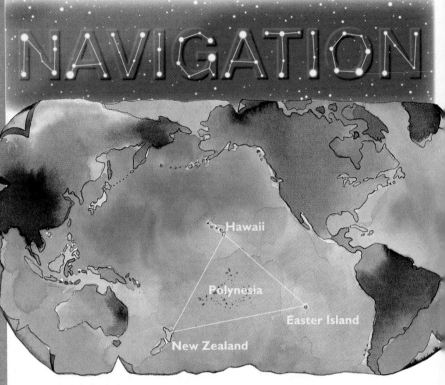

Over four thousand years ago, experienced navigators from Southeast Asia set off across the Pacific in wooden canoes. They had no charts or instruments. Navigating by the stars, the wind, the waves, the birds, and the clouds, they settled the tiny islands scattered over a triangular area covering millions of square miles of open ocean — now Polynesia.

All modern navigators use maps. But before maps were drawn, they were carried in memory. The mental maps of the ancient Polynesians were based on time rather than distance and included up to 80 islands spread out over open ocean.

The people of the Marshall Islands in the Pacific made **stick–charts** to show directions of currents. The shells mark islands.

migration

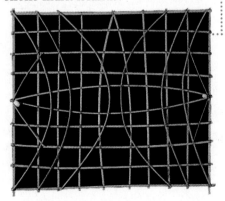

The migratory flight of the **arctic tern** may be the greatest navigational feat among animals. Each year this bird travels 22,000 miles — from the North Pole to the South Pole and back again. Migrating birds, insects, bats, fishes, whales, and land animals use many of the navigational clues used by the ancient navigators.

Plan a Treasure Hunt

Your project is to plan a treasure hunt that can be solved with pencil and paper using a protractor and a ruler.

Your group should create a treasure map, a set of numbered clues, and a solution map showing how the clues lead to the treasure.

Your clues should apply at least three of the topics from the unit:

➤ polar coordinates
➤ vectors
➤ law of cosines and law of sines
➤ parametric equations

Some animals have a sixth sense referred to as *magnetic direction finding*. Bees, robins, and some fish can feel the directed lines of force of Earth's magnetic field. Lacking this sixth sense, people use a **magnetic compass** which was developed separately in ancient China and in Europe.

In Greenland, the native people carved driftwood to make three-dimensional maps. The earliest printed maps date back over 2000 years in China.

Abraham Ortelius included this map in his atlas, published in Antwerp, Belgium, in 1570. The atlas is famous for being the first collection of maps not done by the original mapmaker. He credited 87 others.

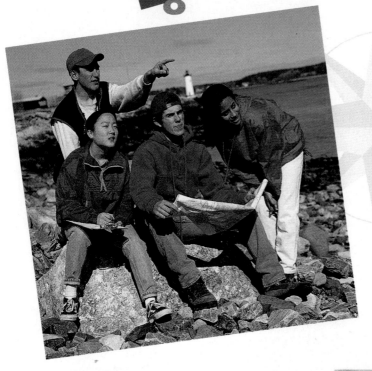

For this project you should work in a group of four students. Here are some ideas to help you get started.

☞ In your group select a location for your treasure hunt. You may want to consider using the school yard, an open field, a park, or a beach.

☞ Obtain a map of the location you selected, or plan to make one if none is available.

☞ Decide where to locate the buried treasure.

Can We Talk NAVIGATION

Working on the Unit Project

Your work in Unit 8 will help you plan your treasure hunt.

Related Exercises:

Section 8-1, Exercise 39
Section 8-2, Exercise 60
Section 8-3, Exercise 24
Section 8-4, Exercise 26
Section 8-5, Exercise 39
Section 8-6, Exercise 32
Section 8-7, Exercise 38

Alternative Projects p. 475

➤ There are four major ways to navigate:

(1) celestial navigation, or using the sun, the stars, and the planets

(2) dead reckoning, or keeping track of how long and how far you have traveled

(3) piloting, or using landmarks

(4) with instruments, such as a magnetic compass

Do you ever use any of these techniques? If you do, tell how you apply them in various situations.

➤ In many cultures, people learn special "tricks" for determining direction. In North America, people used the fact that tree rings are thicker on the north side. In the Tropics, people know that coconut palms lean into the prevailing wind. In northern Australia, the aboriginal people use the fact that termite mounds are oriented north-south.

Have you ever used any special "tricks" to find your way around or avoid getting lost? How do you think you can improve your sense of direction?

Polar Coordinates

Get Your Bearings

Turquoise Lake is an alpine glacial lake just outside Leadville, Colorado. To hike from the picnic area to the entrance of Baby Doe campground, you walk about 1.7 km at a *bearing* of 29°.

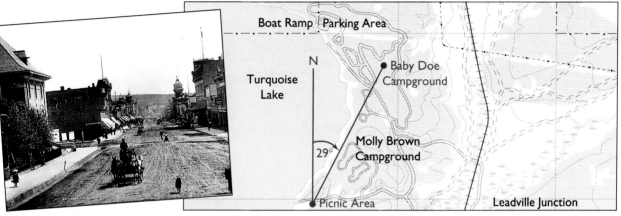

Leadville, Colorado, was the site of a gold and silver rush in the 1870s and 1880s.

A **bearing** is an angular direction given by a magnetic compass. Bearings are used in orienteering and navigation.

In bearings, 0° is at the north and angles are measured clockwise.

From the picnic area, the bearing of Baby Doe campground is 29°.

Polar coordinates use both a distance from a reference point and an angle to describe locations. They are used in mathematics, science, and technology.

In polar coordinates, 0° is along a horizontal ray to the right of the reference point. Angles are measured counterclockwise. Polar coordinates are written as an ordered pair.

Polar coordinates of Baby Doe campground from the picnic area are (1.7, 61°).

$$(r, \theta)$$

r (for radius) is the polar distance.

θ *(theta)* is the measure of the polar angle.

Use the map to name the site with each pair of polar coordinates.

a. (0.8, 175°)   **b.** (0.4, 330°)

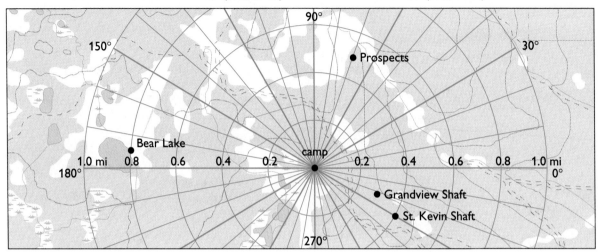

Sample Response

a. Move out 0.8 mi to the right from the campsite along the horizontal ray, and then travel counterclockwise around the circle from 0° to 175°.

The site at this location is the shore of Bear Lake.

b. Move out 0.4 mi to the right from the campsite, and then travel counter-clockwise around the circle to 330°.

The site at this location is St. Kevin Shaft.

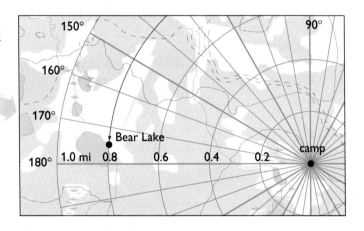

Negative angles are measured clockwise.

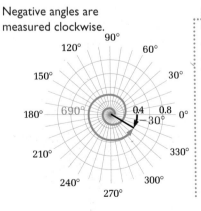

Talk it Over

When working with polar coordinates, angles do not need to have values between 0° and 360°.

1. Two other ways of giving coordinates for St. Kevin Shaft are (0.4, −30°) and (0.4, 690°). How are these coordinate pairs related to the coordinates given in Sample 1, part (b)?

2. Name two other pairs of polar coordinates that give the location of Bear Lake.

3. Describe how to find other pairs of polar coordinates for any point (r, θ).

Use the map in Sample 1 to write polar coordinates for each location.

a. Prospects

b. Grandview Shaft

Sample Response

Draw a circle through each site, centered at the camp.
Then use the markings of the polar grid to estimate r and θ.

a.

b.
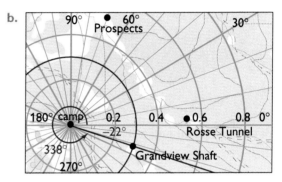

Polar coordinates for Prospects are about $(0.5, 70°)$.

Polar coordinates for Grandview Shaft are about $(0.3, 338°)$ or $(0.3, -22°)$.

Talk it Over

4. Two pairs of polar coordinates are given in Sample 2, part (b). Which one do you prefer? Why?

5. How can you find polar coordinates on a map that does not contain a polar grid? What tools do you need?

Look Back

Describe some differences between a rectangular coordinate ordered pair (x, y) and a polar coordinate ordered pair (r, θ).

8-1 Exercises and Problems

1. **Reading** Describe the similarities and differences between bearings and the angles used in polar coordinates.

For each compass direction, find the bearing and an angle used in polar coordinates.

2. west

3. south

4. northwest

5. northeast

6. southeast

7. southwest

8-1 Polar Coordinates

427

The horizon is along the circumference of the circle.

The center of the map is the point directly overhead.

connection to SCIENCE

Astronomers sometimes locate a star by measuring its *azimuth*, the angle along the horizon from North. The star map shows the night sky in Shanghai, China, on June 5, 1996.

Estimate the azimuth of each star to the nearest five degrees.

8. Vega

9. Polaris

10. Deneb

11. Altair

Name a star with each azimuth.

12. 240°

13. 190°

14. 310°

15. 263°

Graph each point on polar graph paper.

16. $A(3, 45°)$

17. $B(2, -42°)$

18. $C(2.5, 790°)$

19. $D(2, -1000°)$

20. $E(3.2, 250°)$

21. $F(2.4, 640°)$

connection to LITERATURE

J. R. R. Tolkien created a world of fantasy in his trilogy *The Lord of the Rings.* The story takes place in an invented land called "Middle Earth."

Name the place in Middle Earth with each pair of polar coordinates.

22. (280, 138°)

23. (640, 29°)

24. (740, -32°)

Estimate polar coordinates for each place in Middle Earth.

25. Weather Hills

26. Gladden Fields

27. Dead Marshes

THE WEST OF
MIDDLE-EARTH
AT THE END OF
THE THIRD AGE

Miles
100   200

Open-ended Draw an example of each regular polygon centered at the origin and write polar coordinates for its vertices.

28. equilateral triangle

29. regular pentagon

30. regular octagon

Chess Each square on a standard chessboard is labeled by its *file* (a–h) and *rank* (1–8). The player with the white pieces is called "White," and the player with the black pieces is called "Black." White's queen is at d1.

Use the circular chessboard shown. The ranks are wrapped into circles. White's queen is at (1, 112.5°).

31. White starts a game by moving a pawn from d2 to d3. Write polar coordinates of the piece before and after the move.

32. Black responds by moving a pawn from g7 to g6. Write polar coordinates of the piece before and after the move.

33. Black announces "Check" because the bishop at f8 threatens White's king at e1. Write polar coordinates of each position along the indicated path from the bishop to the king.

34. a. Research Find out how pieces move in a standard chess game. Describe how they should move on the circular chessboard.

    b. Find at least three ways for White to block Black's bishop by moving a piece into its path. Write polar coordinates of the pieces before and after the moves. Which move do you think is best?

    c. Group Activity Work with another student.

    Play a game of chess on a circular chessboard. At the end of the game, write the polar coordinates of the remaining pieces.

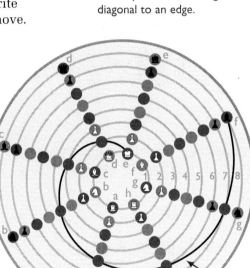

On a standard chessboard, a bishop can move along a diagonal to an edge.

A bishop can move along a spiral until it reaches the inner or outer circle.

Ongoing **ASSESSMENT**

35. Open-ended Create a map of a real or an imaginary place. Use polar coordinates to give references to at least four locations.

Review **PREVIEW**

36. What is the probability of getting 6 or more correct answers when you guess randomly on a quiz of 10 true-or-false questions? *(Section 7-6)*

37. A die is rolled. Find the probability of the event "less than 2 or greater than 4." *(Section 7-2)*

38. Explain how to find the cosine and sine of an acute angle in a right triangle by measuring the sides of the triangle. *(Toolbox Skill 36)*

Working on the Unit Project

39. Choose a starting point on your treasure-hunt map and write a clue that uses polar coordinates to describe the location of the next clue.

Converting Coordinates

One Way / **Or Another**

Convert from polar to rectangular coordinates, and vice versa; extend the definitions of cosine, sine, and tangent; and use a Pythagorean identity.

A call to a hospital in Michigan says that help is needed at an accident at the intersection of Seven Mile Road and Farmington. The hospital sends two response teams, one by helicopter and one by ambulance.

The polar coordinates and rectangular coordinates locate the same point.

The helicopter flies 2.5 mi at an angle of about 53.1° north of east.

The ambulance travels 1.5 mi east on Five Mile Road, then 2 mi north on Farmington.

Both response teams arrive at the accident site, but they use different coordinate systems to get there.

Converting Polar Coordinates to Rectangular Coordinates

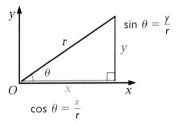

$$\sin \theta = \frac{y}{r}$$

$$\cos \theta = \frac{x}{r}$$

The coordinate system you have used most often is called a *rectangular coordinate system.* You can use what you know about trigonometry to convert polar coordinates in the first quadrant to rectangular coordinates.

$$x = r \cos \theta \qquad y = r \sin \theta$$

$$(x, y) = (r \cos \theta, r \sin \theta)$$

Sample 1

Convert the polar coordinates (38, 82°) to rectangular coordinates. Round decimal answers to the nearest hundredth.

Sample Response

Method ❶ Use a formula.

$$x = r \cos \theta$$
$$= 38 \cos 82°$$ ← Substitute **38** for r and **82°** for θ.
$$\approx 5.289$$

$$y = r \sin \theta$$
$$= 38 \sin 82°$$ ← Substitute **38** for r and **82°** for θ.
$$\approx 37.630$$

The rectangular coordinates for the point are about (5.29, 37.63).

Method ❷ Use a calculator that converts polar coordinates to rectangular coordinates.

Be sure the calculator is in degree mode.

The rectangular coordinates for the point are about (5.29, 37.63).

```
P▶Rx (38, 82)
           5.288577836
P▶Ry (38, 82)
           37.63018661
```

Talk it Over

1. The accident location described on page 430 has polar coordinates (2.5, 53.1°). Show that its rectangular coordinates are about (1.5, 2).

2. a. How are the points with polar coordinates (38, 82°), (38, 442°), and (38, −278°) related?

   b. Convert (38, 442°) and (38, −278°) to rectangular coordinates.

·····▶ **Now you are ready for:**
: **Exs. 1–11 on p. 436**

What are the cosine, sine, and tangent of angles less than 0° or greater than 90°?

• **Materials: polar graph paper, scientific calculators**

• **Work with another student.**

(1) On polar graph paper, draw a large circle and graph points with polar angles of 20°, 160°, 200°, and 340°.

(2) Describe the symmetry in your diagram.

(3) Use a calculator to find the cosine of each angle. What do you notice?

(4) Use a calculator to find the sine of each angle. What do you notice?

(5) Repeat steps 1–4 for angles of 42°, 138°, −42°, and −138°.

(6) Make and test a conjecture about the cosines of angles like 42° and −42° whose measures are opposites.

(7) Test a conjecture about the sines of supplementary angles.

(8) In which quadrants is the cosine of an angle positive? negative? In which quadrants is the sine of an angle positive? negative?

(9) In which quadrants is the tangent of an angle positive? negative?

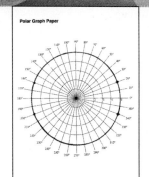

Polar Graph Paper

Expanding the Definitions of Cosine, Sine, and Tangent

The Exploration suggests that you can define the trigonometric ratios for angles of any measure.

COSINE, SINE, AND TANGENT OF ANY ANGLE

The trigonometric ratios are defined as

$$\cos \theta = \frac{x}{r} \qquad \sin \theta = \frac{y}{r} \qquad \tan \theta = \frac{y}{x} \qquad (\text{when } x \neq 0)$$

where

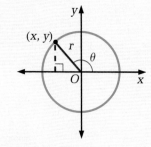

➤ x and y represent the x- and y-coordinates of a point with polar coordinates (r, θ).

➤ x and y can be positive, negative, or zero (except as indicated).

➤ r is positive.

To find the measure of an angle when you know its sine, cosine, or tangent, you can use the *inverse sine* ($\sin^{-1}$), *inverse cosine* ($\cos^{-1}$), or *inverse tangent* feature of a graphics calculator. Entering $\sin^{-1} 0.3420$ into a calculator is like asking, "What is an angle whose sine is 0.3420?"

You saw in the Exploration that there are *two* angles between 0° and 360° whose sine is 0.3420. When you use the *inverse sine* feature on a calculator, the calculator gives only 20° as the answer. You need to use what you know about symmetry to find the other angle, 160°.

Sample 2

a. Find all angles θ between 0° and 360° for which $\sin \theta = 0.4000$.

b. Find all angles θ between 0° and 360° for which $\cos \theta = -0.2567$.

Sample Response

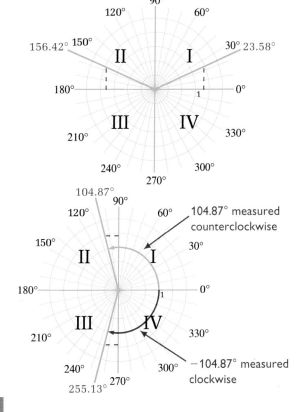

a. $\sin^{-1} 0.4000 \approx 23.58°$ ⟵ Use SIN⁻¹.

This angle is in Quadrant I.

There is also an angle in Quadrant II whose sine is 0.4000.

By symmetry, the other angle is its supplement, about $180° - 23.58°$, or about 156.42°.

Two angles with a sine of 0.4000 are about 23.58° and about 156.42°.

b. $\cos^{-1}(-0.2567) \approx 104.87°$ ⟵ Use COS⁻¹.

This angle is in Quadrant II.

There is also an angle in Quadrant III whose cosine is −0.2567.

By symmetry, this angle has the opposite measure, about −104.87°, or about 255.13°.

Two angles with a cosine of −0.2567 are about 104.87° and about 255.13°.

Talk it Over

3. Find all angles θ between 0° and 360° for which $\cos \theta = 0$.

4. Find all angles θ between 0° and 360° for which $\sin \theta = 0$.

5. Find all angles θ between 0° and 360° for which $\tan \theta = -2$.

▶ Now you are ready for:
Exs. 12–41 on pp. 436–438

Converting Rectangular Coordinates to Polar Coordinates

To convert from rectangular coordinates to polar coordinates, you can use the Pythagorean theorem and the inverse trigonometric features of a calculator.

Sample 3

Convert the rectangular coordinates (−3, −7) to polar coordinates, where θ is an angle between 0° and 360°.

Sample Response

Method ❶ Use a formula.

1 Find r.

$r^2 = x^2 + y^2$ ←——— Use the Pythagorean theorem.

$r = \sqrt{x^2 + y^2}$

$\quad = \sqrt{(-3)^2 + (-7)^2}$

$\quad = \sqrt{58}$

$\quad \approx 7.616$

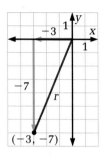

2 Find the polar angle θ.

You can use the inverse trigonometric feature of a calculator.

$\cos^{-1} \dfrac{x}{r} = \cos^{-1} \dfrac{-3}{7.616}$ ←——— Substitute −3 for x and **7.616** for r.

$\quad = \cos^{-1}(-0.3939)$

$\quad \approx 113.20°$

The polar angle 113.20° has the correct cosine value, but it lies in Quadrant II. The angle with the opposite measure, −113.20°, lies in Quadrant III and has the same cosine value.

The positive angle with the same cosine value is 360° − 113.20°, or 246.80°.

Polar coordinates for (−3, −7) are about (7.62, 246.80°).

Method ❷ Use a calculator that converts rectangular coordinates to polar coordinates.

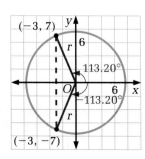

The positive angle with the same cosine value is 360° − 113.20°, or 246.80°.

Polar coordinates for (−3, −7) are about (7.62, 246.80°).

Talk it Over

6. How can you find the polar angle of $(-3, -7)$ using $\sin^{-1} \frac{y}{r}$?

7. How can you find the polar angle of $(-3, -7)$ using $\tan^{-1} \frac{y}{x}$?

8. Explain how to convert $(5, -8)$ to polar coordinates.

A Pythagorean Identity

Applying the Pythagorean theorem to the right triangle shown leads to an important relationship between $\cos \theta$ and $\sin \theta$ for any angle θ:

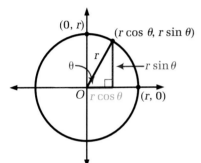

$(r \cos \theta)^2 + (r \sin \theta)^2 = r^2$ ⟵ Use the Pythagorean theorem.

$r^2 (\cos \theta)^2 + r^2 (\sin \theta)^2 = r^2$ ⟵ Use the fact that $(ab)^2 = a^2 b^2$.

$\cos^2 \theta + \sin^2 \theta = 1$ ⟵ Divide both sides by r^2.

↑

"$(\cos \theta)^2$" is written "$\cos^2 \theta$."

This result is sometimes called a **Pythagorean identity.** It shows how $\sin \theta$ and $\cos \theta$ are related and allows you to find one when the other is known.

Sample 4

Find $\cos \theta$ when $\sin \theta = -0.2955$ and θ is in Quadrant III.

Sample Response ·······································

$\cos^2 \theta + \sin^2 \theta = 1$ ⟵ Use this Pythagorean identity.

$\cos^2 \theta + (-0.2955)^2 = 1$ ⟵ Substitute -0.2955 for $\sin \theta$.

$\cos \theta = \pm\sqrt{1 - (-0.2955)^2}$ ⟵ Solve for $\cos \theta$.

$\cos \theta \approx \pm 0.9553$ ⟵ Simplify.

In Quadrant III, $\cos \theta$ is negative, so $\cos \theta \approx -0.9553$.

Look Back ⟵

Make a graph or chart showing where $\sin \theta$, $\cos \theta$, and $\tan \theta$ are positive, negative, zero, or undefined.

······▶ Now you are ready for:
Exs. 42–60 on pp. 438–439

Exercises and Problems

1. **Reading** Explain why the equations $x = r \cos \theta$ and $y = r \sin \theta$ can be used to find rectangular coordinates when you know polar coordinates of a point.

For Exercises 2–4, use the map on page 430.

2. Suppose a helicopter from the hospital flies 2.24 mi at an angle of 63.4° north of east to reach the site of another emergency. What is the nearest intersection?

3. Convert (2.24, 63.4°) to rectangular coordinates. Describe how an ambulance can drive to the site of the emergency.

4. a. **Open-ended** Choose another location somewhere northeast of the hospital. Use a protractor and a ruler to estimate polar coordinates of the location using the hospital as the origin. (Assume that the distance between Five Mile Road and Six Mile Road is one mile.)

   b. Convert the polar coordinates from part (a) to rectangular coordinates.

Convert each pair of polar coordinates to rectangular coordinates. Round decimal answers to the nearest hundredth.

5. (1, 0°)   6. (1, 30°)   7. (1, 45°)   8. (1, 60°)

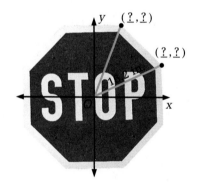

For Exercises 9 and 10, use this stop sign.

9. Two vertices of the stop sign lie in Quadrant I. What are their polar coordinates?

10. Convert the polar coordinates of the vertices in Quadrant I to rectangular coordinates.

11. **Open-ended** On polar graph paper, draw a polygon in Quadrant I with at least four vertices.

    a. Write polar coordinates for each vertex.

    b. Convert the polar coordinates you wrote in part (a) to rectangular coordinates.

    c. Find the lengths of all sides of the polygon.

12. a. Polar coordinates for the vertices of a rectangle are (6, 30°), (6, 150°), (6, −150°), (6, −30°). What are the rectangular coordinates of the vertices?

    b. **Open-ended** Use polar coordinates to describe the vertices of a rectangle. What are the rectangular coordinates of the vertices?

13. **Writing** Explain why $\tan \theta = \dfrac{\sin \theta}{\cos \theta}$.

At the South Pole, every direction is north. To talk about locations, scientists at the United States' Amundsen-Scott station near the South Pole sometimes use a coordinate system in which the Greenwich Meridian is called "north."

A polar grid with 0° at "east" is shown on the map of Antarctica.

Convert the polar coordinates of each scientific research station to rectangular coordinates. Distances are in miles. Describe the location of each station in words.

14. Syowa
(Japan)
(1440, 50°)

15. Belgrano II
(Argentina)
(840, 125°)

16. Scott Base
(New Zealand)
(840, 283°)

17. Vostok
(Russia)
(790, −17°)

18. Mawson
(Australia)
(1540, 27°)

19. Troll
(Norway)
(1240, 88°)

20. Byrd Surface
Camp (U.S.)
(690, 209°)

21. Dumont D'Urville
(France)
(1600, −50°)

Example

The Bay of Whales is at about (820, 254°). Its rectangular coordinates are about (820 cos 254°, 820 sin 254°), or about (−230, −790).

The Bay of Whales is about 230 mi "west" and about 790 mi "south" of the South Pole.

BY THE WAY...

Roald Amundsen and four other Norwegians began the first successful trip to the South Pole from the Bay of Whales in 1911. Their round-trip journey took 99 days.

Complete each statement with *opposite* or *the same*.

22. Supplementary angles have _?_ sines.

23. Supplementary angles have _?_ cosines.

24. Angles with opposite measures have _?_ sines.

25. Angles with opposite measures have _?_ cosines.

For each angle, find another angle between 0° and 360° with the same cosine.

26. 60°   **27.** 145°   **28.** 200°   **29.** −10°

For each angle, find another angle between 0° and 360° with the same sine.

30. 100°   **31.** −15°   **32.** 260°   **33.** 25°

For each angle, find another angle between 0° and 360° with the same tangent.

34. 45°   **35.** 170°   **36.** −150°   **37.** −80°

Find all angles θ between 0° and 360° that fit each condition.

38. $\sin \theta = 0.5$ **39.** $\cos \theta = -0.89$ **40.** $\cos \theta = 0.25$ **41.** $\sin \theta = -0.75$

Convert each pair of rectangular coordinates to polar coordinates, where θ is an angle between 0° and 360°.

42. $(12, -5)$ **43.** $(4, 4)$ **44.** $(-7.5, -7.5)$

45. $(-27.8, 3)$ **46.** $(0, 7)$ **47.** $(-4.3, 0)$

48. $(4, -3)$ **49.** $(-1, \sqrt{3})$ **50.** $(4\sqrt{3}, -4)$

51. Convert the rectangular coordinates of the pentagon to polar coordinates.

Use the Pythagorean identity $\cos^2 \theta + \sin^2 \theta = 1$.

52. Find all possible values of $\sin \theta$ when $\cos \theta = \frac{2}{3}$.

53. Find $\cos \theta$ when $\sin \theta = \frac{3}{5}$ and θ is in Quadrant II.

54. Find $\sin \theta$ when $\sin \theta < 0$ and $\cos \theta = -\frac{5}{13}$.

55. Find $\cos \theta$ when $\cos \theta < 0$ and $\sin \theta = 0.2121$.

Group Activity Work in a group of four students.

56. a. Copy and complete the table for all the angles θ between 0° and 360° whose measures are multiples of 10.

 b. Graph the ordered pairs.

 c. Connect the points. Describe the shape.

 d. Does the graph represent a function?

 e. Describe any connections between this activity and the Exploration on page 432.

$m \angle \theta$	$\cos \theta = x$	$\sin \theta = y$	(x, y)
0°	1	0	(1, 0)
10°	?	?	?
20°	?	?	?
⋮	⋮	⋮	⋮
350°	?	?	?
360°	?	?	?

57. Polar coordinates of two vertices of an equilateral triangle are (0, 0°) and (2, 60°). Find polar coordinates of all the points that can be the third vertex. *(Section 8-1)*

58. Write the first six terms of the sequence defined by the recursive formula $a_1 = 2000$, $a_n = 1.07a_{n-1} + 2000$. *(Section 4-3)*

59. Find the distance from $(-1, 1)$ to $(-4, 5)$. *(Toolbox Skill 31)*

 Working on the Unit Project

60. Use polar coordinates to locate the next spot on your map. Write a clue that uses mathematics from this section.

> *To find the next clue, travel the same distance as you would if you went 40 m north and 22 m east. The polar angle you should use has a sine of −0.2 and lies in Quadrant III.*

245

The Geometry of Vectors

Straight and *Arrow*

EXPLORATION

······ (*How*) *can you use distances and angles to travel from place to place?*

- **Materials: rulers, protractors, graph paper**
- **Work with another student.**

Draw a horizontal line through the origin, or starting point.

Measure a 60° angle as on a polar coordinate system.

1 Make one copy of the map on graph paper.

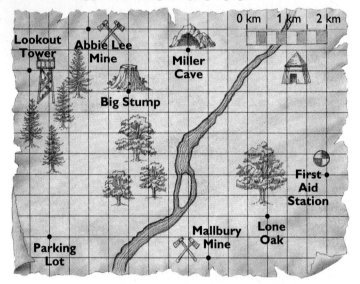

2 Take turns following the directions below. Use each point along the way as a new origin.

➤ Begin at the parking lot and travel 4.0 km at an angle of 60°. (The diagrams at the left show how to complete this instruction.)

➤ From this point travel 4.6 km at −41°.

➤ Now travel 1.8 km at 34°.

➤ Finally, travel 4.6 km at 139°.

3 You should now be at Miller Cave. If you are not, go back and check each other's work.

4 Suppose you walk in a straight line from the parking lot to Miller Cave. About how far will you walk and at what angle?

Draw a point 4.0 km from the starting point.

The instructions that guided your moves in the Exploration, such as "4.0 km at 60°," are examples of vectors. A **vector** is a quantity that has both a **magnitude,** or size, and a direction.

Vectors are commonly named with a bold letter, such as **v.** Here are some ways to represent a vector **v:**

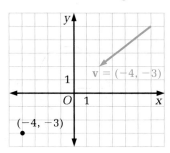

starting point, or **tail**

endpoint, or **head**

216.9°

5

−3

−4

➤ Draw an arrow, as shown in the graph. Each blue arrow represents the same vector, since each describes the same magnitude and direction. You can draw a vector anywhere in a plane.

➤ Use polar form: **v** = (5, 216.9°)

➤ Use rectangular form: **v** = (−4, −3)

Talk it Over

1. Discuss the difference between the two uses of (−4, −3) in this diagram.

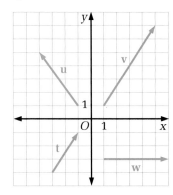

v = (−4, −3)

(−4, −3)

For questions 2 and 3, use this diagram.

2. a. Write **t** in rectangular form.

   b. Write **u** in polar form.

3. a. Which two vectors have the same magnitude?

   b. Which two vectors have the same direction?

Jamal and Ja-Wen are in the marching band's half-time show at a football game. They start from the same corner of the field and march to the same point. Jamal's path can be represented by two vectors in polar form: (20 paces, 60°) then (36 paces, 30°). Ja-Wen marches in a straight line. Draw a vector that represents the path Ja-Wen follows.

Sample Response

3 Draw the first vector for Jamal's path with its tail at the origin.

4 Draw the second vector for Jamal's path with its tail at the head of the first vector.

2 Tear off a piece of grid paper to use as a ruler. Let the width of a grid square represent four paces.

5 Draw a vector for Ja-Wen's path from the tail of the first vector to the head of the second vector.

1 Let the origin represent the corner of the field.

In Sample 1, the vector for Ja-Wen's path is the sum of the two vectors that represent Jamal's path. You add vectors by placing them head to tail. The sum is a vector from the tail of the first vector to the head of the second. It is called a **resultant vector.**

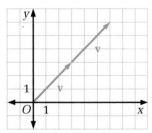

Talk it Over

4. **a.** In Sample 1, suppose the order of Jamal's vectors is reversed. Does this affect Ja-Wen's vector?

   b. Use the diagram to explain why the order in which you add two vectors does not affect the sum.

5. **a.** Let $\mathbf{u} = \mathbf{v} + \mathbf{v}$. How does $\mathbf{u}$ compare with $\mathbf{v}$ in magnitude and direction?

   b. Another way to write $\mathbf{u}$ is $2\mathbf{v}$. Describe the vector $\mathbf{w} = 3\mathbf{v}$. Describe $\mathbf{t} = \frac{1}{2}\mathbf{v}$.

   c. Let $(-1)\mathbf{v}$ be the vector $\mathbf{v}$ with its head and tail interchanged. How does $(-1)\mathbf{v}$ compare with $\mathbf{v}$ in magnitude and direction?

Unit 8 Angles, Trigonometry, and Vectors

A vector **v** = k**u** is called a **scalar multiple** of **u**. For k > 0, **v** has the same direction as **u** and a magnitude k times as great. For k < 0, **v** has the opposite direction as **u** and a magnitude |k| times as great.

A special case is **v** = (−1)**u**, where **v** has the same magnitude as **u** but the opposite direction. In this case, **v** can be written as −**u**, and **v** and **u** are called **opposite vectors.** The sum of two opposite vectors is the zero vector.

Sample 2

Draw the vector w = u − 2v, with u = (8, 83°) and v = (3.5, 144°). Use a protractor and a ruler to draw each sum. Write the resultant vector in polar form and in rectangular form.

Sample Response

Think of **w** as the sum of the vectors **u** and −2**v**.

1 Start at the origin. Draw **u**.

2 Draw **v** from the head of **u**.

3 Draw −2**v** from the head of **u**. It is a vector with twice the magnitude of **v** and the opposite direction.

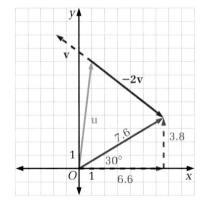

4 Draw the resultant vector **u** + (−2**v**) from the tail of **u** to the head of −2**v**.

5 To write the vector in polar form, measure to find the magnitude and direction of the resultant vector.

6 To write the vector in rectangular form, estimate the horizontal shift and the vertical shift from the tail to the head of the resultant vector.

The polar form of the resultant vector is about (7.6, 30°).
The rectangular form is about (6.6, 3.8).

Look Back

Describe a geometric method for adding two vectors.

1. **Group Activity** Work with another student. Use the map on page 440.

   a. Create your own set of instructions for traveling from one point on the map to another. Use at least four steps in your instructions.

   b. Follow each other's instructions. Did you each arrive at the correct destination? If not, go back and check each other's work.

2. **Reading** Which instructions in the Exploration on page 440 can be represented by opposite vectors?

3. Janice and Malcolm are dance partners. During a dance, Janice walks from Malcolm at a 45° angle for eight steps and then continues at a −25° angle for another eight steps. When she stops, Malcolm walks in a straight line to join her. Draw a vector that represents the path Malcolm follows.

4. Suppose you are given these instructions in a treasure hunt: Walk five paces from the doorstep at a 30° angle and then 10 paces at a 120° angle. Draw a vector that represents your new position relative to the doorstep.

For Exercises 5–10, copy the map of landmarks on an island. Use Little Lake as the origin. Use the given coordinates to locate each landmark.

5. Slate Lagoon is at (3.3, 5.3).

6. Hermit's Cave is at (4.7, −40°).

7. Cool Spring:
   (12, −36°) from Palm Grove

8. Black Cliffs:
   (−7, 4.7) from the Abandoned Shack

9. Thinking Spot:
   (−9, −2) from Slate Lagoon

10. Feather Falls:
    (10, 100°) from the Loading Docks

Let t = (1, 3), u = (−7, 3), v = (3, 60°), and w = (4, 90°). Use a protractor and a ruler to draw each sum. Write the resultant vector in polar form and in rectangular form. Estimate answers to the nearest tenth.

11. $t + u$

12. $t - u$

13. $-t + 2u$

14. $v + 3w$

15. $-v + (-w)$

16. $-(v + w)$

17. **Writing** Compare the results of Exercises 15 and 16. Make a conjecture about the relationship between $-a + (-b)$ and $-(a + b)$. Test your conjecture with another pair of vectors.

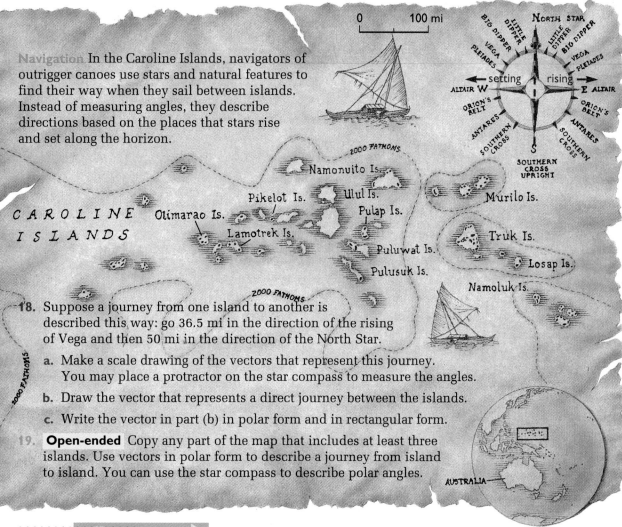

Navigation In the Caroline Islands, navigators of outrigger canoes use stars and natural features to find their way when they sail between islands. Instead of measuring angles, they describe directions based on the places that stars rise and set along the horizon.

18. Suppose a journey from one island to another is described this way: go 36.5 mi in the direction of the rising of Vega and then 50 mi in the direction of the North Star.

   a. Make a scale drawing of the vectors that represent this journey. You may place a protractor on the star compass to measure the angles.

   b. Draw the vector that represents a direct journey between the islands.

   c. Write the vector in part (b) in polar form and in rectangular form.

19. **Open-ended** Copy any part of the map that includes at least three islands. Use vectors in polar form to describe a journey from island to island. You can use the star compass to describe polar angles.

Ongoing **ASSESSMENT**

20. a. **Open-ended** Draw any three vectors **a**, **b**, and **c**.

   b. Draw (**a** + **b**) and (**b** + **c**).   **c.** Draw (**a** + **b**) + **c** and **a** + (**b** + **c**).

   d. What is the relationship between the two vectors in part (c)?

Review **PREVIEW**

21. Convert the rectangular coordinates (7.2, −4.8) to polar coordinates. *(Section 8-2)*

22. Three students are chosen at random from 8 juniors and 10 seniors. What is the probability that at least 2 seniors are chosen? *(Section 7-4)*

23. Convert the polar coordinates (12.8, −83°) to rectangular coordinates. *(Section 8-2)*

8 Working on the Unit Project

24. Write a clue for your treasure hunt that requires someone to draw the sum of two vectors to get to the place where the next clue is.

The Algebra of Vectors

Up Up And Away

Focus

Use algebra to solve problems involving vectors.

When an airplane takes off, it moves horizontally and vertically at the same time.

The speed of the airplane in the vertical direction is called the *rate of climb*.

200 mi/h

The speed of the airplane in the horizontal direction is called the *ground speed*.

15°

Sample 1

A passenger jet takes off at an angle of 15°. Suppose the speed of the jet is 200 mi/h after the jet takes off.

a. Find the jet's ground speed to the nearest mile per hour.

b. Find the jet's rate of climb to the nearest mile per hour.

Sample Response

Use a vector **v** to represent the speed and direction of the jet. **v** is the sum of a horizontal vector $\mathbf{v}_x$ and a vertical vector $\mathbf{v}_y$.

a. The ground speed is the magnitude of $\mathbf{v}_x$.
Use trigonometry to find this magnitude.

$$\cos 15° = \frac{\text{magnitude of } \mathbf{v}_x}{200}$$

$$200 \cos 15° = \text{magnitude of } \mathbf{v}_x$$

$$193.2 \approx \text{magnitude of } \mathbf{v}_x$$

The ground speed is about 193 mi/h.

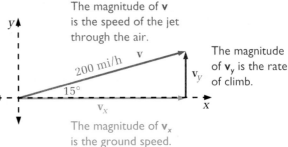

The magnitude of **v** is the speed of the jet through the air.

The magnitude of $\mathbf{v}_y$ is the rate of climb.

200 mi/h

$\mathbf{v}_y$

15°

$\mathbf{v}_x$

The magnitude of $\mathbf{v}_x$ is the ground speed.

b. The rate of climb is the magnitude of $\mathbf{v}_y$.
You can use trigonometry to show that the magnitude of $\mathbf{v}_y = 200 \sin 15° \approx 51.8$.

The rate of the climb is about 52 mi/h.

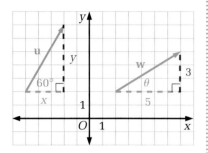

1. Explain why it makes sense to use *ground speed* and *rate of climb* for an airplane's horizontal and vertical speeds.

2. **a.** What is a polar form of the vector **v** in Sample 1? What information about the jet does the polar form give?

   b. What is the rectangular form of **v**? What information does the rectangular form give?

3. **a.** Complete this statement: The rectangular form (x, y) of **u** in the diagram is **u** = (_?_ cos _?_, _?_ sin _?_).

   b. Complete this statement: You can find a polar form (r, θ) of **w** in the diagram using the equations $r^2 = (\_?\_)^2 + (\_?\_)^2$ and $\tan \theta = \_?\_$.

4. Compare converting between polar and rectangular forms of vectors with converting between polar and rectangular coordinates.

Adding Vectors in Rectangular Form

The vectors **u** = (5, 2) and **v** = (3, 4) are shown, along with their sum **u** + **v**. Notice that:

$$\mathbf{u} + \mathbf{v} = (5, 2) + (3, 4)$$
$$= (5 + 3, 2 + 4)$$
$$= (8, 6)$$

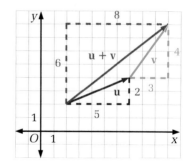

This result illustrates the following rule.

ADDING TWO VECTORS IN RECTANGULAR FORM

For any two vectors **u** = (x_1, y_1) and **v** = (x_2, y_2):

Example
$(3, -2) + (4, 6) = (3 + 4, -2 + 6)$
$= (7, 4)$

$$\mathbf{u} + \mathbf{v} = (\mathbf{x_1}, \mathbf{y_1}) + (\mathbf{x_2}, \mathbf{y_2})$$
$$= (\mathbf{x_1 + x_2}, \mathbf{y_1 + y_2})$$

◄ ∘ ∘ ∘

Watch Out!

When two vectors are in polar form, you *cannot* use the above rule. You must convert the vectors to rectangular form before adding.

An airplane is flying at a speed of 300 mi/h and at a bearing of 40° at a constant altitude. The airplane meets a wind whose speed is 60 mi/h and whose bearing is 155°. Find the resulting speed and bearing of the airplane as it flies through the wind.

Sample Response

Let **a** = the speed and direction of the airplane with no wind.

Let **w** = the speed and direction of the wind.

Then **v** = **a** + **w** represents the resulting speed and direction of the airplane as it flies through the wind.

Find **v** in polar form.

Step 1 Write **a** and **w** in polar form.

$$\mathbf{a} = (300, 50°) \quad \longleftarrow \quad \text{The measure of the polar angle is } 90° - 40° = 50°.$$

$$\mathbf{w} = (60, -65°) \quad \longleftarrow \quad \text{The measure of the polar angle is } 90° - 155° = -65°.$$

Step 2 Convert **a** and **w** to rectangular form.

P▶Rx (300, 50)
    192.8362829
P▶Ry (300, 50)
    229.8133329

P▶Rx (60, −65)
    25.3570957
P▶Ry (60, −65)
    −54.37846722

$$\mathbf{a} \approx (192.84, 229.81) \qquad \mathbf{w} \approx (25.36, -54.38)$$

Step 3 Find **v** in rectangular form.

$$\mathbf{v} = \mathbf{a} + \mathbf{w}$$
$$\approx (192.84, 229.81) + (25.36, -54.38)$$
$$\approx (192.84 + 25.36, 229.81 + (-54.38))$$
$$\approx (218.20, 175.43)$$

Step 4 Convert **v** to polar form.

$$\mathbf{v} \approx (279.98, 38.80°)$$

R▶Pr (218.20, 175.43)
    279.9766506
R▶Pθ (218.20, 175.43)
    38.79883507

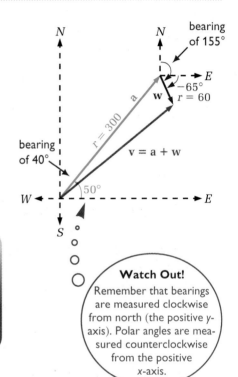

Watch Out!
Remember that bearings are measured clockwise from north (the positive *y*-axis). Polar angles are measured counterclockwise from the positive *x*-axis.

The resulting speed of the airplane as it flies through the wind is the magnitude of **v**, about 279.98 mi/h.

The airplane's bearing is about 90° − 38.80°, or about 51.20°.

Questions 5–7 refer to Sample 2 on page 448.

5. Why was it necessary to convert **a** and **w** to rectangular form in Step 2?

6. Why was it necessary to convert **v** to polar form in Step 4?

7. a. Does the wind increase or decrease the airplane's speed?

   b. Suppose the wind's bearing is 30°. Does this change your answer to part (a)? Explain.

   c. What wind bearing maximizes the airplane's speed? What wind bearing minimizes the airplane's speed?

Look Back

How do you add two vectors given in rectangular form? How do you add two vectors given in polar form?

8-4 Exercises and Problems

1. **Reading** What are the missing steps in the solution in part (b) of Sample 1?

Convert each vector to polar form.

2. (3, 5)   3. (−6, 2)   4. (−4, −9)

Convert each vector to rectangular form.

5. (7, 60°)   6. (1, 143°)   7. (2.5, −35°)

8. **Writing** Janet and Alma were asked to express the sum of **u** = (9, 10°) and **v** = (6, 82°) in rectangular form. Write a paragraph comparing their solutions. Be sure to identify any mistakes.

Janet Kazdan

$$u + v = (9, 10°) + (6, 82°)$$

$$= (9 + 6, 10° + 82°)$$

$$= (15, 92°)$$

$$= (15 \cos 92°, 15 \sin 92°)$$

$$\approx (-0.52, 14.99)$$

Alma Van Dorn

$$u + v = (9, 10°) + (6, 82°)$$

$$= (9 \cos 10°, 9 \sin 10°)$$
$$+ (6 \cos 82°, 6 \sin 82°)$$

$$\approx (8.86, 1.56) + (0.84, 5.94)$$

$$\approx (8.86 + 0.84, 1.56 + 5.94)$$

$$\approx (9.70, 7.50)$$

Find each vector sum in rectangular form.

9. $(4, 0) + (0, 3)$ **10.** $(9, 2) + (5, -11)$ **11.** $(3\sqrt{2}, -1) + (-\sqrt{2}, 2)$

Find each vector sum in polar form.

12. $(1, 70°) + (2, 10°)$ **13.** $(85, -98°) + (6, -7°)$ **14.** $(5, 50°) + (10, -50°)$

15. An airplane takes off at an angle of 10° and at a speed of 250 mi/h. Find the airplane's ground speed and rate of climb.

16. An airplane is flying at a speed of 180 mi/h and at a bearing of 350°. The airplane meets a wind whose speed is 45 mi/h and whose bearing is 15°. Find the speed and bearing of the airplane as it flies through the wind.

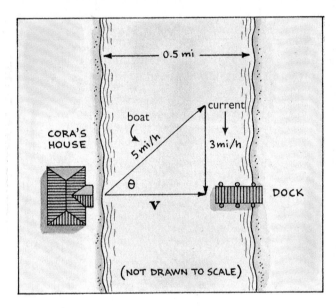

17. Cora Turner wants to row her boat to a dock directly across a river from her house. Cora can row at 5 mi/h. The speed of the current is 3 mi/h.

   a. At what angle θ should she point the boat in order to reach the dock?

   b. How long will it take her to reach the dock? (*Hint:* Find the magnitude of **v**, the vector representing the combined speed and direction of the boat and current.)

18. **Group Activity** Work with another student. You will need a ruler and graph paper.

   a. Draw the vector 3**u** where **u** = (1, 2). Use your drawing to find the rectangular form of 3**u**. Complete:
   $$3\mathbf{u} = (\underline{\ ?\ } \cdot 1, \underline{\ ?\ } \cdot 2)$$

   b. What do you think is the rectangular form of k**u** where **u** = (x, y) and k is any real number? Justify your answer.

   c. Draw the vector **u** − **v** where **u** = (4, 5) and **v** = (1, 3). Use your drawing to find the rectangular form of **u** − **v**. Complete:
   $$\mathbf{u} - \mathbf{v} = (\underline{\ ?\ } - \underline{\ ?\ }, \underline{\ ?\ } - \underline{\ ?\ })$$

   d. What do you think is the rectangular form of **u** − **v** where **u** = (x_1, y_1) and **v** = (x_2, y_2)? Justify your answer.

   e. Find the rectangular form of 2**u** − 3**v** for the vectors in part (c).

A *force* is a push or a pull. Physicists use vectors to represent forces.

19. Etenia is pulling her brother Ben in a sled. Etenia pulls with a force of 7.5 lb at an angle of 39° with respect to the horizontal.

   a. What amount of force pulls the sled forward? (*Hint:* Find the magnitude of $\mathbf{F_x}$.)

   b. **Writing** How can Etenia increase the amount of force that pulls the sled forward *without* increasing the total amount of force she exerts?

20. A car that weighs 3000 lb is at rest on a hill. The diagram shows the three forces acting on the car: the car's weight **W**, the upward force **U** of the road, and the force **F** of friction between the tires and the road.

   a. Write **W** in rectangular form. (*Hint:* First write **W** in polar form.)

   b. Let *f* be the magnitude of **F**. Write **F** in rectangular form. (Your answer will involve *f*.)

   c. Let *u* be the magnitude of **U**. Write **U** in rectangular form. (Your answer will involve *u*.)

   d. Since the car is at rest, the sum of the forces acting on the car is zero:

   $$\mathbf{W} + \mathbf{U} + \mathbf{F} = (0, 0)$$

   Use this fact to find the values of *u* and *f*.

BY THE WAY...

The Ojibwa people of North America and Canada made flat wooden sleds called *nobugidabans* to carry people and supplies over the snow. British traders mispronounced this word as *toboggans.*

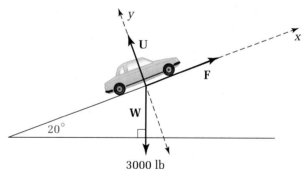

Ongoing **ASSESSMENT**

21. **Group Activity** Work with another student. You will need a ruler, a protractor, and graph paper.

   a. Draw a vector **u** on a coordinate grid. Draw a second vector **v** whose tail is at the head of **u**.

   b. Use the ruler and protractor to find a polar form (r_1, θ_1) of **u**. Then find a polar form (r_2, θ_2) of **v**.

   c. Draw the vector $\mathbf{w} = (r_1 + r_2, \theta_1 + \theta_2)$ on the same coordinate grid you used in part (a). Based on your drawing, does $\mathbf{w} = \mathbf{u} + \mathbf{v}$? What does this tell you about adding vectors in polar form?

22. Let **u** = (2, −5). Write −3**u** in rectangular form. *(Section 8-3)*

Solve. *(Section 5-8)*

23. $200(1.08)^t = 500$

24. $\log_2 (x - 3) + \log_2 (x - 7) = 5$

25. **Sports** Mark puts a shot as shown. *(Section 2-4)*

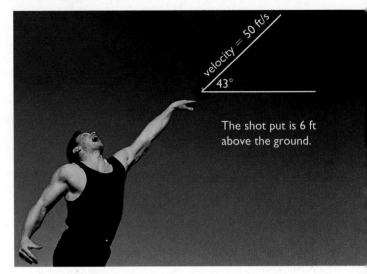

velocity = 50 ft/s

43°

The shot put is 6 ft above the ground.

   a. Use the equation

$$h(t) = -16t^2 + (v_0 \sin \theta)t + h_0$$

   to express the height of the shot put above the ground as a function of time.

   b. When does the shot put hit the ground?

Working on the Unit Project

26. Write a clue for your treasure hunt that requires someone to add two or more vectors in rectangular form in order to locate the next clue.

Unit 8   CHECKPOINT

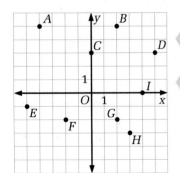

1. **Writing** Suppose the magnitude of **u** is r_1 and the magnitude of **v** is r_2. Is it always true that the magnitude of **u** + **v** is $r_1 + r_2$? Explain your answer.

Name the point with each given pair of polar coordinates.   **8-1**

2. (3, 90°)   **3.** (2.8, −135°)   **4.** (2.8, −45°)

Find polar coordinates for each point.

5. *A*   **6.** *H*   **7.** *I*

8. Convert (8, 110°) to rectangular coordinates.   **8-2**

9. Convert (3, −5) to polar coordinates.

10. Find all angles θ between 0° and 360° for which $\cos \theta = 0.6243$.

11. Find $\sin \theta$ when $\cos \theta = -0.4892$ and θ is in Quadrant II.

12. Draw the vector **w** = 3**u** − **v** where **u** = (2, 50°) and **v** = (3, −70°).   **8-3**

13. Find **u** = (7, 12) + (−4, 2) in rectangular form.   **8-4**

14. Find **v** = (5, 41°) + (9, −100°) in polar form.

Parametric Equations

TIMED TRAVEL

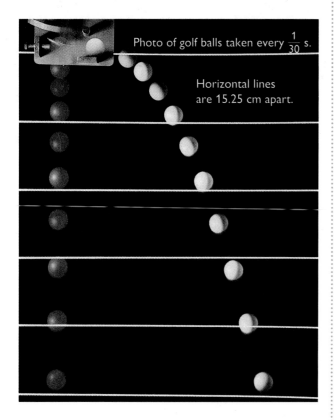

Photo of golf balls taken every $\frac{1}{30}$ s.

Horizontal lines
are 15.25 cm apart.

Talk it Over

The photo shows two golf balls falling from
the same starting point. The ball on the right
was given an initial horizontal velocity of
2 m/s.

1. **a.** Compare the horizontal motion of the
   two golf balls. What do you notice?

   b. Compare the vertical motion of the
   two golf balls. What do you notice?

   c. Would you say that the second golf
   ball's horizontal motion has an effect
   on its vertical motion? Explain.

2. **a.** When an object falls, its vertical
   position varies as the square of the
   time it falls:

   $$y = at^2$$

   The vertical position of each golf ball
   at the bottom of the photograph is
   about -0.784 m after 0.4 s. Use this to
   determine the constant of variation a.

   b. The second ball traveled the
   horizontal distances given in this
   table. Find an equation giving x as
   a function of t.

Time t (seconds)	Horizontal position x (meters)
0.1	0.2
0.2	0.4
0.3	0.6

launch velocity
vector

vertical
v_y component
of velocity

v_x
horizontal component
of velocity

$x = v_x t$

magnitude
of vector $\mathbf{v_x}$

$y = v_y t - \frac{1}{2}gt^2$

magnitude
of vector $\mathbf{v_y}$

When an object falls, whether or not it is given an initial push, its
horizontal and vertical movements are independent of each other.

Suppose an object is given a launch velocity $\mathbf{v}$ with horizontal
and vertical components as shown. Then at time t the object's
horizontal position x and vertical position y are given by these
equations, where g, the acceleration due to gravity, is about
9.8 m/s^2 or $g \approx 32$ ft/s^2. The variables x and y each depend on
a third variable, t. The equations relating x and y to t are called
parametric equations and t is called a **parameter**.

11 ft/s

41°

3 ft

Suppose that when a skateboarder flies off a ramp, the skateboarder is moving at an angle of 41° with a velocity of 11 ft/s.

a. Express the horizontal and vertical positions, relative to the launch point of the skateboarder, using parametric equations.

b. Use a graphics calculator to graph the path of the moving skateboarder. Use this graph to find the skateboarder's position 0.2 s after the jump.

c. Combine the two parametric equations into a single equation relating y to x.

Sample Response

a. Find v_x and v_y.

$$(11, 41°) \approx (8.3, 7.2)$$

↑   ↑   ↑
velocity v_x v_y
vector

← Convert the velocity vector from polar to rectangular form.

$$x = v_x t \qquad y = v_y t - \frac{1}{2}(32)t^2$$

$$= 8.3t \qquad = 7.2t - 16t^2$$ ← Substitute **8.3** for v_x and **7.2** for v_y.

The parametric equations for the horizontal and vertical positions are $x = 8.3t$, and $y = 7.2t - 16t^2$.

b. An appropriate viewing window is $0 \le x \le 7$ and $-3 \le y \le 3$. Set the parameter t to go from 0 to 1 with a t-step of 0.01.

After 0.2 s, the skateboarder is 1.66 ft to the right of and 0.8 ft above the end of the ramp.

The skateboarder moves along a parabola.

Trace the graph.

T = .2
X = 1.66   Y = .8

c. **1** Solve one of the equations for t.

$$x = 8.3t$$

$$\frac{x}{8.3} = t$$

2 Then substitute for t in the other equation.

$$y = 7.2t - 16t^2$$

$$= 7.2\left(\frac{x}{8.3}\right) - 16\left(\frac{x}{8.3}\right)^2$$ ← Substitute $\frac{x}{8.3}$ for t.

$$= 0.87x - 0.24x^2$$

An equation of the path is $y = 0.87x - 0.24x^2$.

TECHNOLOGY NOTE

When graphing parametric equations, make these settings:

t-min ← the minimum value of t

t-max ← the maximum value of t

t-step ← the increment of time in each step from t-min to t-max

You also need to set the calculator mode to Parametric.

3. a. What is the *y*-value when the skateboard hits the ground?

   b. When does the skateboard hit the ground?

4. Graph $y = 0.87x - 0.24x^2$. Do you think it is the same as the graph of the parametric equations?

5. How does changing the launch vector to (11, 20°) affect the path of the skateboard?

Sample 2

TECHNOLOGY NOTE

Make sure your calculator is in degree mode. In these equations, θ stands for *t*.

Suppose an object's motion is described by these parametric equations.

$$x = 2 \cos \theta \qquad y = 2 \sin \theta \qquad \text{where } 0° \le \theta \le 360°$$

a. Plot the path of this object.

b. Combine the two parametric equations into a single equation in terms of *x* and *y*.

Sample Response

a. An appropriate viewing window is $-6 \le x \le 6$, and $-4 \le y \le 4$. Set the parameter to go from 0 to 360 with a step of 1.

The path appears to be a circle of radius 2 centered at the origin.

b. Solve $x = 2 \cos \theta$ and $y = 2 \sin \theta$ for $\cos \theta$ and $\sin \theta$.

$\cos \theta = \dfrac{x}{2}$

$\sin \theta = \dfrac{y}{2}$

$\cos^2 \theta + \sin^2 \theta = 1$ ◄———— Use this Pythagorean identity.

$\left(\dfrac{x}{2}\right)^2 + \left(\dfrac{y}{2}\right)^2 = 1$ ◄———— Substitute $\dfrac{x}{2}$ for **cos** θ and $\dfrac{y}{2}$ for **sin** θ.

$\dfrac{x^2}{4} + \dfrac{y^2}{4} = 1$ ◄———— Simplify.

$x^2 + y^2 = 4$

An equation of the path is $x^2 + y^2 = 4$.

Look Back ◄

Describe the effect of launch velocity on a falling object.

1. **Reading** What does g represent in the equation for the vertical position of a falling object as a function of time? What is the value of g?

2. What is the relationship between these two different equations for y?

$$y = at^2 \quad \text{and} \quad y = v_y t - \frac{1}{2}gt^2$$

3. A billiard ball with a horizontal velocity of 3 m/s and a vertical velocity of 0 m/s rolls off of a table that is 1 m high.

   a. Write parametric equations to describe the position of the billiard ball at any time t.

   b. Complete the following table using the equations.

TIME (seconds)	Horizontal position x	Vertical position y	Ordered pair
0.0	?	?	?
0.1	?	?	?
0.2	?	?	?
0.3	?	?	?
0.4	?	?	?
0.5	?	?	?

   c. Estimate the time it takes for the billiard ball to hit the floor. Explain your answer.

BY THE WAY...

During the 1971 Apollo 14 mission, astronaut Alan B. Shepard surprised Mission Control when he played golf on one of his moon walks. He estimated that his best shot traveled 400 yd.

4. **Golf** Suppose you hit a golf ball on Earth at an angle of 10° with a velocity of 235 ft/s.

   a. Write parametric equations that describe the path of the ball.

   b. Suppose you play golf on the moon, where $g = 2.7$ ft/s². How far will the ball travel?

Combine each pair of parametric equations into a single equation relating y to x.

5. $x = 2.5t$, $y = 3.4t$

6. $x = 53.9t$, $y = -4.9t^2$

7. $x = 9.1t$, $y = 3.23t - 4.9t^2$

8. $x = 4.03t$, $y = 4.03t - 16.1t^2$

9. $x = 3.6 \cos t$, $y = 3.6 \sin t$

10. $x = (6 \cos t) + 3$, $y = (6 \sin t) - 2$

11. **Baseball** A batter hits a baseball with a velocity of 43 m/s and at an angle of 38°. The ball is 1 m above the ground when it is hit.

a. Write and graph parametric equations to describe the path of the ball.

b. Convert the parametric equations into a single equation.

c. Graph the single equation.

d. Compare the graphs.

e. What are the advantages and disadvantages of each type of equation?

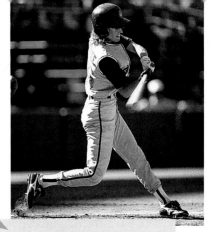

12. **Gardening** To be sure her whole garden gets water, Wynona changes the angle of the hose so the water sprays farther. The water flows out of her garden hose at a velocity 7.8 m/s, and the end of the hose is about 1.5 m above the ground.

8 m

5 m

a. Write parametric equations that describe the path of the water when the hose is held at an angle of 30°, 40°, 50°, and 60°.

b. Graph the equations.

c. **Writing** Can Wynona water the whole garden while standing in one place? Does it matter where she stands? Explain your reasoning.

BY THE WAY...

The Silver Bullets professional women's baseball team was founded in 1994. It is the first all-female team to be recognized by the National Association of Professional Baseball Leagues and compete against all-male minor-league teams.

TECHNOLOGY **In the parametric equations for Exercises 13–32, the variable t stands for θ. Use the following settings on a graphics calculator:**

$0 \le t \le 360$ t-step = 1 $-12 \le x \le 12$ $-8 \le y \le 8$

For Exercises 13–15, describe the graph of each pair of parametric equations.

13. $x = 8 \cos t$
    $y = 8 \sin t$

14. $x = 5 \cos t$
    $y = 5 \sin t$

15. $x = 7.5 \cos t$
    $y = 7.5 \sin t$

16. Write parametric equations for a circle with radius 3 centered at the origin.

17. Graph the equations $x = (4 \cos t) + 4$ and $y = (4 \sin t) - 3$.

18. Write parametric equations for a circle with radius 7 centered at the point $(-3, -2)$.

19. What can you conclude about the graph of the parametric equations $x = (a \cos t) + b$ and $y = (a \sin t) + c$ where $a > 0$?

For Exercises 20–22, graph Exercise 13. Then change each setting on the calculator as indicated. Describe how the graph changes.

20. Change *t*-step to 10.

21. Change *t*-min to 90.

22. Change *t*-max to 285.

23. Write parametric equations for a semicircle with radius 6 units in quadrants III and IV.

24. Write parametric equations for a circular arc with measure 47° and radius 7 units starting at 115°.

25. **Open-ended** Graph a pair of parametric equations. Change the *t*-step setting on the calculator. Predict the change in the graph. Check it.

TECHNOLOGY **A geometric shape called an *ellipse* can be graphed using parametric equations. Use the following settings on a graphics calculator:**

$0 \le t \le 360$ t-step = 1 $-12 \le x \le 12$ $-8 \le y \le 8$

For Exercises 26–28, describe the graph of each pair of parametric equations.

26. $x = 8 \cos t$
    $y = 6 \sin t$

27. $x = (5.5 \cos t) - 1$
    $y = 8 \sin t$

28. $x = (4 \cos t) + 3$
    $y = (7 \sin t) - 1$

29. What can you conclude about the graph of the parametric equations
    $x = (a \cos t) + b$ and $y = (c \sin t) + d$ where $a > 0$ and $c > 0$?

Write parametric equations for each graph.

30.

31.

32.

Ongoing **ASSESSMENT**

33. **Group Activity** Work with another student.

    a. Write parametric equations for a circle or an arc.

    b. Trade equations with your partner. Sketch the graph of the equations without using a graphics calculator.

34. **Writing** Describe a situation that can be modeled using parametric equations. Write three questions that can be answered using the parametric equations.

Review **PREVIEW**

For Exercises 35 and 36: *(Section 8-4)*

  a. **Find v + u.**   b. **Find u − v.**

35. $\mathbf{v} = (1, 5)$, $\mathbf{u} = (2, -7)$ 36. $\mathbf{v} = (-2, 3)$, $\mathbf{u} = (5, -6)$

37. Find the length of the hypotenuse of a right triangle whose legs are 10 cm and 5 cm long. *(Toolbox Skill 30)*

38. Find the distance between (3, 7) and (5, 0). *(Toolbox Skill 31)*

 Working on the Unit Project

39. Plot two more locations on your treasure hunt map: the location of the last clue and the location of the treasure. You will use these in Sections 8-6 and 8-7.

The Law of Cosines

Focus

Derive the law of cosines and use it to find measures of sides and angles in triangles.

MONUMENTAL TASK

Devils Tower National Monument looms above the plains in the northeastern corner of Wyoming.

The map shows distance and angle measurements to the base of the tower from three viewpoints along the hiking trail that circles the tower.

EXPLORATION

(How) can you find the length of the third side of a triangle from the lengths of the other two sides and the measure of their included angle?

- **Materials: centimeter rulers, protractors**
- **Work in a group of three students.**

1 Choose one of the three viewpoints along the trail.

2 Use the side-length and angle measures in the table below to make a scale drawing of △ABC, where C is your viewpoint, and A and B are points on Devils Tower. Use the scale 1 cm = 100 ft.

3 Measure AB to the nearest millimeter on your scale drawing and record it in a table like the one below. How many feet does this represent through Devils Tower?

4 Draw an x-axis through points C and B, and a y-axis through point C. Find rectangular coordinates for point A.

5 Find AB using the distance formula. Record your results in the table. Compare your answers with the measurements on your scale drawing.

	Find AB using a scale drawing.				Find AB using the distance formula.			
	CB	m∠C	CA	AB	C	B	A	AB
1	18 cm	40°	18 cm	?	(0, 0)	(18, 0)	(?, ?)	?
2	10.5 cm	55°	13.5 cm	?	(0, 0)	(10.5, 0)	(?, ?)	?
3	14.8 cm	36°	15.5 cm	?	(0, 0)	(14.8, 0)	(?, ?)	?

The triangles in the Exploration on page 459 are SAS (side-angle-side) constructions. These constructions yield unique triangles.

It is useful to be able to find the length of the third side without doing the construction and measuring. If the triangle is a right triangle, you can use the Pythagorean theorem. Otherwise, you can use the *law of cosines,* which is derived from the distance formula like this:

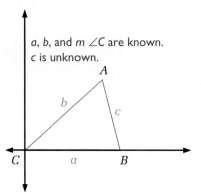

a, *b*, and $m \angle C$ are known. *c* is unknown.

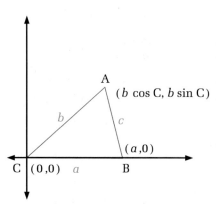

1 Given a triangle, place it so that one vertex is at the origin and one side lies on the x-axis.

2 Label the triangle. It is customary to label length *a* opposite $\angle A$, length *b* opposite $\angle B$, and length *c* opposite $\angle C$.

3 Identify the coordinates of each vertex in terms of the known measurements. You can use trigonometry to find the coordinates of A.

4 Use the distance formula to find *c*.

$$d = \sqrt{(x_2 - x_1)^2 + (y_2 - y_1)^2}$$ ⟵ Write the distance formula.

$$c = \sqrt{(a - b \cos C)^2 + (0 - b \sin C)^2}$$ ⟵ Substitute *c* for *d*, $(a, 0)$ for (x_2, y_2), and $(b \cos C, b \sin C)$ for (x_1, y_1).

$$c^2 = (a - b \cos C)^2 + (0 - b \sin C)^2$$ ⟵ Square both sides.

$$= a^2 - 2ab \cos C + b^2 \cos^2 C + b^2 \sin^2 C$$ ⟵ Simplify.

$$= a^2 - 2ab \cos C + b^2(\cos^2 C + \sin^2 C)$$ ⟵ Factor b^2 from the last two terms.

$$= a^2 - 2ab \cos C + b^2(1)$$ ⟵ Substitute 1 for $\cos^2 C + \sin^2 C$.

$$= a^2 + b^2 - 2ab \cos C$$ ⟵ Simplify and reorder terms.

$$c = \sqrt{a^2 + b^2 - 2ab \cos C}$$ ⟵ Take the positive square root of both sides.

The result resembles the Pythagorean theorem for right triangles, but it works for all triangles. You can use it to find the length of the third side of a triangle when you know the lengths of two sides and the measure of the included angle. If you put vertex *A* or *B* at the origin instead of vertex *C*, you can derive the related expressions for a^2 or b^2.

LAW OF COSINES

In any $\triangle ABC$:

$$a^2 = b^2 + c^2 - 2bc \cos A$$

$$b^2 = a^2 + c^2 - 2ac \cos B$$

unknown
side length $\longrightarrow$ $c^2 = a^2 + b^2 - 2ab \cos C$

                known   known   measure of the
             side length side length included angle

Sample 1

Find the distance from the picnic area to the boat ramp across Turquoise Lake.

Sample Response

The map shows two sides of a triangle that have lengths 1.26 km and 1.42 km, and an included angle that measures 74°.

$c^2 = a^2 + b^2 - 2ab \cos C$ ←   Use the law of cosines.

$ = (1.26)^2 + (1.42)^2 - 2(1.26)(1.42) \cos 74°$ ←   Substitute **1.26** for **a**, **1.42** for **b**, and **74°** for **C**.

$ \approx 2.62$

$c \approx 1.62$ ←   Take the positive square root of both sides.

The boat ramp is about 1.6 km from the picnic area.

Talk it Over

1. In the derivation of the law of cosines, why can you substitute 1 for the expression $\cos^2 C + \sin^2 C$?

2. Use the law of cosines to calculate AB in the triangle you drew in the Exploration on page 459. Compare your answer to the results you found in the Exploration.

3. Can you use the law of cosines to find the hypotenuse of a right triangle? How is the Pythagorean theorem related to the law of cosines?

······► **Now you are ready for:**
Exs. 1–16 on pp. 463–465

(How) *can you find the measures of the angles of a triangle when you know the lengths of the three sides?*

- **Materials: rulers, compasses, protractors**
- **Work in a group of three students.**

① Construct the triangles whose side lengths are given in rows 2, 3, and 4 of the table below.

	AB	*AC*	*BC*	*m ∠A*	*m ∠B*	*m ∠C*
1	8.6 cm	6.4 cm	4.1 cm	27°	45°	108°
2	6.7 cm	7.2 cm	4.4 cm	?	?	?
3	8.2 cm	3.5 cm	6.5 cm	?	?	?
4	4.2 cm	6.9 cm	3.6 cm	?	?	?
5	8.7 cm	3.7 cm	4.0 cm	?	?	?

Example:
Use row 1 of the table.

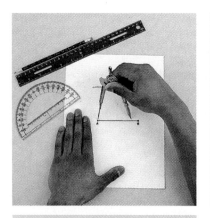

Draw $\overline{AB}$. From point A, draw an arc with radius AC.

From point B, draw an arc with radius BC. Label the intersection of the arcs as point C.

Draw $\overline{AC}$ and $\overline{BC}$ to complete the triangle.

② Measure the angles of your triangles with a protractor. Record them in a table like the one above.

③ Is the sum of the angle measures in each triangle 180°? Why or why not?

④ What happens when you try to construct a triangle using the lengths given in row 5 of the table above?

The triangles in the Exploration are SSS (side-side-side) constructions. If the sides can form a triangle, it is a unique triangle.

Verify the measure of ∠A for the triangle in row 1 of the table in the Exploration on page 462.

Sample Response

$$a^2 = b^2 + c^2 - 2bc \cos A$$ ← Write the law of cosines that involves ∠A.

$$\cos A = \frac{b^2 + c^2 - a^2}{2bc}$$ ← Solve for cos A.

$$= \frac{(6.4)^2 + (8.6)^2 - (4.1)^2}{2(6.4)(8.6)}$$ ← Substitute **6.4** for **b**, **8.6** for **c**, and **4.1** for **a**.

$$\approx 0.8913$$ ← Simplify.

$$m \angle A \approx 26.96°$$ ← Use the inverse cosine feature of a calculator.

cos⁻¹ 0.8913
   26.96293842

The measure of ∠A is about 27°.

Look Back ←

Under what conditions can you use the law of cosines to find an unknown side length or an unknown angle measure in a triangle?

▶ Now you are ready for:
Exs. 17–32 on pp. 465–466

8-6 Exercises and Problems

1. **Reading** What measurements of a triangle do you need to know to use the law of cosines to find an unknown side length?

For Exercises 2–4, use the given information to draw △ABC. Measure the length of the third side. Then use the law of cosines to calculate the length of the missing side. Compare your results.

2. $a = 8.3$ cm, $b = 11.3$ cm, $m \angle C = 37°$

3. $b = 4.7$ cm, $c = 7.1$ cm, $m \angle A = 112°$

4. $c = 9.2$ cm, $a = 3.9$ cm, $m \angle B = 67°$

5. **Writing** Place any △ABC on a coordinate grid so that ∠B is at the origin. Using the method on page 460, derive this form of the law of cosines:

$$b^2 = a^2 + c^2 - 2ac \cos B$$

6. Suppose two sides of a triangle are 3 in. long and the measure of their included angle is 60°. What is the length of the third side?

7. Open-ended Draw any large quadrilateral *ABCD*. Measure the sides and ∠ *A* and ∠ *C*. Find *BD* using the law of cosines with two different triangles. Check your answers by measuring.

connection to **CHEMISTRY**

Chemists model molecules by measuring bond angles and the distances between atoms. Molecules are in constant motion, so the measurements are constantly changing. The distances and bond angles given are average values. (Note: 1 picometer (pm) = 10^{-12} m.)

Find the distance between two hydrogen atoms in each molecule.

8. water (H_2O)

9. methane (CH_4)

Find the length of a side of each inscribed regular polygon.

10.

10 cm

11.

4 in.

12.

15 ft

13. Dome-shaped tents often have regular hexagons as a base.

a. One popular dome-shaped tent has a base shaped like a regular hexagon with sides of length 48 in. How tall is the tallest person who can sleep stretched out full length in this tent along the line shown?

b. Open-ended How long must each side of the hexagonal base of a dome-shaped tent be for you to sleep stretched out full length?

? ⊢ 48 in. ⊣

Career The design competition for the Vietnam Veterans Memorial in Washington, D.C., attracted more than 1400 entries. Maya Ying Lin, the winner, was 21 when her design was selected.

14. In her design, two walls of polished black granite meet at an angle of 125.2°. Each wall is 246.75 ft long. Find the distance between the ends of the memorial.

15. The walls are 10.1 ft high at the center. The walkway that leads to the center of the memorial slopes downward. Find the measure of the angle that this walkway makes with the top edge of the monument, which is horizontal.

ground level   246.75 ft

10.1 ft →

walkway down

(Not drawn to scale.)

16. The 125.2° angle she chose allows the Vietnam Veterans Memorial to point to two other nearby landmarks.

    Find the distance between the Lincoln Memorial and the Washington Monument.

17. Find the other two angles in the triangle formed by the Vietnam Veterans Memorial, the Lincoln Memorial, and the Washington Monument.

Vietnam Veterans Memorial

900 ft   125.2°   3500 ft

Lincoln Memorial

Washington Monument

The west wall points to the Lincoln Memorial, which is 900 ft away.

The east wall points to the Washington Monument, which is 3500 ft away.

18. a. Solve the equation $c^2 = a^2 + b^2 - 2ab \cos C$ for $\cos C$.
    b. Solve the equation $b^2 = a^2 + c^2 - 2ac \cos B$ for $\cos B$.

19. Use the law of cosines to verify the measures of $\angle B$ and $\angle C$ in row 1 of the table on page 462.

20. The side lengths in row 5 of the table on page 462 do not form a triangle. What happens if you try to use these lengths and the law of cosines to find the angles of a triangle?

21. **Writing** Explain how you can use the law of cosines several times to find the length of the fourth side of a quadrilateral when you know the lengths of three sides and the measures of all four angles.

A _dihedral angle_ of a polyhedron is the angle between adjacent faces. Use the labeled triangles to find the measure of a dihedral angle in each regular polyhedron.

22. tetrahedron

$\sqrt{3}$

2

$\sqrt{3}$

23. octahedron

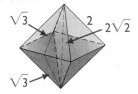

$\sqrt{3}$ 2 $2\sqrt{2}$

$\sqrt{3}$

24. icosahedron $\sqrt{3}$

$\sqrt{3}$

$\sqrt{5} + 1$ 2

8-6 The Law of Cosines

In Edgar Allan Poe's story "The Gold-Bug," William Legrand decodes a pirate's clue to buried treasure. The clue leads him to a skull hidden in a tree. An assistant drops a gold charm through one eye of the skull, and Legrand places a peg where the charm lands. When he digs 50 ft away, as instructed by the clue, he finds nothing. He realizes the charm was dropped through the wrong eye.

> "This mistake made a difference ... in the position of the peg...; of course the error, however trivial in the beginning, increased as we proceeded with the line, and by the time we had gone fifty feet threw us quite off the scent."

25. Suppose the gold charm lands 18 in. from the tree. To correct the mistake, Legrand moves the peg 3 in. but keeps it 18 in. from the tree.

Use the law of cosines to find the angle from peg position 1 to the tree to peg position 2.

26. Use the law of cosines to find how far away from the first dig site the treasure lies buried.

27. Show how to solve Exercise 26 using similar triangles.

Ongoing **ASSESSMENT**

28. **Group Activity** Use the law of cosines to fill in the unknown lengths and angle measures for the triangles in the table.

a	b	c	m∠A	m∠B	m∠C
129	43	?	?	?	76°
78	?	53	?	157°	?
52	17	60	?	?	?

Review **PREVIEW**

29. Write parametric equations for a circle that has a radius of 5 and its center at the origin. *(Section 8-5)*

30. Tell whether each statement is *True* or *False*? *(Toolbox Skill 36)*

    a. $h = a \sin C$ **b.** $h = c \sin A$

31. Solve the proportion $\dfrac{7}{\sin 30°} = \dfrac{196}{x}$. *(Toolbox Skill 37)*

Working on the Unit Project

32. Write a clue for your treasure hunt that requires the use of the law of cosines.

8-7

The Law of Sines

Going to **GREAT** Lengths

······Focus

Use the law of sines to
find measures of sides
and angles in triangles.

MT. EVEREST

Upper Rauje
Lower Rauje
Sollung
Pike Sub
Pangu
Chhulyāmu
Aisyālukharka
Lāori Danda
Mayām
SCALE: 1/2 INCH = 3 MILES

27°45'

27°30'

The Great Trigonometric
Survey of India in 1852
declared Mt. Everest to be
the highest mountain in
the world.

In the 1950s, surveyors measured angles of elevation from
eight different sites. These
angles are useful for finding
the height only if you know the
distance of each observation
site from Mt. Everest. These distances cannot be measured
directly, but the *law of sines*,
developed below, can be used to
find them.

In any $\triangle ABC$, if the altitude from B has length h, then

$$h = c \sin A \quad \text{and} \quad h = a \sin C.$$

$$c \sin A = a \sin C \qquad \longleftarrow \quad \text{The two expressions for } h \text{ are equal.}$$

$$\frac{c \sin A}{\sin A \sin C} = \frac{a \sin C}{\sin A \sin C} \qquad \longleftarrow \quad \text{Divide both sides by } \sin A \sin C.$$

$$\frac{c}{\sin C} = \frac{a}{\sin A} \qquad \longleftarrow \quad \text{Simplify.}$$

By using other altitudes, you can show that in any $\triangle ABC$, the
ratio $\dfrac{b}{\sin B}$ has the same value as $\dfrac{c}{\sin C}$ and as $\dfrac{a}{\sin A}$.

LAW OF SINES

In any $\triangle ABC$, the lengths of the sides are in
proportion with the sines of the opposite angles.

$$\frac{a}{\sin A} = \frac{b}{\sin B} = \frac{c}{\sin C}$$

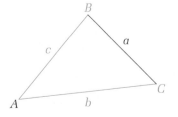

Sample 1 shows that you can use the law of sines to find unknown measures in a triangle given the measures of two angles and the length of an included side (ASA).

Sample 2 shows that you can also use this law to find unknown measures in a triangle given the measures of two angles and the length of a non-included side (AAS).

Sample 1

Find the distance from Aisyālukharka to Mt. Everest.

Sample Response

On the map, $m \angle U = 123.32°$, $m \angle E = 21.47°$, and $e = 102,990$.

$$\frac{u}{\sin U} = \frac{e}{\sin E}$$ ⟵ Use the law of sines for $\triangle UEA$.

$$\frac{u}{\sin 123.32°} = \frac{102,990}{\sin 21.47°}$$ ⟵ Substitute **123.32°** for **U**, **102,990** for e, and **21.47°** for E.

$$u = \frac{102,990 \sin 123.32°}{\sin 21.47°}$$ ⟵ Solve for u.

$$\approx 235,128$$ ⟵ Simplify.

The distance from Aisyālukharka to Mt. Everest is about 235,130 ft.

Sample 2

Find the distance from Mayām to Mt. Everest.

Sample Response

On the map, $m \angle A = 95.98°$, $m \angle M = 63.19°$, and $m = 235,130$.

$$\frac{a}{\sin A} = \frac{m}{\sin M}$$ ⟵ Use the law of sines for $\triangle AEM$.

$$\frac{a}{\sin 95.98°} = \frac{235,130}{\sin 63.19°}$$ ⟵ Substitute **95.98°** for **A**, **235,130** for m, and **63.19°** for M.

$$a = \frac{235,130 \sin 95.98°}{\sin 63.19°}$$ ⟵ Solve for a.

$$\approx 262,015$$ ⟵ Simplify.

The distance from Mayām to Mt. Everest is about 262,020 ft.

▶ Now you are ready for:
Exs. 1–14 on pp. 471–472

Talk it Over

1. Use the tangent ratio and the information in the table to estimate the height of Mt. Everest measured from either Aisyālukharka or Mayām.

Observation site	Station altitude	Distance to Mt. Everest	Angle of elevation
Aisyālukharka	8670 ft	235,130 ft	4.95°
Mayām	10,948 ft	262,020 ft	3.88°

2. Sample 1 uses the law of sines with ASA information. Sample 2 uses the law of sines with AAS information. What other triangle information can you use with the law of sines?

EXPLORATION

(How) many triangles can you construct if you are given SSA information?

- **Materials: protractors, rulers, compasses**
- **Work in a group of four students.**

Each student should follow steps 1–6 to complete one row of the table below.

① Draw a long baseline. Label the left endpoint A.

② Use a protractor to draw a 30° angle at point A.

③ Measure 8 cm from point A and mark point C as shown.

④ Put one end of the compass at C and draw an arc with radius a.

⑤ If your arc intersects the baseline, label the point(s) of intersection B.

⑥ List the number of triangles you can construct using the SSA information in each row. Then tell whether the triangles formed are *acute, right,* or *obtuse.*

a	b	$m \angle A$	Number of triangles	Type(s) of triangles
3 cm	8 cm	30°	?	?
4 cm	8 cm	30°	?	?
6 cm	8 cm	30°	?	?
10 cm	8 cm	30°	?	?

⑦ Write a conjecture about how the relationship between a, b, and $b \sin A$ influences the number of triangles formed.

Two triangles can be formed from the same SSA information when two conditions are met:

$$a > b \sin A \qquad\qquad a < b$$

The arc from C is long enough to intersect the baseline twice.

The arc is not long enough to intersect the baseline to the left of A outside the triangle.

This situation is called the **ambiguous case.** This means you cannot tell whether one, two, or no triangles are formed.

Sample 3

Find the unknown measures for $\triangle ABC$ with $a = 4$ cm, $b = 7.2$ cm, and $m\angle A = 30°$.

Sample Response

Step 1 Find the measure of one of the unknown angles.

Since $4 > 7.2 \sin 30°$ and $4 < 7.2$, two triangles can be formed.

$\dfrac{a}{\sin A} = \dfrac{b}{\sin B}$ ⟵ Use the law of sines to find $m\angle B$.

$\dfrac{4}{\sin 30°} = \dfrac{7.2}{\sin B}$ ⟵ Substitute **4** for **a**, **30°** for **A**, and **7.2** for **b**.

$\sin B = \dfrac{7.2 \sin 30°}{4}$ ⟵ Solve for sin B.

$\quad\ = 0.9$ ⟵ Simplify.

$m\angle B \approx 64°$ or $116°$ ⟵ Use the inverse sine feature of a calculator. The two angles whose sine is 0.9 are supplementary.

Step 2 Find $m\angle C$ and c for each of the two cases.

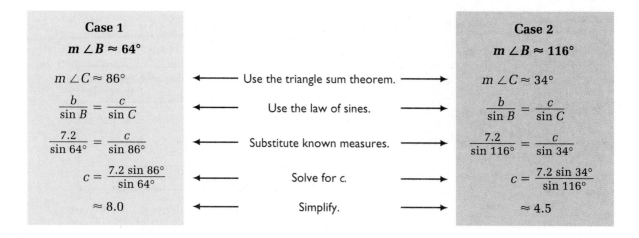

Case 1		Case 2
$m\angle B \approx 64°$		$m\angle B \approx 116°$
$m\angle C \approx 86°$	⟵ Use the triangle sum theorem. ⟶	$m\angle C \approx 34°$
$\dfrac{b}{\sin B} = \dfrac{c}{\sin C}$	⟵ Use the law of sines. ⟶	$\dfrac{b}{\sin B} = \dfrac{c}{\sin C}$
$\dfrac{7.2}{\sin 64°} = \dfrac{c}{\sin 86°}$	⟵ Substitute known measures. ⟶	$\dfrac{7.2}{\sin 116°} = \dfrac{c}{\sin 34°}$
$c = \dfrac{7.2 \sin 86°}{\sin 64°}$	⟵ Solve for c. ⟶	$c = \dfrac{7.2 \sin 34°}{\sin 116°}$
≈ 8.0	⟵ Simplify. ⟶	≈ 4.5

Measurements for the two triangles that meet the SSA conditions in Sample 3 are summarized in this table.

	$m \angle A$	$m \angle B$	$m \angle C$	a	b	c
Case 1	30°	64°	86°	4 cm	7.2 cm	8.0 cm
Case 2	30°	116°	34°	4 cm	7.2 cm	4.5 cm

Look Back ◄

Of all the combinations of side lengths and angle measures used to construct triangles, which do not always produce a unique triangle? Why?

·····► **Now you are ready for:**
: **Exs. 15–38 on pp. 473–474**

8-7 Exercises and Problems

1. **Reading** How can surveyors use trigonometry to find the height of Mt. Everest without measuring distances to the mountain?

2. Find the height of Mt. Everest using the observation site you did not choose in *Talk it Over* question 1. Compare your answer with the other height you found. Explain any difference in the answers. How can you get a better estimate of the height of Mt. Everest?

Find the unknown measures in each triangle.

3.

4.

5.
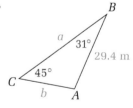

Copy and complete the table. Sketch each triangle.

	$m \angle A$	$m \angle B$	$m \angle C$	a	b	c
6.	?	28°	13°	?	6.2	?
7.	109°	?	25°	58	?	?
8.	52°	?	74°	?	?	62
9.	90°	38°	?	?	19	?

10. The diagram shows measurements a surveyor has made. Find x and y, the two distances to the flag.

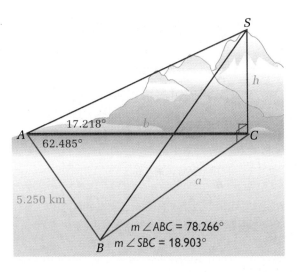

11. **Surveying** The diagram shows measurements taken by a surveyor at sea level to determine the height of a mountain.

   a. Find $m \angle ACB$.

   b. Use the law of sines to find a and b.

   c. Find h using right $\triangle ACS$.

   d. Find h using right $\triangle BCS$.

   e. What is the average of the two heights in parts (c) and (d)?

   f. Repeat parts (a) through (e), rounding all angle measurements to whole numbers. How does this reduction in accuracy affect the estimate of the mountain's height?

12. **Astronomy** When you hold a finger in front of your face and look at your finger with one eye at a time, your finger appears to shift against the background. This principle, known as *parallax*, has been used to estimate the distance to nearby stars, using the diameter of Earth's orbit (about 3.0×10^8 km) as the base of a triangle.

   a. Suppose an isosceles triangle models the position of Alpha Centauri, a bright star near Earth. The angle at Alpha Centauri is $0.000417°$. Find the distance from Alpha Centauri to Earth.

   b. Light travels 9.46×10^{12} km in one year. How many years does it take light to travel from Alpha Centauri to Earth?

13. **Carpentry** Part of a roof has a slope of $\frac{4}{12}$, and the other part of the roof has a slope of $\frac{6}{12}$.

   a. Find the measures of $\angle A$ and $\angle B$.

   b. Find the measure of the angle at the peak of the roof.

   c. Find a and b.

   d. Find h.

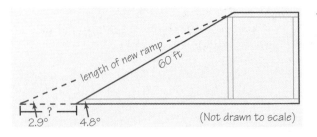

(Not drawn to scale)

14. **Access Standards** A 60 ft ramp makes an angle of $4.8°$ with the ground. To meet new accessibility guidelines, the ramp must make an angle of $2.9°$ with the ground.

   a. How long will the new ramp be?

   b. How much farther along the ground will the new ramp extend?

Unit 8 Angles, Trigonometry, and Vectors

15. The *angular separation* of the sun and a planet is the angle formed by the sun, Earth, and the planet. The average distance from the sun to Earth is called 1 *astronomical unit* (a.u.).

On January 5, 1997, the angular separation of the sun and Venus is 21.147°. The distance from the sun to Earth on that day is 0.983 a.u. and from the sun to Venus is 0.724 a.u. On the same day, the angular separation of the sun and Mercury is 8.206°. The distance from the sun to Mercury is 0.323 a.u.

a. Find the unknown angle measures and side length in $\triangle V_1 SE$ and $\triangle V_2 SE$, which represent the possible positions of Venus, the sun, and Earth.

b. Find the unknown angle measures and side length in $\triangle M_1 SE$ and $\triangle M_2 SE$, which represent the possible positions of Mercury, the sun, and Earth.

c. Suppose a high-powered telescope reveals the sun shining on the planets as shown.

Is Venus at V_1 or V_2?

Is Mercury at M_1 or M_2?

d. Using your answers from parts (a)–(c), make a scale drawing showing the positions of the sun, Earth, Venus, and Mercury on January 5, 1997. Label all the distances among them. (*Hint:* Use the law of cosines to find the distance from Mercury to Venus.)

BY THE WAY...

Because the orbit of Venus is inside Earth's orbit, Venus appears near the Sun at dawn or dusk. That is why it is called the "morning star" or "evening star."

$a < b \sin A$

$a = b \sin A$

$a > b \sin A$
$a < b$

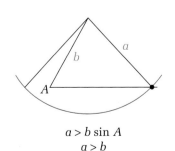

$a > b \sin A$
$a > b$

16. Four constructions that contain SSA information are shown.

  a. For each construction, find the number of triangles formed and explain how you found the answer.

  b. How many triangles will be formed when $a > b \sin A$ and $a = b$? Explain.

17. Draw diagrams, similar to those in Exercise 16, showing all the possibilities when A is an obtuse angle.

For each angle measure and pair of side lengths, tell how many triangles can be formed.

18. $m\angle A = 47°$, $b = 6$, $a = 7$

19. $m\angle A = 112°$, $b = 11$, $a = 20$

20. $m\angle A = 32°$, $b = 9$, $a = 6$

21. $m\angle A = 57°$, $b = 11$, $a = 4$

22. $m\angle A = 12°$, $b = 192$, $a = 40$

23. $m\angle A = 149°$, $b = 27$, $a = 24$

Find the unknown measures in each $\triangle ABC$.

24. $m\angle A = 72°$, $m\angle C = 19°$, $b = 15.1$

25. $m\angle A = 111°$, $a = 12$, $c = 9$

26. $m\angle C = 76°$, $a = 18$, $c = 12.4$

27. $m\angle B = 108°$, $b = 10.9$, $c = 11.6$

Find the unknown measures in each $\triangle RST$. Tell whether you used the *law of cosines*, the *law of sines*, or both.

28. $r = 8$ cm, $s = 4$ cm, $t = 9$ cm

29. $m\angle R = 62°$, $m\angle T = 49°$, $s = 13$ km

30. $m\angle S = 81°$, $r = 16.2$ cm, $t = 9.1$ cm

31. $m\angle S = 119°$, $m\angle T = 15°$, $t = 4$ in.

32. $m\angle T = 57°$, $r = 6.3$ cm, $s = 17$ cm

33. $m\angle R = 17°$, $m\angle T = 91°$, $r = 3.2$ km

Ongoing **ASSESSMENT**

34. **Group Activity** Work with another student.

Write *triangle sum theorem, law of sines,* or *law of cosines* to complete each row. Then tell whether it is easier to find *angles* first or *sides* first.

GIVEN	To find sides, use...	To find angles, use...	Example
SAS	?	?	8–6 Sample 1, p. 461
SSS	all sides known	?	8–6 Sample 2, p. 463
ASA	?	?	8–7 Sample 1, p. 468
AAS	?	?	8–7 Sample 2, p. 468
SSA	?	?	8–7 Sample 3, p. 470

Review **PREVIEW**

35. Write a form of the law of cosines for a triangle with sides of length x, y, and z and angles X, Y, and Z. *(Section 8-6)*

36. Write an indirect proof to show that no regular polygon has an interior angle whose measure is $80°$. *(Section 3-7)*

37. **Open-ended** Write an eight-number data set. Find the standard deviation of the data set. *(Section 6-2)*

Working on the Unit Project

38. Write a last clue for your treasure hunt that leads to the treasure and that can be answered only by applying the law of sines. An example is shown.

To get to the treasure, walk x ft at a bearing of y°, where x and y are found by applying the law of sines to the triangle shown.

Completing the Unit Project

Unit Project 8

Now you are ready to share your map and clues with another group so that they can search for the buried treasure.

Your completed project should include these things:

➤ **a treasure map**

➤ **numbered clues written on separate pieces of paper**

➤ **a solutions map on which you write the clues at the points where searchers stop to pick up new clues**

➤ **a written critique of your treasure hunt by the group that tries it**

Solution Map

CLUE 3

CLUE 1

Use your answer for clue 1 as your starting place. Draw vector V (-20, 30) and vector W (-30, 70). The location of your next clue is at V + W.

1 INCH = 10 YARDS

Look Back

Were the members of another group able to locate the buried treasure from your group's clues? Were any of the clues too imprecise? too easy or too difficult to follow?

Alternative Projects

····· **Project 1:** Ocean Navigation

Write a research report on ocean navigation. Find out how boat pilots use bearings and maps to stay on course by using information about currents, tides, and so on.

····· **Project 2:** Orienteering

Find out about the sport of orienteering. Create a classroom display that shows how participants use maps and magnetic compasses to plot courses between *control points*.

For Questions 1–13, use this diagram.

Carol Grant Gould and James L. Gould
studied the behavior of honey bees to find
out how they navigate and communicate.
In one study, a bee was trained to find food
at three stations about 180 m from the hive.

Find polar coordinates for each station.   8-1
Use the hive as the origin.

1. blue station

2. white station

3. red station

Bee landing at hive entrance

Find rectangular coordinates for each station.   8-2

4. blue station

5. white station

6. red station

The bee was first trained to fly along vector **a** to get food at
the blue station. When the food was moved to the white station, the bee flew along vectors **a** and **b** to get it. When the
food was moved again, the bee flew along vectors **a**, **b**, and **c**
to get it. The bee returned directly to the hive along vector **d**.

Draw and label each vector.   8-3

7. **a** + **b**

8. **b** + **c**

9. **a** + **b** + **c**

10. the vector that the bee traveled to return to the hive
    from the red station

Find each vector sum in rectangular form. Use the rectangular   8-4
coordinates you found in Questions 4–6.

11. **a** + **b**   12. **a** + **b** + **c**   13. **a** + **b** + **c** + **d**

Describe the graph of each pair of parametric equations. Use these   8-5
settings: $0 \leq t \leq 360$, t-step = 1, $-12 \leq x \leq 12$, and $-8 \leq y \leq 8$.

14. $x = \cos t$
    $y = \sin t$

15. $x = \cos t + 4$
    $y = \sin t - 5$

16. $x = 4 \cos t$
    $y = 5 \sin t$

17. Find the distance between the tips of the stunt kite's wings.

18. Sketch a regular pentagon inscribed in a circle of radius 2 in. What is the length of each side?

Use the information from Sarah's journal.

19. Draw a sketch of the area and Sarah's hike back to camp.

20. How many paces is it from the rocks to camp?

21. What is the distance in paces across the lake from the cottonwood tree to camp?

22. Suppose Sarah walked at a rate of 100 paces/min and rested at the rocks for 17 min. At what time did she return to camp?

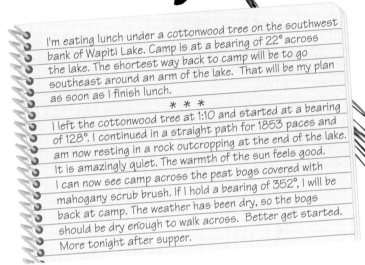

48 in.
95°
48 in.

8-6

8-7

I'm eating lunch under a cottonwood tree on the southwest bank of Wapiti Lake. Camp is at a bearing of 22° across the lake. The shortest way back to camp will be to go southeast around an arm of the lake. That will be my plan as soon as I finish lunch.

* * *

I left the cottonwood tree at 1:10 and started at a bearing of 128°. I continued in a straight path for 1853 paces and am now resting in a rock outcropping at the end of the lake. It is amazingly quiet. The warmth of the sun feels good. I can now see camp across the peat bogs covered with mahogany scrub brush. If I hold a bearing of 352°, I will be back at camp. The weather has been dry, so the bogs should be dry enough to walk across. Better get started. More tonight after supper.

23. **Self-evaluation** What dimensions of a triangle do you need to know in order to use the law of cosines? the law of sines? How can you be sure you remember the laws and know when to use them?

24. **Group Activity** Work in a group of four students.

a. Copy and complete the table of angle measures for the five types of triangles in this geodesic dome. Round answers to the nearest hundredth of a degree.

b. **Open-ended** Choose a vertex of the dome and show that the sum of the measures of the angles at the vertex is less than 360°.

	Side lengths			Angle measures		
I	*a*	*a*	*b*	?	?	?
II	*b*	*c*	*c*	?	?	?
III	*c*	*d*	*f*	?	?	?
IV	*d*	*d*	*e*	?	?	?
V	*e*	*e*	*e*	60°	60°	60°

This geodesic dome is based on an icosahedron whose faces are each subdivided into 16 triangles.

Each vertex is 15 ft from the center of the dome.

The triangles in the geodesic dome appear to be equilateral, but most of them are not.

Side	Length (in.)
a	45.57
b	53.14
c	53.02
d	56.32
e	58.49
f	53.75

IDEAS AND (FORMULAS)=x^2

GEOMETRY

➤ Polar coordinates (r, θ) describe the location of a point using a distance r from a reference point and an angle θ measured from $0°$ along a horizontal to the right of the reference point. *(p. 425)*

➤ Positive polar angles are measured counterclockwise from $0°$. Negative polar angles are measured clockwise from $0°$. *(pp. 425, 426)*

➤ The rectangular coordinates of a point with polar coordinates (r, θ) are $(r \cos \theta, r \sin \theta)$. *(p. 431)*

➤ Vectors are quantities with both magnitude and direction. *(p. 441)*

➤ You can add vectors by placing them in a head-to-tail arrangement. The sum is the vector with its tail at the tail of the first vector and its head at the head of the last vector. *(p. 442)*

➤ The opposite of a vector **v** is a vector with the same magnitude as **v** but the opposite direction. *(p. 443)*

➤ The vector $k\mathbf{v}$ is a scalar multiple of vector **v**. It has the same direction as **v** and a magnitude that is k times the magnitude of **v**. *(p. 443)*

➤ You can use the law of cosines to find the length of the third side of a triangle when you know the lengths of two sides of a triangle and the measure of their included angle (SAS). *(p. 461)*

➤ You can use the law of cosines to find any angle in a triangle when you know the lengths of all three sides (SSS). *(p. 463)*

➤ You can use the law of sines to find unknown dimensions in a triangle when you know the measures of two angles in the triangle and the length of one side (ASA or AAS) or when you know the lengths of two sides and the measure of a non-included angle (SSA). *(pp. 468, 470)*

➤ SSA information does not always define a unique triangle. Sometimes no triangle or two triangles can be formed. *(p. 470)*

ALGEBRA $)x^2$

➤ The sum of two vectors $\mathbf{u} = (x_1, y_1)$ and $\mathbf{v} = (x_2, y_2)$ is the vector $(x_1 + x_2, y_1 + y_2)$. To add vectors given in polar form, you must first convert them to rectangular form. *(p. 447)*

➤ Parametric equations define x and y in terms of a third variable t. *(p. 453)*

Unit 8 Angles, Trigonometry, and Vectors

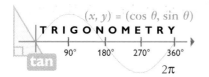

(x, y) = (cos θ, sin θ)

T R I G O N O M E T R Y

tan

90°   180°   270°   360°

2π

➤ The cosine, sine, and tangent ratios can be defined for any angle. The values of x and y used are the coordinates of a point with polar coordinates (r, θ). *(p. 432)*

$$\cos \theta = \frac{x}{r} \quad \sin \theta = \frac{y}{r} \quad \tan \theta = \frac{y}{x} \quad \text{(when } x \neq 0\text{)}$$

➤ Supplementary angles have the same sine. *(p. 433)*

➤ Angles with opposite measures have the same cosine. *(p. 433)*

➤ To convert rectangular coordinates to polar coordinates, use the Pythagorean theorem to find r. Then use the inverse trigonometric feature of a calculator to find the measure of θ. The calculator may not display the correct polar angle. Use what you know about the quadrant the point lies in to find the correct polar angle. *(p. 434)*

➤ A Pythagorean identity relates the sine and cosine of any angle. *(p. 435)*

$$\cos^2 \theta + \sin^2 \theta = 1$$

➤ The law of cosines is related to the Pythagorean theorem but it applies to all triangles. *(p. 461)*

$$a^2 = b^2 + c^2 - 2bc \cos A$$

➤ The law of sines states that lengths of the sides of any triangle are in proportion with the sines of the opposite angles. *(p. 467)*

$$\frac{a}{\sin A} = \frac{b}{\sin B} = \frac{c}{\sin C}$$

········**Key Terms**

• **bearing** (p. 425)
• **vector** (p. 441)
• **tail of a vector** (p. 441)

• **polar coordinates** (p. 425)
• **magnitude** (p. 441)
• **resultant vector** (p. 442)

• **Pythagorean identity** (p. 435)
• **head of a vector** (p. 441)
• **scalar multiple of a vector** (p. 443)

• **opposite vectors** (p. 443)
• **law of cosines** (p. 461)

• **parametric equations** (p. 453)
• **law of sines** (p. 467)

• **parameter** (p. 453)
• **ambiguous case** (p. 470)

9

Transformations of Graphs and Data

Suppose you could travel back through time. In the 4th millennium B.C. in Mesopotamia, you meet a wheelwright making wheels out of three planks clamped together. In the 1600s you meet a village blacksmith forging wagon parts in colonial America. You tell the wheelwright and the blacksmith about the role of computer graphics in the career of a 20th century automobile designer. They never heard of the job.

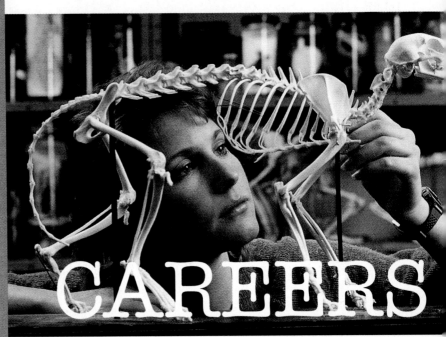

CAREERS

Growing office in downtown area seeks individual for part time employment. Must be flexible, service minded, have strong organization skills, attn. to detail, ability to take initiative & handle diverse duties. Most interest

skills

When you go job hunting, you bring a résumé of your schooling, job experiences, honors, and special skills. Employers may also be looking for traits you take for granted, traits that followed you from childhood into adulthood.

interests

The sucessful candidate must be self-motivated and possess strong communication skills and enjoy customer contact. We offer

Job Interview

A job interview is an opportunity for you to ask questions about a company and the job it is offering, as well as to answer questions about yourself. For your project, your group will plan to invite someone in one career field to visit your class and answer questions.

As you work through the Working on the Unit Project exercises, you will understand some of the topics to bring up in a job interview, such as the role and scoring of any special tests needed for entry and the expected availability of job openings in the future.

Your completed project will include a list of questions to use in interviewing a career representative, a completed interview, and an analysis of the information gained in the interview.

Statistics show that an adult working in the United States will probably change jobs six or seven times in a lifetime. In today's global economy, your special interests and skills may take you far from home to a part of the world that has the right job for you.

Civil Engineering – Japan

Medicine – Spain

City Planning – Kenya

Archaeology – Mexico

For this project you should work in a group of four students. Here are some ideas to help you get started.

☞ Ask your guidance counselor for the *Kuder General Interest Survey*. This survey will give you a profile of your interests and a rating in nine career fields.

☞ In your group, discuss career fields you might be interested in exploring.

☞ Ask parents, neighbors, teachers, and friends for the names of individuals working in the career you have chosen to investigate. You may wish to ask some of them about working conditions and job satisfaction.

☞ The class as a whole may wish to discuss career choices so that each group investigates a different career.

☞ Plan to meet with your group later to contact a career resource person and prepare questions for the interview.

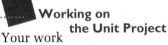

Can We Talk CAREERS

Working on the Unit Project

Your work in Unit 9 will help you plan questions for the interview.

Related Exercises:

Section 9-1, Exercise 28
Section 9-2, Exercise 31
Section 9-3, Exercise 19
Section 9-4, Exercises 45, 46
Section 9-5, Exercise 28
Section 9-6, Exercise 21
Section 9-7, Exercise 22

Alternative Projects p. 533

➤ What jobs exist today that were unheard of when your great grandparents were looking for their first jobs?

➤ Do you see any shifts in the nature of the jobs available from the 1800s to the 1900s? Can you give some reasons for these changes?

➤ Do you prefer a 9-to-5 job, or one with flexible hours? working alone or with a team? working outdoors or indoors? Do you want a job that requires extensive travel?

➤ Have you ever been interviewed for a job? What kinds of questions were you asked? Did any surprise you?

➤ What are some jobs that require mathematical skills? What are those skills?

➤ Many employers expect to train new employees in the details of a job, but they want people to have problem solving skills. List characteristics that you think make a person a good problem solver.

Adding a Constant to Data

········Focus

Recognize the effect that adding a constant to data values has on the mean, median, range, and standard deviation.

NEED A LIFT?

People who plaster ceilings sometimes walk on stilts. This allows the plasterers to reach high ceilings without having to move a ladder. The table shows the heights of a group of plasterers without stilts and with stilts.

Heights of Plasterers

Name	Without stilts (inches)	With stilts (inches)
Bob	72	86
Karl	65	79
Portia	63	77
Kendra	66	80
Ralph	74	88
Marcus	68	82
Jenny	64	78
Jordan	66	80
Sandra	62	76

Talk it Over

1. How are the numbers in the second and third columns of the table related?

2. Find the mean of the heights without stilts. Find the mean of the heights with stilts. How do the means compare?

3. Repeat question 2 using the median.

4. Repeat question 2 using the range.

5. The histograms show the distribution of heights for the plasterers without stilts and with stilts. Describe the relationship between the two histograms.

Height Distribution

without stilts   with stilts

9-1 Adding a Constant to Data

483

Use the table on page 483. Find the standard deviation of the heights without stilts and of the heights with stilts. Compare the values.

Sample Response

Method ❶ Use a calculator.

Put your calculator in statistics mode or select the statistics menu. Enter the data and have the calculator compute the standard deviation for each data set.

standard deviation without stilts

1–Var Stats
$\bar{x} = 66.66666667$
$\Sigma x = 600$
$\Sigma x^2 = 40130$
$Sx = 4.031128874$
$\sigma x = 3.80058475$
$\downarrow n = 9$

standard deviation with stilts

1–Var Stats
$\bar{x} = 80.66666667$
$\Sigma x = 726$
$\Sigma x^2 = 58694$
$Sx = 4.031128874$
$\sigma x = 3.80058475$
$\downarrow n = 9$

The standard deviation is the same for both data sets, about 3.8 in.

Method ❷ Use a formula.

$$\text{standard deviation} = \sqrt{\frac{\displaystyle\sum_{i=1}^{n}(x_i - \bar{x})^2}{n}}$$

This represents the mean height.

This represents the number of heights.

Compute the mean height without stilts as you did in *Talk it Over* question 2 on page 483: $\bar{x} \approx 66.7$.

standard deviation without stilts

$$\approx \sqrt{\frac{(72 - 66.7)^2 + (65 - 66.7)^2 + \cdots + (62 - 66.7)^2}{9}}$$

$$\approx \sqrt{\frac{5.3^2 + (-1.7)^2 + \cdots + (-4.7)^2}{9}}$$

$$\approx 3.80$$

Compute the mean height with stilts as you did in *Talk it Over* question 2 on page 483: $\bar{x} \approx 80.7$.

standard deviation with stilts

$$\approx \sqrt{\frac{(86 - 80.7)^2 + (79 - 80.7)^2 + \cdots + (76 - 80.7)^2}{9}}$$

$$\approx \sqrt{\frac{5.3^2 + (-1.7)^2 + \cdots + (-4.7)^2}{9}}$$

$$\approx 3.80$$

The standard deviation is the same for both data sets, about 3.8 in.

ADDING A CONSTANT TO A DATA SET

When a constant value is added to every value in a data set,

(1) the graph of the distribution, the mean, and the median are translated by the constant value, and

(2) the range and the standard deviation (σ) remain the same.

Example

Add 8 to each data value.

$\bar{x} = 3$
median $= 3.5$
range $= 3$
$\sigma \approx 1.1$

$\bar{x} = 3 + 8 = 11$
median $= 3.5 + 8 = 11.5$
range $= 3$
$\sigma \approx 1.1$

Talk it Over

6. Explain why the standard deviations in Sample 1 are the same with or without stilts.

7. Suppose the same constant negative value is added to every value in a data set. Tell whether each statistical measure will *increase*, *decrease*, or *stay the same*. Explain your choice.

   a. mean
   b. median
   c. range
   d. standard deviation

8. For the situation in question 7, will a histogram of the data be translated to the left or to the right? Explain your choice.

Sample 2

Suppose the stilts that the plasterers wear in the situation on pages 483 and 484 are 18 in. stilts. Find the mean and the standard deviation of the plasterers' heights with 18 in. stilts.

Sample Response

Use the mean of the heights without stilts from Sample 1: about 66.7. Add 18 to find the mean with stilts: $66.7 + 18 = 84.7$. The mean of the plasterers' heights with 18 in. stilts is about 84.7 in.

The standard deviation of the heights with 18 in. stilts is the same as it is without stilts in Sample 1: about 3.8 in.

Look Back
Identify three effects of adding a constant value to every value
in a data set.

9-1 Exercises and Problems

1. **Reading** Which statistical measures are not affected by adding a constant
   value to every value in a data set?

2. Find the mode of the heights without stilts in the table on page 483 and the
   mode of the heights with stilts. Compare the modes.

3. Compare the medians for the two distributions shown in the box-and-whisker
   plots. Do the same for the lower extremes, the upper extremes, and the ranges.
   Which of these statistical measures are different for the two distributions?
   Which are the same?

Height Distributions

For Exercises 4–8, use the table.

4. Find the mean and the median of the Calories
   per serving for these cereals without milk.

5. Find the range and the standard deviation of the
   Calories per serving for these cereals without milk.

6. If you use a $\frac{1}{2}$ cup of skim milk, this adds 44 Cal.
   Predict the mean and the standard deviation of the
   Calories per serving for these cereals served with
   $\frac{1}{2}$ cup of skim milk.

7. Test your prediction from Exercise 6. Add 44 Cal
   to each entry in the Calorie column of the table.
   Then compute the mean and the standard deviation. Do you get the results you predicted? If not,
   why not?

8. **a.** Draw a box-and-whisker plot of cereal prices.

   b. Suppose there is a $.25 coupon for each box of
   cereal. Draw a box-and-whisker plot that shows
   how this will affect the amount customers will
   pay for the cereal.

BRAND	Calories per serving without milk	Price of a 15-oz box (dollars)
A	160	2.19
B	80	1.89
C	70	3.20
D	90	2.99
E	110	1.65
F	110	1.99
G	130	3.10
H	210	2.89
I	110	2.19
J	120	1.89
K	110	2.79
L	50	1.80

A musical composition can be transposed by raising or lowering the pitch of each note by the same amount. On a piano, intervals between notes are measured in half steps. The symbol ♯ indicates a half step up and the symbol ♭ represents a half step down.

Suppose a composition is transposed up two half steps (one whole step). What does each note become?

9. D   **10.** F♯   **11.** A♭   **12.** B

13. Suppose you want a composition that starts on a G to start lower, on a C. What must you do to each note in the composition?

14. What would you have to do to a composition in order to transpose it up an octave?

15. **Writing** When a piece of music is transposed, you can still recognize the melody. Why is that? How does this relate to what you have learned in this section?

Football The 1993 Dallas Cowboys football team had 58 players. The table shows the distribution of weights. All weights are given to the nearest pound. The mean weight for the team was 238.3 lb.

16. Draw a histogram for the data. Locate the mean on your histogram.

17. The clothes and equipment that football players wear for a game add about 10 lb to each player's weight.

   a. How does adding 10 lb to each player's weight affect the mean weight of the team?

   b. How does adding 10 lb to each player's weight affect the position, size, and shape of the histogram you drew in Exercise 16?

Distribution of Weights of 1993 Dallas Cowboys Players			
Weight range in pounds	Frequency	Weight range in pounds	Frequency
180–189	8	260–269	2
190–199	5	270–279	4
200–209	7	280–289	6
210–219	3	290–299	0
220–229	5	300–309	2
230–239	4	310–319	1
240–249	5	320–329	3
250–259	3		

18. Suppose the mean annual contribution to an environmental organization is $50. The organization spends $3 per year for a newsletter to each contributor. What effect does it have on the mean, the median, the range, and the standard deviation of the annual contributions when you subtract the cost of the newsletters from the contributions?

19. Annual wages for hourly workers at Fit-Rite Corporation have a mean of $21,300 and a standard deviation of $3500. All hourly workers receive the same end-of-year bonus that increases the mean to $22,100.

a. How much is the end-of-year bonus?

b. What is the standard deviation of the hourly workers' annual wages at Fit-Rite when the bonus is included?

Review **PREVIEW**

20. The measures of two angles of a triangle are 30° and 120°. The length of the side opposite the 30° angle is 12 cm. Find the length of the side opposite the 120° angle. *(Section 8-7)*

Suppose u = (8, −3) and v = (−1, 2). Find each sum. *(Section 8-4)*

21. u + v   **22. 2u + v**   **23. 2u − v**

For each function, draw a graph and find the domain and the range. *(Sections 2-1, 2-3)*

24. $f(x) = |x|$ **25.** $f(x) = |x| + 3$ **26.** $f(x) = |x + 3|$

Ongoing **ASSESSMENT**

27. **Writing** Write a paragraph proof of this statement:

If a constant number is added to each item in a data set, then the mean of the data set is increased by that number.

Given n data values $x_1, x_2, x_3, \ldots, x_n$ with mean $\bar{x}$

Prove The mean of the n data values $x_1 + k, x_2 + k, x_3 + k, \ldots, x_n + k$ is $\bar{x} + k$.

Working on the Unit Project

28. a. Draw a histogram for the data.

b. Draw a histogram for the same group 10 years later.

c. Describe the relationship between the graphs in parts (a) and (b).

d. Suppose that 65 is retirement age. Predict the number of faculty who will retire within the next 10 years.

e. **Open-ended** What factors besides retirement might affect the number of job openings for new college faculty over the next 10 years?

College Faculty in 1990	
Ages in years	Number of faculty
20–24	5,000
25–29	45,000
30–34	55,000
35–39	93,000
40–44	85,000
45–49	80,000
50–54	99,000
55–60	150,000
60–64	100,000

Translating Graphs

····Focus

Recognize the relationship between the graph of $y - k = f(x - h)$ and the parent graph of $y = f(x)$.

EXPLORATION

How do h *and* k *affect the graph of*
$$y - k = f(x - h)?$$

• **Materials: graphics calculators or graphing software**
• **Work in a group of four students.**

parent function: $y = x^2$

① Graph these equations and the *parent* function on the same set of axes. You may have to solve for *y* first. Use a window that will give you equal unit spacing on the two axes.

   a. $y - 1 = x^2$
   b. $y = (x - 2)^2$
   c. $y - 1 = (x - 2)^2$

② Describe how the graph of each equation in step 1 is related to the graph of the parent function.

③ Repeat steps 1 and 2 for each equation below.

parent function: $y = |x|$

   a. $y - 1 = |x|$
   b. $y = |x - 2|$
   c. $y - 1 = |x - 2|$

④ Repeat steps 1 and 2 for each equation below.

parent function: $y = \sqrt{x}$

   a. $y - 1 = \sqrt{x}$
   b. $y = \sqrt{x - 2}$
   c. $y - 1 = \sqrt{x - 2}$

⑤ Repeat steps 1 and 2 for each equation below.

parent function: $y = 10^x$

   a. $y - 1 = 10^x$
   b. $y = 10^{x - 2}$
   c. $y - 1 = 10^{x - 2}$

⑥ Make a conjecture about how the graph of $y - k = f(x - h)$ is related to the graph of the parent function $y = f(x)$.

TRANSLATING GRAPHS

The graph of $y - k = f(x - h)$ can be found by translating the graph of the parent function $y = f(x)$ by the vector (h, k).

Example

$f(x) = \log x$; $(h, k) = (-5, 2)$

Talk it Over

1. In step 1 of the Exploration, what is the vertex of the parent graph? What is the vertex of the graph of $y - 1 = (x - 2)^2$? What vector transforms the first vertex into the second?

2. Which graphs in the Exploration were horizontal translations of the parent graph? Which were vertical translations? How can you identify horizontal and vertical translations if you are given values for h and k?

3. Complete each rule for the translation $P \rightarrow P'$ that transforms the graph of the parent function $y = f(x)$ into the graph of $y - k = f(x - h)$.

   a. $P(x, y) \rightarrow P'(\underline{\,?\,}, \underline{\,?\,})$

   b. $\begin{array}{c} P \\ \begin{bmatrix} x \\ y \end{bmatrix} \end{array} + \begin{bmatrix} ? \\ ? \end{bmatrix} = \begin{array}{c} P' \\ \begin{bmatrix} x' \\ y' \end{bmatrix} \end{array}$

Sample 1

Sketch the graph of $y - 3 = (x + 2)^3$.

Sample Response

1 Find the parent function, h, and k.

The parent function is a cubic: $f(x) = x^3$
$y - k = (x - h)^3$ is
$y - 3 = (x + 2)^3$, so
$k = 3$ and $h = -2$.

2 Sketch the graph of the parent function $y = x^3$.

3 Translate the graph by the vector $(-2, 3)$.

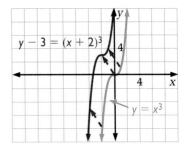

•••••▶ **Now you are ready for:**
⋮ Exs. 1–14 on pp. 492–493

Finding Equations for Graphs

You can use what you have learned about translating graphs to find an equation of a graph. To do this, you first have to decide which parent function has a graph with the same shape. There is a Visual Glossary of Functions on page 672.

Sample 2

Write an equation for each graph.

a.

b.
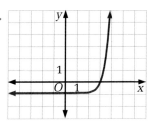

Sample Response

Step 1 Look at the shape of each graph to identify its parent function.

a. The parent function is the square root function.

b. The parent function is an exponential function.

Step 2 Identify the translation vector by finding a key point on the parent graph and its image on the translated graph.

a.
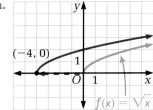

$O(0, 0) \rightarrow O'(-4, 0)$

The translation vector (h, k) is $(-4, 0)$.

b.

$P(0, 1) \rightarrow P'(3, 0)$

The translation vector (h, k) is $(3, -1)$.

Step 3 Write an equation of the form $y - k = f(x - h)$ for each graph.

a. $f(x) = \sqrt{x}$, $h = -4$, $k = 0$

$$y - k = f(x - h)$$
$$y - 0 = \sqrt{x - (-4)}$$
$$y = \sqrt{x + 4}$$

b. $f(x) = 10^x$, $h = 3$, $k = -1$

$$y - k = f(x - h)$$
$$y - (-1) = 10^{x - 3}$$
$$y + 1 = 10^{x - 3}$$

4. The point (4, 9) is on the graph given in part (b) of Sample 2. Show that this ordered pair is a solution of the equation found in step 3 of part (b).

5. In part (a) of Sample 2, the origin was the key point used to find the translation. Why was the origin not used in part (b)?

6. How is the domain of the function in part (a) of Sample 2 related to the domain of its parent function?

7. How is the asymptote for the graph in part (b) of Sample 2 related to the asymptote of its parent graph?

Look Back ←

How can you use translations and parent functions to sketch the graph of a function? How can you use translations and parent graphs to write an equation of a graph?

·······► Now you are ready for:
Exs. 15–31 on pp. 494–495

9-2 Exercises and Problems

For Exercises 1–3, the equations are in the form $y - k = f(x - h)$. For each equation, find the parent function and the translation vector.

1. $y - 7 = (x + 2)^2$ 2. $y - 2 = \log(x - 1)$ 3. $y = 10^{x + 9}$

4. **Reading** Choose the letter of the translation that transforms the graph of $y = f(x)$ into the graph of $y - 2 = f(x + 5)$.

   A. left 2, up 5   B. right 5, down 2   C. left 5, down 2   D. left 5, up 2

Sketch the graph of each function.

5. $y + 9 = \sqrt{x - 4}$

6. $y + 1 = |x - 3|$

7. $y - 4 = \log x$

8. $y = (x + 6)^3$

9. **a.** Show that the vertices of trapezoid $ABCD$ are on the graph of $y = x^2$.

   b. Find the coordinates of the vertices of trapezoid $ABCD$ after the translation $P \to P'$.

   $$\overset{P}{\begin{bmatrix} x \\ y \end{bmatrix}} + \begin{bmatrix} -1 \\ -8 \end{bmatrix} = \overset{P'}{\begin{bmatrix} x' \\ y' \end{bmatrix}}$$

   c. Suppose you transform the graph of $y = x^2$ using the translation in part (b). Write an equation of the new graph.

   d. Show that each vertex you found in part (b) is on the parabola whose equation you found in part (c).

Toll Roads The Kansas Turnpike is a toll road. It begins at the border of Oklahoma and Kansas and continues for 236 mi to the border of Kansas and Missouri, near Kansas City.

Suppose a car enters the turnpike at South Topeka.

Let x = the number on the mile marker where the car exits the turnpike.

Let y = the toll in dollars.

You can use this equation to estimate the toll for a car:

toll equation: $y - 0.30 = 0.03 |x - 177|$

For Exercises 10–13, use the toll equation.

10. Emporia is at mile marker 127. Estimate the toll from South Topeka to Emporia.

11. East Lawrence is at mile marker 204. Estimate the toll from South Topeka to East Lawrence.

12. a. Consider $y = 0.03 |x|$ as the parent function. Explain how the graph of the toll equation is related to the parent graph.

    b. Sketch a graph of the toll equation.

    c. Give a real-world interpretation of each of these quantities in the toll equation: 0.03, 0.30, 177.

13. The toll equation does not give the same values used by the Kansas Turnpike Authority. For example, to travel from South Topeka to Mulvane (at mile 33) or to Haysville-Derby (at mile 39) actually costs the same amount, $4.50.

    a. Compare the actual toll to the toll given by the toll equation for Mulvane and for Haysville-Derby.

    b. **Open-ended** Why do you think the Turnpike Authority charges $4.50 instead of the amounts given by the toll equation?

14. **Income Tax** In 1993 a single person who was self-supporting and had no other dependents paid no federal income tax on the first $6050 of *earned* income. The tax rate for the first $22,100 of *taxable* income was 15%.

    a. Let x = taxable income. Let y = income tax. Sketch a graph of the function $y = 0.15x$.

    b. On the same set of axes, let x = earned income. Let y = income tax. Sketch the graph of the function $y = 0.15(x - 6050)$.

    c. Consider the graph in part (a) as a parent graph. Describe the translation that transforms it into the graph in part (b).

    d. **Writing** Explain why both graphs, if properly interpreted, give correct values for the income tax of a single person with no other dependents.

    e. Do either of the equations in parts (a) and (b) apply to a single person earning $3500? Explain.

Write an equation for each graph.

15.

16.

17.

18.

19.

20.

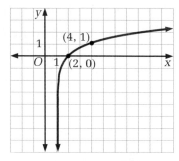

21. For the graph shown at the right, $y = \frac{1}{x}$ is the parent function.

   a. Find the values of h and k.

   b. Find the equations of the asymptotes for the translated graph.

Space Exploration In July of 1994, surgeon Chiaki Mukai became the first Japanese woman in space. She was the payload specialist on an international mission aboard the space shuttle *Columbia*.

The Spacelab module in the payload bay held most of the experiments performed during the mission. The following equation approximates the module's weight w (in pounds) at a distance d (in miles) above the surface of Earth.

$$w = \frac{3.68 \times 10^{11}}{(4000 + d)^2}$$

For Exercises 22–24, use the equation above.

22. About how much does the Spacelab module weigh on the surface of Earth?

23. *Columbia*'s altitude while in orbit was 184 mi. About how much did the Spacelab module weigh while in orbit?

24. a. Graph the function at the bottom of page 494.

b. Graph the parent function $w = \dfrac{3.68 \times 10^{11}}{d^2}$ on the same set of axes.

c. Compare the graphs in parts (a) and (b).

d. Give a real-world interpretation of the function in part (b). (*Hint:* The radius of Earth is about 4000 mi.)

e. What values of d would you substitute into the function in part (b) to answer the questions asked in Exercises 22 and 23?

BY THE WAY...

On July 17, 1975, astronauts from the United States shook hands with Russian cosmonauts in outer space as part of the Apollo-Soyuz mission. This was the first time that spacecraft from two different countries met in orbit.

Ongoing ASSESSMENT

25. **Open-ended** Choose a radius. Write an equation for a circle that has this radius and is centered at the origin. Write an equation for a congruent circle with its center in the fourth quadrant. What translation transforms the original circle into the congruent circle?

Review PREVIEW

26. The mean of a set of test scores is 72 and the standard deviation is 9. The highest score is 90. Suppose 10 points are added to each score. What will be the mean and the standard deviation of the new scores? *(Section 9-1)*

27. Evaluate $\displaystyle\sum_{n=1}^{4} \left(\dfrac{2}{3}\right)^n$. *(Section 4-6)*

Multiply each pair of matrices. *(Toolbox Skill 11)*

28. $\begin{bmatrix} 5 & 0 \\ 0 & 2 \end{bmatrix} \begin{bmatrix} 1 & 0 \\ 0 & 4 \end{bmatrix}$

29. $\begin{bmatrix} 2 & 0 \\ 0 & \frac{1}{4} \end{bmatrix} \begin{bmatrix} \frac{4}{5} & 0 \\ 0 & 2 \end{bmatrix}$

30. $\begin{bmatrix} 3 & 0 \\ 0 & 2 \end{bmatrix} \begin{bmatrix} 2 & 3 & 2 & 4 \\ 1 & 0 & 2 & 1 \end{bmatrix}$

Working on the Unit Project

31. **Research** Read about the qualifications, salaries, working conditions, and job opportunities for the careers you are investigating. Here are some books that contain information:

➤ *Occupational Outlook Handbook*
by the U.S. Bureau of Labor Statistics

➤ *Statistical Abstract of the United States*
by the U.S. Bureau of the Census

➤ *The American Almanac of Jobs and Salaries*
by John W. Wright

➤ *What Color Is Your Parachute?*
by Richard N. Bolles

Multiplying Data by a Constant

CONSTANT CHANGES

········Focus

Recognize the effect that multiplying data values by a constant has on the mean, median, range, and standard deviation.

The French unit of money is the *franc*. The number of dollars equivalent to one franc is called the *exchange rate*. The table shows the numbers of francs spent by students in a high school French club during a trip to France. It also shows the equivalent numbers of dollars spent.

STUDENT	Francs spent	Equivalent dollars
Abdul	1630	326
Adriana	1285	257
Carrie	1480	296
Hamid	1870	374
Hannah	1190	238
Jared	1705	341
Kimiko	1570	314
Matthew	1120	224
Rosa	1860	372
Tanya	1550	310
Teodoro	1240	248

Talk it Over

1. Find the number that makes this equation true:
$$\text{number of francs spent} \times \underline{?} = \text{number of dollars spent}$$
   What was the exchange rate at the time of the trip?

2. **a.** Find the mean of the francs data.
   b. Find the mean of the dollars data.
   c. Find the number that makes this equation true:
$$\text{mean of francs data} \times \underline{?} = \text{mean of dollars data}$$

3. Repeat question 2 using the median.

4. Repeat question 2 using the range.

5. The histograms show the distributions of the francs and dollars data. How are the histograms alike? different?

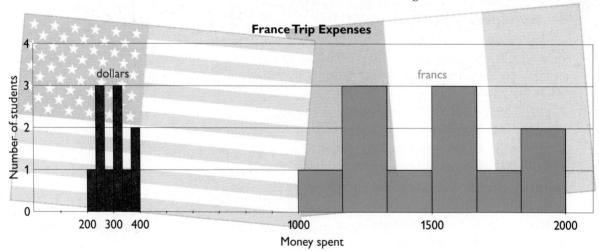

France Trip Expenses

dollars   francs

Number of students

Money spent

Use the table on page 496. Find the standard deviation of the francs data and of the dollars data.

Sample Response

Enter the francs and dollars data on a calculator. Have the calculator compute the standard deviation for each data set.

standard deviation
of francs data →

1–Var Stats
$\bar{x} = 1500$
$\Sigma x = 16500$
$\Sigma x^2 = 25437550$
$Sx = 262.2117465$
$\sigma x = 250.0090907$
$\downarrow n = 11$

standard deviation
of dollars data →

1–Var Stats
$\bar{x} = 300$
$\Sigma x = 3300$
$\Sigma x^2 = 1017502$
$Sx = 52.4423493$
$\sigma x = 50.00181815$
$\downarrow n = 11$

The standard deviation of the francs data is about 250 francs. The standard deviation of the dollars data is about $50.

Talk it Over

6. Use the results of Sample 1. Find the number that makes this equation true:

$$\text{standard deviation of francs data} \times \underline{\ ?\ } = \text{standard deviation of dollars data}$$

7. Suppose each of these data values is multiplied by 4:

6, 10, 7, 1, 16

Predict how the mean, the median, the range, and the standard deviation change. Check your prediction by computing these statistics for the original and transformed data sets.

MULTIPLYING DATA VALUES BY A CONSTANT

When each value in a data set is multiplied by the same positive constant a, then the mean, the median, the range, and the standard deviation are also multiplied by a.

Sample 2

The mean annual salary for employees at a tree nursery is $18,000. The standard deviation of the salaries is $7000. Suppose the nursery owner gives all employees a 4% raise. Find the mean and the standard deviation of the new salaries.

Sample Response

The effect of a 4% raise is that each salary is multiplied by 1.04. Therefore, the mean and the standard deviation are also multiplied by 1.04.

$$\text{new mean} = 1.04 \times \text{old mean} = (1.04)(18{,}000) = 18{,}720$$

$$\text{new standard deviation} = 1.04 \times \text{old standard deviation} = (1.04)(7000) = 7280$$

The mean of the new salaries is $18,720. The standard deviation is $7280.

Look Back

Identify at least three effects of multiplying each value in a data set by a positive constant.

9-3   Exercises and Problems

1. **Reading** Explain how you can use the histograms on page 496 to compare the ranges of the dollars and francs data.

For Exercises 2 and 3:

a. **Find the mean, the median, the range, and the standard deviation of the given data.**

b. **Repeat part (a) for the data obtained by multiplying each value by a.**

c. **Make histograms of the original and transformed data. Draw your histograms on the same set of axes.**

2. data: 93, 71, 96, 62, 85, 99, 75

   $a = 0.5$

3. data: 7.3, 9.2, 9.7, 9.6, 5.8, 5.5, 6.1, 5.2

   $a = 3$

4. **Consumer Economics** At an electronics store, the mean price of a VCR is $330. The standard deviation of the prices is $45. During a clearance sale, all merchandise in the store is discounted by 15%. Find the mean and standard deviation of the new VCR prices.

connection to **SCIENCE**

The table shows the diameters of the nine planets in Earth's solar system.

5. Let d be the diameter of a planet expressed as a multiple of Earth's diameter. Complete each sentence with an inequality involving d.

   a. If a planet is larger than Earth, then ? .

   b. If a planet is smaller than Earth, then ? .

6. Find the mean, the median, the range, and the standard deviation of the data in the second column.

7. a. Find the number that makes this equation true:

   $$\frac{\text{diameter}}{\text{in miles}} \times \underline{\ ?\ } = \frac{\text{diameter as a multiple}}{\text{of Earth's diameter}}$$

   b. Find the mean, the median, the range, and the standard deviation of the data in the third column.

   c. **Writing** Aaron looked at the median from part (b) and concluded that Earth is an average-sized planet. Yolanda looked at the mean and concluded that Earth is much smaller than average. Explain why both conclusions are reasonable.

PLANET	Diameter in miles	Diameter as a multiple of Earth's diameter
Mercury	3,030	0.38
Venus	7,520	0.95
Earth	7,930	1.00
Mars	4,200	0.53
Jupiter	88,700	11.19
Saturn	74,600	9.41
Uranus	31,600	3.98
Neptune	30,800	3.88
Pluto	1,420	0.18

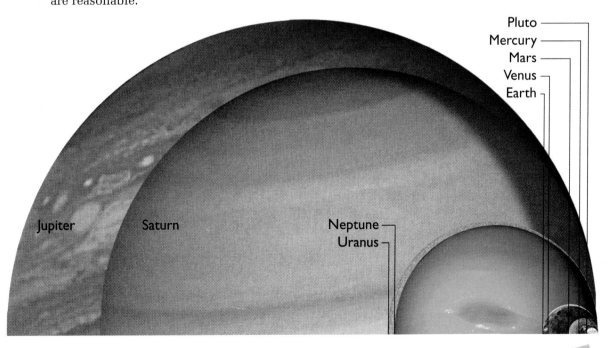

8. **Biology** The table shows the recommended average weights for men of different heights.

Height in inches	Weight in pounds
64	145
66	153
68	161
70	170
72	179
74	188
76	199

a. TECHNOLOGY Use a graphics calculator to find an equation of the least-squares line for the data.

b. Make a new table giving the heights in centimeters and the weights in kilograms. (*Hint:* 1 in. = 2.54 cm and 1 lb ≈ 0.45 kg)

c. TECHNOLOGY Use a graphics calculator to find an equation of the least-squares line for the centimeter/kilogram data in part (b).

d. **Writing** What is the relationship between the vertical intercepts of the least-squares lines in parts (a) and (c)? What is the relationship between the slopes of the lines?

Ongoing ASSESSMENT

9. **Writing** Write a paragraph proof of this statement: If each value in a data set is multiplied by a, then the mean is also multiplied by a. (*Hint:* Let $x_1, x_2, \ldots, x_n$ be the original data values, and let $\bar{x}$ be their mean. You need to show that the mean of $ax_1, ax_2, \ldots, ax_n$ is $a\bar{x}$.)

Review PREVIEW

Without using graphing technology, sketch the graph of each function. *(Section 9-2)*

10. $y = |x - 3|$ 11. $y - 2 = x^2$ 12. $y + 4 = \sqrt{x - 5}$

Evaluate to three decimal places. *(Section 5-7)*

13. $\log_2 5$ 14. $\log_7 3$ 15. $\log_{1/3} 9.68$ 16. $\log_{11} \frac{3}{4}$

Write an equation for the parabola passing through the given points. *(Section 6-5)*

17. $(1, 8), (2, 3), (4, 10)$ 18. $(-5, -2), (3, 1), (6, -0.5)$

 Working on the Unit Project

19. The table shows average starting salaries for college graduates entering certain occupations in 1993.

a. Display these data on a bar graph.

b. Suppose that starting salaries will be 34% greater in 2003. What will the average starting salaries be then? Display these data on a bar graph.

c. Describe the transformation that relates the graphs you drew in parts (a) and (b).

OCCUPATION	Average starting salary
teaching	$22,505
sales/marketing	$28,536
business administration	$27,564
engineering	$35,004
computer science	$31,164

Stretching Graphs

Focus

Recognize the effects of horizontal and vertical stretches on sets of points and graphs of functions.

Pulled In Many Directions

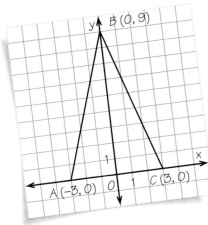

EXPLORATION

What happens to a figure when you multiply its coordinates by positive constants a *and* b?

- **Materials:** graph paper, graphics calculators (optional)
- **Work in a group of three students.**

① You can use a **transformation matrix** to represent a transformation. Use the transformation matrix $T = \begin{bmatrix} 3 & 0 \\ 0 & 1 \end{bmatrix}$ and the matrix M shown. Find the product matrix $M' = TM$.

$$M = \begin{array}{ccc} A & B & C \\ \begin{bmatrix} -3 & 0 & 3 \\ 0 & 9 & 0 \end{bmatrix} \end{array} \quad \leftarrow \begin{array}{l} \text{Matrix } M \text{ represents the} \\ \text{vertices of the triangle.} \end{array}$$

② Draw triangle $A'B'C'$ represented by the matrix M'. Describe the effect of transformation T on the original triangle.

③ Repeat steps 1 and 2 for each transformation matrix.

a. $T = \begin{bmatrix} 1 & 0 \\ 0 & 2 \end{bmatrix}$ **b.** $T = \begin{bmatrix} 3 & 0 \\ 0 & 1 \end{bmatrix}\begin{bmatrix} 1 & 0 \\ 0 & 2 \end{bmatrix} = \begin{bmatrix} 3 & 0 \\ 0 & 2 \end{bmatrix}$ **c.** $T = \begin{bmatrix} \frac{1}{3} & 0 \\ 0 & \frac{1}{2} \end{bmatrix}$

④ Suppose a and b can be any positive numbers. Make a conjecture about the effects of the transformation matrix $T = \begin{bmatrix} a & 0 \\ 0 & b \end{bmatrix}$.

⑤ Write an equation of the parabola that passes through the vertices of the original triangle. Graph the equation.

⑥ Use the form $\frac{y}{b} = -\left(\frac{x}{a}\right)^2 + 9$.

a. Write an equation of the parabola that passes through the vertices of the triangle you drew in step 2. What is the value of a? of b?

b. Repeat part (a) for the triangle you drew in part (a) of step 3.

c. Graph your equations from parts (a) and (b). Compare the graphs with your graph from step 5.

Student Resources Toolbox
p. 634 *Matrices*

▶ **Now you are ready for:**
Exs. 1–15 on pp. 504–505

When you transformed the coordinates of the triangles in the Exploration, the triangles stretched.

The segment with endpoints (x_1, y_1) and (x_2, y_2) is stretched by a factor of a in the horizontal direction.

$$\begin{bmatrix} a & 0 \\ 0 & b \end{bmatrix}\begin{bmatrix} x_1 & x_2 \\ y_1 & y_2 \end{bmatrix} = \begin{bmatrix} ax_1 + 0y_1 & ax_2 + 0y_2 \\ 0x_1 + by_1 & 0x_2 + by_2 \end{bmatrix} = \begin{bmatrix} ax_1 & ax_2 \\ by_1 & by_2 \end{bmatrix}$$

The segment is stretched by a factor of b in the vertical direction.

You can stretch the graphs of functions as well.

STRETCHING GRAPHS

When the graph of $y = f(x)$ is stretched horizontally by the positive factor a,

(1) all points where the original graph crosses the y-axis remain fixed, and

(2) an equation of the new graph is $y = f\left(\dfrac{x}{a}\right)$.

When the graph of $y = f(x)$ is stretched vertically by the positive factor b,

(1) all points where the original graph crosses the x-axis remain fixed, and

(2) an equation of the new graph is $\dfrac{y}{b} = f(x)$.

Sample 1

Writing The parent function $y = x(x - 2)(x + 3)$ and the function $y = 2x(x - 2)(x + 3)$ are graphed on the same set of axes. Describe the relationship between the two graphs using the language of transformations.

Sample Response

The function $y = 2x(x - 2)(x + 3)$ is related to the parent function in this way:

$$\frac{y}{2} = x(x - 2)(x + 3) = f(x)$$

The parent graph can be stretched vertically by the factor 2 to transform it into the graph of $y = 2x(x - 2)(x + 3)$.

The points where the parent graph crosses the x-axis remain fixed in the new graph: $(0, -3)$, $(0, 0)$, and $(0, 2)$.

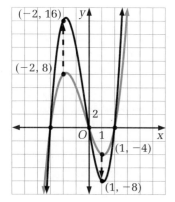

Unit 9 Transformations of Graphs and Data

Talk it Over

1. Use the parent function $y = x(x - 2)(x + 3)$ from Sample 1.

   a. Find the stretch factor and the direction of stretch for the graph of the function $y = \frac{x}{2}\left(\frac{x}{2} - 2\right)\left(\frac{x}{2} + 3\right)$.

   b. Sketch the graph of the function in part (a).

2. Suppose you stretch the graph of the parent function horizontally by the factor $\frac{1}{2}$ and vertically by the factor 3.

   a. Find an equation of the new graph.

   b. Which points on the original graph will remain fixed?

Watch Out!
When the stretch factor in a given direction is between 0 and 1, the graph *shrinks* in that direction.

Sample 2

Andy Martinez manages a parking lot. He originally charged $3 for the first hour or fraction of an hour plus $2 for each additional hour or fraction of an hour. He is increasing his rates.

a. Use the graphs. Describe how the rates are changing.

b. Suppose the function that represents the original rates is $y = f(x)$. Write a function that represents the new rates.

Original Rates

New Rates

Sample Response

a. The time intervals are shrinking by 50%, to half hours instead of hours, but the fees per interval stay the same.

b. The graph shrinks only in the horizontal direction, so $y = f\left(\frac{x}{a}\right)$.

   Since $a = \frac{1}{2}$, $y = f\left(\frac{x}{\frac{1}{2}}\right)$. This can also be written $y = f(2x)$.

····▶ **Now you are ready for:**
Exs. 16–46 on pp. 505–509

Look Back ◀

For what values of a is the graph of $\frac{y}{b} = f\left(\frac{x}{a}\right)$ produced by stretching the graph of $y = f(x)$? In what direction?

9-4 Stretching Graphs

Exercises and Problems

Matrix M represents the polygon OPQRS.

a. Multiply M by each transformation matrix and draw the image.

b. Describe the effect of each transformation on the polygon.

$$M = \begin{array}{c} \begin{array}{ccccc} O & P & Q & R & S \end{array} \\ \begin{bmatrix} 0 & 8 & 8 & 4 & 0 \\ 0 & 0 & 6 & 10 & 6 \end{bmatrix} \end{array}$$

1. $\begin{bmatrix} 1 & 0 \\ 0 & \frac{1}{2} \end{bmatrix}$

2. $\begin{bmatrix} \frac{3}{2} & 0 \\ 0 & 1 \end{bmatrix}$

3. $\begin{bmatrix} 1 & 0 \\ 0 & 2 \end{bmatrix}$

4. $\begin{bmatrix} \frac{3}{2} & 0 \\ 0 & 2 \end{bmatrix}$

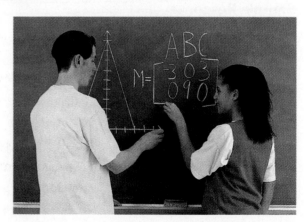

For each pair of matrices in Exercises 5 and 6:

a. Describe the transformation represented by each matrix.

b. Find the product matrix and describe the transformation it represents.

5. $\begin{bmatrix} 4 & 0 \\ 0 & 1 \end{bmatrix}\begin{bmatrix} 1 & 0 \\ 0 & 3 \end{bmatrix}$

6. $\begin{bmatrix} 1 & 0 \\ 0 & \frac{1}{3} \end{bmatrix}\begin{bmatrix} \frac{3}{2} & 0 \\ 0 & 1 \end{bmatrix}$

7. **Open-ended** Draw a polygon on a coordinate plane and use a matrix to represent its coordinates. Then choose two 2 × 2 matrices, one representing a horizontal stretch and one a vertical stretch. Find the image of your polygon after each of the transformations represented by your matrices.

8. **a.** Identify the set of points that remain unchanged after the transformation represented by $T = \begin{bmatrix} a & 0 \\ 0 & 1 \end{bmatrix}$, $a > 0$.

   b. Identify the set of points that remain unchanged after the transformation represented by $T = \begin{bmatrix} 1 & 0 \\ 0 & b \end{bmatrix}$, $b > 0$.

Matrix M represents △ABC shown on page 501. Apply each transformation to matrix M. Then describe the effect.

$$M = \begin{array}{c} \begin{array}{ccc} A & B & C \end{array} \\ \begin{bmatrix} -3 & 0 & 3 \\ 0 & 9 & 0 \end{bmatrix} \end{array}$$

9. $\begin{bmatrix} -3 & 0 \\ 0 & 1 \end{bmatrix}$

10. $\begin{bmatrix} 1 & 0 \\ 0 & -\frac{1}{2} \end{bmatrix}$

11. $\begin{bmatrix} -3 & 0 \\ 0 & -\frac{1}{2} \end{bmatrix}$

12. $\begin{bmatrix} 1 & 0 \\ 0 & -3 \end{bmatrix}$

For Exercises 13–15, use matrix M and the circle.

A stretched circle is called an *ellipse.*

13. **a.** Find the image of matrix M after the transformation represented by the matrix $\begin{bmatrix} 1 & 0 \\ 0 & 2 \end{bmatrix}$.

   b. Plot the image points and draw the ellipse formed by this transformation.

   c. Show that the image points are solutions of this equation:

   $$x^2 + \left(\frac{y}{2}\right)^2 = 25$$

14. **a.** Find the image of matrix M after the transformation represented by the matrix $\begin{bmatrix} 3 & 0 \\ 0 & 1 \end{bmatrix}$.

   b. Plot the image points and draw the ellipse formed by this transformation.

   c. Show that the image points are solutions of this equation:

   $$\left(\frac{x}{3}\right)^2 + y^2 = 25$$

15. Sketch the graph of the ellipse whose equation is $\left(\frac{x}{3}\right)^2 + \left(\frac{y}{2}\right)^2 = 25$.

16. **Reading** What set of points remains fixed when you stretch a graph horizontally by the factor a? vertically by the factor b?

17. For the situation in Sample 2 on page 503, suppose Andy Martinez had decided to double his fees for each hour instead of shrinking the time intervals by 50%.

   a. Sketch a graph to represent the new rates.

   b. Suppose the function that represents the original rates is $y = f(x)$. Write a function that represents the new rates.

For Exercises 18–21, use the parent function shown.

a TECHNOLOGY Use a graphics calculator or graphing software to graph each function on the same set of axes as the parent function.

b. Describe the transformation that transforms the parent graph into the graph of each function.

18. $y = 3x(x - 2)(x + 2)$

19. $y = \frac{1}{3}x(x - 2)(x + 2)$

20. $y = 3x(3x - 2)(3x + 2)$

21. $y = \frac{x}{3}\left(\frac{x}{3} - 2\right)\left(\frac{x}{3} + 2\right)$

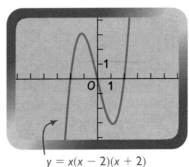

$y = x(x - 2)(x + 2)$

$$M = \begin{matrix} A & B & C & D & E & F \\ \begin{bmatrix} 5 & 4 & 0 & -4 & -5 & 0 \\ 0 & 3 & 5 & 3 & 0 & -5 \end{bmatrix} \end{matrix}$$

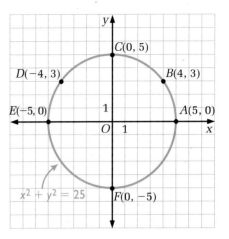

22. **Telephone Rates** Between 8:00 A.M. and 5:00 P.M. a telephone company charges these weekday rates for a long distance call made between Boston and Worcester:

$.29 for the first minute (or fraction of a minute)

$.12 for each additional minute (or fraction of a minute)

a. Let t = the length of a call in minutes. Let c = the cost of a call in dollars. Sketch a graph of the relationship between c and t for values of t in the domain $0 \le t \le 10$.

b. Evening rates apply between 5:00 P.M. and 11:00 P.M. They are 60% of the weekday rates. Sketch a graph of the evening rates between the two cities on the same set of axes as in part (a).

c. Describe the relationship between the graphs you drew in parts (a) and (b) using the language of transformations.

d. Suppose the function that represents the weekday rates is $y = f(x)$. Write a function that represents the evening rates.

For Exercises 23–26, the parent function is $y = -x^2 + 4$. Match each transformed graph with its equation.

23.

24.

25.

26.
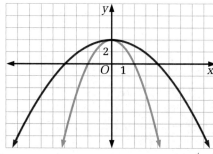

A. $\dfrac{y}{2} = -x^2 + 4$ **B.** $y = -\left(\dfrac{x}{2}\right)^2 + 4$ **C.** $\dfrac{y}{\frac{1}{2}} = -x^2 + 4$ **D.** $y = -\left(\dfrac{x}{\frac{1}{2}}\right)^2 + 4$

Without using graphing technology, sketch the graph of each function.

27. $y = 4|x|$ 28. $y = 10^{x/3}$ 29. $y = 5 \log x$

30. Let x represent the length of a side of a square and an edge of a cube.

a. Graph the area of the square as a function of x.

b. On the same set of axes, graph the surface area of the cube as a function of x.

c. **Writing** Describe the relationship between the two graphs using the language of transformations.

Drama A community theater company is presenting a musical. The manager wants to know how the ticket price will affect the profit. Here is the general form of the profit equation.

$$\text{profit} = \left(\begin{array}{ccc} \text{number of} & & \text{average size} & & \text{ticket} \\ \text{shows} & \times & \text{of audience} & \times & \text{price} \end{array} \right) - \text{costs}$$

The maximum seating capacity of the theater is 100 people. The theater company plans to do five shows.

31. In the worst case, suppose the average audience size is 50 people. Let x = the ticket price. Let y = the profit.

    a. Use the information above and in the table to write a profit equation for this situation.

    b. Graph your equation.

    c. What ticket price must the company charge in order to break even?

32. Repeat Exercise 31 using an average audience size of 100 people, which is the best case.

33. Suppose the theater company wants to reserve 5% of the price of each ticket for a scholarship fund. How will this affect the equations, the graphs, and the break-even points for the best and worst case situations?

MUSICAL BUDGET

ITEM	COST IN DOLLARS
orchestra	800
sound system	400
publicity	300
director	500
lighting/set	600
costumes	200
rental of rehearsal materials	630
royalties (5 shows at $300 each)	1500
miscellaneous	70
TOTAL	5000

Write an equation for each graph. Assume that each graph is a transformation of the graph of one of these parent functions: $y = x^2$, $y = x^3$, $y = |x|$, $y = \sqrt{x}$, $y = \log x$, $y = 10^x$.

34.

35.

36.

37.

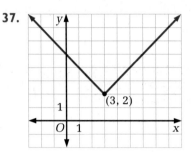

Ongoing **ASSESSMENT**

38. Group Activity Work with another student.

a. Copy and complete the table.

b. Use the values in the table to sketch the graphs of $y = \log x$ and $y = \log_2 x$ on the same set of axes.

c. Describe the transformation that transforms the graph of $y = \log x$ into the graph of $y = \log_2 x$.

d. Use the change-of-base property of logarithms to rewrite $y = \log_2 x$ in terms of $\log x$. Find the stretch factor to the nearest hundredth for the transformation in part (c).

x	$\log_2 x$	$\log x$
$\frac{1}{4}$	?	?
$\frac{1}{2}$	?	?
1	?	?
2	?	?
4	?	?
8	?	?

Review **PREVIEW**

39. The mean price of a pair of shoes at one store is $30. The standard deviation is $10. Suppose prices are reduced by 20%. How does this affect the mean and the standard deviation? *(Section 9-3)*

For each given angle, find another angle between 0° and 360° with the same cosine. *(Section 8-2)*

40. 50°   **41.** 135°   **42.** 240°   **43.** −25°

44. Write an equation for the graph shown. Assume that the shape matches the shape of the graph of $y = |x|$. *(Section 9-2)*

45. The number of farm operators and managers in the United States has been declining in recent years. The function $y = 1{,}444{,}000\left(\frac{1}{2}\right)^{x/34}$ approximates the number of jobs in this field, where x is the number of years since 1983. Describe how you can transform the graph of $y = \left(\frac{1}{2}\right)^{x}$ into the graph of this function.

46. The number of computer analysts/scientists in the United States has been growing in recent years. The function $y = 280{,}000 \cdot 2^{x/6.6}$ approximates the number of jobs in this field, where x is the number of years since 1983. Describe how you can transform the graph of $y = 2^{x}$ into the graph of this function.

Unit 9 CHECKPOINT

1. **Writing** Describe how adding a constant to each value in a data set affects the mean, the median, the range, and the standard deviation of the data set. Then describe how multiplying each data value by a positive constant affects these four statistics.

2. The mean age of workers at a company is 34. The standard deviation of the ages is 10. Suppose the same people worked for the company 5 years ago. What were the mean and the standard deviation of their ages then?   **9-1**

Without using graphing technology, sketch the graph of each equation.   **9-2**

3. $y - 2 = |x + 4|$ 4. $y + 1 = (x - 2)^2$ 5. $y = 10^{x - 3}$

6. At an appliance store, the median price of small microwave ovens is $147.50. The range of the prices is $90. When you include the sales tax, the actual price of each oven is 5% higher. Find the median and the range of the actual prices with the sales tax.   **9-3**

Business Expenses Claudia Pyle travels for her job. Her gasoline mileage is about 24 mi/gal and she usually pays $1.20 per gallon. This is an average of $.05 per mile.   **9-4**

Let x = the number of miles she travels in a week. Then the cost function $y = 0.05x$ represents the amount she spends on gasoline in a week.

7. Suppose a tax increases the cost of gasoline by 5%. Find the new cost function.

8. Suppose Claudia buys a more fuel-efficient car that reduces her gasoline costs by 25%. Find the new cost function.

9-4 Stretching Graphs

9-5 Multiple Transformations

Sliding Scale

········Focus

Recognize the effects of
multiple transformations on
sets of data and graphs of
functions.

Average April Temperatures		
Year	Beijing (°C)	Phila. (°F)
1961	15.0	49.8
1962	13.3	52.0
1963	12.8	52.5
1964	11.8	50.7
1965	10.9	48.9
1966	12.6	47.8
1967	12.8	51.6
1968	14.2	54.7
1969	12.9	55.2
1970	13.6	51.4
1971	13.0	51.6
1972	13.8	49.6
1973	14.6	53.4
1974	13.6	55.8
1975	14.6	48.7
1976	11.4	56.7
1977	14.3	57.2
1978	14.0	50.5
1979	10.5	52.3
1980	10.5	54.7
Mean	13.0	52.3
Standard deviation	1.3	2.7

Philadelphia

Beijing

Philadelphia, Pennsylvania, and Beijing, China, are both located
at a latitude of 40°N.

The table gives temperature data for the two cities over a period
of 20 years.

Talk it Over

1. What do you need to know in order to compare the temperatures for the two cities?

2. Use the formula $C = \frac{5}{9}(F - 32)$. Find the mean April
   temperature in degrees Celsius for Philadelphia for the
   20-year period. How does it compare to Beijing's mean
   April temperature for the period?

3. What factors besides latitude may account for variations
   in temperatures between different locations?

The temperature conversion formula, $C = \frac{5}{9}(F - 32)$, is a combination of transformations.

boiling point of water ← 212

freezing point of water ← 32

Fahrenheit Scale

− 32

On the temperature scale invented by Anders Celsius, the freezing point is $0°$.

− 32

The first step is to translate temperatures by subtracting 32.

← 180

← 0

$\times \frac{5}{9}$

On the Celsius scale, the boiling point is $100°$.

$\times \frac{5}{9}$

The next step is to stretch the scale by the factor $\frac{5}{9}$, since $\frac{5}{9}(180) = 100$.

← 100

← 0

Celsius Scale

Sample 1

Writing Describe the effect of the transformations from Fahrenheit to Celsius on the mean and the standard deviation of the Philadelphia temperatures.

Sample Response

Michael Von Dohlen

From the table on page 510, the mean of the Philadelphia temperatures is 52.3°F and the standard deviation is 2.7°F.

① Since translating and stretching both affect the mean, you can substitute into the formula to find the mean temperature in degrees Celsius.

$C = \frac{5}{9}(52.3 - 32)$

$\approx 11.3°C$

② Since only stretching affects the standard deviation, the standard deviation in degrees Celsius is $\frac{5}{9}$ of the standard deviation in degrees Fahrenheit.

$\frac{5}{9}(2.7) = 1.5°C$

These histograms show the effect of the transformation $C = \frac{5}{9}(F - 32)$ on the distribution of April temperatures for Philadelphia.

**Average Temperature for April, 1961–1980
Philadelphia**

Frequency

Distribution of temperatures in °C

Distribution of temperatures in °F

Temperature

mean = 11.3
standard deviation = 1.5

mean = 52.3
standard deviation = 2.7

······▶ **Now you are ready for:**
: **Exs. 1–9 on pp. 514–516**

9-5 Multiple Transformations

Multiple transformations can be performed on functions as well as on data sets.

Sample 2

Transform the function $f(x) = 2^x$ with a vertical stretch by a factor of 3 followed by a translation 4 units to the right.

a. Write an equation for the transformed function.

b. Graph the transformed function.

Sample Response

a. The vertical stretch gives $\frac{y}{3} = f(x)$ or $y = 3f(x)$.

The horizontal translation then gives $y = 3f(x - 4)$.

The resulting function is $y = 3(2^{x-4})$.

b. First graph the parent function $y = 2^x$.

Stretch the graph of $y = 2^x$ vertically by a factor of 3. This produces the graph of $y = 3(2^x)$.

Translate the graph of $y = 3(2^x)$ 4 units to the right. This produces the graph of $y = 3(2^{x-4})$.

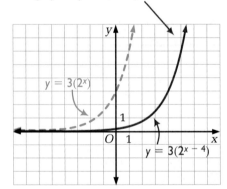

Talk it Over

4. Describe the effects of these transformations on the function $y = 2^x$:

   a vertical stretch by a factor of 2 followed by a translation 1 unit to the right

5. Find the function and sketch the graph when $y = x^3$ is first stretched by a factor of 1.5 in the horizontal direction and then translated 2 units up.

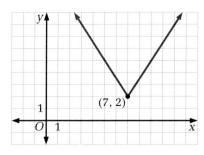

Write an equation of the graph. Assume that the parent function is one of the following:

$$y = x^2, \; y = x^3, \; y = |x|, \; y = \sqrt{x}, \; y = \log x, \text{ or } y = 10^x$$

Sample Response

Step 1 Identify the parent graph.

The given graph looks like a transformation of the graph of the absolute value function, $y = |x|$.

Since the vertex of the parent graph is located at the origin, the vertex is affected only by translations.

Step 2 Find the stretch factor.

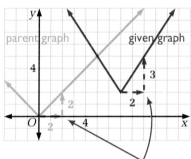

When you move two units to the right of the vertex, the given graph rises 3 units, while the parent graph rises 2 units. So the vertical stretch factor is $\frac{3}{2}$.

Step 3 Find the translation vector.

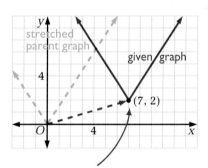

The vertex is translated by the vector (7, 2).

Step 4 Write an equation.

$$\frac{y - k}{b} = \left| \frac{x - h}{a} \right|$$

$$\frac{y - 2}{\frac{3}{2}} = |x - 7|$$

← There is no horizontal stretch, so a is 1.
Substitute **2** for k, **7** for h, and $\frac{3}{2}$ for b.

$$y - 2 = \frac{3}{2}|x - 7|$$

An equation of the graph is $y - 2 = \frac{3}{2}|x - 7|$.

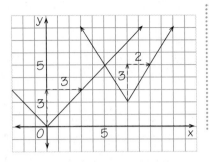

Now you are ready for:
Exs. 10–28 on pp. 516–518

Talk it Over

6. a. In Sample 3, Céline assumed the stretch was horizontal and not vertical. Using her diagram at the left, find the horizontal stretch factor.

b. What is an equation of the graph using the horizontal stretch factor?

c. Is this equation equivalent to the one in Sample 3?

Look Back

Describe the effect of combining stretching with translating on the graphs of data sets and functions.

9-5 Exercises and Problems

1. **Reading** Which types of transformations affect the mean of a set of data? Which affect the standard deviation?

2. The school nurse takes the temperatures of a class of twelve first-grade students. The temperatures (in °F) are:

   98.6, 98.4, 98.0, 99.9, 98.9, 98.6, 98.3, 97.9, 100.2, 98.7, 99.0, 98.8

   Find the mean and the standard deviation of the data. What are the mean and the standard deviation in degrees Celsius?

3. Use the Philadelphia temperature data on page 510.

   a. In what years was the average April temperature more than one standard deviation above the mean? In what years was it more than one standard deviation below the mean?

   b. According to the 68-95-99.7 rule, about 68% of the data of a normal distribution lie within one standard deviation of the mean. Does this rule appear to hold for the Philadelphia temperature data?

   c. Repeat parts (a) and (b) for the Beijing temperature data.

BY THE WAY...

In Canada, the following rhyme is used to help people remember Celsius temperatures:

Thirty is hot, twenty is pleasing,
Ten is not, and zero is freezing.

4. **a.** Use the formula

   $$F = \frac{9}{5}C + 32$$

   to convert the mean April temperature for Beijing to degrees Fahrenheit.

   b. Describe this formula in terms of transformations.

In Ann C. Crispin's novel *Starbridge*, the main character, Mahree, is a 16-year-old space colonist. She and her human companion, Rob, arrive on an alien planet. Their host, Shirazz, offers to provide them with food and to take care of other needs.

"Could we have a *bath*?" Mahree blurted… "A real *bath*?"

Shirazz was unperturbed. "Of course. Sand or mud? Or if with other cleansing medium, please provide its chemical composition."

Mahree stared at Rob, dismayed, but he gave her a reassuring grin, and put in, smoothly, "Liquid H_2O, Esteemed One, in quantity deep enough for immersion."…

"What temperature?"

Rob and Mahree stared at each other, blankly. Precise Simiu temperature measurements were still foreign to them. "This air," Rob said, finally, "is approximately ten of our temperature units less than our body temperatures, which you no doubt determined when you scanned us. We would like our liquid H_2O eight of those units *higher* than our body temperatures, if that is possible."

"Entirely possible," the CLS Liaison said. "It shall be as you have requested."

5. Normal human body temperature is 37°C. Rob was using the Celsius scale as the human temperature unit. Find the temperature of the air and the temperature of the bath water in both Celsius and Fahrenheit degrees.

6. Suppose Shirazz measures Rob's and Mahree's body temperatures at 1135.5 Simiu temperature units and the air at 1098.9 Simiu temperature units.

  a. Find the temperature of the bath water in Simiu temperature units.

  b. Find the freezing point of H_2O to the nearest whole Simiu temperature unit.

For Exercises 7 and 8, use this list of annual salaries for the 10 employees of a small business.

  A. $17,500   **B.** $23,000   **C.** $28,000   **D.** $35,000   **E.** $46,700

  F. $18,300   **G.** $24,500   **H.** $31,500   **I.** $40,400   **J.** $53,000

7. Find the mean and the standard deviation of this set of salaries.

8. Suppose each employee must pay state income tax at a rate of 4.8% on all income above $6000. The formula $T = 0.048(S - 6000)$ gives the tax on a salary of S dollars.

  a. Describe the formula using the language of transformations.

  b. Find the amount of tax each employee pays.

  c. Find the mean and the standard deviation of the taxes.

  d. **Writing** Explain how the mean and the standard deviation of the taxes are related to the mean and the standard deviation of the salaries.

9. This matrix equation shows how the polygon *ABCD* with vertices *A*(0, 0), *B*(1, 1), *C*(1, 5), and *D*(0, 5) is transformed.

$$\begin{bmatrix} 3 & 0 \\ 0 & 1 \end{bmatrix}\begin{bmatrix} x \\ y \end{bmatrix} + \begin{bmatrix} -10 \\ 2 \end{bmatrix} = \begin{bmatrix} x' \\ y' \end{bmatrix}$$

   a. Sketch the original polygon *ABCD* and its image *A′B′C′D′*.

   b. Describe the transformations used to produce the image.

For Exercises 10 and 11, apply the given transformations to the parent function. Then sketch the graphs of the parent function and the transformed function on the same set of axes.

10. $y = \sqrt{x}$; a vertical stretch by a factor of 3 followed by a translation 4 units to the right

11. $y = |x|$; a horizontal stretch by a factor of 3 followed by a translation 8 units down

12. On page 493, you saw the function $y - 0.30 = 0.03|x - 177|$, which approximates the toll, *y*, for a car as a function of *x*, the mile marker where the car exits the Kansas turnpike. Describe the multiple transformations used to produce this function from the parent function $y = |x|$.

13. A stone is dropped from a bridge above a deep, narrow canyon. The height of the bridge is 160 ft. The height in feet of the stone as it falls is given by $y = 160 - 16x^2$ where *x* is the elapsed time in seconds. Consider this function to be the result of multiple transformations on the parent function $y = -x^2$. Sketch the graphs of both functions and describe the transformations used to produce the height function.

For Exercises 14–16, use this postage information and the graph.

The cost of first class postage in the United States depends on the weight of the letter. In 1995 the cost of postage was $.32 for the first ounce and $.23 for each additional ounce or fraction of an ounce.

14. The blue graph is the ceiling function, $y = c(x)$, where *y* is the least integer greater than or equal to *x*. Find $c(2.7)$, $c(2.1)$, $c(-0.5)$, $c(1)$, and $c(7.4)$.

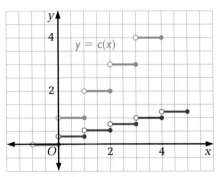

15. The red graph shows the cost of postage in dollars, *y*, for the weight of a letter in ounces, *x*, in 1995.

   a. Why is there an open circle at (0, $.32)?

   b. Use the postage formula to find the vertical distance between the steps of the red graph.

   c. What is the vertical distance between the steps of the graph of the ceiling function?

16. Write an equation for the red graph using $y = c(x)$ as the parent function.

17. Think about the relationship between Fahrenheit and Celsius temperatures. Graph $y = x$ and $y = \frac{5}{9}(x - 32)$ on the same set of axes.

  a. Describe how to transform the first graph to get the second.

  b. Interpret the point where the second graph crosses the y-axis in terms of Fahrenheit and Celsius temperatures.

  c. Find the temperature at which the Fahrenheit and Celsius readings are the same.

Write an equation for each graph. Assume that the parent graph is one of the six listed in Sample 3 on page 513.

18.

19.

20.

21.

22.

23.

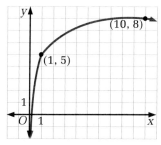

Ongoing **ASSESSMENT**

24. Group Activity Work in a group of four students.

  a. Each of you should choose a different pair of transformations, one from column A and one from column B.

  b. Each of you should choose a nonlinear parent function.

  c. Find the result of performing transformation A followed by transformation B, using the parent function from part (b).

  d. Then find the result of performing transformation B followed by transformation A, using the parent function from part (b).

  e. Share results with your group.

  f. Discuss whether composition of transformations is commutative. That is, do you always get the same results in parts (c) and (d)?

Column A	Column B
• vertical stretch by a factor of 3	• translation 5 units down
• horizontal stretch by a factor of $\frac{1}{2}$	• translation 6 units to the right

25. Without using graphing technology, sketch the graph of the function
$y = 2x(2x + 3)(2x + 3)$. Use $y = x(x + 3)(x + 3)$ as the parent function.
Identify the stretch factor and the direction of the stretch. *(Section 9-4)*

26. A basketball player has a 60% free-throw average. What is the probability
that the player makes at least three baskets in the next five free-throw
attempts? *(Section 7-6)*

27. Each person in a group of 20 journalists and a group of 20 randomly
selected people is asked to write an essay. The number of grammatical
errors in each essay for each group is counted. Which group do you think
has the higher mean number of errors? the higher standard deviation?
Explain. *(Section 6-2)*

Working on the Unit Project

A certain career interest survey gives results in terms of *percentiles*. For
example, a score in the 65th percentile for a particular category on this
survey means that 65% of the general population are less interested in that
category than you are.

28. The table shows Will's scores on the interest survey described above.

Category	Percentile
outdoor	64
mechanical	34
scientific	83
musical	9
literary	61
computational	58
artistic	22
persuasive	91
clerical	31

a. For which categories is Will's interest level above the median for
the general population?

b. For which categories is Will's interest level above the upper quartile?

c. For which category is Will's interest level below that of 90% of the
general population?

Standardizing Data

LET'S Z WHO'S BEST

Every April, runners from all over the world compete in the Boston Marathon. Thousands of runners gain a sense of accomplishment just from completing the race.

In 1994, 8181 runners finished the Boston Marathon. They competed in eight divisions determined by age and gender. Statistics about the women's divisions are shown. The data form a normal distribution.

Women's divisions (age in years)	Number of runners finishing	Mean time $\bar{x}$ (minutes)	Standard deviation σ (minutes)
18–39	1195	225.31	26.64
40–49	447	231.91	26.24
50–59	94	242.58	21.78
60 and over	5	249.90	27.23

Talk it Over

A 57-year-old woman from Georgia finished the race in 4:09:08 (hours:minutes:seconds). A 34-year-old woman from Texas finished the race in 4:00:15.

1. Do you think it is fair to compare the two women's times directly and conclude that the woman from Texas is a better runner? Explain.

2. a. Find the difference between each woman's time and the mean time in her division. (*Hint:* First convert the women's times to minutes.)

   b. Is each woman's time *above* or *below* the mean in her division? In a race like this, is it better to be *above* or *below* the mean? Why?

   c. Divide each difference from part (a) by the standard deviation for the division. This tells you the number of standard deviations from the mean for each time. How many standard deviations above or below the mean was each woman's time?

   d. Based on the calculations in part (c), which woman performed better relative to her division? Explain.

BY THE WAY...

In the 1994 Boston Marathon, 13 men and 2 women competed in the visually impaired category, and 71 men and 9 women competed in the wheelchair race.

To compare the runners in different divisions, you did some calculations in *Talk it Over* question 2 on page 519 to adjust or *standardize* the times. These standardized values are called **z-scores**.

CALCULATING z-SCORES

A z-score for a data value is the number of standard deviations it is above or below the mean of the data set. To find a z-score:

➤ subtract the mean to find the deviation from the mean,

➤ then divide by the standard deviation.

$$z = \frac{x - \bar{x}}{\sigma}$$

Sample 1

A 40-year-old Louisiana woman's time was 3:50:28. Compare her time to the times of the women from Texas and Georgia. Use the statistics from page 519.

Sample Response

Step 1 Convert the woman's time to minutes.

$$x = 3{:}50{:}28 = 3(60) + 50 + \frac{28}{60} \approx 230.47$$

Step 2 Calculate the z-score.
The woman is in the 40–49 division. The mean time in this division is 231.91 min and the standard deviation is 26.24 min.

$$z = \frac{x - \bar{x}}{\sigma}$$

$$\approx \frac{230.47 - 231.91}{26.24} \qquad \longleftarrow \text{ Substitute } \mathbf{230.47} \text{ for } x,$$
$$\mathbf{231.91} \text{ for } \bar{x}, \text{ and } \mathbf{26.24} \text{ for } \sigma.$$

$$\approx -0.055$$

The z-score for the Louisiana woman is about -0.06. Her time is about 0.06 standard deviations below the mean in her division.

The z-scores for the women from Georgia and Texas are positive. The z-score for the woman from Louisiana is negative, which represents a better-than-average performance.

The woman from Louisiana did better relative to her division than the other two women did relative to theirs.

Talk it Over

3. Does a positive z-score indicate a value *below* or *above* the mean? Does a negative z-score indicate a value *below* or *above* the mean? What does a z-score of 0 indicate?

4. Explain how z-scores allow you to compare the performance of women marathoners in different age divisions.

·······➤ Now you are ready for:
Exs. 1–4 on pp. 523–524

z-scores are often used with data that is normally distributed. The parent graph of any normal distribution is called the **standard normal curve.**

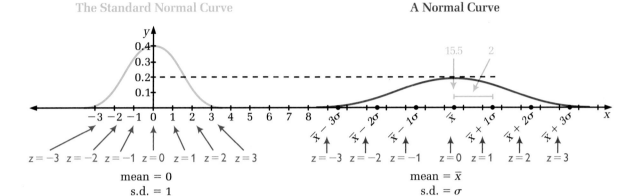

The Standard Normal Curve   A Normal Curve

mean = 0   mean = $\bar{x}$
s.d. = 1   s.d. = σ

In Unit 6 you saw that in any normal distribution, the data are arranged around the mean in a predictable way. The percents of data in six regions of the distribution are shown below. These percents are estimates based on the standard normal curve.

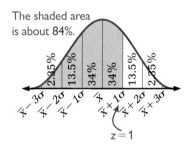

The shaded area is about 84%.

The *standard normal table,* shown below, gives these percents more accurately than the estimates you used in Unit 6. Also, you can use it with z-scores that are not integers.

If you know the z-score for a data value, you can use the table to find the percent of data that is less than the given value.

Standard Normal Table

z	.0	.1	.2	.3	.4	.5	.6	.7	.8	.9	
−3	.0013	.0010	.0007	.0005	.0003	.0002	.0002	.0001	.0001	.0000+	← slightly more than 0
−2	.0228	.0179	.0139	.0107	.0082	.0062	.0047	.0035	.0026	.0019	
−1	.1587	.1357	.1151	.0968	.0808	.0668	.0548	.0446	.0359	.0287	
−0	.5000	.4602	.4207	.3821	.3446	.3085	.2743	.2420	.2119	.1841	
0	.5000	.5398	.5793	.6179	.6554	.6915	.7257	.7580	.7881	.8159	
1	.8413	.8643	.8849	.9032	.9192	.9332	.9452	.9554	.9641	.9713	
2	.9772	.9821	.9861	.9893	.9918	.9938	.9953	.9965	.9974	.9981	
3	.9987	.9990	.9993	.9995	.9997	.9998	.9998	.9999	.9999	1.0000−	← slightly less than 1

The heights of women 18 years old in the United States are normally distributed with a mean of 64 in. and a standard deviation of 2.2 in.

a. Sara is 18 years old and 60.5 in. tall. What percent of 18-year-old women in the United States are shorter than she is? taller than she is?

b. Margaret is 18 years old. 76% of 18-year-old women in the United States are shorter than Margaret. How tall is she?

Sample Response

a. **1** Find Sara's z-score.

$$z = \frac{x - \bar{x}}{\sigma}$$

$$= \frac{60.5 - 64}{2.2}$$ ◄——— Substitute **60.5** for **x**, **64** for $\bar{x}$, and **2.2** for σ.

$$\approx -1.59$$

2 Use the table.

For $z \approx -1.6$, the value from the table is 0.0548, or about 5.5%.

z	.0	.1	.2	.3	.4	.5	.6	.7	.8	.9
-3	.0013	.0010	.0007	.0005	.0003	.0002	.0002	.0001	.0001	.0000+
-2	.0228	.0179	.0139	.0107	.0082	.0062	.0047	.0035	.0026	.0019
-1	.1587	.1357	.1151	.0968	.0808	.0668	.0548	.0446	.0359	.0287
-0	.5000	.4602	.4207	.3821	.3446	.3085	.2743	.2420	.2119	.1841

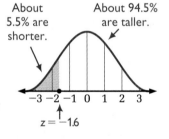

About 5.5% are shorter. About 94.5% are taller.

$z = -1.6$

About 5.5% of the 18-year-old women in the United States are shorter than Sara. This means that about 100% − 5.5% = 94.5% are taller than Sara.

b. In the table, find the value that is closest to 0.76.

z	.0	.1	.2	.3	.4	.5	.6	.7	.8	.9
-0	.5000	.4602	.4207	.3821	.3446	.3085	.2743	.2420	.2119	.1841
0	.5000	.5398	.5793	.6179	.6554	.6915	.7257	.7580	.7881	.8159
1	.8413	.8643	.8849	.9032	.9192	.9332	.9452	.9554	.9641	.9713

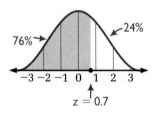

76% ➤ ◄ 24%

$z = 0.7$

The closest value is 0.7580, which corresponds to a z-score of 0.7.

$$z = \frac{x - \bar{x}}{\sigma}$$ ◄——— Use this equation to find x, Margaret's height.

$$0.7 \approx \frac{x - 64}{2.2}$$ ◄——— Substitute **0.7** for **z**, **64** for $\bar{x}$, and **2.2** for σ.

$$x \approx (0.7)(2.2) + 64$$ ◄——— Solve for x.

$$\approx 65.54$$

Margaret is about 65.5 in. tall.

In Sample 2, Margaret's height of about 65.5 in. is said to be at the 76th *percentile* for adult female heights. A **percentile** is a whole number between 0 and 100 that tells what percent of the data in a set are less than or equal to a given value.

Talk it Over

5. Explain why Sara's height in Sample 2 is at the 5th percentile.

6. At what percentile is the median of a distribution?

Look Back ◄

······► Now you are ready for:
Exs. 5–21 on pp. 524–525

How are z-scores useful in comparing data from different distributions?

9-6 Exercises and Problems

1. **Reading** In what kinds of situations are z-scores useful? Why?

2. **Swimming** At a Central Masters Swimming Association meet in 1991, swimmers competed in categories by age, gender, stroke, and length of course.

   One 28-year-old man entered the competition for the 25–29 age category in both 100-yard freestyle and 100-yard backstroke.

   He swam the 100-yard freestyle in 53.76 s. The mean for this race was 56.23 s, and the standard deviation was 6.28 s. He swam the 100-yard backstroke in 62.74 s. The mean for this race was 65.04 s, and the standard deviation was 5.94 s.

   a. Find his z-score for each race.

   b. For which stroke did this swimmer do relatively better?

3. **Swimming** At the same swimming meet, 10 swimmers competed in the 50-yard butterfly for women in the 25–29 age category. Here are their times in seconds:

27.68	28.26	28.62	29.35	30.66
33.03	34.01	34.42	35.15	35.39

   a. Find the mean and the standard deviation of these times.

   b. Find the z-score for each swimmer.

   c. Find the mean and the standard deviation of the z-scores. What do you notice?

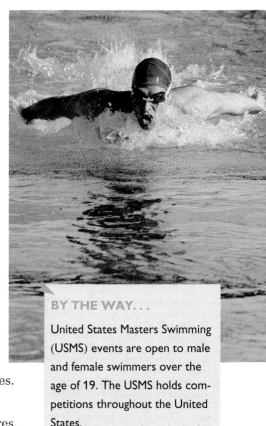

BY THE WAY...

United States Masters Swimming (USMS) events are open to male and female swimmers over the age of 19. The USMS holds competitions throughout the United States.

4. Sandy took two tests in her physics class.

On the first test her score was 73. The class average was 65.1, and the standard deviation was 6.8.

On the second test her score was 88. The class average was 79.3, and the standard deviation was 7.5.

a. Find her z-score for each test.

b. On which test did she do relatively better?

For each z-score:

a. Sketch the standard normal curve and shade the region under the curve for values of z less than the given score.

b. Use the table on page 521 to find the percent of data less than the given score.

5. $z = 0.7$ **6.** $z = -1.3$ **7.** $z = -0.4$ **8.** $z = 2.1$

For each percent, use the table on page 521 to find the corresponding z-score for the standard normal distribution.

9. 25%   **10.** 85%   **11.** 60%   **12.** 0.1%

13. Two normal curves are shown.
For distribution 1, $\bar{x} = 0$ and $\sigma = 1$.
For distribution 2, $\bar{x} = 0$ and $\sigma = 2$.
What transformation transforms curve 1 into curve 2?

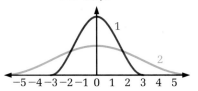

14. **Running** The winning times for the women's divisions in the 1994 Boston Marathon are shown.

a. Find the z-score for each of the four winners based on her age group. Use the means and the standard deviations given on page 519.

b. Suppose the winner in the 40–49 division had run in the 18–39 division. Find her z-score for that division. What percent of the runners in the 18–39 division would she have beaten?

c. Suppose the winner in the 50–59 division had run in the 40–49 division. Find her z-score for that division. What percent of the runners in the 40–49 division would she have beaten?

Women's divisions (age in years)	Winning time (minutes)
18–39	141.75
40–49	153.60
50–59	200.47
60 and over	219.38

15. **Career** Pediatricians monitor the height and weight of children as they grow.

Suppose the weights of one-year-old boys in the United States have a normal distribution with a mean of 11.8 kg and a standard deviation of 1.9 kg.

a. What percent of one-year-old boys weigh less than 13.1 kg?

b. What percent of one-year-old boys weigh more than 13.1 kg?

16. When he was 12 years old and in the seventh grade, Corey had a height advantage playing basketball in his school league, since he was in the 95th percentile for 12-year-old boys.

    a. Find the *z*-score for Corey's height.

    b. Suppose the mean height for 12-year-old boys is 60 in. and the standard deviation is 3 in. Find Corey's height, to the nearest inch, when he was 12 years old.

Ongoing **ASSESSMENT**

17. Use the standard normal table on page 521.

    a. Find the percent of data less than 1 standard deviation from the mean ($z = 1$). Find the percent less than -1 standard deviation from the mean. Subtract the values. What percent is *within* 1 standard deviation of the mean?

    b. Repeat part (a) for ±2 standard deviations and for ±3 standard deviations.

    c. **Writing** Do your answers to parts (a) and (b) support the 68-95-99.7 rule? Explain.

Review **PREVIEW**

18. Sketch both the parent and transformed graphs when the graph of $y = \sqrt{x}$ is stretched vertically by a factor of 2 and then translated 3 units to the left. *(Section 9-5)*

19. Sketch the graphs of $y = 2^x$ and $y = \left(\dfrac{1}{2}\right)^x$ on the same set of axes. Explain why these functions are not inverses of each other. Describe the relationship between the two graphs. *(Section 5-5)*

20. Graph the equations $y = e^{2x}$ and $y = e^{-2x}$. Find the point of intersection of the graphs. *(Section 5-4)*

Working on the Unit Project

Many careers require a college degree and many colleges require applicants to submit standardized test scores. Two tests that are commonly required are the SAT and the ACT.

21. Use the data in the table.

    a. Find Joan's *z*-score for each of the tests.

    b. Find an approximate percentile for her score on each of the tests.

Test	Joan's scores	Mean score	Standard deviation
SAT verbal	490	423	113
SAT math	510	479	124
ACT composite	23	20.8	4.6

Reflecting Graphs

On The Flip Side

On The Flip Side

Focus

Recognize the effect of a
reflection on a graph and on
the graph's equation.

EXPLORATION

*(How) are the graphs of $y = -f(x)$ and
$y = f(-x)$ related to the graph of $y = f(x)$?*

- **Materials: graphics calculators or graphing software,
  graph paper**
- **Work with another student.**

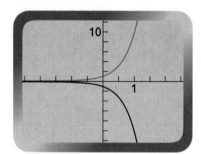

① Let $f(x) = 10^x$.

   a. Write a rule for $-f(x)$.

   b. Use a graphics calculator to graph $y = f(x)$ and
$y = -f(x)$ on the same screen. What is the relationship
between the two graphs?

② **a.** Write a rule for $f(-x)$ where f is the function in step 1.

   b. Use a graphics calculator to graph $y = f(x)$ and
$y = f(-x)$ on the same screen. What is the relationship
between the two graphs?

③ Repeat steps 1 and 2 using the function $f(x) = \sqrt{x}$. Are
your observations about the graphs of $y = f(x)$, $y = -f(x)$,
and $y = f(-x)$ the same?

④ Use the function $f(x) = 4\,|x - 5|$.

   a. Sketch the graph of $y = f(x)$.

   b. Based on your results from steps 1–3,
sketch the graphs of $y = -f(x)$ and
$y = f(-x)$. Use a graphics calculator
to check your graphs.

REFLECTIONS OF GRAPHS

For any function f, the graph of $y = -f(x)$ is the graph of $y = f(x)$ reflected over the x-axis.

For any function f, the graph of $y = f(-x)$ is the graph of $y = f(x)$ reflected over the y-axis.

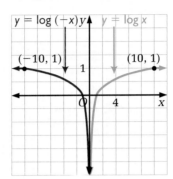

Sample 1

Sketch the graph of $y = 2\sqrt{-x + 4} + 1$.

Sample Response

The parent function is $y = \sqrt{x}$. To identify the transformations, rewrite the given equation as $\dfrac{y - 1}{2} = \sqrt{-(x - 4)}$. Graph this equation using these steps:

1 Reflect the graph of $y = \sqrt{x}$ over the y-axis.

2 Stretch the graph of $y = \sqrt{-x}$ vertically by a factor of 2.

3 Translate the graph of $y = 2\sqrt{-x}$ by the vector $(4, 1)$.

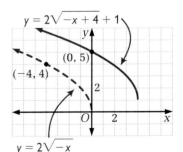

┈┈▶ **Now you are ready for:**
Exs. 1–7 on p. 530

A skydiver jumps from an airplane at an altitude of 13,000 ft. The graph shows the approximate distance $d(t)$ that the skydiver has fallen after t minutes.

a. Let $h(t)$ be the height of the skydiver above the ground after t minutes. Write an equation that gives $h(t)$ in terms of $d(t)$.

b. Sketch the graph of $y = h(t)$.

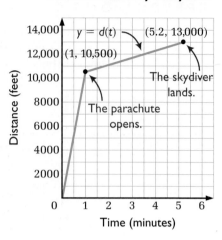

Distance Fallen by a Skydiver

Sample Response

a. **Problem Solving Strategy:** Use a diagram.

Notice from the diagram that:

$$d(t) + h(t) = 13,000$$
$$h(t) = -d(t) + 13,000$$

An equation is $h(t) = -d(t) + 13,000$.

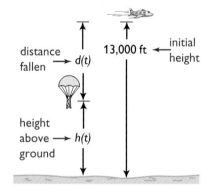

b. The equation in part (a) shows that the graph of $y = h(t)$ is a result of transforming the graph of $y = d(t)$. Follow these steps:

1 Reflect the graph of $y = d(t)$ over the t-axis.

2 Translate the graph of $y = -d(t)$ by the vector $(0, 13,000)$.

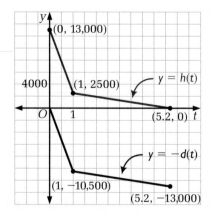

Unit 9 Transformations of Graphs and Data

1. List the steps you would use to sketch the graph of the function $y = -\frac{1}{2}|x - 6| - 3$.

2. Use the graphs of $y = d(t)$ and $y = h(t)$ in Sample 2.

   a. How far above the ground does the skydiver open the parachute?

   b. How long does it take for the skydiver to reach the ground?

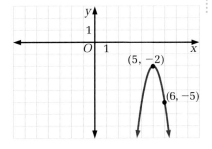

Sample 3

Find an equation for the graph shown. Assume the parent function is one of the following: $y = x^2$, $y = x^3$, $y = \sqrt{x}$, $y = |x|$, $y = 10^x$, or $y = \log x$.

Sample Response

Use the shape of the graph to identify the parent function as $y = x^2$. Apply transformations to the graph of $y = x^2$ until you produce the given graph.

1 Reflect the graph of $y = x^2$ over the x-axis.

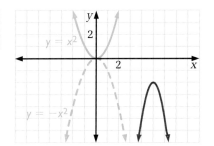

2 Stretch the graph of $y = -x^2$ vertically by a factor of $\frac{-3}{-1} = 3$.

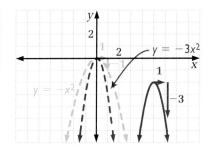

3 Translate the graph of $y = -3x^2$ by the vector $(5, -2)$.
The translated graph is the given graph.

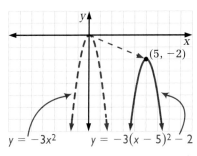

An equation of the given graph is $y = -3(x - 5)^2 - 2$.

:·····▶ **Now you are ready for:**
: **Exs. 8–22 on pp. 530–532**

Look Back ◀────

For any function f, how are the graphs of $y = -f(x)$ and $y = f(-x)$ related to the graph of $y = f(x)$?

Exercises and Problems

1. **Reading** What are the domain and the range of the function in Sample 1?

Sketch the graph of each function.

2. $y = -x^3$

3. $y = 10^{-x - 3}$

4. $y = -3(x + 6)^2 + 4$

5. $y = -\frac{2}{3}|x - 2| - 5$

6. $y = \log(-2x - 9)$

7. $y = -4\sqrt{-x + 2} + 7$

BY THE WAY...

Chinese acrobats may have used parachute-like devices as early as 1306. The first known parachute jump was made by the French physicist Sebastian Lenormand in 1783.

8. **Skydiving** The speed of a skydiver t seconds after opening a parachute can be modeled by the function

$$s(t) = 10 + 166e^{-3.2t}$$

where $s(t)$ is measured in feet per second.

a. **Writing** What transformations can you apply to the graph of $y = e^t$ to obtain the graph of $y = s(t)$?

b. Sketch the graph of $y = s(t)$. Based on your graph, what speed does a skydiver approach as the time t increases?

c. **Research** Look up "parachute" in an encyclopedia. Write a short report on the history of parachuting.

Career A financial consultant helps people decide how to invest their money.

The graph shows what one consultant thinks is the percent of money $m(x)$ that a person x years old should invest in stocks.

9. a. Let $b(x)$ be the percent of money that a person x years old should invest in bonds.

Write an equation that gives $b(x)$ in terms of $m(x)$. (Assume any money not invested in stocks is invested in bonds.)

b. Sketch the graph of $y = b(x)$.

10. **Writing** In general, stocks are more profitable than bonds over long periods of time. However, stocks are usually riskier investments over short periods of time.

Use these facts to explain why the graphs of $y = m(x)$ and $y = b(x)$ make sense.

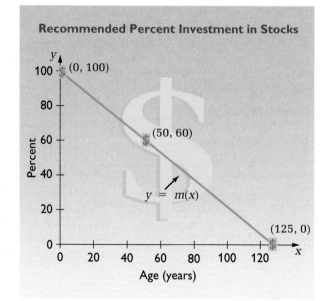

Recommended Percent Investment in Stocks

11. Scuba Diving An ocean diver is working in water 200 ft deep. The graph shows the total atmospheric and water pressure $p(d_s)$ on the diver as a function of the diver's distance d_s from the surface.

a. Let d_b be the distance of the diver from the ocean bottom. Complete this equation with an expression involving d_s:

$$p(d_b) = p(\underline{\ ?\ })$$

b. Use the equation in part (a) to graph $y = p(d_b)$.

Total Atmospheric and Water Pressure on a Diver

Find an equation for each graph. Assume the parent function of each graph is one of the following: $y = x^2$, $y = x^3$, $y = \sqrt{x}$, $y = |x|$, $y = 10^x$, **or** $y = \log x$.

12.

13.

14.

15.

16.

17.

18. **Using Manipulatives** Work with another student. Use a MIRA® transparent mirror and graph paper.

    a. Graph the function $f(x) = 2|x - 4| + 3$.

    b. Use the MIRA® to sketch the reflection of the graph of f over the x-axis. What is an equation of the reflected graph?

    c. Use the MIRA® to sketch the reflection of the graph of f over the y-axis. What is an equation of the reflected graph?

Ongoing **ASSESSMENT**

19. **Open-ended** This design was made by graphing $y = f(x)$, $y = -f(x)$, $y = f(-x)$, and $y = -f(-x)$ where $f(x) = |x - 5|$. Use a different function to make your own design.

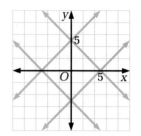

Review **PREVIEW**

20. Elaine's score on a chemistry test is 87. The mean of the scores in Elaine's class is 75, and the standard deviation is 16. Find Elaine's z-score. *(Section 9-6)*

21. Use the diagram. Show that $\angle PQR$ is a right angle. (*Hint:* Use the converse of the Pythagorean theorem: If $(PQ)^2 + (QR)^2 = (PR)^2$, then $\triangle PQR$ is a right triangle.) *(Toolbox Skill 31)*

Working on the Unit Project

22. Claudia estimates that she will owe about $20,000 in student loans when she finishes college. She plans to make gradually increasing monthly payments after she graduates to pay off her loans. The function

    $$A(n) = (-15.3)(1.007)^n + 35.3$$

    gives the amount of money (in thousands of dollars) that Claudia will still owe after making n monthly payments.

    a. **Writing** What transformations can you apply to the graph of $y = (1.007)^n$ to obtain the graph of $y = A(n)$?

    b. Sketch the graph of $y = A(n)$.

    c. **TECHNOLOGY** Graph $y = A(n)$ on a graphics calculator. Use the graph to find how long it will take Claudia to pay off her student loans.

Completing the Unit Project

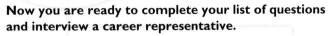

Now you are ready to complete your list of questions and interview a career representative.

Your questions should include these topics:

➤ **college or other training needed for entry and advancement**

➤ **the role of mathematics on the job**

➤ **required tests and their scoring**

➤ **potential for job openings and job security**

➤ **working conditions, hours, and benefits**

The completed project should include a well-organized set of notes for reviewing and analyzing what you learned in the interview.

Look Back ◄

Compare your interview questions with those of other groups. What additional questions would you ask if you had a second job interview?

Alternative Projects

Project 1: Re-scaling the SAT Test

In 1994 the College Board announced that beginning in 1995 scores on the Scholastic Assessment Test (SAT) would be re-scaled. In the years leading up to the change, the mean SAT verbal score was 424 and the mean SAT math score was 478. Under the new system, the mean for both sections of the test is 500.

This decision was based on the concept of transforming a data set. Use articles from newspapers and magazines and literature from the College Board to research this question. Write a paper explaining why the College Board decided to "re-center" the scores and how students and parents should interpret the new scores.

Project 2: Transformations of Functions

You have studied linear, quadratic, polynomial, rational, exponential, logarithmic, and absolute value functions. In applications, the functions that model a real-life situation are often transformations of these parent functions. Find at least six examples of transformed functions that model real-life applications. Make a poster that presents these applications along with graphs of the transformed functions.

1. The table shows the heights of the ten tallest buildings in Denver, Colorado.

9-1

Name of building	Height (ft)
Amoco Building	448
Anaconda Tower	507
Arco Tower	527
First Interstate Tower North	434
Mountain Bell Center	709
1999 Broadway	544
Republic Plaza	714
17th Street Plaza	438
Stellar Plaza	437
United Bank of Denver	698

a. Find the mean, the median, the range, and the standard deviation for the heights of the buildings.

b. Denver is about 5280 ft above sea level. Find the height of each building above sea level.

c. Use what you know about adding a constant to each value in a data set to find the mean, the median, the range, and the standard deviation for the heights of the buildings above sea level.

Sketch a parent graph and translate it to obtain a graph of each equation.

9-2

2. $y = |x + 6|$ 3. $y - 8 = 10^x$ 4. $y + 1 = \sqrt{x - 3}$

5. **Writing** Danielle built a large scale model of the ten tallest buildings in Denver. The scale is 1 ft = 100 ft. Describe two ways you could use the scale to find the mean and the standard deviation of the heights for the ten buildings in Danielle's model.

9-3

The matrix $M = \begin{bmatrix} 0 & 5 & 6 & 1 \\ 0 & 0 & 3 & 3 \end{bmatrix}$ represents the vertices of a trapezoid.

9-4

Multiply M by each transformation matrix and then describe the effect of each transformation.

6. $\begin{bmatrix} 4 & 0 \\ 0 & 1 \end{bmatrix}$ 7. $\begin{bmatrix} 1 & 0 \\ 0 & \frac{1}{3} \end{bmatrix}$ 8. $\begin{bmatrix} 2 & 0 \\ 0 & 5 \end{bmatrix}$

Without using graphing technology, sketch the graph of each function.

9. $y = 3\sqrt{x}$ 10. $y = \left|\frac{x}{5}\right|$ 11. $y = (x - 2)^3$

12. For 1961–1980, the mean of the average September temperatures in   **9-5**
Beijing, China, was 66.7°F, and the standard deviation was 1.2°F.
What are the mean and the standard deviation in degrees Celsius?

13. **Open-ended** The ten students in an advanced class received the
following scores on a 100-point test:

$$47 \quad 52 \quad 39 \quad 44 \quad 51 \quad 63 \quad 50 \quad 48 \quad 45 \quad 56$$

The teacher has decided to rescale the scores using a linear function
$f(x) = mx + b$ where x is a student's actual score and $f(x)$ is the
rescaled score. Find a function that brings all rescaled scores within
the range 60–100. Explain your choice of m and b.

Find an equation for each graph. The parent function is given.

14. parent function: $y = |x|$ **15.** parent function: $y = x^3$

          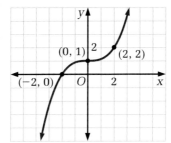

16. Use the standard normal table on page 521 to find the percent of   **9-6**
data less than the given z-score.

a. $z = 0.6$ **b.** $z = -1.3$

17. The heights of men 18 years old or older in the United States are
normally distributed with a mean of 69.1 in. and a standard deviation
of 2.8 in. What percent of men in the United States are taller than
72 in.?

18. Sketch the graph of $y = -3|x + 4| + 2$.   **9-7**

19. Jerry drops a stone into an empty well that is 80 ft deep. The graph
shows the stone's distance $f(t)$ from the top of the well after t seconds.

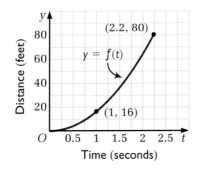

a. Let $g(t)$ be the stone's distance from the bottom of the well after
t seconds. Write an equation that gives $g(t)$ in terms of $f(t)$.

b. Sketch the graph of $g(t)$.

20. **Self-evaluation** Make a concept map to show your understanding of the transformations of data and functions discussed in this unit.

21. **Group Activity** Work in a group of three students. The group should sketch graphs on the same set of axes.

   a. Student 1 should choose a parent function.

   b. Student 2 should sketch the graph of the parent function from part (a). Then student 2 should decide whether student 3 should reflect the graph over the x-axis or over the y-axis.

   c. Student 3 should sketch the reflected graph. Then student 3 should choose a horizontal stretch or a vertical stretch for student 1 to graph.

   d. Student 1 should sketch the stretched graph. Then student 1 should choose a horizontal translation or a vertical translation for student 2 to graph.

   e. Student 2 should sketch the translated graph.

   f. Student 3 should write an equation of the graph sketched in part (e).

IDEAS AND (FORMULAS)$= X^2$ $_5P_5$

STATISTICS & PROBABILITY

➤ When the same constant value is added to each value in a data set:
  • the mean, the median, and the graph of the distribution are translated by the constant value. *(p. 485)*
  • the range and the standard deviation remain the same. *(p. 485)*

➤ When each value in a data set is multiplied by the same positive constant:
  • the graph of the distribution is stretched by the constant value. *(p. 496)*
  • the mean, the median, the range, and the standard deviation are multiplied by the constant value. *(p. 498)*

➤ To find the z-score for a data value, subtract the mean to find the deviation from the mean, and then divide the difference by the standard deviation *(p. 520)*:

$$z = \frac{x - \bar{x}}{\sigma}$$

➤ The parent curve of any normal distribution is the standard normal curve. *(p. 521)*

➤ The standard normal table gives the percent of data less than any given z-score. *(p. 521)*

ALGEBRA

➤ When the graph of $y = f(x)$ is translated horizontally by the constant h, an equation of the new graph is $y = f(x - h)$. *(p. 490)*

➤ When the graph of $y = f(x)$ is translated vertically by the constant k, an equation of the new graph is $y - k = f(x)$. *(p. 490)*

➤ When the graph of $y = f(x)$ is stretched horizontally by the positive factor a:

   • the original graph crossing the y-axis remains fixed. *(p. 502)*

   • an equation of the new graph is $y = f\left(\dfrac{x}{a}\right)$. *(p. 502)*

➤ When the graph of $y = f(x)$ is stretched vertically by the positive factor b:

   • all points where the original graph crosses the x-axis remain fixed. *(p. 502)*

   • an equation of the new graph is $\dfrac{y}{b} = f(x)$. *(p. 502)*

➤ The temperature conversion formula $C = \dfrac{5}{9}(F - 32)$ is a combination of the transformations of translating and stretching. *(p. 511)*

➤ When the graph of $y = f(x)$ is reflected over the x-axis, an equation of the new graph is $y = -f(x)$. *(p. 527)*

➤ When the graph of $y = f(x)$ is reflected over the y-axis, an equation of the new graph is $y = f(-x)$. *(p. 527)*

➤ Combinations of translation, stretching, and reflection may be used to produce a new function from a given parent function. *(p. 527)*

GEOMETRY

➤ A figure in the coordinate plane can be stretched in the horizontal or vertical direction by multiplying the coordinates of its vertices by a transformation matrix. *(pp. 501, 502)*

DISCRETE MATH

➤ For positive numbers a and b, the transformation matrix $\begin{bmatrix} a & 0 \\ 0 & b \end{bmatrix}$ represents stretching by a factor of a in the horizontal direction and by a factor of b in the vertical direction. *(p. 502)*

······· **Key Terms**

  • **transformation matrix** (p. 501)   • **z-score** (p. 520)
  • **standard normal curve** (p. 521)   • **percentile** (p. 523)

Periodic Models

When a total eclipse of the sun occurred during a battle fought in ancient Mesopotamia, the armies were so frightened that they dropped all their weapons and made peace. Because eclipses occur in predictable cycles, modern astronomers have determined that the battle ended on May 28, 585 B.C. — making this historical event the earliest for which a specific date is known.

CYCLES

Every autumn millions of monarch butterflies **migrate** from the eastern United States to a small region of central Mexico — a journey of 2000 mi. In January they fly back north for the summer. The next autumn their offspring repeat the cycle.

monarchs

Make a Functional Scrapbook

Your project is to make a scrapbook describing specific situations that can be modeled using a graph. Your scrapbook should include situations from your life, as well as local, national, and international topics. Use at least one page for each situation.

Describe each situation and include a sketch of a graph that models it. Explain why the situation can be modeled by the graph you selected. Include pictures or sketches to help describe each situation or each model.

Include at least ten different types of graphs in your scrapbook. About half of the graphs you include should be from previous units and half should be from Unit 10. Describe the features of each graph. Explain what these features tell about each situation.

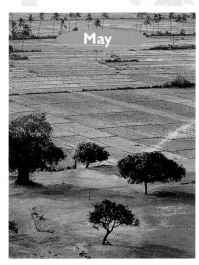

Rice fields in Goa are dry and brown in May.

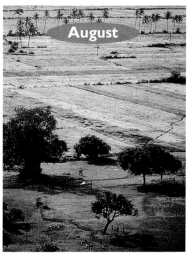

The same fields turn bright green by August due to the monsoon.

Between June and September, the winds blow across the Indian Ocean from the southwest instead of the northeast, causing large downpours throughout Asia. Because the rain is essential to the agriculture and economy in the area, the people of India celebrate the return of the monsoon season with the festival of *Teej*.

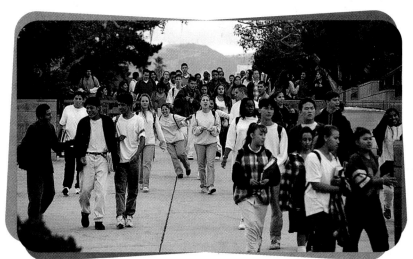

The agricultural cycles of planting, growing, and harvesting once determined when school would start and end. Now school vacations influence economic cycles. Each year many industries focus their products or services on students — stores stock back-to-school supplies in September, movie companies release major films during school vacations, and travel agents and airlines plan trips during spring break.

For this project you should work in a group of four students. Here are some ideas to help you get started.

☞ Make a list of all the functions you can graph. Decide which of these functions to include in your scrapbook.

☞ Think about situations that you would like to model. Decide which type of graph best models these situations.

☞ Decide what materials you will use to make your scrapbook. How will you keep your scrapbook together?

Working on the Unit Project

Your work in Unit 10 will help you make your scrapbook.

Related Exercises:

Section 10-1, Exercises 35–40
Section 10-2, Exercise 37
Section 10-3, Exercise 28
Section 10-4, Exercise 48
Section 10-5, Exercises 21, 22
Section 10-6, Exercises 24, 25
Section 10-7, Exercise 35

Alternative Projects p. 589

Can We Talk   CYCLES

➤ What types of things happen every day? every week? every month? every year?

➤ Halley's Comet returns about every 76 years. What events happen in regular intervals longer than one year?

➤ Meteorologists study patterns in the weather. What are some patterns that you notice in the weather?

➤ A popular saying states that "history repeats itself." Do you think history repeats itself? Why or why not? Give examples of events from history to support your position.

➤ Do you know of any annual events or holidays that are celebrated in other parts of the world? If so, when do they occur?

Describing the Behavior of Functions

From The Looks Of It

The Indianapolis 500 automobile race, first run in 1911, attracts about 300,000 spectators each year. The winner is the first driver to complete 200 laps around the track, a distance of 500 mi.

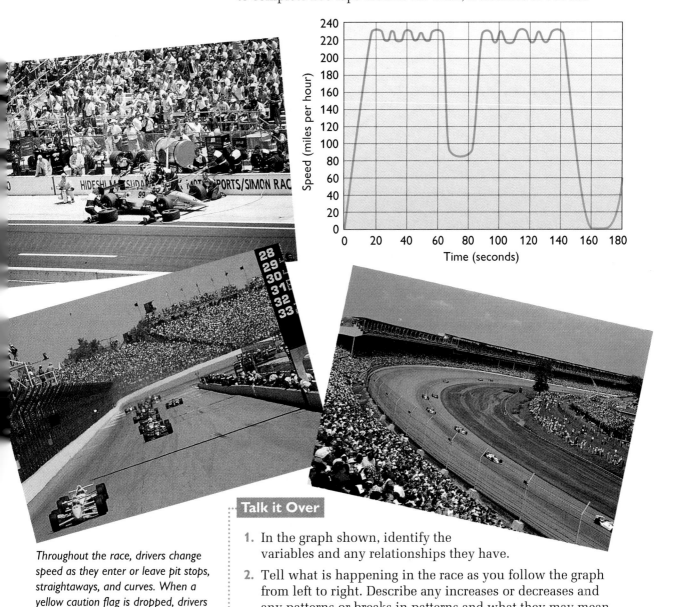

Throughout the race, drivers change speed as they enter or leave pit stops, straightaways, and curves. When a yellow caution flag is dropped, drivers must slow down to 80 mi/h.

Talk it Over

1. In the graph shown, identify the variables and any relationships they have.

2. Tell what is happening in the race as you follow the graph from left to right. Describe any increases or decreases and any patterns or breaks in patterns and what they may mean.

Choose the letter of the graph on the next page that best matches each situation shown below. Tell what variable goes on each axis.

3. The iris of your eye widens as you enter a dark room.

4. As a pot of water boils, the temperature of the water is recorded.

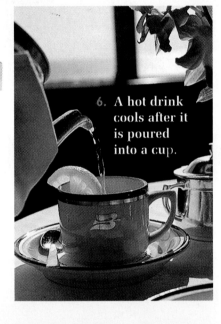

6. A hot drink cools after it is poured into a cup.

5. As a bouncing spring with an attached weight slows to a stop, the height of the weight changes.

7. An electrocardiograph traces a record of the electric currents of a person's heart muscle activity.

8. When a bathtub is filling with water, the height of the water changes as time passes.

A.

B.

C.

D.

E.

F.

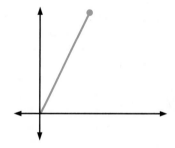

9. Which of graphs A–F can be described by each term?

  a. constant

  b. increasing

  c. decreasing

  d. **periodic**, or repeating the same pattern

  e. **saturating**, or continually increasing or decreasing toward a constant value

  f. **damping**, or moving toward a constant value by alternately increasing and decreasing around that value

Two functions may behave similarly but have important differences. For example, increasing functions do not all grow at the same rate.

Sample

Compare the rates of growth in the first quadrant of these linear, quadratic, and exponential functions:

$$y = 2x \quad y = x^2 \quad y = 2^x$$

Sample Response

Method ❶ Make tables for integer values of x. Look at the differences in the y-values to reach a conclusion about the growth rates.

$y = 2x$

x	y
0	0
1	2
2	4
3	6
4	8
5	10

differences: 2, 2, 2, 2, 2

The differences are constant.

$y = x^2$

x	y
0	0
1	1
2	4
3	9
4	16
5	25

differences: 1, 3, 5, 7, 9

The differences are increasing by 2, in an arithmetic sequence.

$y = 2^x$

x	y
0	1
1	2
2	4
3	8
4	16
5	32

differences: 1, 2, 4, 8, 16

The differences are increasing in a geometric sequence.

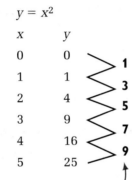

Method ❷ Graph the three functions on the same set of axes.

$y = 2^x$ — $y = x^2$

10 — $y = 2x$

The tables and the graphs show that the exponential function $y = 2^x$ grows the fastest, followed by the quadratic function $y = x^2$, and then the linear function $y = 2x$.

10. Repeat the Sample for the functions $y = 4x$, $y = x^4$, and $y = 4^x$. Are the results the same? Explain.

11. Compare the rates of growth in the first quadrant for these linear, square root, and logarithmic functions:

$$y = \frac{1}{2}x \qquad y = \sqrt{x} \qquad y = \log_2 x$$

12. The graph shows the price of prerecorded videocassettes, in dollars, between 1980 and 1990. Tell whether the prices decreased quickly or decreased slowly for each interval.

a. 1982–1986   b. 1986–1990

Price (dollars) vs. Year

Look Back

Describe a situation that can be modeled by each type of graph.

a. periodic   b. damping   c. saturating   d. constant

10-1 Exercises and Problems

1. a. Interpret this graph of the height of an elevator in an office building.

b. What part of the graph is periodic? What do you think this represents?

c. When do most workers arrive at work?

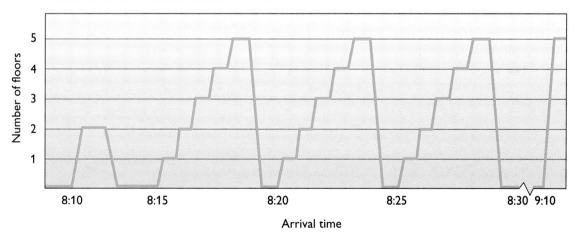

Number of floors vs. Arrival time

2. **Reading** How are saturating functions and damping functions alike? How are they different?

3. **Writing** Refer to the graphs in *Talk it Over* questions 5 and 7 on page 542. How are the graphs alike? How are they different?

Open-ended Describe a situation that can be modeled by each type of graph.

4. increasing   5. decreasing   6. constant

For Exercises 7–12, which of the terms *constant, increasing, decreasing, periodic, damping,* **or** *saturating* **best describes each graph?**

7.

8.

9.

10.

11.

12.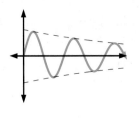

For Exercises 13–16, choose the number of the graph above that best models each situation.

13. the volume of air in your lungs as you breathe normally

14. the amount of radioactivity in a rock as years pass

15. the height of a candle as it burns

16. the constant subzero temperature maintained in an experiment to study low-temperature phenomena

17. Compare the rates of growth in the first quadrant for these functions:

$$y = 3x \qquad y = x^3 \qquad y = 3^x$$

18. **a.** Does a function of the form $y = x^n$, where $n > 0$, grow faster or slower as n increases?

    b. Does an exponential function of the form $y = b^x$ $(b > 1)$ grow faster or slower as b gets close to 1?

19. Compare the rates of decay of these reciprocal, exponential decay, and linear decay functions when $x \geq 2$:

$$y = \frac{2}{x} \qquad y = 2^{-x} \qquad y = 2 - x$$

20. **Writing** Can a periodic function be constantly increasing? Explain.

21. **a.** In the Sample on page 544, in which interval(s) is $y = 2x$ greater than the other two functions?

    b. In which interval(s) is $y = x^2$ greater than the other two functions?

For Exercises 22–24, use the graph of yearly revenues of a state lottery.

22. Identify an interval of the graph where the revenues increased sharply.

23. Identify an interval of the graph where the revenues increased slowly.

24. Describe the graph. Use as many of the terms *constant*, *increasing*, *decreasing*, *periodic*, *damping*, and *saturating* as you can.

Lottery Revenues

1992 revenues $1,870,385,726

1972 revenues $56,390,250

Millions of dollars

'73 '75 '77 '79 '81 '83 '85 '87 '89 '91 '93

Source: Massachusetts State Lottery

Ongoing **ASSESSMENT**

25. **Writing** Compare the rates of growth of the periodic, constant, and linear functions shown.

Review **PREVIEW**

26. **a.** Sketch the graphs of $y = x^2 + 4x$ and $y = -(x^2 + 4x)$ on the same set of axes.

   b. What transformations can you apply to the graph of $y = x^2 + 4x$ to obtain the graph of $y = -(x^2 + 4x)$? *(Section 9-7)*

Simplify. *(Section 5-3)*

27. $64^{2/3}$

28. $5^{1/2} \cdot 5^{4/3}$

29. $\left(\dfrac{36}{100}\right)^{3/2}$

Sketch each graph. *(Toolbox Skill 28)*

30. $y = x^2$

31. $y = (x - 2)^2$

32. $y - 2 = x^2$

33. $y = -x^2$

34. Tell what kinds of transformations are used to obtain the graphs in Exercises 31 – 33 from the original graph in Exercise 30.

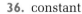 **Working on the Unit Project**

35. Bob made this graph to describe the sound produced by a cymbal. What type of graph did Bob make? Do you think his graph accurately models the situation? Why or why not?

Describe a situation that can be modeled by a graph having each given characteristic. Make a graph to model the situation. Explain why each situation can be modeled by each type of graph. Include each graph on a page of your scrapbook.

36. constant

37. increasing

38. decreasing

39. saturating

40. damping

10-2 Periodic Functions

········Focus
Recognize periodic functions
and features of their graphs.

The automatic dishwasher in a busy restaurant is in constant use. The graph shows the volume of water in the dishwasher as a function of time.

Volume of Water in a Restaurant Dishwasher

Amplitude:

$$\frac{\text{maximum value} - \text{minimum value}}{2}$$

Axis: the horizontal line halfway between the minimum and maximum values of the function

Cycle: the smallest portion of the graph that repeats

Frequency: the reciprocal of the period, or $\dfrac{1}{\text{period}}$

Period: the length of one cycle

Talk it Over

1. How long is the period of the dishwasher graph?

2. How many washing cycles are completed in 1 h? What is this in cycles per minute? Which of the key terms does your answer describe?

3. What is the amplitude of the dishwasher graph?

4. Predict what will be happening in the dishwashing process 4 min, 5.5 min, and 18 min from the start time. Explain how you decided.

Many things, such as the dishwasher, have patterns that repeat. A repeating pattern can be represented by a *periodic graph*, which has a piece that is repeatedly translated horizontally. For a periodic function, the amplitude is the distance of the graph from a high point (or low point) to its axis.

Sam is jumping on a trampoline in a national competition. The graph shows how high his feet are off the ground.

a. Find the cycle.

b. Find the period.

c. Find the frequency.

d. Find the amplitude.

e. Write an equation of the axis.

Sample Response

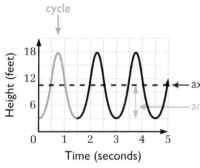

a. The cycle is the part of the graph shown in green.

b. The period is the length of one cycle, or 1.5 s.

c. The frequency is the reciprocal of the period.

$$\frac{1}{\text{period}} = \frac{1}{1.5} \quad \longleftarrow \quad \text{Substitute 1.5 for the period.}$$

$$= \frac{2}{3}$$

The frequency is $\frac{2}{3}$ cycle per second.

d. The amplitude is half the difference between the maximum and minimum values of the function.

$$\frac{\text{maximum value} - \text{minimum value}}{2} = \frac{18 - 3}{2}$$

$$= 7.5$$

The amplitude is 7.5 ft.

e. The axis is the horizontal line halfway between the minimum and maximum values 3 and 18.

$$y = \frac{\text{maximum value} + \text{minimum value}}{2}$$

$$= 10.5$$

An equation of the axis is $y = 10.5$.

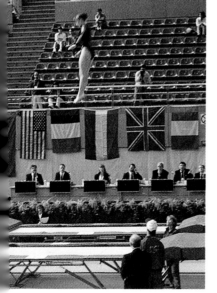

Jennifer Sans was the United States Women's National Champion Trampolinist in 1992, 1993, and 1994.

Talk it Over

5. When Jennifer jumps on the trampoline with the same frequency as Sam, she can jump 2 ft higher than Sam. How is a graph of Jennifer's jumping different from a graph of Sam's?

6. When Jennifer jumps rope, she jumps faster and not as high as when she jumps on a trampoline. How is a graph of Jennifer's jumping rope different from a graph of her jumping on a trampoline?

Sketch a periodic graph with period 3 and amplitude 5.

Sample Response

Many graphs are possible. An amplitude of 5 means

$\dfrac{\text{maximum} - \text{minimum}}{2} = 5$, so maximum − minimum = 10.

Here are two responses.

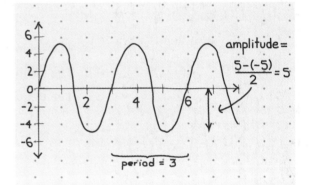

Look Back

On a periodic graph, how do you find the amplitude? the period? the frequency? an equation of the axis?

10-2 Exercises and Problems

1. **Reading** How is the period of a graph related to its frequency?

For Exercises 2–5, use the graph. It shows the way one person's body temperature changes over time.

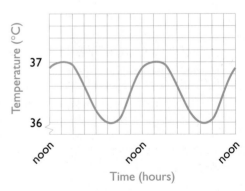

2. What is the amplitude of the function?

3. What is the period of the function?

4. Write an equation of the axis of the graph.

5. At what times of day is the temperature highest? lowest?

For Exercises 6–8, sketch a periodic graph with each set of characteristics.

6. amplitude: 4
   period: 3
   equation of axis: $y = 4$

7. amplitude: 10
   period: 5
   equation of axis: $y = -1$

8. amplitude: 32
   frequency: $\frac{1}{4}$
   equation of axis: $y = 0$

For Exercise 9–12, use this graph that shows the color of a traffic signal light over time.

9. Describe one cycle of the traffic signal light.

10. How many times per hour does the traffic signal light repeat its pattern?

11. At rush hour, the pattern is changed so that the light stays green for 110 s. The length of the red and yellow lights are unchanged. How many times per hour does the traffic signal light repeat this pattern?

12. Explain how changing the length of the pattern changes the frequency with which it occurs.

For each graph in Exercises 13–16:

 a. Find the period. **b. Find the frequency.**

 c. Write an equation of the axis. **d. Find the amplitude.**

13.

14.

15.

16.

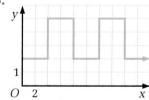

Redraw the graph in Exercise 13 using each given transformation.

17. a horizontal translation of 3

18. a vertical translation of 6

19. a period that is doubled

20. a vertical stretch by a factor of $\frac{1}{2}$

21. a horizontal stretch by a factor of 2

22. a frequency that is doubled

The snowshoe hare population gets large.

The hares threaten the willows by eating too much new growth.

Biologists suggest that the size of the snowshoe hare population is related to the number of willow trees in an area by this cycle of events.

The willows respond by producing a chemical that tastes bad to the hares.

The willows stop producing the bad-tasting chemical.

This causes a food shortage that reduces the hare population.

The willows grow back.

The graph shows how the numbers of hares and willows can change through several cycles.

23. What is the period of the hare's population cycle?

24. What is the period of the willow's population cycle?

25. Identify the intervals when the willows produce the chemical that makes them taste bad.

26. When will the next peak in the hare population occur?

27. When will the next drop in the willow population occur?

28. **Writing** What do you think this ecosystem will be like 37 years after the "0" year on the graph?

Biomass is a measure of the weight of an organism per unit area.

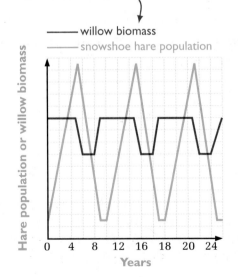

29. Biology The cicada, or *Magicicada septendecim,* is an insect that develops underground for 17 years. In the spring of the year when the cicadas reach adulthood, they all leave the ground at the same time, and 20,000–40,000 may appear under one tree. Adults live for 30–40 days.

a. Indiana, Ohio, Pennsylvania, Kentucky, Tennessee, and North Carolina had adult cicada populations in 1991. What was the year of the previous adult cicada population? What will be the year of the next one?

b. Sketch a graph of the population of adult 17-year cicadas for one location for the 100 years after 1991. Explain why you cannot label the *y*-axis accurately.

c. How would the graph for 13-year cicadas be different from the graph for 17-year cicadas?

Ongoing **ASSESSMENT**

30. Group Activity Work with another student.

a. Draw a periodic graph.

b. Trade graphs with your partner. Identify the cycle, the period, the frequency, and the amplitude, and write an equation of the axis.

Review **PREVIEW**

31. Compare the growth rates in the first quadrant for these functions:
$y = 5x$ $y = 5x^2$ $y = 5^x$ *(Section 10-1)*

32. Use right triangle *ABC.* *(Toolbox Skills 30 and 36)*

a. $m\angle A + m\angle B = \underline{\ ?\ }$.

b. Find an expression for sin *A* in terms of *a* and *c*.

c. Find an expression for cos *B* in terms of *a* and *c*.

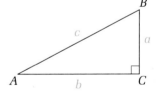

For Exercises 33–36, find the missing parts of each △ABC using the law of cosines or the law of sines. *(Sections 8-6, 8-7)*

33. $c = 10$ cm, $a = 5$ cm, $m\angle B = 30°$

34. $b = 15.4$ cm, $c = 2$ cm, $m\angle A = 110°$

35. $m\angle A = 30°$, $m\angle C = 50°$, $b = 45$ cm

36. $m\angle B = 22°$, $m\angle C = 95°$, $c = 17$ cm

Working on the Unit Project

37. Describe a situation that can be modeled by a periodic function. Make a graph to model the situation. Find or identify the cycle, the period, the frequency, the amplitude, and an equation of the axis of the graph. Include this graph on a page of your scrapbook.

Focus
Recognize and understand characteristics of the graphs of the sine function and the cosine function.

As the Wheel Turns

The Ferris wheel built by George Ferris in Chicago for the World's Columbian Exposition in 1893 was the largest Ferris wheel ever built. The wheel was 250 ft in diameter and each cab could hold 60 people.

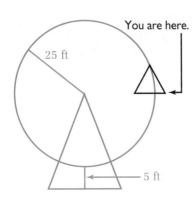

You are here.

25 ft

5 ft

Talk it Over

1. Suppose that you are on a Ferris wheel in the seat shown. For each angle (measured counterclockwise) through which the Ferris wheel turns, make a sketch to show your position.

   a. 90°   b. 180°   c. 270°

   d. 360°   e. 400°   f. 800°

2. How does your height above the ground change as the wheel turns?

3. The graph shows your height above the ground as the Ferris wheel turns. Answer parts (a)–(c) for points A–F.

   a. What is your position on the Ferris wheel?

   b. How many degrees did you turn from the starting point?

   c. How many *revolutions,* or complete turns, did you make?

4. What is the period of the graph from question 3? What does this represent in terms of the Ferris wheel ride?

5. Answer question 4 for the amplitude of the graph.

6. The graph shows your height after t seconds.

   a. How long does it take to make one complete revolution on the Ferris wheel?

   b. How many revolutions do you make in 1 min?

   c. Suppose the Ferris wheel completes one revolution in 20 s. How would the graph change?

Height as a Function of Angle

Height (feet)

Angle of turn (degrees)

Height as a Function of Time

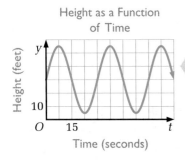

Height (feet)

Time (seconds)

The Sine Function

Many situations, like the height of a seat on a Ferris wheel, can be modeled by a periodic function whose control variable is angle measure or time. Often the graphs of these functions are transformations of the graph of the *sine function*.

A circle with a radius of 1 and its center at the origin is called a *unit circle*. Suppose you move an object around the unit circle in a counterclockwise direction starting at (1, 0). The **sine function**, $y = \sin \theta$, measures the vertical position of the object.

One revolution around the unit circle creates one cycle of the sine function.

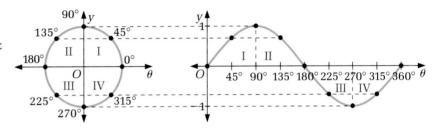

The domain of the sine function is any angle θ, positive or negative. The range of $y = \sin \theta$ is $-1 \le y \le 1$.

TECHNOLOGY NOTE

Set your calculator in degree mode. When you enter the sine function on your graphics calculator, the screen may show sin x, not sin θ.

Sample 1

a. Graph the function $y = \sin \theta$.

b. Describe the graph of $y = \sin \theta$.

Sample Response

a.

The cycle repeats every 360°.

b. The graph is periodic. The period is 360°.

The amplitude is 1.

The graph crosses the θ-axis when θ is a multiple of 180°. The θ-intercepts are . . . , $-360°$, $-180°$, 0°, 180°, 360°, ...

The y-intercept is 0.

The **cosine function**, $y = \cos \theta$, measures the horizontal position of an object moving around a unit circle.

Talk it Over

7. Suppose an object is moving around a unit circle in a counterclockwise direction as shown. Explain why each statement describes the object's horizontal position as it moves through each of the four quadrants.

I. decreasing from 1 to 0   **II.** decreasing from 0 to -1

III. increasing from -1 to 0   **IV.** increasing from 0 to 1

   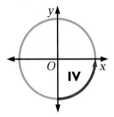

8. Use your answers to question 7 to sketch a graph of the cosine function for $0° \leq \theta \leq 360°$.

GRAPHS OF SINE AND COSINE

For an object moving counterclockwise (forward) or clockwise (backward) around a unit circle, the sine function gives the **vertical** position of the object.

$$y = \sin \theta$$

⟵ The amplitude is 1. ⟶

⟵ The period is 360°. ⟶

For an object moving counterclockwise (forward) or clockwise (backward) around a unit circle, the cosine function gives the **horizontal** position of the object.

$$y = \cos \theta$$

Because the cosine graph can be obtained from the sine graph through a horizontal translation, both graphs and all similarly-shaped graphs produced by transforming the sine or cosine graph can be called *sine waves*.

Writing How is the graph of a cosine function like the graph of a sine function? How are they different?

Sample Response

The graph of the cosine function is a 90° horizontal translation of the graph of the sine function. The two functions have the same period, range, and amplitude, but the intercepts of the two graphs are different. The y-intercept of the sine function is 0, but the y-intercept of the cosine function is 1.

Both graphs are periodic functions that have a period of 360° and an amplitude of 1. The domain of each function is all real angles. The range of each function is $-1 \leq y \leq 1$.

The graph of the sine function crosses the θ-axis when θ is a multiple of 180°. The graph of the cosine function crosses the θ-axis when θ is an odd multiple of 90°.

Look Back

Which function, *sine* or *cosine*, gives the horizontal position of an object moving around a unit circle? Which function gives the vertical position?

10-3 Exercises and Problems

1. **Reading** What is a unit circle? How is a unit circle related to the sine and cosine functions?

Tell whether each statement describes a characteristic of the *sine function*, the *cosine function*, *both functions*, or *neither function*.

2. The function has a period of 360°.

3. The function has an amplitude of 2.

4. The *y*-intercept is 1.

5. The *y*-intercept is 0.

6. The range of the function is $-1 \leq y \leq 1$.

7. The horizontal intercepts occur only at multiples of 90°.

8. The function decreases in the interval $0° \leq \theta \leq 90°$.

9. The function increases in the interval $0° \leq \theta \leq 90°$.

Water power During the Industrial Revolution, water wheels provided power to run factories. Suppose a water wheel is rotating at the rate of 3 revolutions per minute (rev/min). A bucket's height above the water level is a function of the amount of time the wheel has turned. Its graph is a sine wave.

Use the information above for Exercises 10–14.

10. Choose the most reasonable graph for the height of bucket P at t seconds. Explain.

A.   B.   C.

11. What is the amplitude of the function?

12. Describe an interval in which the height of the bucket changes quickly.

13. The height of the bucket at 23 s is the same as its height at 3 s. Why? When is the next time the height will be the same as the height at 3 s?

14. Suppose the speed of the water flowing in the river caused the wheel to turn at 4 rev/min. How would the graph change?

15. **a.** TECHNOLOGY Use a graphics calculator or graphing software to graph the function $y = \sin \theta$ for $-360° \leq \theta \leq 360°$. How many cycles does the graph show?

   b. For what values of θ is $\sin \theta = 0.5$?

   c. What is the maximum value of the function? What is the minimum value of the function? What values of θ give the maximum value of the function? the minimum value of the function?

   d. In what intervals are the values of the function positive? negative?

   e. When are the values of the function increasing? When are they decreasing?

16. Repeat Exercise 15 for the function $y = \cos \theta$.

17. **a.** What is the relationship between $\sin 45°$ and $\sin (-45°)$? $\sin 210°$ and $\sin (-210°)$? $\sin 270°$ and $\sin (-270°)$?

   b. Make a conjecture based on any pattern you see in your answers to part (a).

In factories during the Industrial Revolution, a spinning water wheel caused gears to turn. The gears operated pulleys and belts throughout the mill, which gave power to the machines.

18. **Group Activity** Work with another student.

TECHNOLOGY You will each need a graphics calculator or graphing software. Each of you should set your calculator to degree mode and parametric mode and use the following window:

$$0 \le t \le 360, \ t\text{-step} = 10 \qquad -1.25 \le y \le 1.25, \ y\text{-scale} = 0.5$$

a. One student should graph the unit circle and the other should graph the sine function. Adjust your viewing window to fit the x-values appropriate for your graph.

unit circle	sine function
$x_1 = \cos t$	$x_1 = t$
$y_1 = \sin t$	$y_1 = \sin t$
$-1.88 \le x \le 1.88, \ x\text{-scale} = 0.5$	$0 \le x \le 360, \ x\text{-scale} = 30$

b. Trace along each graph for various values of t. Select a common t-value and compare where the cursor is on each graph. What does the y-value represent on each graph? What does the x-value represent on each graph?

c. **Writing** Compare where the cursor is on each graph for other values of t. How is the position of the cursor on the graph of the unit circle related to the position of the cursor on the sine function?

19. Repeat Exercise 18 using the cosine function instead of the sine function. The person who graphed the unit circle in Exercise 18 should graph the cosine function.

20. Sketch a graph of a periodic graph that has an amplitude of 2 and a period of 4. *(Section 10-2)*

For Exercises 21–24, use the functions $f(x) = x^2$, $g(x) = \frac{x}{2}$, and $h(x) = \sqrt{x} - 1$. Find each function rule or value. *(Section 2-8)*

21. $(f \circ g)(x)$
22. $(h \circ f)(x)$
23. $(f \circ g)(-8)$
24. $(g \circ h)(25)$

Without using graphing technology, sketch the graph of each function. *(Section 9-2)*

25. $y + 2 = (x - 4)^2$
26. $y = \sqrt{x + 3}$
27. $y - 1 = x^3$

 Working on the Unit Project

28. Make a list of all the types of functions you know how to graph. Include the list and examples of each type of graph in your scrapbook.

Transforming Sine and Cosine Graphs

WAVES IN MOTION

Recognize and understand
characteristics of the graphs
of sine functions and cosine
functions that are
transformed.

EXPLORATION

*(What) happens when sine and cosine graphs
are transformed?*

- **Materials: graphics calculators or graphing software**
- **Work with another student.**

Set your calculator in degree mode.
Use this viewing window:
$-360 \le x \le 360$, x-scale = 90
$-3.6 \le y \le 3.6$, y-scale = 0.5

(1) Graph $y = \sin \theta$. What is the amplitude? the period? the
frequency? What is the y-intercept of the graph?

(2) Graph each equation on the same screen as $y = \sin \theta$.
(Have only two graphs on screen.) How is each graph like
the graph of $y = \sin \theta$? How is each graph different?

  a. $y = 2 \sin \theta$ **b.** $y = \sin 2\theta$

  c. $y = \sin (\theta - 45°)$ **d.** $y = \sin \theta + 1$

(3) Use your answers from step 2 to sketch each graph in parts
(a)−(h). To check your prediction, graph each function.
How is each graph like the graph of $y = \sin \theta$? How is each
graph different?

  a. $y = 0.5 \sin \theta$ **b.** $y = -\sin \theta$

  c. $y = \sin 3\theta$ **d.** $y = \sin (-\theta)$

  e. $y = \sin (\theta - 60°)$ **f.** $y = \sin (\theta + 90°)$

  g. $y = \sin \theta + 2$ **h.** $y = \sin \theta - 1.5$

(4) For each equation, write a general rule to tell the effect of
A, B, C, or D on the graph of $y = \sin \theta$.

  a. $y = A \sin \theta$ **b.** $y = \sin B\theta$

  c. $y = \sin (\theta - C)$ **d.** $y = \sin \theta + D$

(5) Use your rules from step 4 to tell what transformation(s) of
the graph of $y = \sin \theta$ will give you the graph of each equation in parts (a)−(d). Then sketch each graph. Graph each
equation using technology to check your sketch.

  a. $y = 4 \sin 2\theta$ **b.** $y = 0.5 \sin (\theta - 30°)$

  c. $y = \sin 0.75(\theta + 45°)$ **d.** $y = \sin (\theta + 180°) - 1.5$

(6) For each graph sketched in step 5, find the amplitude, the
frequency, and the period.

TRANSFORMATIONS OF THE SINE GRAPH

The graph of a function of the form $y = A \sin B(\theta - C) + D$ differs from the graph of $y = \sin \theta$ in the following ways.

➤ The graph is vertically stretched or shrunk by a factor of $|A|$. If $A < 0$, there is a reflection over the θ-axis.

➤ The graph is horizontally stretched or shrunk by a factor of $\frac{1}{|B|}$. The period is $\frac{360°}{|B|}$. If $B < 0$, there is a reflection over the y-axis.

➤ The graph is translated horizontally C units.

➤ The graph is translated vertically D units.

Example
$y = 3 \sin 2(\theta - 45°) + 8$

➤ **Now you are ready for:**
Exs. 1–21 on pp. 563–564

In Exercises 2–5, you will verify that the same properties apply to the graph of the cosine function.

Sample 1

Without using graphing technology, sketch the graph of $y = -0.25 \cos 2(\theta - 90°) - 1$.

Sample Response

Sketch the graph of the parent function, $y = \cos \theta$.

The equation has the form $y = A \cos B(\theta - C) + D$.

The value of A is -0.25. The amplitude is 0.25. $A < 0$, so the graph is reflected over the θ-axis.

The value of B is 2. The period of the graph is $\frac{1}{2} \cdot 360° = 180°$.

The value of C is 90°. The graph is translated 90° to the right.

The value of D is -1. The graph is translated 1 unit down.

10-4 Transforming Sine and Cosine Graphs

561

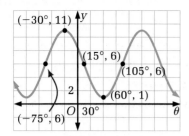

Write an equation for the graph shown.

Sample Response

The values of A, B, and D are the same for a sine function or a cosine function. Find these values first.

Step 1 Find the amplitude, A.

$$A = \frac{\text{maximum value} - \text{minimum value}}{2}$$

$$= \frac{11 - 1}{2}$$

$$= 5$$

Step 2 Find the period, $\frac{360°}{B}$, and solve for B.

$$\text{period} = \frac{360°}{B} \quad \longleftarrow \quad \begin{array}{l}\text{The period is}\\ 105° - (-75°) = 180°.\end{array}$$

$$180° = \frac{360°}{B} \quad \longleftarrow \quad \text{Solve for B.}$$

$$B = \frac{360°}{180°}$$

$$= 2$$

Step 3 Find the axis, or the vertical translation, D.

$$D = \frac{\text{maximum value} + \text{minimum value}}{2}$$

$$= \frac{11 + 1}{2}$$

$$= 6$$

Step 4 Write an equation.

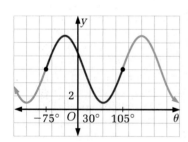

Method ❶ Use a sine function.

$$y = A \sin B(\theta - C) + D$$

$$= 5 \sin 2(\theta - C) + 6 \quad \longleftarrow \quad \begin{array}{l}\text{Substitute 5 for A,}\\ \text{2 for B, and 6 for D.}\end{array}$$

$$= 5 \sin 2(\theta + 75°) + 6 \quad \longleftarrow \quad \begin{array}{l}\text{The sine graph is shifted}\\ \text{left 75°, so C} = -75°.\end{array}$$

An equation of the graph is $y = 5 \sin 2(\theta + 75°) + 6$.

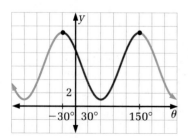

Method ❷ Use a cosine function.

$$y = A \cos B(\theta - C) + D$$

$$= 5 \cos 2(\theta - C) + 6 \quad \longleftarrow \quad \begin{array}{l}\text{Substitute 5 for A,}\\ \text{2 for B, and 6 for D.}\end{array}$$

$$= 5 \cos 2(\theta + 30°) + 6 \quad \longleftarrow \quad \begin{array}{l}\text{The cosine graph is shifted}\\ \text{left 30°, C} = -30°.\end{array}$$

An equation of the graph is $y = 5 \cos 2(\theta + 30°) + 6$.

······► Now you are ready for:
Exs. 22–48 on pp. 564–567

Look Back ◄──────────────

Consider the function $y = A \cos B(\theta - C) + D$. Tell how its graph is different from the graph of $y = \cos \theta$.

10-4 Exercises and Problems

1. **Reading** On the graph of $y = A \sin B(\theta - C) + D$, what do the values of A, B, C, and D represent?

▓ TECHNOLOGY **Use a graphics calculator or graphing software. Graph each equation. Then tell how each graph is different from the graph of $y = \cos \theta$.**

2. $y = \cos \theta - 3$ 3. $y = \cos 2\theta$ 4. $y = -2 \cos \theta$ 5. $y = \cos (\theta + 30°)$

Choose the letter of the graph that best matches each equation.

6. $y = 4 \cos \theta$ 7. $y = 2 \sin \theta$ 8. $y = 2 \sin 2\theta$

9. $y = 0.25 \cos \theta - 1$ 10. $y = 2 \cos (\theta - 45°)$ 11. $y = \sin 2\theta + 1$

A.   B.   C.

D.   E.   F.

For each equation:

a. Find the amplitude, the period, and the frequency of its graph.

b. Sketch the graph without using graphing technology.

12. $y = \cos 2\theta$ 13. $y = 3 \sin \theta$ 14. $y = -\cos \theta + 3$

15. $y = \sin (\theta + 60°)$ 16. $y = 0.5 \cos \theta - 2$ 17. $y = \sin 2(\theta - 45°)$

18. **Writing** How is the graph of $y = \sin (\theta - 90°)$ like the graph of $y = \sin (\theta + 90°)$? How is it different?

19. **Health** The graph shows the maximum flow of air out of the lungs of a person with asthma and a person without asthma.

    a. In what ways are the graphs similar?

    b. In what ways are the graphs different?

    c. How is the graph of the maximum air flow for the asthmatic patient a transformation of the graph for the non-asthmatic patient?

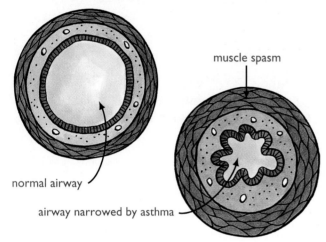

20. Suppose $f(\theta) = \sin \theta$. Rewrite each equation in the general form $\dfrac{y - h}{a} = f\left(\dfrac{\theta - k}{b}\right)$. Then tell which transformations are applied to the graph of f to obtain the graph of each equation.

    a. $y = 2 \sin \theta + 1$ b. $y = \sin 3(\theta + 45°)$ c. $y = \sin 4\theta - 3$ d. $y = 0.5 \sin (\theta - 60°)$

21. **Writing** Tell how the values of A, B, C, and D in the equation $y = A \sin B(\theta - C) + D$ compare to the values of a, b, h, and k in the equation $\dfrac{y - h}{a} = f\left(\dfrac{x - k}{b}\right)$.

For each equation:

a. Find the amplitude, the period, and the frequency of its graph.

b. Sketch the graph without using graphing technology.

22. $y = 3 \sin 4\theta - 2$

23. $y = \cos 2(\theta - 75°) + 1$

24. $y = 0.3 \cos 0.5(\theta - 45°)$

25. $y = -2 \sin 0.25(\theta + 30°) + 3$

Choose the letter of the graph that best matches each equation.

26. $y = 0.5 \cos (\theta - 90°) - 2$ 27. $y = 2 \sin 0.5(\theta - 60°) - 2$ 28. $y = -\cos 2(\theta + 45°) - 1$

A.

B.

C.

For Exercises 29 and 30, the graph of a function is described. Write an equation for each function. Then sketch the graph.

29. The graph is a cosine function with amplitude = 3, period = 45°, and a horizontal translation 30° to the left.

30. The graph is a sine function with amplitude = 1, period = 60°, and a vertical translation 1.5 units up.

Write an equation for each graph.

31.

32.

33.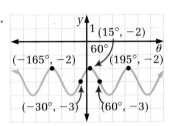

For a particular location on Earth, the number of hours of daylight in a 24-hour period depends on the time of year. There are always 12 hours of daylight at the equator.

The graph below shows the number of hours of daylight for two different locations north of the equator. Locations south of the equator experience the same pattern six months later than locations in the Northern Hemisphere.

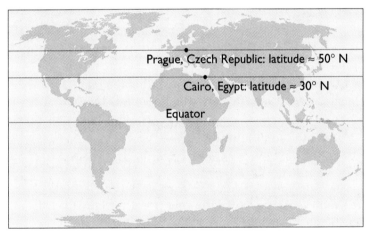

Prague, Czech Republic: latitude ≈ 50° N

Cairo, Egypt: latitude ≈ 30° N

Equator

34. a. What axis do the two graphs have in common? What do you think this axis represents in this situation? Why?

b. What do the points represent where the two graphs cross their common axis?

35. The function $y = 4 \sin\left(\dfrac{360}{365}(t - 80)\right)^{\circ} + 12$ describes the number of hours of daylight as a function of t, the day of the year, for Prague. Use this function to write a function for the number of hours of daylight for Cairo.

36. a. Describe two ways that you can transform the graphs to show the number of hours of daylight for regions in the Southern Hemisphere.

b. Write a function for the number of hours of daylight for Pôrto Alegre, Brazil, which has a latitude of about 30°S.

The Canterbury Tales were written by Geoffrey Chaucer in the late fourteenth century. The following passage is from the prologue to *The Parson's Tale.*

When the Manciple's tale was wholly ended,
From the south line the broad sun had decended
So low that it appeared now, to my sight,
Not more than twenty-nine degrees in height.
And it was four o-clock, as I should guess,
For eleven feet, or somewhat more or less,
My shadow at that time appeared to be,
Of such feet as, proportioned equally,
Would fix my height at six, by calculation.
And the moon also, in his exaltation,
Libra I mean, continued to ascend,
As we were entering a hamlet's end.

37. **a.** According to the passage, how tall is the man? How long is his shadow? How high above the horizon is the sun?

    b. Use trigonometry and the man's estimates of his shadow and height to verify the sun's altitude.

The function $y = 19.3 \sin\left(\frac{360}{365}(t - 71)\right)^\circ + 17.6$ can be used to find the height of the sun, in degrees, at 4:00 P.M. each day at the latitude of Canterbury, where t represents the day of the year ($t = 1$ for January 1, $t = 2$ for January 2, $\ldots t = 365$ for December 31). Use this information to answer Exercises 38–40.

38. Why is the period of the function 365?

39. An *equinox* occurs when the number of hours of daylight equals the number of hours without daylight. In 1387 when scholars think Chaucer began writing *The Canterbury Tales*, the spring equinox occurred on March 12th.

    a. If January 1 is the first day of the year, what day of the year is March 12th?

    b. How is this value used in the equation? Why?

40. **a.** TECHNOLOGY Graph the function $y = 19.3 \sin\left(\frac{360}{365}(t - 71)\right)^\circ + 17.6$.

    On what days of the year is the height of the sun about 29° at 4:00 P.M.?

    b. **Research** Read the prologue to *The Canterbury Tales*. Which of your answers from part (a) represents the date referred to in the prologue to *The Parson's Tale*? Why?

41 TECHNOLOGY Graph each of the equations found in Sample 2 on page 562 to verify that they represent the same graph.

42. Suppose you are on a Ferris wheel that completes 2.5 revolutions per minute. The function $h = 25 \sin \theta + 5$ can be used to model your height, in feet, above the ground as a function of the angle the wheel has turned.

a. How many degrees are in 1 revolution?

b. Convert 2.5 revolutions per minute to degrees per second.

c. Write an equation for the angle, θ, the wheel has turned as a function of t, the amount of time the wheel has turned.

d. In part (c), you found an equation for θ as a function of t. The equation $h = 25 \sin \theta + 5$ gives the height as a function of θ. Use these equations and composition of functions to write an equation for the height as a function of time.

Ongoing ASSESSMENT

43. **Group Activity** Work with a partner. You will each need a graphics calculator or graphing technology.

a. Enter a function of the form $y = A \sin B(x - C) + D$ or the form $y = A \cos B(x - C) + D$ on your calculator. Graph the function in an appropriate window. Trade calculators with your partner.

b. Trace along the graph you receive to determine its properties. Write an equation for the graph.

c. Does your equation match the one your partner entered? Graph your equation on the same screen as the original to see if the graphs match.

d. Repeat parts (a)–(c) using other graphs.

Review PREVIEW

44. Graph the function $y = \sin \theta$ for $-360° \le \theta \le 360°$. For what values of θ is $\sin \theta \approx 0.86$? *(Section 10-3)*

Tell whether each series appears to have a sum. If it does, give its value.
(Section 4-7)

45. $6 + 3.5 + 1 + (-1.5) + \cdots$

46. $\displaystyle\sum_{n=1}^{\infty} (-0.99)^{n-1}$

47. A wheel is turning at 5 revolutions per minute. How many degrees will a point on the wheel rotate in 1 min? in 1 s? *(Section 10-3)*

Working on the Unit Project

48. Write a function for the number of hours of daylight at a location on this map. Graph your function. Put it in your scrapbook. Include pictures and describe the location.

Modeling with Sine and Cosine

Reinventing The Wheel

Focus

Use sine and cosine functions to model periodic situations.

25 ft

2 rev/min

You start here.

5 ft

Transformations of the sine graph and the cosine graph can be used to model many periodic situations, such as the Ferris wheel ride discussed in Section 10-3.

Sample 1

Find an equation that models your height above the ground as you ride on a Ferris wheel.

Sample Response

Step 1 Choose the sine function or the cosine function.

Since you know that you are halfway between the minimum height and the maximum height at time $t = 0$, choose the sine function. The general model is $h(t) = A \sin B(t - C) + D$ where h is the height, in feet, and t is the time, in seconds, since starting.

The Sine Graph

Step 2 Find A, the amplitude.

$$A = \frac{\text{maximum value} - \text{minimum value}}{2}$$

$$= \frac{55 - 5}{2} \qquad \longleftarrow \quad \begin{array}{l}\text{maximum value} = \text{the diameter of the wheel} + \text{the}\\ \text{distance from the bottom of the wheel to the ground} = 55\end{array}$$

$$= 25$$

Step 3 Find B, the number of degrees the wheel turns each second.

Convert revolutions per minute to degrees per second.

$$2 \text{ rev/min} = \frac{2 \text{ revolutions}}{1 \text{ min}} \cdot \frac{360°}{1 \text{ revolution}} \cdot \frac{1 \text{ min}}{60 \text{ s}}$$

$$= \frac{720°}{60 \text{ s}}$$

$$= 12°/s$$

$$B = 12$$

Step 4 Find C, the horizontal translation.

You start halfway between the maximum and minimum heights, so there is no horizontal translation. $C = 0$

> **BY THE WAY...**
>
> A Ferris wheel operator places riders around the wheel so that the weight is distributed symmetrically. The order of loading may vary, depending on the operator's estimation of the size of the load.

Step 5 Find D, the vertical translation.

$$D = \frac{\text{maximum value} + \text{minimum value}}{2}$$

$$= \frac{55 + 5}{2}$$

$$= 30$$

Step 6 Substitute the values of A, B, C, and D into the general model.

An equation that models your height, in feet, above the ground after t seconds is $h(t) = 25 \sin (12t)° + 30$.

Height Curve

Height (feet)

10

O 15 t

Time (seconds)

•····▶ Now you are ready for:
Exs. 1–8 on p. 572

Talk it Over

1. What is your height above the ground after riding the Ferris wheel for each given time?

   a. 90 s   **b.** 2.5 min   **c.** 200 s

2. Suppose you chose the cosine function. How does this change the equation that models your height?

Time	Altitude
midnight	10.23°
1:00 A.M.	8.02°
2:00 A.M.	6.75°
3:00 A.M.	6.53°
4:00 A.M.	7.35°
5:00 A.M.	9.17°
6:00 A.M.	11.88°
7:00 A.M.	15.32°
8:00 A.M.	19.30°
9:00 A.M.	23.58°
10:00 A.M.	27.93°
11:00 A.M.	32.07°
noon	35.65°
1:00 P.M.	38.40°
2:00 P.M.	40.02°
3:00 P.M.	40.32°
4:00 P.M.	39.25°
5:00 P.M.	36.97°
6:00 P.M.	33.70°
7:00 P.M.	29.77°
8:00 P.M.	25.48°
9:00 P.M.	21.13°
10:00 P.M.	16.98°
11:00 P.M.	13.28°

Sample 2

In northern latitudes around the beginning of summer (June 21), there are days when the sun never sets. A region where this occurs is called "the land of the midnight sun."

a. Graph the data provided for the altitude (angle above the horizon) of the sun in Arctic Bay, Northwest Territories, Canada, for June 23, 1994. What parent function does the graph suggest?

b. Find an equation that models the altitude of the sun on this day.

c. Graph the equation and compare it to your graph for part (a).

Continued on next page.

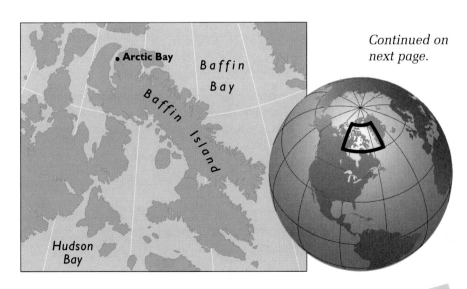

• **Arctic Bay**

Baffin Bay

Baffin Island

Hudson Bay

Time-lapse photo of the midnight sun in Norway

Sample Response

a.

The Sun in Arctic Bay on 6/23/94

(Graph: x-axis "Time (hours since midnight)" from 0 to 22; y-axis "Altitude" from 0° to 50°)

The graph looks like a sine wave. The maximum altitude is 40.32°, and the minimum altitude is 6.53°. The period is 24 h.

b. Step 1 Choose the sine function or the cosine function.

> The time of the maximum altitude is known, so choose the cosine function. The general model is $h(t) = A \cos B(t - C) + D$, where h is the sun's altitude in degrees, and t is the time, in hours, since midnight.

Step 2 Find A, the amplitude.

$$A = \frac{\text{maximum value} - \text{minimum value}}{2}$$

$$= \frac{40.32 - 6.53}{2}$$

$$\approx 16.90$$

Step 3 Find B, the factor that relates the period of the cosine function to the period of the altitude function.

$$1 \text{ cycle in } 24 \text{ hours} = \frac{360°}{24 \text{ h}}$$

$$= 15°/\text{h} = 15t° \text{ in } t \text{ hours}$$

$$B = 15$$

Step 4 Find C, the horizontal translation.

The maximum occurs at 3 P.M., or 15 h after midnight. $C = 15$

Step 5 Find D, the vertical translation.

$$D = \frac{\text{maximum value} + \text{minimum value}}{2}$$

$$= \frac{40.32 + 6.53}{2}$$

$$\approx 23.43$$

Step 6 Substitute the values of A, B, C, and D into the general model.

An equation that models the altitude, in degrees, of the sun in Arctic Bay on June 23, 1994, as a function of the number of hours after midnight is $h(t) = 16.90 \cos 15(t - 15)° + 23.43$.

c. The model fits the data well.

The Sun in Arctic Bay on 6/23/94

— model
☀ data

Talk it Over

3. Suppose you use the sine function as the parent graph for this model. What is the value of C?

4. Sketch the graph of the altitude of the sun when sunrise is at 6:00 A.M., the sun's altitude reaches a maximum of 60° at noon, and there are 12 hours of daylight. What happens to the graph when the sun sets?

······▶ **Now you are ready for:**
Exs. 9–22 on pp. 573–575

Look Back ◀───────

Describe the process for fitting a sine wave to data.

10-5 Exercises and Problems

1. **Reading** Explain step 3 of Sample 1.

For Exercises 2 and 3, use $h(t) = 25 \sin (12t) + 30$.

2. Find your height at each given time after the Ferris wheel starts.

   a. 10 s   **b.** 25 s   **c.** 100 s

3. **a.** Graph the equation.

   b. At what times will you be back at your starting position?

   c. Which points on the graph do these times correspond to?

For Exercises 4–6, change the dimensions of the Ferris wheel in Sample 1 as indicated.

a. How does the graph change?

b. What is the new equation?

4. The radius of the Ferris wheel is 17.5 ft.

5. The bottom of the Ferris wheel is 4 ft off the ground.

6. The Ferris wheel makes 5 revolutions in 2 min.

7. **Physics** A weight attached to a spring is pulled down so that it is 10 cm from the floor and is released so that it bounces up and down. When the effects of friction and gravity are ignored, its height can be modeled by a sine function of the time since it started bouncing. The weight reaches its first maximum height of 50 cm at 1.5 s.

   a. Write an equation for the height, in centimeters, of the weight as a function of time, in seconds.

   b. Graph the equation from part (a).

   c. When is the weight moving up fastest?

   d. When is it moving down fastest?

   e. At what times is the weight changing direction?

8. High and low tides for Buenos Aires, Argentina, on February 17, 1993, are shown:

   a. Sketch a graph of the function. Assume that the water height can be modeled by a sine function.

   b. Find an equation for the height of the water as a function of the number of hours after midnight.

   c. Predict the time and height of the next high tide.

   d. **Research** Why do tides behave like sine waves? Why are they not exactly sine waves?

Tide	Time	Height
High	4:09 A.M.	118 cm
Low	10:52 A.M.	57 cm

Thomas Jefferson recorded the temperatures at Monticello, his home near Charlottesville, Virginia, from 1810 to 1816. During this time Jefferson was experimenting with new farming techniques and new crops. (*Note:* Jefferson mistakenly switched the "max." and "min." listings.)

Jefferson began designing Monticello in 1768 at the age of 24.

	1810.			1811.			1812.			1813.			1814.			1815.			1816.			mean of every month
	min.	mean	max	min.	mean	max.	min.	mean	max.	min.	mean	max.	min.	mean	max	min.	mean	max	min.	mean	max.	
Jan.	5½	38	66	20	39	68	5½	34	53	13	35	59	16½	36	55	8½	35	60	16	34	51	36
Feb.	12	43	73				21.	40	75		38	65	14	42	65	16	36	57	15½	41	62	40
Mar.	20	41	61	28	44	78	31½	46	70	28	48	71	13½	43	73	31	54	80	25	48	75	46
April	42	55	81	36	58	86	31	56	86	40	59	80	35	59	82	41	60	82	30	49	71	56.5
May	43	64	88	46	62	79	39	60.86		46	62	81	47	65	91	37	58	77	43	60	79	61.5
June	53	70	87	58	73	89	58	74	92½	54	75	93	57	69	87	54	71	88	51	70	86	72
July	60	75	88	60	76	89½	57	75	91	61	75	94½	60	74	89	63	77	89	51	71	86	75
Aug.	55		90	59	75	85	61	71	87	62	74	92	56	75	88	58	72	84	51	73	90	73
Sep.	50	70	81	50	67	81	47		75	54	69	83	52	70	89	45	61	82	54	63	90½	67
Oct.	32	57	82	35	62	65	39	55	80	32	53	70	37	58	83	38½	59	76	37	57	73	57
Nov.	27	44	69	32	46	62	10	43	76	20	48	71	23	47	71	20	46	70	24	46	71	45.5
Dec.	14	32	62	20	38	49	13	35	63	10	37	53	18	38	59	12	36	57	23	43	69	37.
mean of each year		660 / 55			63 / 50.			66 / 55.			673 / 56			676 / 56½			663 / 55½			66 / 54½		55¼

mean of 7 years

9. Graph the mean monthly temperatures in the last column of Jefferson's chart using a number for the month of the year (January = 1, February = 2, and so on).

10. **a.** Find an equation that models the temperature at Monticello as a function of time.

b. Graph your equation from part (a).

c. According to your equation, what was the mean temperature in May? Does this agree with the recorded temperatures?

11. Jefferson comments that many people believed "that the degrees of both cold & heat are moderated" since the country was settled.

a. How would a moderation in temperature affect the graph?

b. Graph these monthly mean temperatures in Charlottesville, Virginia, for 1931 to 1960.

It is a common opinion that the climates of the several states of our union have undergone a sensible change since the dates of their first settlements; that the degrees both of cold & heat are moderated.

Jan.	Feb.	Mar.	Apr.	May	June	July	Aug.	Sept.	Oct.	Nov.	Dec.
37.2	38.4	45.3	56.6	66.3	73.7	77.3	76.0	69.9	59.5	48.4	38.7

c. What kind of change appears to have occurred in the mean temperatures for this area of Virginia since Jefferson's time?

12. Earth Science In 1815, the Indonesian volcano Tambora erupted. The volcanic ash thrown into the atmosphere from this eruption may have caused unusually cold weather in many places in 1816.

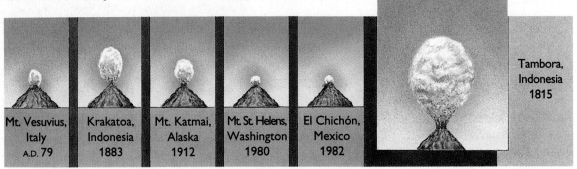

Graph Monticello's mean temperatures in 1816. Compare this graph to your graph of mean temperatures in Exercise 9 or 10. Does the eruption seem to have affected the observed temperatures?

A pictorial comparison of the amounts of ash from six major volcanic eruptions

13. a. Open-ended Find an equation that models the data in the graph. Let t be the number of months since January 1992.

Residential and Commercial Electricity Use in the United States from January 1992 to June 1994

Months

b. Graph your equation. Is it a good model?

c. Writing How is electricity use related to temperature? Explain why a mathematical model cannot predict the exact amount of electricity used.

Ongoing **ASSESSMENT**

14. Radio stations broadcast in one of two ways: AM, which means amplitude modulation, or FM, which means frequency modulation.

a. Which of these graphs represents AM? Which represents FM?

i.

ii.

b. Writing Can either of these waves be modeled with a sine wave? Explain.

**Number of Women Employed in the
United States Who Are at Least 20 Years Old**

15. Fit a linear model to this data.
(Section 6-4)

Year	1989	1990	1991	1992
Number Employed	49,745,000	50,455,000	50,535,000	51,180,000

16. You and a friend agree to meet for lunch between 12:10 P.M. and 12:20 P.M. You decide to wait 5 min for each other before sitting with someone else. What is the probability that you will meet? *(Section 7-3)*

For Exercises 17–20, tell whether each shape has *vertical reflection symmetry, horizontal reflection symmetry,* or *180° rotational symmetry.*
(Toolbox Skill 39)

17.

18.

19.

20.

 Working on the Unit Project

21. Katherine's group gathered data on the number of cars passing through an intersection at different times during the day.

  a. What function do you think best models the data? Why?

  b. Write an equation to model the data. Graph your equation and the data on the same set of axes. How accurate is your model?

22. Include your answers to parts (a)–(e) in your scrapbook.

  a. **Research** Think of a situation that can be modeled by a sine or cosine function. Gather any data you need to develop a model. Remember to include the source of your data or to describe the methods you used to gather data.

  b. Make a graph of your data. Label each axis.

  c. Write an equation to model your data.

  d. Graph the equation you wrote in part (c) on the same set of axes as the data. How well does your model fit the data? What are some reasons why the data may not fit the model for all points?

  e. **Writing** Do you think your model can be used to make accurate predictions about the future of the situation? Why or why not?

Daily Traffic through an Intersection

1. **Writing** When $0° \leq \theta \leq 360°$, for which values of θ is $\sin \theta > \cos \theta$? Explain your reasoning.

2. Compare the rates of growth in the first quadrant of $y = 5x$, $y = x^5$, and $y = 5^x$.   **10-1**

3. Draw a periodic graph with period 2, amplitude 3, and axis at $y = 2$.   **10-2**

Tell whether each statement is true for the *sine function*, the *cosine function*, *both functions*, or *neither function*.   **10-3**

4. The amplitude is 1.

5. The y-intercept is 1.

6. The domain of the function is all angles.

7. The function increases in the interval $0° \leq \theta \leq 90°$.

For each graph, find the period, the amplitude, and the frequency. Then write an equation for each graph.   **10-4**

8.

9.

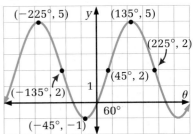

10. The graph of a transformed cosine function has period $180°$, amplitude 2, and a vertical translation 3 units down. Without using graphing technology, make a sketch of the graph.

11. Use the table to answer parts (a)–(c).   **10-5**

Ice Cream Production in the United States (millions of gallons)											
	Jan.	Feb.	Mar.	Apr.	May	June	July	Aug.	Sept.	Oct.	Nov.	Dec.
1991	56.4	60.8	72.8	73.7	81.8	91.5	88.1	83.7	72.9	68.0	57.2	58.0
1992	58.7	62.3	77.1	78.9	79.7	89.7	87.4	79.2	73.8	64.6	58.3	58.3
1993	53.7	64.3	76.7	75.9	78.0	90.3	89.7	84.4	74.2	62.8	57.9	58.3

a. Graph the mean monthly ice cream production in the United States for 1991–1993. What type of function do you think best models the data? Why?

b. Write an equation to model the data.

c. Graph your equation and the data on the same set of axes. How accurate is your model? What are some reasons why some of the data points do not fit the model?

Patterns and Transformations

Focus
Recognize periodic
border patterns. Use
transformations to classify
and create border patterns.

FRIEZE FRAME

In many cultures people use border patterns to decorate edges of pottery, curtains, belts, and ribbons. Mathematicians have found that all border patterns fall into one of seven types. Examples of each type from various cultures are shown below.

A.

Native American

B.

Incan

C.

Zairean

D.

Chinese

E.

Egyptian

F.

Islamic

G.

Greek

Mosaic floor in Delos, Greece

Talk it Over

1. Explain why these patterns are periodic.

2. List all the border patterns that have each type of symmetry.

   a. vertical reflection symmetry

   b. horizontal reflection symmetry

   c. 180° rotational symmetry

Student Resources Toolbox
p. 663 *Transformations*

This table shows the seven types of border patterns and how each is constructed. To classify a border pattern by type, you have to identify all the types of symmetry it has.

The Seven Types of Border Patterns		
Symmetry Type	**How to Construct**	**Example**
Translation	Translate an asymmetric figure repeatedly.	
Vertical reflection	Reflect an asymmetric figure over a vertical line. Translate the pair repeatedly.	
Horizontal reflection	Reflect an asymmetric figure over a horizontal line. Translate the pair repeatedly.	
Glide reflection	Reflect an asymmetric figure over a horizontal line, then translate the image to the next space. Translate the pair repeatedly.	
Horizontal and vertical reflection	Reflect an asymmetric figure over a horizontal line, then reflect the pair over a vertical line. Translate all four repeatedly.	
180° rotation	Rotate an asymmetric figure 180° into the next space. Translate the pair repeatedly.	
180° rotation and vertical reflection	Rotate an asymmetric figure 180°, then reflect the pair over a vertical line. Translate all four repeatedly.	

You can use a tree diagram to classify border patterns by the type(s) of symmetry they have. Every border pattern has translational symmetry, so begin by looking for a vertical reflection.

┈┈▶ Now you are ready for:
Exs. 1–4 on p. 580

Sample 1

Classify this border pattern by its symmetry.

Sample Response

Is there vertical reflection?

Yes.

Is there horizontal reflection?

No.

Is there 180° rotation?

Yes.

This border pattern has 180° rotation and vertical reflection symmetry.

Sample 2

Use this asymmetric figure. Create a border pattern that has vertical reflection symmetry.

Sample Response

┈┈▶ Now you are ready for:
Exs. 5–25 on pp. 580–581

Look Back ◀

What transformations are used in creating border patterns?

1. **Reading** What one transformation is used in all types of border patterns?

2. The capital letter A is an example of a letter that has vertical reflection symmetry.

   a. Name two other capital letters that have vertical reflection symmetry.

   b. Name two capital letters that have horizontal reflection symmetry.

   c. Name two capital letters that have horizontal and vertical reflection symmetry.

   d. Name two capital letters that have 180° rotational symmetry.

3. Suppose a border pattern has both vertical and horizontal reflection symmetry. What other type of symmetry must it also have?

4. **a.** How are glide reflection symmetry and horizontal reflection symmetry alike? How are they different?

   b. **Writing** Explain why horizontal reflection is a special case of glide reflection.

Classify each border pattern by its symmetry.

5.

Native American

6.

Native American

7.

Native American

8.

Native American

9.

Native American

10.

Islamic

11. **a.** Why can a border pattern *not* have rotational symmetries other than 180°, such as 60° rotational symmetry?

   b. Why can a border pattern *not* have other lines of symmetry besides those that are parallel or perpendicular to the edges?

12. **Open-ended** Create your own asymmetric basic element. Use it to generate two different border patterns. Tell the type of symmetry that each border pattern has.

13. Find all the types of border patterns in the table on page 578 that have both 180° rotational symmetry and horizontal reflection symmetry.

Suppose the asymmetric figure used to construct a border pattern contains the letter "b." In which types of border patterns constructed with this figure will each of these letters appear?

14. d   **15.** p   **16.** q

17. Find all the types of border patterns in the table on page 578 that contain glide reflection symmetry.

18. Classify this sine wave by its symmetry.

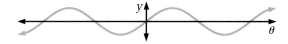

Ongoing **ASSESSMENT**

19. **Group Activity** Work with another student.
Without showing your partner your work, choose one type of symmetry and create a border pattern. Trade papers and classify your partner's border pattern by its symmetry.

Review **PREVIEW**

20. Find an equation to model the mean monthly temperatures shown in the table. *(Section 10-5)*

Mean Monthly Temperatures at Yellowstone Park, WY											
Jan.	Feb.	Mar.	Apr.	May	June	July	Aug.	Sept.	Oct.	Nov.	Dec.
18.3°	21.6°	26.9°	38.1°	46.9°	53.8°	62.9°	61.1°	52.4°	42.6°	29.1°	22.2°

21. Convert the vector $(-7, 4)$ to polar form. *(Section 8-4)*

22. Convert the vector $(5, -25°)$ to rectangular form. *(Section 8-4)*

23. Find the measures of each interior and each exterior angle of a regular hexagon. *(Section 3-4)*

Working on the Unit Project

24. Create a border design to include on the cover of your scrapbook. On the inside front cover of your scrapbook, describe the symmetry used to make the border design.

25. Make another border design and describe its symmetry. Use this design to highlight items in your scrapbook.

Periodic Tessellations

It All Fits

EXPLORATION

What do regular and semiregular tessellations look like?

- **Materials: paper cutouts of 8 of each type of regular polygon — 3-, 4-, 5-, 6-, 8-, 10-, and 12-gon — with sides that are the same length, or geometric drawing software**
- **Work in a group of four students.**

Focus
Recognize, classify, and create tessellations.

1. By placing regular polygons so their vertices touch, make a tiling — a design that covers the plane without gaps or overlaps. Your design is called a **tessellation.**

2. A **regular tessellation** is a tessellation made from only one kind of regular polygon. Which regular polygons can you use to create regular tessellations?

3. A **semiregular tessellation** is a tessellation made from two or more kinds of regular polygons arranged the same way at every vertex.

3.3.4.3.4   3.3.3.3.6

Explain how each number code describes the semiregular tessellation above it.

4. Make as many semiregular tessellations as you can that use *two* kinds of regular polygons. Draw a sketch and write a code for each tessellation.

5. Make a semiregular tessellation that uses *three* kinds of regular polygons.

6. Which polygons did you use in your semiregular tessellations? Which polygons did you *not* use?

BY THE WAY...

The word *tessellation* comes from the Latin word "tessera," a small square piece of stone used in mosaics.

Tilings have been used by many cultures to cover floors, walls, ceilings, and columns.

Detail of Moorish-style wall tile in Córdoba, Spain

Ceiling in Junagarh Fort, Bikaner Rajasthan, India

Tile dating from 1325, in Fez, Morocco

Sample 1

Use an indirect proof to show that each group of polygons cannot tessellate a plane.

a. regular pentagons

b. regular hexagons and squares

Sample Response

a. Suppose regular pentagons tessellate a plane. Let p = the number of regular pentagons that surround a vertex.

Each interior angle of a regular pentagon has a measure of 108°, so

$$108p = 360$$

$$p = 3\frac{1}{3}$$

Since p does not have an integer value, the assumption that regular pentagons tessellate a plane is false.

b. Suppose regular hexagons and squares tessellate a plane. Let h = the number of regular hexagons at each vertex and let s = the number of squares at each vertex.

The measures of the interior angles of regular hexagons and squares are 120° and 90°, so

$$120h + 90s = 360$$

Since the number of regular hexagons at each vertex, h, can be 0, 1, 2, or 3, the solutions to this equation include (0, 4), $\left(1, 2\frac{2}{3}\right)$, $\left(2, 1\frac{1}{3}\right)$, and (3, 0).

The only solutions with integer values are the first and last, which involve only squares or only regular hexagons, but not both shapes.

Since there is no combination of regular hexagons and squares that can surround a vertex, the assumption that regular hexagons and squares tessellate a plane is false.

······▶ Now you are ready for:
Exs. 1–13 on pp. 585–586

cell

cell

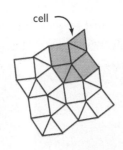

cell

A **periodic tessellation** is a tessellation that matches itself exactly when it is translated.

Every periodic tessellation has a fundamental unit, called a **cell,** that can be copied and translated to generate the pattern.

Talk it Over

1. Choose one of the regular tessellations you made in the Exploration. Is it periodic? If so, shade a cell.

2. Choose one of the semiregular tessellations you made in the Exploration. Is it periodic? If so, shade a cell.

Tessellations with Nonregular Polygons

Regular and semiregular tessellations are made from regular polygons. You can also make tessellations with nonregular polygons.

All parallelograms tessellate.   All triangles tessellate.

BY THE WAY...

The Dutch artist Maurits Cornelius Escher (1898–1972) spent much of his career creating tessellations inspired by those he admired in the Alhambra, a 14th century Moorish palace in Granada, Spain.

Talk it Over

3. Explain why the sum of the measures of the angles around each vertex is 360° in a tessellation of congruent parallelograms.

4. Explain why the sum of the measures of the angles around each vertex is 360° in a tessellation of congruent triangles.

Sample 2

Create a new tessellation by modifying a tessellation of parallelograms.

1 Start with a parallelogram.

 2 Make a change on one side and translate the change to the opposite side.

 3 Make a different change to the other pair of opposite sides.

 4 Draw details inside the cell if you wish.

······► Now you are ready for:
Exs. 14–35 on pp. 586–588

Look Back

Which of these polygons will tessellate periodically — *any triangle, any quadrilateral, any pentagon?*

10-7 Exercises and Problems

1. **Reading** How does a regular tessellation differ from a semiregular one?

Write a code for each tessellation.

2.

3.

4.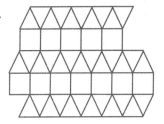

Sketch the tessellation represented by each code.

5. 3.3.3.3.3.3   6. 8.8.4   7. 6.3.6.3   8. 6.4.3.4

Use an indirect proof to show that each group of regular polygons cannot tessellate a plane.

9. regular pentagons and equilateral triangles   10. regular heptagons

11. regular decagons   12. regular octagons and equilateral triangles

13. You can prove that there are only three regular tessellations by considering the way regular polygons fit around a vertex.

The measure of each angle of a regular n-gon is $\dfrac{(n-2)180°}{n}$.

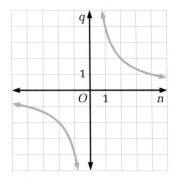

a. Explain why the equation $\dfrac{(n-2)180q}{n} = 360$ is true for all regular tessellations in which q regular n-gons surround each vertex.

b. Use algebra to show that the equation in part (a) is equivalent to the equation $(n-2)(q-2) = 4$. Explain each step.

c. A graph of $nq = 4$ is shown. How should you translate it to obtain the graph of $(n-2)(q-2) = 4$? Make a careful drawing of the translated graph.

d. Name the points on the graph of $(n-2)(q-2) = 4$ whose coordinates are positive integers. How are these points related to regular tessellations?

e. Explain how the graph of $(n-2)(q-2) = 4$ shows that there are no more than three regular tessellations.

Which region in each semiregular tessellation is *not* a cell?

14.

15.

16.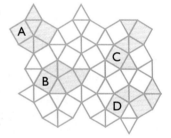

For Exercises 17–23, use this information. A *dual* is made by drawing segments that connect the centers of adjacent polygons in a regular or semiregular tessellation.

The *center of a regular polygon* is the point where the perpendicular bisectors of the sides meet.

17. The 3.3.4.3.4 semiregular tessellation and its dual are shown.

  a. Describe the polygons in the dual.

  b. Regular pentagons cannot tessellate a plane. Explain why the polygons in the dual are able to tessellate a plane.

  c. The dual is periodic. What is a cell for the dual?

Draw the dual of each regular tessellation. If the dual is periodic, shade a cell.

18.

19.

20.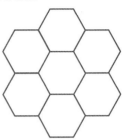

Draw each semiregular tessellation and its dual. If the dual is periodic, shade a cell.

21

22.

23.

24. **Open-ended** Draw a nonperiodic tessellation using regular polygons.

25. Any quadrilateral will tessellate a plane.

   a. Draw any quadrilateral and show how congruent copies can be placed around it to tessellate a plane.

   b. Draw a concave quadrilateral like the one shown and show how congruent copies can be placed around it to tessellate a plane.

26. **Using Manipulatives** The three types of hexagons shown tessellate a plane.

   a. Choose one of the three types of hexagons. Create an example using side lengths and angle measures that follow the rules shown for the type of hexagon you choose.

$m\angle A + m\angle B + m\angle C = 360°$ $m\angle A + m\angle B + m\angle D = 360°$ $m\angle A = m\angle C = m\angle E = 120°$

   b. Cut out at least 12 copies of your hexagon from a piece of paper. Use your copies to make a periodic tessellation. Draw a sketch of it.

   c. How many hexagons form a cell for your periodic tessellation?

27. **Open-ended** Use the method of Sample 2 to make a creative tessellation by modifying each pair of opposite sides of a parallelogram.

28. Open-ended Use the method of Sample 2 to make a creative tessellation by modifying each pair of opposite sides of a hexagon whose opposite sides are parallel and congruent.

29. Modify each side of a triangle so that the modified side has 180° rotational symmetry about the midpoint of the segment. Make a creative tessellation based on this method.

30. Modify each side of a quadrilateral so that the modified side has 180° rotational symmetry about the midpoint of the segment. Make a creative tessellation based on this method.

Ongoing ASSESSMENT

31. Writing Describe how periodic tessellations are like periodic functions and border patterns. How are they different?

Review PREVIEW

32. Use this shape. Create a border pattern having horizontal reflection symmetry. *(Section 10-6)*

33. Transform the function $f(x) = x^2$ with a horizontal stretch by a factor of 4 followed by a translation of 5 units down. Write an equation for the transformed function and graph it. *(Section 9-5)*

34. Evaluate each logarithm. Round decimal answers to the nearest hundredth. *(Section 5-6)*

   a. log 1000   **b.** log 1   **c.** ln 5

Working on the Unit Project

35. a. Make a polygonal tessellation to include in your scrapbook. Tell whether the tessellation is *regular* or *semiregular*.

   b. Write a number code to describe your tessellation. Explain how the code describes the tessellation.

Completing the Unit Project

Now you are ready to complete your scrapbook. Your project should include these things:

➤ **at least ten different types of graphs modeling specific situations, including the graphs you made in the "Working on the Unit Project" exercises**

➤ **a description and a picture of situations from your life, as well as local, national, and international topics**

➤ **a list of the functions you know how to graph**

➤ **an explanation of each graph in your scrapbook, including why the graph can be used to model a specific situation**

➤ **a description of how you gathered any data you needed to model a situation with a graph**

➤ **a description of the symmetry used to make the border design for the scrapbook cover**

Look Back ◄

Look at the scrapbooks made by other groups. Which graphs did they include? What situations did they describe? How would you change your scrapbook to make it better?

Alternative Projects

Project 1: Predict Future Trends

Think of a situation in nature that can be modeled by a sine wave. Gather data to develop an accurate model and graph your data.

Write an equation to model your data. Graph your equation and the data on the same set of axes Use your model to make predictions about the situation. Do you think your predictions are accurate? Explain.

Project 2: Penrose Tiles

Roger Penrose is a mathematician who worked with two kite-shaped tiles that always create nonperiodic tessellations when certain rules are followed. Research Penrose and the Penrose tiles that are named for him. How are the dimensions of the tiles related to the golden ratio? What kinds of nonperiodic tessellations can you make with Penrose tiles? Can you make periodic tessellations with the tiles if you ignore the rules Penrose used?

Which of the terms *constant, increasing, decreasing, periodic, damping,* or *saturating* **best describes the graph of each function?**

10-1

1. $y = \sin \theta$ **2.** $y = 5x$ **3.** $y = \dfrac{2}{3}$ **4.** $y = (2.1)(0.6)^x$

5. Compare the rates of growth in the first quadrant of $y = 4x$, $y = x^4$, and $y = 4^x$.

6. Sketch a periodic graph with amplitude 4, period 3, and an axis with the equation $y = 4$.

10-2

7. For the graph shown, identify the following:

a. a cycle

b. the period

c. the frequency

d. the amplitude

e. an equation of the axis

8. **Writing** What is a sine wave and how can it be obtained from the graph of the sine or the cosine function?

10-3

For each equation, find the amplitude, the period, and the frequency of its graph. Then sketch the graph without using graphing technology.

10-4

9. $y = 3 \sin (\theta - 45°) + 1$ **10.** $y = \cos 2\theta - 4$ **11.** $y = 0.5 \sin 3\theta + 2$

Write an equation for each graph.

12.

13.

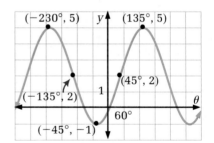

Use the table for Exercise 14.

10-5

Natural Gas Use by United States Electricity Utilities in 1992												
Month	Jan.	Feb.	Mar.	Apr.	May	June	July	Aug.	Sept.	Oct.	Nov.	Dec.
Natural gas use (billion cubic ft)	169	170	208	229	236	266	334	303	274	213	189	176

14. a. Graph the data in the table.

b. Write an equation to model the data. Let $x =$ the month expressed as a number. (Jan. = 1, Feb. = 2, . . .)

c. What type of function did you write an equation for in part (b)? Why did you choose this type?

Classify each border pattern by its symmetry.

15.

16.

17.

18. **Open-ended** Draw an asymmetric figure. Use it to create three different border patterns that each have a different type of symmetry. Describe the symmetry of each pattern.

For Exercises 19 and 20, tell whether each group of polygons can tessellate a plane.

19. squares and equilateral triangles

20. regular decagons

21. Use an indirect proof to show that regular 9-gons and squares cannot tessellate a plane.

22. **Self-evaluation** Describe the process of modeling data with a sine wave. How have you helped yourself to be more successful with these steps?

23. **Group Activity** Work in a group of three students.

a. Write the names of the seven types of border patterns on separate slips of paper. Fold each slip of paper in half. Each member of the group should pick two slips of paper at random. Set aside the seventh slip.

b. Each of you should draw an asymmetric figure on a piece of paper. Pass your drawing to the person on your right.

c. Choose one of the border patterns you selected in part (a). Draw the chosen border pattern using the figure you receive. Pass your border design and the original figure to the person on your right.

d. Repeat part (c) using the other border pattern you selected.

e. Identify the types of border patterns made from your asymmetric figure. Check your answers with the members of your group.

IDEAS AND (FORMULAS)=x^2

> The terms *constant*, *increasing*, *decreasing*, *periodic*, *saturating*, and *damping* can be used to describe the graph of a function. *(p. 543)*

> You can use tables or graphs to compare the rates of growth of functions. *(p. 544)*

> You can find the period, the frequency, the amplitude, and the equation of the axis of a periodic graph by looking at the graph. *(p. 548)*

> period = the length of one cycle
>
> frequency = the reciprocal of the period
>
> amplitude = $\dfrac{\text{maximum value} - \text{minimum value}}{2}$
>
> equation of the axis: $y = \dfrac{\text{maximum value} + \text{minimum value}}{2}$

> You can make predictions about the future behavior of periodic events by analyzing a part of the graph that includes at least one complete cycle. *(p. 568)*

> For an object moving counterclockwise (forward) or clockwise (backward) around a unit circle, the sine function gives the vertical position of the object. *(p. 555)*

> The graph of the sine function has an amplitude of 1 and a period of 360°. *(p. 556)*

> For an object moving counterclockwise (forward) or clockwise (backward) around a unit circle, the cosine function gives the horizontal position of the object. *(p. 556)*

> The graph of the cosine function has an amplitude of 1 and a period of 360°. *(p. 556)*

> The graph of the cosine function is a 90° horizontal translation of the graph of the sine function. *(p. 557)*

> The general form for the equation of a sine wave is $y = A \sin B(\theta - C) + D$ or $y = A \cos B(\theta - C) + D$. The graph of each of these functions has the following properties:

> > $|A|$ is the amplitude.
> >
> > $\dfrac{360°}{|B|}$ is the period.
> >
> > The graph of the parent function is translated horizontally C units.
> >
> > The equation of the axis is $y = D$. *(p. 561)*

Unit 10 Periodic Models

- The graph of a function of the form $y = A \sin B(\theta - C) + D$ can be obtained from the graph of $y = \sin \theta$ by the following transformations.

  - The graph is vertically stretched or shrunk by a factor of $|A|$. If $A < 0$, then there is also a reflection over the θ-axis.
  - The graph is horizontally stretched or shrunk by a factor of $\frac{1}{|B|}$. If $B < 0$, then there is also a reflection over the y-axis.
  - The graph is translated horizontally C units.
  - The graph is translated vertically D units.

  The same transformations apply to the graphs of $y = A \cos B (\theta - C) + D$ and $y = \cos \theta$. *(p. 561)*

- You can determine the period, the amplitude, the horizontal translation, and the vertical translation of a sine wave from its graph. *(p. 562)*

- You can write an equation for the graph of a sine wave by using the general model $y = A \sin B(\theta - C) + D$ and finding the values for A, B, C, and D. *(p. 562)*

- The general model for a sine wave can be used to write an equation that models a set of periodic data. *(p. 568)*

GEOMETRY

- There are seven types of border patterns. *(p. 577)*
- Border patterns are periodic. *(p. 577)*
- All border patterns are created using some combination of vertical reflection, horizontal reflection, and 180° rotation with repeated translations. *(p. 578)*
- You can use indirect proof to show that a group of polygons cannot tessellate a plane. *(p. 583)*
- Some nonregular polygons tessellate a plane, for example, all triangles and all parallelograms. *(p. 584)*
- You can make a creative tessellation by modifying the sides of a polygon that tessellates a plane. *(pp. 584–585)*

··········**Key Terms**

- **periodic** (p. 543)
- **cycle** (p. 548)
- **amplitude** (p. 548)

- **cosine function** (p. 556)
- **semiregular tessellation** (p. 582)

- **saturating** (p. 543)
- **period** (p. 548)
- **axis of a periodic function** (p. 548)

- **tessellation** (p. 582)
- **periodic tessellation** (p. 584)

- **damping** (p. 543)
- **frequency** (p. 548)
- **sine function** (p. 555)

- **regular tessellation** (p. 582)
- **cell** (p. 584)

Contents of Student Resources

Student Resources

Student Resources

This handbook introduces you to the basic features of most graphics calculators. Check your calculator's instruction manual for specific keystrokes and any details not provided here.

Performing Calculations

➤ **The Keyboard**

Look closely at your calculator's keyboard. Notice that most keys serve more than one purpose. Each key is labeled with its primary purpose, and labels for any secondary purposes appear somewhere near the key. You may need to press **2nd**, **SHIFT**, or **ALPHA** to use a key for a secondary purpose.

Examples of using the **X²** key:

Press **X²** to square a number.

Press **2nd** and then **X²** to take a square root.

Press **ALPHA** and then **X²** to get the letter I.

➤ **The Home Screen**

Your calculator has a "home screen" where you can do calculations. You can usually enter a calculation on a graphics calculator just as you would write it on a piece of paper.

Shown below are other things to remember as you enter calculations on your graphics calculator.

The calculator may recognize implied multiplication.

The calculator has a subtraction key, **−**, and a negation key, **(−)**. If you use these incorrectly, you will get an error message.

To perform an operation that is not often used, such as to calculate a cube root or $_nC_r$, you may need to press the **MATH** key to display a menu of operations.

1. Use your calculator to find the value of each expression.

   a. $\sqrt{12.25}$ **b.** 2^5 **c.** $\sin 75°$ **d.** $\cos^{-1} 0.5$

   e. $\sqrt[3]{64}$ **f.** $5!$ **g.** $_5P_2$ **h.** $_{12}C_6$

Displaying Graphs

➤ The Viewing Window

Think of the calculator screen as a "viewing window" that lets you look at a portion of the coordinate plane.

On many calculators, the standard viewing window uses values from −10 to 10 on both the x- and y-axes. You can adjust the viewing window by pressing the [RANGE] or [WINDOW] key and entering new values for the window variables.

```
RANGE
Xmin = -10
Xmax = 10
Xscl = 1
Ymin = -10
Ymax = 10
Yscl = 1
Xres = 1
```

The x-axis will be shown for $-10 \le x \le 10$.

The y-axis will be shown for $-10 \le y \le 10$.

With scale variables set to equal 1, tick marks will be 1 unit apart on both axes.

Some calculators have a resolution variable. This controls how "smooth" the graph will look.

➤ Entering and Graphing a Function

To graph a function, enter its equation in the form $y = \ldots$.
If the equation does not use x and y, rewrite the equation.
Let $x =$ the control variable and $y =$ the dependent variable. Set the variables for an appropriate viewing window. The graph of $y = \frac{1}{2}x + 3$ is shown using the standard viewing window.

Use parentheses. If you enter $y = 1/2x + 3$ instead, the calculator may interpret the equation as $y = \frac{1}{2x} + 3$.

You can see both displays at the same time with split-screen mode.

To enter some radical functions, you may need to press [Y=] and then [MATH] to find and enter the menu items $\sqrt[3]{}$ or $\sqrt[x]{}$. Remember to enter $y = \sqrt[3]{x - 1}$ as $y = \sqrt[3]{(x - 1)}$, so the calculator does not interpret the equation as $y = \sqrt[3]{x} - 1$.

➤ Squaring the Screen

A "square screen" is a viewing window with equal unit spacing on the two axes. For example, the graph of $y = x$ is shown for two different windows.

Standard Viewing Window

Square Screen Window

On a square screen, the line $y = x$ makes a 45° angle with the x-axis.

On many graphics calculators, the ratio of the screen's height to its width is about 2 to 3. Your calculator may have a feature that gives you a square screen. If not, choose values for the window variables that make the "length" of the y-axis about two-thirds the "length" of the x-axis:

$$(\text{Ymax} - \text{Ymin}) \approx \frac{2}{3}(\text{Xmax} - \text{Xmin})$$

Try This

2. Enter and graph each equation separately. Use the standard viewing window.

   a. $y = 3x + 1$ **b.** $y = 2^x$ **c.** $y = \left| \dfrac{1}{x} \right|$ **d.** $y = \sqrt[3]{2x + 2}$

3. Find a good viewing window for the graph of $y = 65 - 3x$. Be sure your window shows where the graph crosses both axes.

4. Find a viewing window that will allow you to graph these two lines so that they appear to be perpendicular: $y = 2x + 1$ and $y = -0.5x - 2$.

Reading a Graph
➤ The TRACE Feature

After a graph is displayed, you can use the calculator's TRACE feature. When you press **TRACE**, a flashing cursor appears on the graph. The x- and y-coordinates of the cursor's location are shown at the bottom of the screen. Press the left- and right-arrow keys to move the TRACE cursor along the graph.

X = 2.3684211   Y = 2.3684211

The TRACE cursor is at the point (2.3684211, 2.3684211) on the graph of $y = x$.

Technology Handbook

X = 2.5231579 Y = 20.000402

Suppose you want to find the radius of a circular hole with an area of 20 in². The formula for the area of a circle is $A = \pi r^2$. Rewrite the equation using x and y. Graph the equation $y = \pi x^2$.

Using the TRACE key, move the cursor along the graph until the y-value is approximately equal to 20. This will give you the value of x that is the radius of the circular hole.

X = 2.5231325 Y = 20

Another way to solve the problem is to graph two equations on the same screen: $y = \pi x^2$ and $y = 20$. Use TRACE to move the cursor to the intersection of the two lines to find your answer.

Some calculators have an intersection feature as a menu item that will calculate and display the coordinates of the point of intersection of two graphs.

➤ Friendly Windows

As you press the right-arrow key while tracing a graph, the x-coordinate may increase by "unfriendly" increments.

Your calculator may allow you to control the x-increment, ΔX, directly. If not, you can control it indirectly by choosing an appropriate Xmax for a given Xmin. For example, on a TI-82 graphics calculator, choose Xmax so that

$$Xmax = Xmin + 94\Delta X.$$

This number depends upon the calculator you are using.

RANGE
Xmin = −5 ←
Xmax = 4.4 ←
Xscl = 1
Ymin = −10
Ymax = 10
Yscl = 1
Xres = 1

Suppose you want ΔX to equal 0.1. If Xmin = −5, then set Xmax equal to −5 + 94(0.1), or 4.4. This gives a "friendly window" where the TRACE cursor's x-coordinate will increase by 0.1 each time you press the right-arrow key.

Try This

5. Graph $y = 2\pi x$. Find the value of x when $y = 10$.

6. Graph the equation $y = x^2 + 2x - 1$. Choose a friendly window where $\Delta X = 0.1$. Use the TRACE feature to determine, to the nearest tenth, the x-coordinate of each of the two points where the graph crosses the x-axis.

➤ The TABLE Feature

Instead of tracing the graph of an equation, you may wish to examine a table of values. Not all calculators have a TABLE feature. Check to see if yours does.

The screen shows a table of values for $y = x^2 + 2x - 1$. Here the value of x increases from a minimum of 0 in steps of 0.1. Some calculators have a table set-up feature that allows you to set the table minimum and the change in the control variable.

Notice that the y-values change sign between $x = 0.4$ and $x = 0.5$.

Taking a Closer Look at a Graph

➤ The ZOOM Feature

Suppose you are interested in the point where the graph of the equation $y = x^2 + 2x - 1$ crosses the positive x-axis.

To get a closer look at the point of interest, you can use the ZOOM feature. Your calculator may have more than one way to zoom. A common way is to put a "zoom box" around the point. The calculator will then draw what's inside the box at full-screen size.

Define a "zoom box" . . .   **and then zoom.**

You create a "zoom box" by fixing first one corner and then the opposite corner of the box. (See your calculator's manual.)

Tracing reveals that the graph crosses the x-axis between $x = 0.41$ and $x = 0.42$. Repeat zooming and tracing.

When you graph a rational equation using the standard viewing window, the display may be unclear near asymptotes of the graph.

The graph is unclear.

$x = -\frac{1}{2}$ is an asymptote.

Zoom in to see the graph of $y = \dfrac{2x^2}{2x + 1}$ better near the origin.

On many graphics calculators you can use [▲] and [▼] to move between graphs. This process helps you solve the system:

$$x + y = 3$$
$$x = \frac{2}{3}y - 5$$

Rewrite the equations. Enter $Y_1 = -X + 3$ and $Y_2 = \left(\frac{3}{2}\right)X + \left(\frac{15}{2}\right)$.

1 TRACE along the first line (Y_1) until you are near the intersection.

2 Press [▲]

3 Now you are on the other line.

X = -1.791989 Y = 4.7919889

The x-coordinates are the same. The y-coordinates are close.

X = -1.791989 Y = 4.8120166

You can ZOOM in and repeat the process described above until the y-coordinates are the same to the nearest tenth, hundredth, or any other decimal place.

Try This

7. Try zooming in on the point where the graph of $y = x^2 + 2x - 1$ crosses the negative x-axis. Between what two values, to the nearest hundredth, does the x-coordinate of the point lie?

8. Sketch a clear graph of $y = \dfrac{x^2 - 2}{3x - 3}$.

9. Solve this system by graphing: $9x + 3y = 14$
$$-3x + 2y = 8$$

Student Resources

Comparing Graphs

➤ ### Using a List to Graph a Family of Curves

Some calculators allow you to enter a list as an element in an expression. The calculator can then plot a function for each value in the list and graph a family of curves.

$Y_1 = \{1, -2, 0.5\}X^2$
plots the family of functions
$y = x^2, y = -2x^2, y = 0.5x^2$.

$Y_2 = X^2 + \{-4, 5, 2\}$
plots the family of functions
$y = x^2 - 4, y = x^2 + 5, y = x^2 + 2$.

➤ ### A Function and Its Inverse

When two functions are inverses of each other, their graphs are reflections of each other over the line $y = x$.

Suppose you want to graph $y = 2x + 4$ and its inverse.

:Y_1 ■ 2X + 4 — Enter the equation as Y_1.

:Y_2 ■ .5X − 2

:Y_3 ■ X — Interchange x and y and solve for y. Enter the result as Y_2.

:$Y_4 =$

:$Y_5 =$

:$Y_6 =$ — Enter $Y_3 = X$ to see the symmetry.

:$Y_7 =$

:$Y_8 =$

Some graphics calculators have a DRAW INV feature as a menu item. You can enter $y = 2x + 4$ as Y_1 and then enter DRAW INV Y_1 to graph Y_1 and its inverse. (See page 300, Exercise 27, for a method that uses parametric equations.)

Try This

10. Describe how to use a list to plot the family of functions $y = x$, $y = -x$, $y = \frac{1}{2}x$, $y = 2x$.

11. Graph each family of functions. (Set your calculator in degree mode. Use $-360 \le x \le 360$, x-scale $= 90$; $-4 \le y \le 4$, y-scale $= 1$.)

  a. $y = \{1, -1, 0.5\} \cos x$ **b.** $y = \sin x + \{-1, 0, 1\}$

12. Graph each function and its inverse.

  a. $y = x + 3$ **b.** $y = -3x - 1$ **c.** $y = 2^x$

Technology Handbook

Graphing Parametric Equations

➤ ## Parametric Mode

When a ball is tossed up at an angle, it travels both vertically and horizontally. Suppose its path can be described by these two parametric equations:

$x = 0.3 + 6t$ ⟵——— x is the horizontal distance traveled in t seconds.

$y = 6t - 4.9t^2$ ⟵——— y is the vertical distance traveled in t seconds.

The variables x and y are both expressed in terms of a third variable, the parameter t. A graphics calculator in parametric mode will substitute a t-value in both equations and plot (x, y).

Choose parametric mode (par). In this mode, you set a range for t as well as for x and y.

RANGE
Tmin = 0 ⟵——— the minimum value of t in seconds
Tmax = 1.2 ⟵——— the maximum value of t in seconds
Tstep = .1 ⟵——— increments of time in each step from $t = 0$ to $t = 1.2$
Xmin = 0
Xmax = 7.6
Xscl = .8
↓Ymin = −1.6

➤ ## Exploring a Parametric Graph

Use these settings for the variables:

$0 \leq t \leq 1.2$ with increments of 0.1 for t-values,

$0 \leq x \leq 7.6$ with increments of 0.8 for x-values, and

$-1.6 \leq y \leq 3.44$ with increments of 0.8 for y-values.

: X₁ₜ ▬ .3 + 6T ⟵——— Enter $x = 0.3 + 6t$.
: Y₁ₜ ▬ 6T − 4.9T² ⟵——— Enter $y = 6t - 4.9t^2$.
: X₂ₜ =
: Y₂ₜ =
: X₃ₜ =
: Y₃ₜ =
: X₄ₜ =
: Y₄ₜ =

Use TRACE to graph the position of the ball as a function of time.

T = .1
X = .9   Y = .551

Try This

13. Suppose the path of a baseball t seconds after it is hit is described by the parametric equations $x = 100t$ and $y = -16t^2 + 40t + 3$.

a. Graph the parametric equations using these settings:

$0 \leq t \leq 3$ with increments of 0.05 for t-values,

$0 \leq x \leq 300$ with increments of 50 for x-values, and

$0 \leq y \leq 70$ with increments of 10 for y-values.

b. Use the TRACE feature. In how many seconds will the ball reach its maximum height?

Using Matrices

➤ Entering and Multiplying a Matrix by a Number

Suppose you want to enter this table of sales data as a matrix. Press the matrix function key. Select EDIT and choose matrix [A].

Set the dimensions: 3 rows, 4 columns.

This Month's Sales by Age Group				
	VCRs	CD players	Faxes	Telephone answerers
Under 25	73	211	24	106
25–49	132	188	67	142
Over 49	89	55	46	98

Enter the elements. ➤

$$\begin{bmatrix} 73 & 211 & 24 & 106 \\ 132 & 188 & 67 & 142 \\ 89 & 55 & 46 & 98 \end{bmatrix}$$

```
MATRIX [A] 3 × 4

[ 73   211  24 ...
[ 132  188  67 ...
[ 89   55   46 ...
```

Suppose the data are this month's sales. You want to see what a projected increase of 14% in sales would be.

You have entered the data as matrix [A]. To increase each element by 14%, you can multiply [A] by 1.14.

First return to the home screen.

◀—— Press 1.14 **MATRX** **ENTER** **ENTER** on a TI-82 graphics calculator.

```
1.14 [A]

[ [ 83.22   240.54...
  [ 150.48  214.32...
  [ 101.46  62.7   ...
```

➤ Adding and Subtracting Matrices

You can add or subtract two matrices that have the same dimensions. Suppose you enter two months' sales data as [A] and [B].

To compare the two data sets, you can subtract the matrices. The answer is a matrix with the same dimensions as the original matrices. Its elements are the sums or differences of elements in the same positions in [A] and in [B].

Press **MATRX** **ENTER** **–** **MATRX** 2 **ENTER**.

this month's sales

```
MATRIX [A] 3 × 4

[ 73   211  24 ...
[ 132  188  67 ...
[ 89   55   46 ...
```

last month's sales

```
MATRIX [B] 3 × 4

[ 70   180  30 ...
[ 162  147  51 ...
[ 76   54   41 ...
```

```
[A]–[B]

[ [ 3    31  −6   −12 ...
  [ −30  41  16   4    ...
  [ 13   1   5    14   ...
```

➤ Finding the Product of Two Matrices

You can multiply two matrices when the number of columns of the first matrix is the same as the number of rows of the second matrix.

Suppose you want to find this product: $\begin{bmatrix} 9 & 4 \\ 3 & 1 \\ 2 & 8 \\ 1 & 5 \end{bmatrix} \begin{bmatrix} 4 & 2 & 0 \\ 3 & 0 & 2 \end{bmatrix}$

Enter the two matrices as [A] and [B].
Their dimensions are 4 × 2 and 2 × 3.
Then find the product of the matrices.

[A][B]

```
[[ 48  18   8  ]
 [ 15   6   2  ]
 [ 32   4  16  ]
 [ 19   2  10 ]]
```

Press [MATRX] [ENTER] [MATRX] 2 [ENTER]
on a TI-82 graphics calculator.

➤ Finding the Inverse of a Matrix

You can use a graphics calculator to find the inverse of a matrix when the number of rows is the same as the number of columns.

Suppose you want to find the inverse of this matrix: $\begin{bmatrix} 3 & -1 \\ 4 & 0 \end{bmatrix}$

Enter the elements of the matrix as [A].

MATRIX [A] 2 × 2

```
[ 3 −1 ]
[ 4  0 ]
```

To find [A]⁻¹ press
[MATRX] [ENTER] [X⁻¹] [ENTER].

[A]⁻¹

```
[[ 0  .25 ]
 [ −1 .75 ]]
```

Try This

Use matrices A, B, C, or D to find each answer. If a matrix does not exist, write *not defined*.

$A = \begin{bmatrix} 3 & 4 \\ 6 & 7 \end{bmatrix}$ $B = \begin{bmatrix} 5 & 11 \\ -3 & -7 \end{bmatrix}$ $C = \begin{bmatrix} 9 & 3 \\ 12 & 4 \end{bmatrix}$ $D = \begin{bmatrix} 2 & 0 & -8 & 1 \\ 5 & 7 & 3 & 9 \end{bmatrix}$

14. $A + B$ **15.** $B - C$ **16.** $2A$ **17.** AB

18. $C + D$ **19.** CD **20.** A^{-1} **21.** D^{-1}

Student Resources

Working with Statistics

Histograms, Line Graphs, and Box-and-Whisker Plots

Many graphics calculators can display histograms, line graphs, and even box-and-whisker plots of data that you enter.

Readers of **galaxy** Magazine

Age group	Frequency
10–14	1110
15–19	3398
20–24	4344
25–29	3215
30–34	332
35–39	112

◄— The data about readers of *Galaxy* magazine are displayed in a histogram. ——►

Scatter Plots and Curve Fitting

Curve fitting is the process of finding an equation that describes a set of ordered pairs. Often, the first step is to enter the two lists of data and then graph the paired data in a scatter plot.

Men's Winning Times in Olympic 400 m Freestyle Swimming		
Year	Years after 1960	Time (seconds)
1960	0	258.3
1964	4	252.2
1968	8	249.0
1972	12	240.27
1976	16	231.93
1980	20	231.31
1984	24	231.23
1988	28	226.95
1992	32	225.00

On a TI-82 graphics calculator, press the STAT key to find a menu item for editing, or entering, a list of data.

Enter the years after 1960 as List 1. Enter the time in seconds as List 2.

L1	L2	L3
0		———
4		
8		
12		
16		
20		
24		

L2 (1) = 258.3

Other statistics menu items will fit lines and curves to your data plot, such as the median-median line, the least-squares line (linear regression), and the least-squares parabola (quadratic regression). Below, a least-squares line is fit to a plot of the Olympic data.

LinReg

$y = ax + b$
$a = -1.056041667$
$b = 255.3622222$
$r = -.9621654179$

➤ Mean and Standard Deviation

Most scientific and graphics calculators will calculate and display the mean and the standard deviation of a set of data using formulas that are already programmed into the calculator.

Your calculator may have two formulas for standard deviation. This book (see page 339) uses the standard deviation σ, which uses all n data items. (The other formula uses a sample of data items.)

L1	L2	L3
0	258.3	-----
4	252.2	
8	249.0	
12	240.27	
16	231.93	
20	231.31	
24	231.23	

L2 (7) = 231.23

You have set up List 2 as the y-variable.

Suppose you have entered the table of Olympic swimming data into your graphics calculator as on page 605. You are interested in the mean and the standard deviation of the winning times.

On a TI-82 graphics calculator, press the STAT key to access the menu of statistical calculations and choose the 2-variable statistics.

You will first see calculations for the x-variable, including $\bar{x}$ and σx. Press the down-arrow key until you find the statistical calculations for the y-variable.

number of data items ⟶
mean of the values in List 2 ⟶

standard deviation of the values in List 2 ⟶

2–Var Stats
↑n = 9
$\bar{y}$ = 238.4655556
Σy = 2146.19
Σy^2 = 512948.859
Sy = 12.02325155
↓σy = 11.33563027

Try This

22. The table provides some data values for the eruptions of Old Faithful, a geyser in Yellowstone Park.

Length of eruption (*l*)	3	4.5	4	2.5	3.5	5	2
Time (in minutes) until next eruption (*t*)	68	89	83	62	75	92	57

a. Enter the two lists of data on a graphics calculator.

b. Graph the paired data in a scatter plot.

c. Fit a least-squares line to the data (linear regression).

d. Fit a median-median line to the data.

e. Find the mean and the standard deviation of the data in the second row of the table.

Using a Spreadsheet

In addition to using a graphics calculator, you may want to use a computer with a spreadsheet program. A spreadsheet can help you solve a problem like this one: Suppose you want to buy a CD player that costs $195, including tax. You already have $37 and can save $9 per week. After how many weeks can you buy the player?

A spreadsheet is made up of cells named by a column letter and a row number, like A3 or B4. You can enter a label, a number, or a formula into a cell.

row numbers
column letters

	A	B
		CD Savings
	A	**B**
1	Week number	Total saved
2	0	37
3	= + A2 + 1	= + B2 + 9
4	= + A3 + 1	= + B3 + 9
5	= + A4 + 1	= + B4 + 9
6	= + A5 + 1	= + B5 + 9
7	= + A6 + 1	= + B6 + 9
8	= + A7 + 1	= + B7 + 9
9	= + A8 + 1	= + B8 + 9
10	= + A9 + 1	= + B9 + 9
11	= + A10 + 1	= + B10 + 9
12	= + A11 + 1	= + B11 + 9
13	= + A12 + 1	= + B12 + 9
14	= + A13 + 1	= + B13 + 9
15	= + A14 + 1	= + B14 + 9
16	= + A15 + 1	= + B15 + 9
17	= + A16 + 1	= + B16 + 9
18	= + A17 + 1	= + B17 + 9
19	= + A18 + 1	= + B18 + 9
20	= + A19 + 1	= + B19 + 9

Cell B1 contains the label "Total saved."

Cell B2 contains the number 37.

Cell B3 contains the formula "= +B2+9." This formula tells the computer to take the number in cell B2, add 9 to it, and put the result in cell B3. (Likewise, the formula in cell A3 tells the computer to take the number in cell A2, add 1 to it, and put the result in cell A3.)

Instead of typing a formula into each cell individually, you can use the spreadsheet's copy and fill commands.

In this spreadsheet, the computer has replaced all the formulas with calculated values. You can have the computer draw a scatter plot with a line connecting the plotted points. As you can see, you will have enough money to buy the CD player after 18 weeks.

	A	B
		CD Savings
	A	**B**
1	Week number	Total saved
2	0	37
3	1	46
4	2	55
5	3	64
6	4	73
7	5	82
8	6	91
9	7	100
10	8	109
11	9	118
12	10	127
13	11	136
14	12	145
15	13	154
16	14	163
17	15	172
18	16	181
19	17	190
20	18	199

Extra Practice

Unit 1

1. Mu Lan had two positive integers, A and B. She divided B by A and found that B was not evenly divisible by A. Then she divided $2B$ by A to see if $2B$ was evenly divisible by A. She continued this process using multiples of B until she found a multiple that was evenly divisible by A. **1-1**

   a. What procedure did Mu Lan's algorithm perform?

   b. Did Mu Lan's algorithm contain a loop? If it did, describe the loop.

Solve each equation or inequality in two ways. **1-1**

2. $2x + 3 = 15$

3. $-4 + 7x = 31$

4. $12 = \frac{1}{2}x + 5$

5. $-x + 9 \geq 14$

6. $\frac{1}{3}x + 5 > 2$

7. $30 - 4x \leq 6$

Tell whether each set of measurements can be the lengths of the sides of a triangle. **1-2**

8. 3 in., 5 in., 7 in.

9. 4 ft, 15 ft, 18 ft

10. 2.5 m, 5.5 m, 2.5 m

11. 14 cm, 6 cm, 8 cm

12. 20 yd, 20 yd, 10 yd

13. 25 ft, 18 ft, 6 ft

14. a. Find all the different rectangles that have sides with whole-number lengths and a perimeter of 32.

    b. Which of the rectangles you found in part (a) has the largest area? **1-2**

The table shows the number of books in some large city library systems in 1992 and the amount each system spent that year to buy new library materials. **1-3**

15. Make a scatter plot of the relationship between number of books and amount spent.

16. Describe any trend(s) suggested by the scatter plot.

City	Books (millions)	Amount spent (million $)
Anchorage, AK	0.4	0.7
Boston, MA	6.0	2.0
Chicago, IL	1.7	3.6
Denver, CO	2.2	1.9
Houston, TX	4.0	4.0
Kansas City, MO	1.8	1.6
Los Angeles, CA	5.7	4.5
Milwaukee, WI	2.3	1.8
Philadelphia, PA	3.5	6.2
Toledo, OH	1.8	3.0

Student Resources *(vertical, left margin)*

Weefixit Appliance Service charges $25 for a house call, plus $16 for each hour spent fixing an appliance. Appliance Rehab charges $18 for a house call, plus $19 per hour. 1-4

17. Write an equation that models each company's repair charges.

18. Which company charges less if a repair takes 1.5 h? 4 h?

Use algebra to find each break-even point. Round answers to the nearest tenth. 1-4

19. $E = 12 + 3.5x$
$I = 7.5x$

20. $E = 144 + 2.7x$
$I = 4.3x$

21. $E = 55 + 1.8x$
$I = 8.7x$

Solve. When necessary, round decimal answers to the nearest tenth. 1-5

22. $x + y = 8$
$3x + 4y = 22$

23. $x - y = 5$
$7x + 3y = 7$

24. $-x + 2y = 11$
$5x + y = 22$

25. $x + y = 1$
$y + z = 3$
$x + z = 6$

26. $x + y - z = 9$
$x - y + z = -3$
$x + 2y + 4z = 3$

27. $x + 2y = 6$
$3x - y + z = 9$
$x - y + 4z = 5$

Use a matrix to represent the connections among the vertices of each diagram. 1-6

28.

29.

30.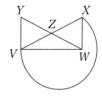

For Exercises 31 and 32, use the table of the routes of a public bus service. 1-6

Buses leaving from	Provide service to . . .		
Central Square	Veterans' Plaza	Zoo	Downtown
Downtown	Veterans' Plaza	Northside Mall	
Northside Mall	Veterans' Plaza	Downtown	
Veterans' Plaza	Central Square		
Zoo	Northside Mall		

31. Make a diagram to represent the bus routes.

32. Make a matrix to represent the bus routes.

Find the value of x that maximizes or minimizes each function. Find the maximum or minimum value. Tell whether it is a *maximum* or a *minimum*. 1-7

33. $y = -x^2 + 6x + 2$

34. $y = 3x^2 - 24x - 5$

35. $y = -2x^2 - 18x + 1$

At Central High's Community Day, some students will go on a walkathon and others will wash cars. At most, 15 students will take part. Each walker will spend about 4 h, and each washer will spend about 6 h. Organizers have agreed to limit the total student time to 72 h. 1-8

36. Let x represent the number of walkers and let y represent the number of washers. Write a system of inequalities that represents all the constraints on x and y. Graph the feasible region and label each vertex with its coordinates.

37. Suppose each walker raises $7 and each washer raises $8. How many walkers and how many washers should there be in order to maximize the Community Day income?

Unit 2

For each function, find $f(3)$, $f(-2)$, and $f(a + b)$. 2-1

1. $f(x) = (x + 2)^2$

2. $f(x) = \dfrac{x + 1}{x}$

3. $f(x) = 7 - \dfrac{1}{2}x$

4. $f(x) = 2x^2 - 5x + 1$

5. $f(x) = |x - 5|$

6. $f(x) = \dfrac{x}{x^2 + 1}$

Tell whether each graph represents a *function*. If it does, tell whether the function is *one-to-one* or *many-to-one*. 2-1

7.

8.

9.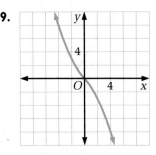

Tell whether each function is *linear*. If it is, find $f(2)$, $f(-3)$, and $f(a - b)$. 2-2

10. $f(x) = \dfrac{1}{2x + 7}$

11. $f(x) = -3x + 2$

12. $f(x) = \dfrac{x}{6} - 5$

13. $f(x) = x^2 - 2x + 1$

14. $f(x) = 8 - 3x$

15. $f(x) = 5 + 4(2 - x)$

Write an equation for each function in the form $f(x) = mx + b$. 2-2

16. $f(0) = -6; m = 3$

17. $f(-1) = 4; f(5) = 7$

18. $m = -2; f(3) = 8$

19. $f(2) = 11; f(-3) = 1$

20. $f(-3) = 2; f(1) = -5$

21. $f\left(\dfrac{1}{2}\right) = 3; f\left(\dfrac{5}{2}\right) = 6$

Graph each piecewise function or absolute value function. 2-3

22. $f(x) = \begin{cases} x & \text{if } 0 \le x < 3 \\ 10 - 2x & \text{if } 3 \le x \le 5 \end{cases}$

23. $f(x) = \begin{cases} x + 1 & \text{if } 0 \le x < 2 \\ 3 & \text{if } 2 \le x \le 4 \\ 1 + 0.5x & \text{if } 4 < x \le 6 \end{cases}$

24. $f(x) = |x - 2|$

25. $f(x) = -2|x| + 3$

26. $f(x) = \dfrac{|x + 1|}{3} - 1$

Tell whether each function is a quadratic function. For each quadratic function: 2-4

a. Find $f(2)$, $f(-3)$, and $f(a - b)$.

b. Graph f.

27. $f(x) = -\dfrac{1}{2}x^2$

28. $f(x) = (x + 3)^2 - 1$

29. $f(x) = \dfrac{1}{x^2 + 4}$

30. $f(x) = 2x^2 - 8x - 1$

31. $f(x) = \dfrac{(x - 1)^2}{4}$

32. $f(x) = x^3 + x^2 + 5$

Write an equation in the form $f(x) = kx^n$ for each direct variation function. 2-5

33. $f(1) = 3$; $n = 5$

34. $k = 4$; $f(3) = 36$

35. $f\left(\dfrac{1}{2}\right) = 3$; $n = 4$

36. $f(2) = 56$; $f(1) = 7$

37. $f(0.2) = 9$; $n = 3$

38. $f(10) = 500$; $f\left(\dfrac{1}{10}\right) = \dfrac{5}{100}$

Graph each polynomial function. 2-5

39. $f(x) = x(x - 1)(x + 3)$

40. $f(x) = x^2(x - 3)$

41. $f(x) = (x + 1)(x - 2)(x - 4)$

42. $f(x) = -x(x + 2)^2$

Solve. 2-6

43. $\sqrt{x + 6} = x$

44. $\sqrt{x} = x - 12$

45. $\sqrt{2x + 1} = x - 7$

46. $\sqrt{3x + 1} + 1 = x$

47. $\sqrt{7x - 3} + 3 = 2x$

48. $\sqrt[3]{4x} = x$

Find the domain and range of each function. 2-6

49. $f(x) = \sqrt[3]{x - 5}$

50. $f(x) = \sqrt{x + 2}$

51. $f(x) = -\sqrt{x - 3}$

52. $f(x) = \sqrt{5 - 2x}$

53. $f(x) = -\sqrt[3]{x + 10}$

54. $f(x) = 2\sqrt{x + 1} - 4$

For Exercises 55–60: 2-7

a. Graph the function.

b. Write the equations of all asymptotes of the graph.

c. Find the domain and range of the function.

55. $f(x) = \dfrac{4}{x - 2}$

56. $f(x) = -\dfrac{3}{x}$

57. $f(x) = \dfrac{x}{x + 3}$

58. $f(x) = \dfrac{x - 5}{x}$

59. $f(x) = \dfrac{x}{2x - 8}$

60. $f(x) = -\dfrac{x - 1}{x + 2}$

For Exercises 61–68, use the functions $f(x) = 7x^2 + 1$, $g(x) = \sqrt{x}$, and $h(x) = \dfrac{x}{2x - 1}$. For each function, (a) find a rule and (b) find the domain of the function. **2-8**

61. $f \cdot g$ **62.** $f + h$ **63.** $g \circ f$ **64.** $h \circ g$

65. $\dfrac{f}{h}$ **66.** $f - g$ **67.** $f \circ g$ **68.** $g \cdot h$

Unit 3

Determine whether each implication is *True* or *False*. Then state the converse, inverse, and contrapositive of each implication. Determine whether each is *True* or *False*. **3-1**

1. If two angles of a triangle are equal in measure, then two sides of the triangle are equal in measure.

2. If the diagonals of a quadrilateral are perpendicular, then the quadrilateral is a rhombus.

3. If n is a prime number greater than 2, then n is a positive odd integer.

4. If at least one of two numbers, a and b, is positive, then their product, ab, is positive.

5. Use the diagram at the right. Write a coordinate proof of the statement: If the midpoints of the sides of a quadrilateral are joined in order, then the resulting figure is a parallelogram. **3-2**

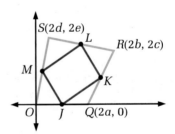

Suppose a kite is defined as a quadrilateral with at least one line of symmetry that passes through two opposite vertices. **3-3**

6. Is this definition *inclusive* or *exclusive*?

7. Using this definition, is it true that if a quadrilateral is a square, then it is a kite?

8. Using this definition, is it true that if a quadrilateral is an isosceles trapezoid, then it is a kite?

9. Suppose the words *at least one* in the definition were changed to read *exactly one*. Would it then be true that if a quadrilateral is a rhombus, then it is a kite?

Find the measure of each interior angle and each exterior angle of a regular polygon with the given number of sides. **3-4**

10. 5 **11.** 7 **12.** 18 **13.** 16

ABCDEFGHIJ is a regular decagon. Find the measure of each arc or angle. `3-5`

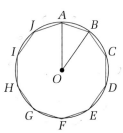

14. $\angle AOB$ **15.** $\overset{\frown}{AC}$

16. $\overset{\frown}{JFC}$ **17.** $\angle OAB$

18. $\angle G$ **19.** $\overset{\frown}{CF}$

In the diagram at the right, $m\angle FCE = 55°$, $m(\overset{\frown}{FC}) = 130°$, and $\overset{\frown}{FCD}$ is a semicircle. Find the measure of each arc or angle. `3-6`

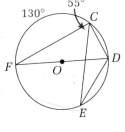

20. $\angle CDF$ **21.** $\overset{\frown}{EF}$

22. $\overset{\frown}{DE}$ **23.** $\angle ECD$

24. $\overset{\frown}{CD}$ **25.** $\angle CDE$

The diagram at the right shows two circles, O and P, placed so that the line m is tangent to both circles at point Q. `3-7`

26. How do you know that $\overline{OQ}$ and $\overline{PQ}$ lie in the same line?

27. Assume temporarily that the circles have another point R in common. Draw $\overline{OQ}$, $\overline{PQ}$, $\overline{OR}$, and $\overline{PR}$. Compare the length OP to the sum $OR + PR$. Which is larger, or are they the same?

28. The triangle inequality states that the sum of the lengths of any two sides of a triangle is greater than the length of the third side. Use the triangle inequality in an indirect proof that two circles such as O and P have no other point in common other than Q.

Use the diagram at the right, in which $\triangle BCD$ is an equilateral triangle circumscribed about a circle of radius 2. `3-8`

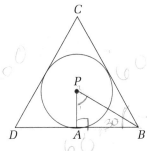

29. Find $m\angle APB$.

30. Use trigonometry to find DB.

31. Find the area of $\triangle BCD$.

Find the area of each triangle with the given sides AB, BC, and AC, and with inscribed circle of radius r. `3-8`

32. $AB = 17$; $BC = 25$; $AC = 26$; $r = 6$

33. $AB = 50$; $BC = 56$; $AC = 34$; $r = 12$

Write the reasoning you would use in an indirect proof of each fact. `3-9`

34. A regular polyhedron cannot have 6 edges meeting at each vertex.

35. A regular polyhedron cannot have octagonal faces.

Unit 4

For each sequence in Exercises 1–6: 4-1

a. Find the next three terms.

b. Find the 10th term.

1. $2, -3, 4, -5, \ldots$ **2.** $0.02, 0.2, 2, 20, \ldots$ **3.** $20, 17, 14, 11, \ldots$

4. $\dfrac{1}{2}, \dfrac{1}{6}, \dfrac{1}{18}, \dfrac{1}{54}, \ldots$ **5.** $4, 2, 1, 4, 2, 1, \ldots$ **6.** $-1, 4, -9, 16, \ldots$

Tell whether each infinite sequence appears to have a limit. If so, give its value. 4-1

7. $0.9, 1.1, 0.99, 1.01, \ldots$ **8.** $\dfrac{3}{2}, \dfrac{9}{4}, \dfrac{27}{8}, \dfrac{81}{16}, \ldots$ **9.** $\dfrac{3}{5}, \dfrac{33}{50}, \dfrac{333}{500}, \dfrac{3333}{5000}, \ldots$

Write the first four terms and the 20th term of each sequence. 4-2

10. $a_n = 3n - 10$ **11.** $b_n = \dfrac{n^2}{n+1}$ **12.** $a_n = \dfrac{1}{2^{n+1}}$ **13.** $t_n = \dfrac{2n-1}{2n+1}$

Write an explicit formula for each sequence. 4-2

14. $1, \dfrac{1}{4}, \dfrac{1}{9}, \dfrac{1}{16}, \ldots$ **15.** $5, 7, 9, 11, \ldots$ **16.** $\dfrac{3}{2}, 2, \dfrac{5}{2}, 3, \ldots$

17. $150, 15, 1.5, 0.15, \ldots$ **18.** $\dfrac{2}{1}, \dfrac{3}{2}, \dfrac{4}{3}, \dfrac{5}{4}, \ldots$ **19.** $125, 25, 5, 1, \ldots$

Write the first six terms of each sequence. 4-3

20. $a_1 = 79$

    $a_n = a_{n-1} - 4$

21. $a_1 = 80$

    $a_n = \dfrac{1}{2}a_{n-1}$

22. $a_1 = 24$

    $a_n = \dfrac{a_{n-1}}{n}$

23. $a_1 = 4$

    $a_n = \dfrac{2}{a_{n-1}}$

24. $a_1 = 256$

    $a_n = \sqrt{a_{n-1}}$

25. $a_1 = 10$

    $a_n = \dfrac{a_{n-1} + 10}{a_{n-1}}$

For each sequence in Exercises 26–31: 4-4

a. Decide whether the sequence is *arithmetic*, *geometric*, or *neither*.

b. Write a recursive formula.

26. $12, 4, -4, -12$ **27.** $16, 20, 25, 31.25, \ldots$ **28.** $7, -7, 7, -7, \ldots$

29. $8, \dfrac{4}{5}, \dfrac{2}{25}, \dfrac{1}{125}, \ldots$ **30.** $1, 1.1, 1.11, 1.111, \ldots$ **31.** $\dfrac{1}{2}, -\dfrac{3}{2}, -\dfrac{7}{2}, -\dfrac{11}{2}, \ldots$

For each sequence in Exercises 32–37: 4-4

a. Find x when the sequence is arithmetic.

b. Find x when the sequence is geometric.

32. $3, x, 12$ **33.** $-4, x, -25$ **34.** $5, x, 45$

35. $2, x, 100$ **36.** $0.5, x, 8$ **37.** $-3, x, -300$

     Student Resources

Find the sum of each finite arithmetic series. 4-5

38. $(-5) + 2 + 9 + 16 + \cdots + 51$

39. $2 + 2.3 + 2.6 + 2.9 + \cdots + 8$

40. $15 + 12.5 + 10 + 7.5 + \cdots + (-10)$

41. $4 + \dfrac{14}{3} + \dfrac{16}{3} + 6 + \cdots + 22$

Write each series in sigma notation. 4-5

42. $4^2 + 4^3 + 4^4 + \cdots + 4^9$

43. $16 + 26 + 36 + 46 + \cdots + 126$

44. $\dfrac{4}{3^5} + \dfrac{5}{3^6} + \dfrac{6}{3^7} + \dfrac{7}{3^8} + \cdots + \dfrac{11}{3^{12}}$

45. $(-12) + (-3) + 6 + 15 + \cdots + 60$

Find the sum of each series. 4-6

46. $125 + 100 + 80 + 64 + \cdots + \dfrac{1024}{25}$

47. $3 + (-6) + 12 + (-24) + \cdots + 768$

48. $\dfrac{1}{2} + \dfrac{1}{3} + \dfrac{2}{9} + \dfrac{4}{27} + \cdots + \dfrac{16}{243}$

49. $50 + 5 + 0.5 + 0.05 + \cdots + 0.00005$

For each series in Exercises 50–52: 4-6

a. Decide whether the series is *arithmetic, geometric,* or *neither.*

b. Find the sum.

50. $1 + 2 + 4 + 7 + \cdots + 22$

51. $\displaystyle\sum_{n=1}^{6} -3(0.5)^n$

52. $\displaystyle\sum_{k=0}^{11} 8(k + 1) - 3$

For each series in Exercises 53–58: 4-7

a. Graph the first six partial sums.

b. Decide whether the series has a sum. If it does, give its value.

53. $10 + 5 + 2.5 + 1.25 + \cdots$

54. $0.64 + 0.8 + 1 + 1.25 + \cdots$

55. $17 + 11 + 5 + (-1) + \cdots$

56. $\dfrac{5}{3} + \dfrac{5}{9} + \dfrac{5}{27} + \dfrac{5}{81} + \cdots$

57. $\displaystyle\sum_{n=1}^{\infty} 30\left(\dfrac{4}{5}\right)^n$

58. $\displaystyle\sum_{n=1}^{\infty} \left(\dfrac{1}{10^n} + 3\right)$

Unit 5

After reaching a peak, the concentration of medication in a person's blood stream decreases exponentially. Suppose the medication loses 18% of its concentration every hour. Suppose that the concentration y of the medication (in µg/mL) at time t (in hours) is modeled by the equation $y = (1.4)(0.82)^t$. 5-1

1. Graph the equation.

2. Find the peak concentration.

3. Find the time when half of the peak concentration of the medication remains.

4. Find the time when the concentration is less than 0.4 µg/mL.

Since 1980, when the Chavez Park public school system installed its first computers, the number of computers in the school system has been growing exponentially. There were 320 computers in the system in 1990 and 368 computers in the system in 1991. **5-2**

5. Write an exponential function that models the number of computers in the Chavez Park school system.

6. How many computers were there in the school system in 1985? In 1980?

7. How many computers did the school system have in 1970?

Simplify. **5-3**

8. $100^{5/2}$

9. $9^{1/3} \cdot 9^{1/6}$

10. $40^{2/3}$

11. $\left(\dfrac{25}{16}\right)^{3/4}$

Simplify. **5-3**

12. $\sqrt{x^7 y^8}$

13. $\sqrt[3]{8a^4 b^6}$

14. $\sqrt{25p^{-8}}$

15. $\sqrt[3]{w^2} \cdot \sqrt[6]{w^{-2}}$

Find the value of each function, to the nearest hundredth, for (a) $x = 1.5$ and (b) $x = -0.8$. **5-4**

16. $f(x) = 480e^{-2.6x}$

17. $f(x) = \dfrac{1}{1 + 14e^{-1.2x}}$

18. $f(x) = 22(e^{x/25} + e^{-x/25})$

Find the value of an investment of $1500 for five years at an annual rate of 8%, if interest is compounded as specified. **5-4**

19. annually

20. monthly

21. daily

Write an equation for the inverse of each function. **5-5**

22. $y = 5 - 4x$

23. $y = \dfrac{3}{7x}$

24. $y = \dfrac{1}{8}x^3$

25. $y = \sqrt{x} + 2,\ x \geq 0$

26. $y = (x + 3)^{5/3}$

27. $y = |2x|,\ x \geq 0$

28. $y = (x - 3)^2,\ x \leq 3$

29. $y = x^3 + 1$

Evaluate each logarithm. Round decimal answers to the nearest hundredth. **5-6**

30. $\log \dfrac{1}{\sqrt{10}}$

31. $\log_3 81$

32. $\log 40$

33. $\log_5 \dfrac{1}{125}$

34. $\ln 20$

35. $\log_6 1$

36. $\ln e^3$

37. $\log_2 \sqrt{32}$

Solve. Round decimal answers to the nearest hundredth. **5-6**

38. $\log_x 1{,}000{,}000 = 3$

39. $\log_x 25 = -2$

40. $e^x = \sqrt[3]{e}$

41. $\ln x = 0$

42. $e^x = 17$

43. $\log x = -0.25$

Write each expression as a single logarithm. **5-7**

44. $\log 48 - 3 \log 2$

45. $\log_3 14 + \dfrac{1}{2} \log_3 16$

46. $\dfrac{1}{3} \log 64 - 2 \log 4 + \log 2$

Write each expression in terms of $\log_7 A$ and $\log_7 B$. 5-7

47. $\log_7 A\sqrt{B}$

48. $\log_7 \dfrac{\sqrt{A}}{B^3}$

49. $\log_7 \sqrt[4]{AB^5}$

Evaluate. 5-7

50. $\log 2000 - \log 2$

51. $\dfrac{1}{2}(\log_6 4 + \log_6 9)$

52. $\log_5 25 - 4\log_5 \sqrt{5}$

Solve. 5-8

53. $4^x = 15$

54. $12^{2x} = 7$

55. $8(1.05)^x = 29$

Solve. 5-8

56. $\log x + \log (x - 15) = 2$

57. $\log_6 3x + \log_6 (x + 7) = -1$

58. $2 \log_4 x - \log_4 (x + 3) = 1$

59. $2 \log_2 x - \log_2 (3x - 10) = 3$

Unit 6

The ages, in months, of members of a mathematics class are given in the table at the right. 6-1

 1. Draw a histogram for the age data.

 2. Identify the type of distribution.

 3. Find the mean and the median ages of the members of Jim Abbott's mathematics class.

Ages of Students in Jim Abbott's Mathematics Class (in months)				
180	192	165	178	182
185	184	182	194	198
172	176	178	184	186
192	186	188	185	182
176	196	188	176	168
174	172	170	183	191

The table at the right shows intervals for the land areas of the 50 states and the number of states that fall into each interval. 6-1

 4. Complete the table.

 5. Draw a relative frequency histogram for the data.

 6. Identify the type of distribution for the histogram.

 7. What percent of the states have land areas less than 60,000 mi²?

Land Area (1000 mi²)	No. of states	Percent of total
0–19	9	?
20–39	6	?
40–59	15	?
60–79	7	?
80–99	5	?
100–119	3	?
120–139	1	?
140–159	2	?
160 and over	2	?

Extra Practice

For Exercises 8–11, the table shows a sampling of prices of regular unleaded gasoline in two communities on the same day.

	Prices of one gallon of unleaded regular gasoline ($)
Midway	1.38 1.25 1.23 1.31 1.32 1.36 1.21 1.34 1.32 1.28 1.39 1.24 1.25
Fairview	1.32 1.31 1.28 1.36 1.35 1.32 1.33 1.37 1.33 1.31 1.32 1.30 1.34

8. Find the mean, the range, and the standard deviation of the data for Midway.

9. Find the mean, the range, and the standard deviation for Fairview.

10. For each of the two data sets, find the percent of the data within one standard deviation of the mean.

11. Suppose histograms based on the two data sets were drawn on the same axes using two different shadings for the bars. Without graphing, predict how the two histograms would differ.

For Exercises 12–14: 6-3

a. **Draw a histogram for each data set.**

b. **Find the mean and the median of each data set.**

c. **Decide whether the data appears to show a normal distribution.**

12. times an airport shuttle bus took to reach the downtown stop (min)

23, 15, 18, 26, 17, 20, 21, 17, 14, 16, 22, 24, 18, 13, 21, 24, 22, 19, 22, 23, 24, 15, 20, 21, 19, 20, 22, 23, 19, 16

13. numbers of raisins in a sample of home-baked oatmeal cookies

8, 7, 8, 4, 9, 6, 5, 5, 6, 7, 4, 10, 8, 11, 9, 12, 10, 6, 7, 7, 9, 8, 10, 9, 9, 8, 11, 8, 6, 7

14. duration of music tracks on albums by the group Live Bait (min)

3.2, 3.3, 5.6, 2.4, 4.2, 2.4, 3.0, 2.8, 4.6, 1.8, 3.2, 4.6, 2.4, 2.0, 1.4, 4.2, 5.0, 2.0, 3.4, 3.6, 5.2, 4.2, 1.6, 3.8, 4.0

For Exercises 15–18, the table shows laboratory trials of an insect repellent. For each trial, various amounts of repellent were applied to a test patch. The numbers of insects landing on the patch during a fixed period of time were recorded. 6-4

Amount of repellent used (oz)	0.5	1.0	1.5	2.0	2.5	3.0	3.5	4.0	4.5
No. of insects landing	38	34	33	30	27	25	20	16	14

15. Make a scatter plot of the data.

16. Find an equation of the least-squares line.

17. Find an equation of the median-median line.

18. How do these two lines compare in this situation?

For Exercises 19–22, the table below shows the numbers of Americans employed on farms in census years since 1920. 6-5

Year	1920	1930	1940	1950	1960	1970	1980	1990
No. of farm workers (millions)	11.4	10.3	9.0	6.9	4.1	2.9	2.8	2.9

19. Make a scatter plot of the data. (Use "Years since 1920" for the x-values.)

20. Find a quadratic model for the data.

21. Graph the quadratic model on the same set of axes as the scatter plot.

22. Use your model to predict the number of farm workers in the year 2000.

Unit 7

Design a formula for a calculator to produce each set of random numbers. 7-1

1. integers from 1 to 6

2. integers from 10 to 20

For Exercises 3 and 4, design a simulation to investigate each situation. 7-1

3. Suppose 5 cards are drawn from a standard deck of cards and each card is replaced before the next card is drawn. What is the probability that cards drawn include at least two cards of the same denomination (that is, two threes, two kings, etc.)?

4. In a certain state, lottery ticket numbers are four-digit numbers. If any three digits match digits of the winning number, the ticket holder wins a prize. Matching digits do not have to be in the same order. Suppose the winning number consists of four different digits. What is the probability of buying a winning ticket?

A card is drawn from a standard deck. Find the probability of each event. 7-2

5. It is a king or a diamond.

6. It is a face card or a red card.

You look at the second hand of a clock at two random times during the day and record the position as a real number between 0 and 60. Find the probability of each event. 7-2

7. The sum of the two readings will be greater than 80?

8. Both of the readings will be less than 20?

You roll a die twice. Find the probability of each event. 7-2

9. The sum of the numbers showing is at least 9.

10. The first number is odd or the second number is 6.

Dao Nguyen has $500 in his bank account. He wants to buy a CD player, which will cost between $100 and $300, and a pair of speakers in the same price range. `7-3`

11. What is the probability that he will have enough in his bank account to cover the cost of those items?

12. What is the probability that the speakers will cost at least $50 more than the CD player?

The table shows the amount of time a sample of students spent listening to music. Use the table in Exercises 13 and 14. `7-4`

Hours per week	Freshmen	Sophomores	Juniors	Seniors	Totals
0–10	8	10	20	24	62
10–20	18	14	16	12	60
20–30	22	18	10	8	58
Totals	48	42	46	44	180

13. Find $P(10\text{–}20 \text{ hours per week} \mid \text{sophomore})$, $P(\text{sophomore})$, and $P(10\text{–}20 \text{ hours per week and sophomore})$.

14. Find $P(10\text{–}20 \text{ hours per week})$. Are the events "$X$ is a sophomore" and "X listens to music 10–20 hours per week" independent?

Box *A* contains 10 white and 10 black marbles. Box *B* contains 10 white and 20 black marbles. One of the two boxes is chosen at random. Then a marble is drawn at random from that box. Find each probability. `7-4`

15. $P(\text{from Box } A \text{ and black})$ **16.** $P(\text{black})$ **17.** $P(\text{from Box } A \mid \text{black})$

In a board game, you roll a die to determine your moves. A roll of 5 or 6 advances your token 4 squares, a roll of 2, 3, or 4 advances your token 3 squares, and a roll of 1 puts your token back 1 square. `7-5`

18. How many squares do you expect to advance each turn?

19. In certain situations during the game, you may pick a card, but you may choose not to. There is an equal likelihood that the card will say "Advance 6 spaces" or "Go back 1 space." Should you pick the card?

At a certain intersection, the light for northbound traffic switches between red for 15 seconds and green for 35 seconds. Find the probability of each event. `7-6`

20. Out of the next 6 northbound cars, exactly 4 will hit the light red.

21. Out of the next 6 northbound cars, 4 or more will hit the light red.

22. Consider the event: "Out of the next 12 northbound cars, exactly 8 will hit the light red." Would you expect the probability of this event to be smaller or larger than the answer to Exercise 20? Calculate this probability.

Unit 8

Graph each point on polar graph paper. 8-1

1. $(4, 150°)$

2. $(2, -70°)$

3. $(3, 230°)$

4. $(1.5, -110°)$

5. $(3.5, 110°)$

6. $(4, 315°)$

Convert the polar coordinates to rectangular coordinates. Give answers to the nearest hundredth. 8-2

7. $(7, 270°)$

8. $(3, 120°)$

9. $(4, 225°)$

10. $(5\sqrt{2}, 45°)$

11. $(2, -155°)$

12. $(6, 32°)$

13. $(5, 142°)$

14. $(8, -40°)$

Convert each set of rectangular coordinates to polar coordinates. 8-2

15. $(-2, 2\sqrt{3})$

16. $(-6\sqrt{2}, -6\sqrt{2})$

17. $(4, -3)$

18. $(12, 5)$

19. $(-4.2, 3.4)$

20. $(-6.5, -1)$

Use the diagram at the right for Exercises 21–29. Write each vector in rectangular form. 8-3

21. t

22. u

23. v

24. w

25. 2u

26. −v

27. t + u

28. u + v

29. v + w

Let t = (5, 240°) and u = (3, 90°). Use a protractor and ruler to draw each sum. Write the resultant vector in polar and rectangular form. 8-3

30. −t

31. 3u

32. t + u

33. u − t

34. t − 2u

35. 2t + u

Find each vector sum in rectangular form. 8-4

36. $(2, -7) + (5, 4)$

37. $(-5, -8) + (3, 8)$

38. $(4, -2) + (11, -9)$

39. $(3.2, 0) + (-4.6, -1.5)$

40. $(3\sqrt{2}, 4) + (-\sqrt{2}, -3)$

41. $(0.2, -1.6) + (-1.9, 0.3)$

Find each vector sum in polar form. 8-4

42. $(3, 40°) + (2, -80°)$

43. $(1, 130°) + (4, 270°)$

44. $(2, 15°) + (3, 148°)$

45. $(4, -160°) + (3, 20°)$

46. $(5, 112°) + (4, 310°)$

47. $(6, 200°) + (7, 75°)$

Write parametric equations for the motion of an object thrown with a velocity vector v (with magnitude in m/s). 8-5

48. $v = (45, 30°)$

49. $v = (63, 28°)$

Combine each pair of parametric equations into a single equation relating y to x. 8-5

50. $x = 3.6t$, $y = 2.5t - 4.9t^2$

51. $x = 15.7t$, $y = 5.8t - 16.1t^2$

52. $x = 4 + 3 \cos t$, $y = -7 + 3 \sin t$

53. $x = 1 + \frac{1}{2} \cos t$, $y = 2 + \frac{1}{2} \sin t$

54. $x = 4 \cos t$, $y = 9 \sin t$

55. $x = 3 + 6 \cos t$, $y = -1 + 5 \sin t$

Use the law of cosines to find the length of the missing side or the measure of the missing angle of $\triangle ABC$. 8-6

56. $a = 6.7$ cm, $b = 4.3$ cm, $m\angle C = 56°$, $c = ?$

57. $b = 12.8$ cm, $c = 10.6$ cm, $m\angle A = 115°$, $a = ?$

58. $a = 9.4$ cm, $c = 8.1$ cm, $m\angle B = 35°$, $b = ?$

59. $a = 12.5$ cm, $b = 5.9$ cm, $c = 9.3$ cm, $m\angle A = ?$

60. $a = 4.7$ cm, $b = 3.2$ cm, $c = 2.8$ cm, $m\angle C = ?$

Use the law of sines to solve for the missing parts of each $\triangle ABC$. 8-7

61. $A = 36°$, $B = 58°$, $c = 11.4$

62. $A = 123°$, $a = 15.7$, $b = 12.1$

63. $B = 72°$, $c = 6.2$, $b = 8.5$

64. $B = 28°$, $C = 53°$, $a = 10.6$

65. $C = 114°$, $a = 21.6$, $c = 25.2$

66. $A = 16°$, $C = 121°$, $b = 9.4$

For each angle measure and side lengths, tell how many triangles can be formed. 8-7

67. $A = 49°$, $b = 12$, $a = 8$

68. $A = 37°$, $b = 7$, $a = 9$

69. $A = 43°$, $b = 6$, $a = 5$

70. $A = 112°$, $b = 10$, $a = 13$

Unit 9

Carmelita works for the fund-raising office of a hospital. Last year she received the following contributions from a group of small donors:

$45, $25, $30, $65, $100, $150, $35, $40, $60, $75, $100, $75 9-1

1. Find the mean, the median, and the standard deviation of the contributions.

2. This year Carmelita is asking each donor in the group to increase his or her contribution by $10. Suppose every donor agrees to this plan. Find the mean, the median, and the standard deviation of the new contributions.

Each equation is in the form $y - k = f(x - h)$. For each equation, find the parent function and the translation vector. 9-2

3. $y + 2 = 10^{x-1}$

4. $y - 6 = \sqrt{x + 4}$

5. $y = \log (x - 9)$

6. $y - 5 = (x - 11)^3$

7. $y + 8 = |x|$

8. $y + 4 = (x + 7)^2$

A parent function and a translation vector are given. **Write the equation of the function after translation, and graph the original function and the translated function on the same set of axes.** 9-2

9. $y = x^3$; $(3, 4)$

10. $y = \log x$; $(-4, 2)$

11. $y = |x|$; $(3, -5)$

12. $y = \sqrt{x}$; $(-2, -3)$

13. $y = x^2$; $(1, -5)$

14. $y = 10^x$; $(3, -4)$

For Exercises 15 and 16: 9-3

a. Find the mean, the median, the range, and the standard deviation of the given data.

b. Repeat part (a) for the data obtained by multiplying each value by a.

c. Make histograms of the original and transformed data. Draw your histograms on the same axes.

15. data: 12, 14, 14, 18, 20, 22, 24, 34, 36, 38, 42, 42, 42, 44, 46

$a = 1.5$

16. data: 54, 57, 65, 66, 66, 68, 68, 71, 74, 77, 79, 83, 85, 88, 92

$a = 2$

Matrix M represents the triangle ABC. Find each product matrix TM. Then describe the effect on the original triangle. 9-4

17. $T = \begin{bmatrix} 4 & 0 \\ 0 & 1 \end{bmatrix}$

18. $T = \begin{bmatrix} 1 & 0 \\ 0 & \frac{3}{2} \end{bmatrix}$

$M = \begin{bmatrix} 4 & 6 & 2 \\ 0 & 2 & 6 \end{bmatrix}$

19. $T = \begin{bmatrix} 1 & 0 \\ 0 & \frac{1}{4} \end{bmatrix}$

20. $T = \begin{bmatrix} 5 & 0 \\ 0 & 1 \end{bmatrix}$

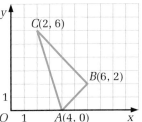

A parent function and two transformations are given. **Write the equation of the transformed function and draw its graph.** 9-5

21. $f(x) = \log x$; a translation of 3 units to the left followed by a vertical stretch by a factor of 2

22. $f(x) = x^2$; a translation of 2 units to the left followed by a translation of 1 unit down

23. $f(x) = |x|$; a vertical stretch by a factor of $\frac{1}{2}$ followed by a translation of 4 units to the right

24. $f(x) = 10^x$; a translation of 5 units to the left followed by a translation of 2 units down

For each z-score: 9-6

a. Sketch the standard normal curve and shade the region under the curve for values of z less than the given score.

b. Use the table on page 521 to find the percent of data less than the given score.

25. $z = 0.2$

26. $z = -1.0$

27. $z = -2.1$

28. $z = 1.9$

For each percent, use the table on page 521 to find the corresponding z-score for the standard normal distribution. 9-6

29. 54%　　　　　　**30.** 10%　　　　　　**31.** 1%　　　　　　**32.** 79%

Use the table on page 521, to find the missing information about a normal distribution from the given information. 9-6

33. $\bar{x} = 34.5$; $\sigma = 2.6$; data value $= 35.2$; z-score $= ?$; percentile $= ?$

34. $\bar{x} = 86.3$; $\sigma = 4.8$; percentile $= 90$; z-score $= ?$; data value $= ?$

35. $\sigma = 2.9$; percentile $= 24$; data value $= 55.2$; z-score $= ?$; $\bar{x} = ?$

Sketch the graph of each function. 9-7

36. $y - 4 = -2\lvert x + 3 \rvert$　　　**37.** $y = 3 \log(-x - 2)$　　　**38.** $y + 6 = -\frac{1}{5}x^3$

39. $y - 1 = 10^{-x+2}$　　　**40.** $y = -4\sqrt{x + 5}$　　　**41.** $y - 2 = -\frac{3}{4}(x - 3)^2$

Unit 10

Use one of the terms *constant, increasing, decreasing, periodic, damping,* **or** *saturating* **to describe each graph.** 10-1

1. 　　　**2.** 　　　**3.**

For each graph in Exercises 4 and 5: 10-2

a. Find the period.　　　　　　**b. Find the frequency.**

c. Write an equation of the axis.　　**d. Find the amplitude.**

4. 　　　　　**5.**

For Exercises 6–9, give the value of each characteristic of each function for $0° \le x \le 360°$. 10-3

a. sine function　　　　**b. cosine function**

6. The x-intercepts　　　　　　　**7.** The y-intercept

8. The intervals where the function increases　　**9.** The range of the function

Give another angle between 0° and 360° where the given function has the same value. `10-3`

10. sin 35° **11.** cos 140° **12.** sin 195° **13.** cos 65°

For each equation: `10-4`

a. Find the amplitude, period, and frequency of the graph.

b. Sketch the graph without using graphing technology, for $-360° \le \theta \le 360°$.

14. $y = 3 \sin (\theta - 60°)$ **15.** $y = 5 \sin (2\theta) + 1$ **16.** $y = -\cos (\theta + 30°) - 2$

17. $y = \cos 2(\theta + 90°) - 1$ **18.** $y = -4 \sin 0.5(\theta - 60°)$ **19.** $y = 2.5 \cos (3\theta) + 3$

Each arm of an amusement park ride called the Terrible Twister has a radius of 15 ft and each arm makes one vertical counterclockwise revolution every 20 seconds. Suppose your seat starts at the 3 o'clock position of the ride, and at its starting position your seat is 20 ft off the ground. `10-5`

20. Find your height at each time.

    a. 5 seconds after the ride starts   **b.** 15 seconds after the ride starts

21. Write an equation of your vertical position (in feet) as a function of time (in seconds).

22. Rewrite the equation you wrote for Exercise 21 to suit each condition.

    a. Each arm takes 24 s to make one complete revolution

    b. You start at the highest position of the ride.

Classify each border pattern by its symmetry. `10-6`

23.

24.

25.

26.

Use the tessellation shown at the right. `10-7`

27. Shade a cell of the tessellation.

28. Tell whether the tessellation is *regular, semiregular,* or *nonregular.*

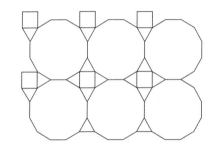

Sketch a tessellation represented by each code. `10-7`

29. 4.4.4.4   **30.** 3.3.3.4.4

Toolbox
. . . .

►Discrete Mathematics

Data Measures and Displays

Skill 1	Finding Mean, Median, Mode, and Range

mean: The sum of the data in a data set divided by the number of items.	**median:** The middle number or the mean of the two middle numbers in a data set arranged in order.
mode: The data item, or items, appearing most often. There may be more than one mode or no mode.	**range:** The difference between the smallest and largest data items.

Examples The following high temperatures were recorded on days in March:

42, 38, 56, 56, 60, 40, 65, 45, 48, 42, 56.

Find the mean, the median, the mode, and the range of the data.

Mean: There are 11 temperatures. Add the numbers. Divide the sum by 11.

$$\frac{42 + 38 + 56 + 56 + 60 + 40 + 65 + 45 + 48 + 42 + 56}{11} = 49.8$$

To the nearest tenth, the mean is 49.8.

Median: List the numbers in order. Find the middle number.

38 40 42 42 45 48 56 56 56 60 65

The median is 48.

Mode: Since 56 appears three times, and no other number appears more than twice, 56 is the mode.

Range: The smallest number is 38. The largest is 65. Subtract to find the range: $65 - 38 = 27$. The range is 27.

Use the table of data, which shows protein per serving of some foods.

1. Find the mean.   **2.** Find the median.

3. Find the mode.   **4.** Find the range.

Protein per serving (g)					
24	36	42	10	32	24
10	18	16	18	12	30

A **histogram** displays grouped data. Each group is defined by an interval on the horizontal axis. The situation and the spread of the data determine how many intervals will be used. Five to 15 intervals are common. The height of the bar for an interval indicates the number of data items that fall in the interval. This number is called a **frequency.**

Example The frequency table and the histogram show the number of supporters for candidate Kaoru Hirakawa in different age groups in her city.

Age Group	Frequency
18–29	70
30–39	140
40–49	130
50–59	40
60 or over	30

Use the table or the histogram to answer each question.

a. How many Hirakawa supporters are between the ages of 50 and 59?

  Histogram: The bar for the interval 50–59 has height 40.
  Frequency table: The frequency for the age group 50–59 is 40.

There are 40 supporters between the ages of 50 and 59.

b. In which age groups does she have the greatest support and the least support?

  Using the histogram, you see that the tallest bar is for the interval 30–39. She has the greatest support in this age group. The shortest bar is for the group "60 or over." She has the least support in this age group.

Use the histogram or the frequency table to answer each question.

Salary Range (thousand $)	Number of subscribers
Below 20	30
20–29	100
30–39	52
40–49	34
50 or over	11

How many subscribers are in each salary range?

1. Below $20,000   **2.** Between $20,000 and $29,000   **3.** $50,000 or over

4. Which salary range has the most subscribers? the least?

Using Counting Techniques

A **permutation** is an arrangement of a certain number of items in a definite order. The symbol for the number of different permutations of r items chosen all possible ways from among n items is $_nP_r$.

Example How many different four-letter arrangements can be made from the letters of the word GRATES? Assume that a letter cannot be used more than once.

The number of four-letter arrangements is $_6P_4$, since there are 6 letters to choose from.

6 choices for the first letter   4 choices for the third letter

$$6 \cdot 5 \cdot 4 \cdot 3 = 360 \longleftarrow \text{number of 4-letter arrangements}$$

5 choices for the second letter   3 choices for the fourth letter

The symbol $n!$ (read "n factorial") means the product of the positive integers through n.

$$n! = n(n-1)(n-2) \cdots 3 \cdot 2 \cdot 1.$$

The example above suggests a formula for $_nP_r$.

Number of permutations of r items selected from n items:

$$_nP_r = \underbrace{n(n-1)(n-2)\cdots}_{r \text{ factors}} = \frac{n!}{(n-r)!}$$

n items $\nearrow$ $\uparrow$

arranged r at a time

Example To solve the example above using the formula, you write:

$$_6P_4 = \frac{6!}{(6-4)!} = \frac{6!}{2!} = \frac{6 \cdot 5 \cdot 4 \cdot 3 \cdot 2 \cdot 1}{2 \cdot 1} = 6 \cdot 5 \cdot 4 \cdot 3 = 360$$

Evaluate each expression.

1. $5!$

2. $7!$

3. $\dfrac{6!}{3!}$

4. $\dfrac{10!}{2!}$

5. $_7P_3$

6. $_8P_5$

7. $_9P_4$

8. $_6P_6$

Find the number of four-letter arrangements that can be made from the letters of each word.

9. COMPUTER

10. HARVEST

11. NUMERATOR

A **combination** is a selection of a definite number of items from a group of items, without regard to order. The symbol for the number of different combinations of r items selected all possible ways from a group of n items is $_nC_r$.

As you saw in Skill 3, each selection of r items can be arranged to form $_rP_r$ (or $r!$) different *permutations*. Therefore, $_nP_r = {_rP_r} \cdot {_nC_r}$. When you solve this equation for $_nC_r$, you get the following formula.

Number of combinations of r items selected from n items:

$$_nC_r = \frac{_nP_r}{_rP_r} = \frac{n!}{(n-r)!\, r!}$$

 Example   How many different groups of 3 actresses can be chosen to play the witches in *Macbeth* from these 6 actresses who audition: Val, Carla, Susan, Pat, Mimi, and Rose?

Order does not matter in this situation. You have to find the number of combinations of 6 items selected 3 at a time.

Method ❶

Problem Solving Strategy: Make a systematic list.

Represent each actress with one letter.

VCS	VSP	VPM	VMR	CSP	CPM	CMR	SPM	SMR	PMR
VCP	VSM	VPR		CSM	CPR		SPR		
VCM	VSR			CSR					
VCR									

20 different groups of 3 actresses can be chosen from 6 actresses.

Method ❷

Problem Solving Strategy: Use a formula.

$$_6C_3 = \frac{6!}{(6-3)!3!} = \frac{6!}{3!3!} = \frac{6 \cdot 5 \cdot 4 \cdot 3 \cdot 2 \cdot 1}{3 \cdot 2 \cdot 1 \cdot 3 \cdot 2 \cdot 1} = 20$$

20 different groups of 3 actresses can be chosen from 6 actresses.

Evaluate each expression.

1. $_6C_4$ **2.** $_8C_3$ **3.** $_7C_5$ **4.** $_9C_4$

5. How many different subcommittees of 5 can be selected from a committee of 11?

6. How many different ways can you select 7 CDs out of 12 to bring to a party?

Toolbox   **629**

Pascal's triangle shows that there is a simple pattern to the numbers $_nC_r$.

Example Use Pascal's triangle to find $_4C_2$.

Some Properties of Pascal's Triangle

Each number (except the 1's) is the sum of the two numbers just above it.

The number in row n, diagonal r, is $_nC_r$.

The sum of the numbers in row n is 2^n.

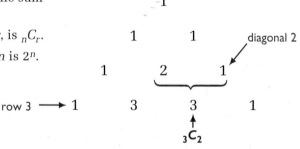

Find each value using Pascal's triangle.

1. $_4C_2$

2. $_5C_3$

3. $_6C_3$

4. $_6C_4$

5. How could you find $_7C_4$ from your answers to Questions 3 and 4 above, using Pascal's triangle?

6. The numbers in diagonal 2 of Pascal's triangle are called *triangular numbers*. Why do you think this name was chosen? (*Hint*: Draw an equilateral triangle made up of dots arranged in a grid.)

7. Make a conjecture about the sums of pairs of consecutive numbers in diagonal 2 of Pascal's triangle.

Probability

The **probability** of an event is a number between 0 and 1 that tells how likely the event is to happen. The closer the probability is to 1, the more likely the event. If the same experiment is performed over and over, you can find the **experimental probability** $P(E)$ of an event E as follows:

$$P(E) = \frac{\text{number of times the event } E \text{ happened}}{\text{number of times the experiment was performed}}$$

Example
Out of a crate of 400 light bulbs, 8 were found to be defective. What is the experimental probability of finding a defective bulb?

$$P(\text{defective bulb}) = \frac{\text{number of defective bulbs found}}{\text{total number of bulbs checked}} = \frac{8}{400} = 0.02, \text{ or } 2\%$$

When all the outcomes of an experiment are equally likely, you can find the **theoretical probability** of an event by calculation. You can think of an event as the group of outcomes that are considered favorable. Theoretical probability is the ratio:

$$P(E) = \frac{\text{number of favorable outcomes}}{\text{number of possible outcomes}}$$

Example
Suppose you pick a card at random from the 13 hearts of a standard deck. What is the probability that it is a face card?

There are 13 possible outcomes:

There are 3 favorable outcomes:

$P(\text{face card}) = \frac{3}{13} \approx 0.23$, or about 23%

The table shows how many of each different size of a particular style of sweatshirt were sold at one store last month. Find the probability that a sweatshirt sold will be each size.

Size	Number Sold
Small	15
Medium	32
Large	44

1. Small   **2.** Medium   **3.** Large

A card is chosen at random from the 13 hearts of a standard deck. Find each probability.

4. $P(\text{ace of hearts})$ **5.** $P(\text{not a face card})$ **6.** $P(\text{a diamond})$ **7.** $P(\text{not a diamond})$

Toolbox

Two events that cannot happen at the same time are said to be **mutually exclusive.** When two events are mutually exclusive, you can find the probability that either one or the other will occur by adding the probabilities of the two events.

For mutually exclusive events A and B: $P(A \text{ or } B) = P(A) + P(B)$

Example ▸ A spinner numbered 1 through 12 is spun. What is the probability that the spinner lands on 12 or an odd number?

Since 12 is not an odd number, these two events are mutually exclusive. Therefore,

$P(\text{odd number or } 12) = P(\text{odd number}) + P(12) = \frac{6}{12} + \frac{1}{12} = \frac{7}{12}.$

Use the spinner from the example above. Find the probability of each event.

1. 3 or 7

2. 8 or a multiple of 3

3. number less than 4 or greater than 8

4. a multiple of 4 or a prime number

Operations with Matrices

A **matrix** (plural: *matrices*) is an arrangement of numbers, called **elements,** in rows and columns. The number of rows followed by the number of columns are the **dimensions** of the matrix. The price matrix below has dimensions 3×2, read "three by two."

Example ▸ What is the daily rental price for a compact car on a weekend?

Daily Car Rental Prices

	Weekday	Weekend
Subcompact	32.50	44.00
Compact	38.00	56.00
Full-size	52.50	68.00

three rows

two columns

The daily rental for a compact car on a weekend is $56.00.

Use the matrix at the right.

1. Give the dimensions of the matrix.

2. How much is a $\frac{1}{4}$ lb burger special? How much is a dinner with a plain burger?

Burger Prices

	$\frac{1}{4}$ lb	$\frac{1}{2}$ lb	dinner
Plain	3.50	4.00	5.50
Special	4.50	5.00	7.00

To multiply a matrix P by a number, you multiply each entry of P by the number. Multiplying a matrix by a number is called **scalar multiplication.**

Example The matrix $P = \begin{bmatrix} 3.50 & 4.00 & 5.50 \\ 4.50 & 5.00 & 7.00 \end{bmatrix}$ represents burger prices, as in the exercises on page 632. Suppose burger prices increase by 8%. Write the matrix for the new pricing scheme.

Each new price will be 100% + 8% of the current price. The new matrix will be:

$$(1.08)P = \begin{bmatrix} (1.08)\,3.50 & (1.08)\,4.00 & (1.08)\,5.50 \\ (1.08)\,4.50 & (1.08)\,5.00 & (1.08)\,7.00 \end{bmatrix}$$

$$= \begin{bmatrix} 3.78 & 4.32 & 5.94 \\ 4.86 & 5.40 & 7.56 \end{bmatrix}$$

Multiply each matrix by the given number.

1. $\begin{bmatrix} 1 & 4 \\ 7 & 0 \\ 6 & 2 \end{bmatrix}; 5$

2. $\begin{bmatrix} 1 & 1 & 0 & 1 \\ 3 & 2 & 4 & 6 \end{bmatrix}; 0.5$

3. $\begin{bmatrix} 24 & 36 & 8 \\ 12 & 48 & 4 \end{bmatrix}; 1.25$

When two matrices have the same dimensions, you can add or subtract the matrices by adding or subtracting the elements in corresponding positions.

Example $\begin{bmatrix} 25 & 46 & 53 \\ 0 & 38 & 22 \end{bmatrix} + \begin{bmatrix} 15 & 16 & -5 \\ 25 & 32 & -12 \end{bmatrix} = \begin{bmatrix} 25+15 & 46+16 & 53+(-5) \\ 0+25 & 38+32 & 22+(-12) \end{bmatrix}$

$$= \begin{bmatrix} 40 & 62 & 48 \\ 25 & 70 & 10 \end{bmatrix}$$

Example $\begin{bmatrix} 5 & 6 \\ -4 & 9 \\ 2 & 3 \end{bmatrix} - \begin{bmatrix} 3 & 6 \\ 5 & 2 \\ -1 & 8 \end{bmatrix} = \begin{bmatrix} 5-3 & 6-6 \\ -4-5 & 9-2 \\ 2-(-1) & 3-8 \end{bmatrix} = \begin{bmatrix} 2 & 0 \\ -9 & 7 \\ 3 & -5 \end{bmatrix}$

Example You cannot add $\begin{bmatrix} 3 & 2 & 4 \\ 6 & 5 & 1 \end{bmatrix}$ and $\begin{bmatrix} 8 & 3 \\ 2 & 5 \end{bmatrix}$, because they have different dimensions.

dimensions: 2 × 2

dimensions: 2 × 3

Toolbox

Add or subtract as indicated.

1. $\begin{bmatrix} 4 & -1 & 6 \\ 9 & 3 & -2 \end{bmatrix} + \begin{bmatrix} 5 & 3 & -7 \\ 6 & -2 & 8 \end{bmatrix}$

2. $\begin{bmatrix} 12 & 15 \\ 22 & 0 \\ 17 & 25 \\ 8 & 16 \end{bmatrix} - \begin{bmatrix} -5 & 6 \\ 15 & 9 \\ 12 & -4 \\ 8 & 20 \end{bmatrix}$

3. $\begin{bmatrix} 1.5 & 3.8 \\ 6.2 & 4.6 \end{bmatrix} - \begin{bmatrix} 2.5 & 1.4 \\ 4.3 & 5.9 \end{bmatrix}$

4. $[62 \quad 112 \quad 58] + [48 \quad 68 \quad 12]$

Skill 11   Multiplying Matrices

The matrix product $L \cdot R$ is defined only when the number of columns of matrix L equals the number of rows of matrix R. If the dimensions of L are $m \times n$ and those of R are $n \times p$, the product will have dimensions $m \times p$.

To multiply a row of L by a column of R, you multiply each element of the row of L by the corresponding element of the column of R and then add.

Example

Multiply the first elements.

Multiply the second elements.

$$[3 \ -1]\begin{bmatrix} 4 \\ 5 \end{bmatrix} = [3 \cdot 4 + (-1)5] = [7]$$

Add.

To multiply a matrix L by a matrix R, you multiply each *row* of L by each *column* of R, and enter the result in the position whose coordinates are (*row, column*).

Example When matrix A has dimensions 2×4 and matrix B has dimensions 4×1, the dimensions of the product matrix are 2×1.

Multiply each row of A by the one column of B.

$$\begin{matrix} A \\ \begin{bmatrix} 1 & 0 & 5 & 7 \\ 2 & 12 & -2 & 10 \end{bmatrix} \end{matrix} \begin{matrix} B \\ \begin{bmatrix} 8 \\ 12 \\ -3 \\ 4 \end{bmatrix} \end{matrix} = \begin{bmatrix} 1(8) + 0(12) + 5(-3) + 7(4) \\ 2(8) + 12(12) + (-2)(-3) + 10(4) \end{bmatrix}$$

$$= \begin{bmatrix} 21 \\ 206 \end{bmatrix} \begin{matrix} \leftarrow \text{(row 1 of A)} \times \text{(column 1 of B)} \\ \leftarrow \text{(row 2 of A)} \times \text{(column 1 of B)} \end{matrix}$$

Multiply.

1. $[5 \ -2]\begin{bmatrix} 3 \\ 6 \end{bmatrix}$

2. $\begin{bmatrix} 4 & -1 \\ 3 & 5 \\ 2 & -2 \end{bmatrix}\begin{bmatrix} 4 & 7 \\ 0 & 1 \end{bmatrix}$

3. $\begin{bmatrix} 6 & 1 \\ 0 & 4 \\ 3 & 2 \end{bmatrix}\begin{bmatrix} 1 & -1 & 2 & 0 \\ 3 & 4 & -5 & -2 \end{bmatrix}$

➤ Algebra and Graphing

Algebraic Expressions

Skill 12	Evaluating Expressions

You evaluate an algebraic expression, such as $7x^2 - 3x + 5$, by substituting a given value for the variable.

Example   Evaluate $7x^2 - 3x + 5$ when $x = -2$.

$$7x^2 - 3x + 5 = 7(-2)^2 - 3(-2) + 5 \quad \longleftarrow \text{Substitute } -2 \text{ for } x.$$
$$= 7 \cdot 4 - 3(-2) + 5 \quad \longleftarrow (-2)^2 \text{ means } (-2)(-2).$$
$$= 28 - (-6) + 5 \quad \longleftarrow \text{Do multiplication next.}$$
$$= 28 + 6 + 5 \quad \longleftarrow \text{To subtract } -6, \text{ add its opposite.}$$
$$= 39 \quad \longleftarrow \text{Do addition last.}$$

Evaluate each expression when $x = 3$.

1. $x^2 - 7x + 12$ **2.** $4x^3 - 5x + 1$ **3.** $15 - 4x^2$

4. $-2x^2 + 6x - 4$ **5.** $2x^5 - 4(x - 1)$ **6.** $(x - 5)^3 - 4(x + 1)^2$

Evaluate each expression when $a = -10$ and $b = 2$.

7. $3(a + b)$ **8.** $-a - b^2$ **9.** $-a^2b$

10. $-4a^2 + b^2$ **11.** $-4(a^2 + b^2)$ **12.** $-4(a + b)^2$

Skill 13	Adding and Subtracting Polynomials

A **monomial** is a number, a variable, or the product of a number and one or more variables. A **polynomial** is a monomial or a sum of monomials.

Terms having the same variables raised to the same powers are called **like terms**. To add two polynomials, **combine like terms**.

Example

$$(2x^2 + 4xy) + (-5x^2 + 7xy) = 2x^2 + 4xy - 5x^2 + 7xy \quad \longleftarrow \text{Rewrite without parentheses.}$$
$$= (2x^2 - 5x^2) + (4xy + 7xy) \quad \longleftarrow \text{Group like terms.}$$
$$= (2 - 5)x^2 + (4 + 7)xy \quad \longleftarrow \text{Use the distributive property.}$$
$$= -3x^2 + 11xy$$

Toolbox

To subtract one polynomial from another, you can remove parentheses and rewrite the difference as the sum of the first polynomial and -1 times the second. Then use the distributive property.

Example

$$(3x^2 - 2xy + 8y^2) - (7x^2 - 5xy + 2y^2) = (3x^2 - 2xy + 8y^2) + (-1)(7x^2 - 5xy + 2y^2)$$
$$= 3x^2 - 2xy + 8y^2 - 7x^2 + 5xy - 2y^2$$
$$= (3 - 7)x^2 + (-2 + 5)xy + (8 - 2)y^2$$
$$= -4x^2 + 3xy + 6y^2$$

Add or subtract, as indicated.

1. $(4a^2 - 3a + 2) + (-5a^2 + 2a)$

2. $(x^2 - xy + y^2) + (2x^2 + xy + y^2)$

3. $(7x^3 - 4x + 9) - (5x^3 + 3x^2 - 4x + 10)$

4. $(3c^2 + cd - 4d^2) - (5c^2 + 7cd + d^2 + 1)$

Skill 14   Using Rules of Exponents

For all real numbers x and all positive integers n,

$$x^n \text{ means } \underbrace{x \cdot x \cdot x \cdot \cdots \cdot x}_{n \text{ factors}}.$$

Product of Powers Rule: $a^m \cdot a^n = a^{m+n}$, for all real numbers a.

Quotient of Powers Rule: $\dfrac{a^m}{a^n} = a^{m-n}$, for all real numbers $a \neq 0$.

Example $3^5 \cdot 3^4 = 3^{5+4}$ ← Use the product of powers rule.
$$= 3^9$$

Example $\dfrac{2^7}{2^4} = 2^{7-4}$ ← Use the quotient of powers rule.
$$= 2^3$$

Example $\dfrac{6.7 \times 10^9}{3.2 \times 10^4} = \dfrac{6.7}{3.2} \times \dfrac{10^9}{10^4}$

$$= \dfrac{6.7}{3.2} \times 10^{9-4} \quad \leftarrow \text{ Use the quotient of powers rule.}$$

$$\approx 2.1 \times 10^5$$

Student Resources

To extend the domain of exponents to include 0 and the negative integers in a way that is consistent with the rules of exponents on page 636, you make the following definitions:

Zero Exponent Rule: For any real number $a \neq 0$, $a^0 = 1$.

Negative Exponent Rule: For any real number $a \neq 0$, $a^{-n} = \dfrac{1}{a^n}$.

Example Simplify $6a^0b^{-4}$. Write the answer without negative exponents.

$$6a^0b^{-4} = 6 \cdot 1 \cdot b^{-4} \qquad \longleftarrow \text{Use the zero exponent rule.}$$
$$= 6\left(\frac{1}{b^4}\right) \qquad \longleftarrow \text{Use the negative exponent rule.}$$
$$= \frac{6}{b^4}$$

If a, b, c, and d are real numbers with $b \neq 0$ and $d \neq 0$, then

$$\frac{ac}{bd} = \frac{a}{b} \cdot \frac{c}{d}.$$

Example Simplify $\dfrac{2x^{12}y^{-2}}{6x^3y^4}$. Write your answer without negative exponents.

$$\frac{2x^{12}y^{-2}}{6x^3y^4} = \frac{2}{6} \cdot \frac{x^{12}}{x^3} \cdot \frac{y^{-2}}{y^4}$$
$$= \frac{2}{6} \cdot x^{12-3} \cdot y^{-2-4} \qquad \longleftarrow \text{Use the quotient of powers rule.}$$
$$= \frac{1}{3} \cdot x^9 \cdot y^{-2} \qquad \longleftarrow \text{Simplify.}$$
$$= \frac{x^9}{3y^2} \qquad \longleftarrow \text{Use the negative exponent rule.}$$

Simplify. Write your answer without negative exponents.

1. $(3t^4)(9t^9)$

2. $\dfrac{6a^{10}}{8a^2}$

3. $(5r^2)(-4r^{-3})$

4. $5a^{-2}b^0$

5. $\dfrac{45u^{-5}}{9}$

6. $(4m^{-2})(3n^{-4})$

7. $(-2x^2y^5)(3x^{-2}y^{-7})$

8. $\dfrac{4v^0w^3}{6v^{-2}w^4}$

9. $\dfrac{14x^{-5}y^{-7}}{7xy^2}$

Skill 15   Multiplying Polynomials

To multiply two polynomials, you use the distributive property as often as needed.

Example

$(2a + 3)(5a + 7) = (2a + 3) \cdot 5a + (2a + 3) \cdot 7$ ← Use the distributive property.

$= 2a \cdot 5a + 3 \cdot 5a + 2a \cdot 7 + 3 \cdot 7$ ← Use the distributive property again.

$= 10a^2 + 15a + 14a + 21$

$= 10a^2 + 29a + 21$ ← Combine like terms.

Example   Expand $(2p + 3)(4p^2 - 5p + 8)$.

$(2p + 3)(4p^2 - 5p + 8) = (2p + 3) \cdot 4p^2 + (2p + 3) \cdot (-5p) + (2p + 3) \cdot 8$

$= 8p^3 + 12p^2 - 10p^2 - 15p + 16p + 24$

$= 8p^3 + 2p^2 + p + 24$ ← Combine like terms.

There are patterns that help you expand certain special products.

Special Products

$(a + b)^2 = a^2 + 2ab + b^2$
$(\text{first} + \text{second})^2 = (\text{first})^2 + 2(\text{first})(\text{second}) + (\text{second})^2$

$(a - b)^2 = a^2 - 2ab + b^2$
$(\text{first} - \text{second})^2 = (\text{first})^2 - 2(\text{first})(\text{second}) + (\text{second})^2$

$(a + b)(a - b) = a^2 - b^2$
$(\text{first} + \text{second})(\text{first} - \text{second}) = (\text{first})^2 - (\text{second})^2$

Example   Expand $(3x + 5y)^2$.

You can use the distributive property, as in the Examples above, or you can use the first pattern above, with a replaced by $3x$ and b replaced by $5y$:

$(3x + 5y)^2 = (3x)^2 + 2 \cdot 3x \cdot 5y + (5y)^2$

$= 9x^2 + 30xy + 25y^2$

Expand.

1. $(a + 2)(a - 2)$

2. $(a + 2)^2$

3. $(a - 2)^2$

4. $(3k + 4)(7k - 2)$

5. $(5x + 2y)^2$

6. $(7c + 6d)(7c - 6d)$

7. $(9w - 4)^2$

8. $(10x - 3y)(2x - 5y)$

9. $(a + 2)(a^2 - 3a + 1)$

10. $(3x + 2y)^2$

11. $(x + 3)(x^2 - 2x + 4)$

12. $(2n - 5)(2n^2 - 3n - 2)$

Student Resources

You can use Pascal's triangle (see Skills 4 and 5) to help you expand a power of a binomial. Notice the pattern of the coefficients in the expansions below.

$$(a + b)^0 = \qquad\qquad 1$$
$$(a + b)^1 = \qquad\qquad 1a + 1b$$
$$(a + b)^2 = \qquad 1a^2 + 2ab + 1b^2$$
$$(a + b)^3 = 1a^3 + 3a^2b + 3ab^2 + 1b^3$$

This pattern suggests that if n is a positive integer, the coefficients in the expansion of $(a + b)^n$ can be found in row n of Pascal's triangle.

The Binomial Theorem

If n is a positive integer, then this is the expanded form of $(a + b)^n$:

$$(_nC_0)a^nb^0 + (_nC_1)a^{n-1}b^1 + (_nC_2)a^{n-2}b^2 + \cdots$$
$$\cdots + (_nC_{n-2})a^2b^{n-2} + (_nC_{n-1})a^1b^{n-1} + (_nC_n)a^0b^n$$

The coefficients of the form $(_nC_r)$ are numbers in the nth row of Pascal's triangle.

Example Write $(x + 3)^4$ in expanded form.

Use the binomial theorem with $n = 4$.

For coefficients, use the fourth row of Pascal's triangle.

```
            1
          1   1
        1   2   1
      1   3   3   1
    1   4   6   4   1
```
$\longrightarrow$ $(a + b)^4 = 1a^4b^0 + 4a^3b^1 + 6a^2b^2 + 4a^1b^3 + 1a^0b^4$

Substitute x for a and 3 for b. Simplify.

$$
\begin{aligned}
(x + 3)^4 &= 1x^4(3)^0 + 4x^3(3)^1 + 6x^2(3)^2 + 4x^1(3)^3 + 1x^0(3)^4 \\
&= 1x^4(1) + 4x^3(3) + 6x^2(9) + 4x^1(27) + 1x^0(81) \\
&= x^4 + 12x^3 + 54x^2 + 108x + 81
\end{aligned}
$$

Expand.

1. $(x + y)^5$

2. $(2r + 3)^4$

3. $(p^2 + q)^6$

4. $(2n - m)^3$

5. $(c + 10d)^5$

6. $(v^2 + 2w^3)^4$

Toolbox

One way to factor a trinomial is to try different combinations of binomial factors.

Example   Factor $2x^2 + 5x + 3$ by trial and error.

You want an answer in this form: $(\underline{\ ?\ } x + \underline{\ ?\ })(\underline{\ ?\ } x + \underline{\ ?\ })$

These terms will be factors of $2x^2$.
For example: $2x, x$

These terms will be factors of 3.
For example: $1, 3$
$-1, -3$

Try different combinations. Focus on getting the correct middle term.

The second pair of factors gives the correct middle term.

$2x^2 + 5x + 3 = (2x + 3)(x + 1)$

To factor certain trinomials, use the patterns from Skill 15.

Perfect Square Trinomials: $a^2 + 2ab + b^2 = (a + b)^2$
$$a^2 - 2ab + b^2 = (a - b)^2$$

Difference of Two Squares: $a^2 - b^2 = (a + b)(a - b)$

Example $49x^2 - 4y^2 = (7x)^2 - (2y)^2$
$$= (7x + 2y)(7x - 2y) \quad \longleftarrow \text{ Use the pattern for } a^2 - b^2.$$

You can factor some polynomials by finding the greatest common (monomial) factor, or **GCF**, of the terms.

Example $6x^5 - 8x^7 + 10x^2 = 6(x^2 \cdot x^3) - 8(x^2 \cdot x^5) + 10x^2$ ← Find the GCF of the variable parts.
$$= 2x^2(3x^3) - 2x^2(4x^5) + 2x^2(5) \longleftarrow \text{ The GCF of the coefficients is 2.}$$
$$\text{The GCF of the variable parts is } x^2.$$
$$= 2x^2(3x^3 - 4x^5 + 5)$$

Factor.

1. $x^2 - 20x + 100$

2. $25y^2 - 81z^2$

3. $a^2 - 5a - 14$

4. $2c^2 + 9c - 5$

5. $3x^2 - 7xy + 2y^2$

6. $49m^2 + 70mn + 25n^2$

7. $4x^5 - 2x^4 + 16x^2$

8. $9p^3q + 15p^2$

9. $45x^3y - 18x^2y^5$

A **rational expression** is a quotient of two polynomials. You can often simplify rational expressions by factoring both the numerator and the denominator of the expression.

Example   Simplify $\dfrac{x^2 + 5x + 6}{x + 2}$.

$$\dfrac{x^2 + 5x + 6}{x + 2} = \dfrac{(x + 3)(x + 2)}{x + 2}$$ ⟵ Factor both the numerator and the denominator.

$$= x + 3$$ ⟵ Look for common factors in numerator and denominator to simplify.

Example   Simplify $\dfrac{x^2 - 6x + 9}{x^2 - 2x - 3}$.

$$\dfrac{x^2 - 6x + 9}{x^2 - 2x - 3} = \dfrac{(x - 3)^2}{(x - 3)(x + 1)}$$ ⟵ Factor both the numerator and the denominator.

$$= \dfrac{x - 3}{x + 1}$$ ⟵ Look for common factors in numerator and denominator to simplify.

Sometimes an algebraic expression includes several rational expressions as terms. You can simplify such an expression by finding the least common multiple (LCM) of the denominators, just as you would when adding fractions.

Example   Simplify $\dfrac{3}{4x^2} - \dfrac{1}{8x}$.

$$\dfrac{3}{4x^2} - \dfrac{1}{8x} = \dfrac{2 \cdot 3}{2 \cdot 4x^2} - \dfrac{x \cdot 1}{x \cdot 8x}$$ ⟵ The LCM is $8x^2$.

$$= \dfrac{6}{8x^2} - \dfrac{x}{8x^2}$$ ⟵ Simplify.

$$= \dfrac{6 - x}{8x^2}$$ ⟵ Subtract the numerators and write the result over the common denominator.

Simplify.

1. $\dfrac{y + 5}{y^2 + 10y + 25}$

2. $\dfrac{x^2 - x - 2}{x^2 - 4}$

3. $\dfrac{a^2 - 7a + 12}{a^2 - a - 12}$

4. $\dfrac{2}{3x} + \dfrac{4}{x}$

5. $\dfrac{2}{x - 5} - \dfrac{3}{2x - 10}$

6. $\dfrac{2}{x^2 + x} - \dfrac{1}{x + 1}$

Toolbox

When a is a nonnegative number, $\sqrt{a}$ is a real number. When a is negative, $\sqrt{a}$ is not a real number.

You may be able to simplify $\sqrt{a}$ by finding the largest perfect-square factor of a, and then using the fact that for all nonnegative numbers a and b,

$$\sqrt{ab} = \sqrt{a} \cdot \sqrt{b}.$$

Example

$\sqrt{18} = \sqrt{9 \cdot 2}$ ◀—— 9 is the largest perfect-square factor of 18. Write 18 as $9 \cdot 2$.

$\quad = \sqrt{9} \cdot \sqrt{2}$ ◀—— Use the fact that $\sqrt{ab} = \sqrt{a} \cdot \sqrt{b}$.

$\quad = 3\sqrt{2}$ ◀—— Write $\sqrt{9}$ as 3.

Note: It would *not* have been helpful to write $\sqrt{18}$ as $\sqrt{6 \cdot 3}$, because neither 6 nor 3 is a perfect square.

To simplify a product of radical factors, you use the fact that for all nonnegative numbers a and b,

$$\sqrt{a} \cdot \sqrt{b} = \sqrt{ab}.$$

Example

$5\sqrt{3} \cdot \sqrt{2} = 5\sqrt{3 \cdot 2}$ ◀—— Use the fact that $\sqrt{a} \cdot \sqrt{b} = \sqrt{ab}$.

$\quad = 5\sqrt{6}$

Example

$4\sqrt{5} \cdot 2\sqrt{15} = 4 \cdot 2 \cdot \sqrt{5} \cdot \sqrt{15}$ ◀—— Group radical terms.

$\quad = 8\sqrt{5 \cdot 15}$ ◀—— Use the fact that $\sqrt{a} \cdot \sqrt{b} = \sqrt{ab}$.

$\quad = 8\sqrt{75}$ ◀—— Simplify.

$\quad = 8\sqrt{25 \cdot 3}$ ◀—— 25 is the largest perfect-square factor of 75.

$\quad = 8\sqrt{25} \cdot \sqrt{3}$ ◀—— Use the fact that $\sqrt{ab} = \sqrt{a} \cdot \sqrt{b}$.

$\quad = 8 \cdot 5\sqrt{3}$ ◀—— Write $\sqrt{25}$ as 5.

$\quad = 40\sqrt{3}$

Simplify.

1. $\sqrt{45}$ **2.** $\sqrt{300}$ **3.** $\sqrt{76}$ **4.** $5\sqrt{12}$ **5.** $12\sqrt{125}$

6. $\sqrt{6} \cdot \sqrt{7}$ **7.** $3\sqrt{5} \cdot \sqrt{2}$ **8.** $4.2\sqrt{11} \cdot \sqrt{3}$ **9.** $8\sqrt{2} \cdot 3\sqrt{3}$

10. $\sqrt{6} \cdot \sqrt{6}$ **11.** $\left(3\sqrt{3}\right)^2$ **12.** $2\sqrt{6} \cdot 3\sqrt{2}$ **13.** $4\sqrt{5} \cdot 3\sqrt{10}$

The equation $x^2 = -1$ has no real-number solution. The **imaginary unit i**, which is not a real number, is defined to be a solution of this equation:

$$i = \sqrt{-1} \quad \text{and} \quad i^2 = -1$$

The square root of a negative number is defined as follows for all real numbers $a > 0$:

$$\sqrt{-a} = \sqrt{-1} \cdot \sqrt{a} = i\sqrt{a}$$

Example   **a.** $\sqrt{-81} = i\sqrt{81} = 9i$ **b.** $\sqrt{-33} = i\sqrt{33} \approx 5.7i$

In order to create a system that includes both the real numbers and the **pure imaginary numbers,** such as i, $2i$, and $i\sqrt{3}$, the **complex numbers** are defined. These are numbers of the form $a + bi$, where a and b are real numbers.

You can use what you know about adding like terms and multiplying binomials to do operations with complex numbers.

Example   Simplify.

a. $(9i)(3i) = 27i^2$

$\qquad = 27(-1)$ ← Substitute -1 for i^2.

$\qquad = -27$

b. $(2 + 6i) - (1 - 3i) = 2 + 6i - 1 + 3i$ ← Rewrite without parentheses.

$\qquad = (2 - 1) + (6 + 3)i$ ← Group real parts and group imaginary parts.

$\qquad = 1 + 9i$

c. $(5 + 7i)(4 + 8i) = (5 + 7i)4 + (5 + 7i)8i$ ← Use the distributive property.

$\qquad = 20 + 28i + 40i + 56i^2$ ← Use the distributive property again.

$\qquad = 20 + 68i + 56(-1)$ ← Combine like terms. Substitute -1 for i^2.

$\qquad = 20 + 68i - 56$ ← Simplify.

$\qquad = -36 + 68i$ ← Combine like terms.

Simplify.

1. $\sqrt{-100}$ **2.** $\sqrt{-0.25}$ **3.** $\sqrt{-17}$ **4.** $\sqrt{-83}$

5. $(5i)(7i)$ **6.** $(4i)(-3i)(0.5i)$ **7.** $9i(1 - 8i)$ **8.** $-7i(12 + 3i)$

9. $(8 - 14i) + (10 - 5i)$ **10.** $(-4 + 2i) - (9 - 9i)$ **11.** $(3 + 4i) - (-7 + 11.5i)$

12. $(5 + 4i)(6 - 12i)$ **13.** $(-2 + 8i)(1 + 0.2i)$ **14.** $(4 - 10i)(4 + 10i)$

Solving Equations

Solving a linear system of equations means finding one pair of numbers (x, y) that satisfies both equations. One method of solving a linear system is **substitution.**

Example Solve the system: $x - 2y = -11$
$$x + y = 4$$

$x + y = 4$	$\longrightarrow$ $y = 4 - x$	$\longleftarrow$ Solve the second equation for y.
$x - 2y = -11$	$\longrightarrow$ $x - 2(4 - x) = -11$	$\longleftarrow$ Substitute $4 - x$ for y in the other equation.
	$x - 8 + 2x = -11$	$\longleftarrow$ Remove parentheses.
	$3x = -3$	$\longleftarrow$ Combine like terms.
	$x = -1$	$\longleftarrow$ Solve for x.
	$-1 + y = 4$	$\longleftarrow$ Substitute the value of x back into either equation.
	$y = 5$	

The solution (x, y) is $(-1, 5)$.

You can also use **addition-or-subtraction** to solve a system.

Example Solve by the addition-or-subtraction method.

a. $3y = 2x + 2$
$3y = x - 2$

b. $5a + 2b = 23$
$7a - 2b = 13$

a. The coefficients of y are *the same.*
Subtract to eliminate the y-terms.

$$\begin{array}{r} 3y = 2x + 2 \\ - \underline{3y = x - 2} \\ 0 = x + 4 \end{array}$$

$0 = x + 4$

$-4 = x$

Solve the new equation.

$3y = -4 - 2$
$3y = -6$
$y = -2$

Substitute in one of the original equations to find the other variable.

The solution (x, y) is $(-4, -2)$.

b. The coefficients of b are *opposites.*
Add to eliminate the b-terms.

$$\begin{array}{r} 5a + 2b = 23 \\ + \underline{7a - 2b = 13} \\ 12a + 0 = 36 \end{array}$$

$12a = 36$

$a = 3$

$5(3) + 2b = 23$
$15 + 2b = 23$
$2b = 8$
$b = 4$

The solution (a, b) is $(3, 4)$.

Some linear systems contain no like terms with the same or opposite coefficients. You can change the coefficients by multiplying both sides of either equation by a constant.

Example Solve the system: $4x - 3y = 11$
$-5x + 2y = -12$

$5(4x - 3y) = 5(11)$ ⟵ Multiply both sides of the first equation by **5**.

$4(-5x + 2y) = 4(-12)$ ⟵ Multiply both sides of the second equation by 4.

$20x - 15y = 55$
$-20x + 8y = -48$ ⟵ The new system has x-terms that are opposites.

Now you can solve the system as in the preceding example.

Solve each system.

1. $y = 4x$
$y = -x - 15$

2. $b = a + 5$
$b = 3a - 1$

3. $x - y = 1$
$x + y = -1$

4. $3a + 5b = 17$
$3a + 8b = 5$

5. $p - 6q = 14$
$2p + 6q = 1$

6. $-2c + 9d = 35$
$6c + 7d = 65$

Skill 22   Solving a Quadratic Equation

A **quadratic** equation is one that contains an x^2-term. Some quadratic equations can be solved by factoring and using the *zero-product property*.

Example Solve $4x^2 - x = 5$.

$4x^2 - x = 5$

$4x^2 - x - 5 = 0$ ⟵ Rewrite the equation in standard form.

$(4x - 5)(x + 1) = 0$ ⟵ Factor the trinomial by trial and error.

$4x - 5 = 0$ *or* $x + 1 = 0$ ⟵ Use the zero-product property. When a product of factors is equal to 0, one or more of the factors equals 0.

$4x = 5$ $x = -1$

$x = 1.25$

The solutions are 1.25 and -1.

Toolbox   **645**

Quadratic Formula: If $a \neq 0$, the solutions of the equation $ax^2 + bx + c = 0$ are

$$x = -\frac{b}{2a} + \frac{\sqrt{b^2 - 4ac}}{2a} \text{ and } x = -\frac{b}{2a} - \frac{\sqrt{b^2 - 4ac}}{2a}.$$

← The discriminant, $b^2 - 4ac$.

Two different real roots when $b^2 - 4ac > 0$.
One real root when $b^2 - 4ac = 0$.
No real roots when $b^2 - 4ac < 0$.

Example Solve $2x^2 + 3x = 4$.

$$2x^2 + 3x - 4 = 0$$ ← Rewrite the equation in standard form: $ax^2 + bx + c = 0$.

$$x = -\frac{b}{2a} \pm \frac{\sqrt{b^2 - 4ac}}{2a}$$ ← Use the formula.

$$= -\frac{3}{2(2)} \pm \frac{\sqrt{3^2 - 4(2)(-4)}}{2(2)}$$ ← Substitute **2** for a, **3** for b, **−4** for c.

$$= -\frac{3}{4} \pm \frac{\sqrt{41}}{4} \approx -0.75 \pm 6.40$$

$$x \approx 5.65 \text{ or } x \approx 7.15$$

Solve.

1. $x^2 - 4x - 5 = 0$ 　　**2.** $2x^2 - 3x = 5$ 　　**3.** $0 = 9x^2 + 6x - 3$

4. $x^2 - 4x + 1 = 0$ 　　**5.** $2x^2 + 3x = 7$ 　　**6.** $5x^2 - 10x = -2$

Skill 23　**Solving Rational Equations**

A **rational equation** is one that involves rational expressions.

Example Solve $\dfrac{1}{x - 4} = \dfrac{2}{x^2 - 16}$.

$$x^2 - 16 = 2(x - 4)$$ ← Use cross products.

$$x^2 - 16 = 2x - 8$$ ← Use the distributive property.

$$x^2 - 2x - 8 = 0$$ ← Write the equation in standard form.

$$(x + 2)(x - 4) = 0$$ ← Factor.

$$x + 2 = 0 \quad or \quad x - 4 = 0$$ ← Use the zero-product property.

$$x = -2 \qquad\qquad x = 4$$

Check Substitute the results in the original equation.

$$\frac{1}{-2 - 4} \overset{?}{=} \frac{2}{(-2)^2 - 16}$$ ← Substitute −2 for x.

$$\frac{1}{-6} = \frac{1}{-6} \checkmark$$ ← This is a valid statement. −2 is a solution.

$$\frac{1}{4 - 4} \overset{?}{=} \frac{2}{4^2 - 16}$$ ← Substitute 4 for x.

$$\frac{1}{0} = \frac{2}{0}$$ ← Division by zero is undefined. 4 is **not** a solution.

The solution is −2. (4 is an **extraneous solution**.)

To solve rational equations, you can eliminate denominators by multiplying both sides by the LCM of all the denominators.

Example Solve $\frac{3}{5} + \frac{4}{x-3} = 7$.

First look for a common multiple of the denominators. A common multiple is an expression that has both denominators as factors.

$$\frac{3}{5} + \frac{4}{x-3} = 7 \quad \longleftarrow \quad 5(x-3) \text{ is a common multiple.} \longleftarrow \cdot \circ \circ \bigcirc$$

Watch Out!
A common multiple of $\frac{3}{5}$ and $\frac{4}{x-3}$ is $5(x-3)$, not $5x - 3$.

Then multiply both sides of the equation by this common multiple.

$$5(x-3)\left(\frac{3}{5} + \frac{4}{x-3}\right) = 5(x-3)(7)$$

$$5(x-3)\left(\frac{3}{5}\right) + 5(x-3)\left(\frac{4}{x-3}\right) = 35x - 105 \quad \longleftarrow \quad \text{Use the distributive property.}$$

$$(x-3)3 + 5(4) = 35x - 105 \quad \longleftarrow \quad \text{Simplify.}$$

$$3x + 11 = 35x - 105$$

$$116 = 32x$$

$$3.625 = x$$

Solve.

1. $\frac{1}{x} = \frac{4}{x-2}$

2. $\frac{3}{y+1} = \frac{y}{2}$

3. $\frac{2a+5}{a-1} = \frac{3a}{a-1}$

4. $\frac{6}{t} - \frac{2}{t-1} = 1$

5. $\frac{x-1}{x} + \frac{9}{4x} = 6$

6. $\frac{x}{x-2} + \frac{30}{x+2} = 9$

Skill 24   Solving Polynomial Equations

Some polynomial equations can be solved using the zero-product property (see Skill 22), even if they are not quadratic.

Example Solve $x^3 + 3x^2 + 2x = 0$

$x(x^2 + 3x + 2) = 0 \quad \longleftarrow \quad$ Factor out the monomial factor x.

$x(x + 2)(x + 1) = 0 \quad \longleftarrow \quad$ Factor the trinomial $x^2 + 3x + 2$ by trial and error.

$x = 0 \quad or \quad x + 2 = 0 \quad or \quad x + 1 = 0 \quad \longleftarrow \quad$ Use the zero-product property.

$\qquad\qquad\qquad x = -2 \qquad\qquad x = -1$

The solutions are 0, -2, and -1.

Solve.

1. $x^3 - 5x^2 + 6x = 0$

2. $x^3 + 4x^2 + 3x = 0$

3. $(x - 1)(x + 3)(3x - 1) = 0$

4. $x^3 + 3x^2 - 4x = 0$

5. $x^3 - 4x = 0$

6. $(x + 6)(x - 2)^2 = 0$

Graphing

The **slope** of a nonvertical line in a coordinate plane is the ratio

$$m = \frac{\text{change in } y}{\text{change in } x}, \text{ or } \frac{\text{rise}}{\text{run}}.$$

The **y-intercept** of such a line is the y-coordinate of the point where the line crosses the y-axis.

A nonvertical line in a coordinate plane always has an equation that can be expressed in **slope-intercept form**, where m is the slope of the line and b is the y-intercept:

$$y = mx + b$$

Example Write an equation of the line with slope 3 and y-intercept -5.

Since $m = 3$ and $b = -5$, an equation is $y = 3x + (-5)$, or $y = 3x - 5$.

Example Write an equation of the line through the points $(-3, 9)$ and $(2, -1)$.

Step 1 Find the slope of the line: $m = \dfrac{\text{change in } y}{\text{change in } x} = \dfrac{-1 - 9}{2 - (-3)} = \dfrac{-10}{5} = -2$.

Step 2 Since $m = -2$, the equation $y = mx + b$ is $y = -2x + b$. Substitute the coordinates of either of the two given points into this equation to find the value of b:

$9 = -2(-3) + b$ ⟵ Substitute the coordinates $(-3, 9)$ into $y = -2x + b$.

$9 = 6 + b$ ⟵ Simplify.

$3 = b$ ⟵ Solve for b.

An equation is $y = -2x + 3$.

You can find the equation of a graphed line by choosing two points on the line and using them to find the slope. If the y-intercept can easily be read off the graph, there is no need to calculate the value of b.

Example Write an equation of the line shown in the graph.

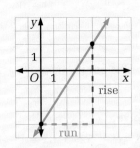

Choose two points on the graph to find m and b: $(0, -4)$ and $(4, 2)$.

Using these two points, you find:

$$m = \frac{\text{change in } y}{\text{change in } x} = \frac{2 - (-4)}{4 - 0} = \frac{6}{4} = 1.5$$

Since the graph crosses the y-axis at $(0, -4)$, you know that $b = -4$.

Therefore, an equation is $y = 1.5x - 4$.

Find an equation of each line.

1. with slope 4, through $(0, 7)$

2. with slope -0.5, through $(2, -3)$

3. through $(6, -7)$ and $(2, 5)$

4. through $(-2, 1)$ and $(7, -5)$

5. the line shown at the right

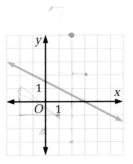

Skill 26   Making a Table of Values to Graph

To graph a function without using graphing technology, you need to make a table of values.

Example   Make a table and graph the function $y = x^2 - 4x - 3$.

Choose any convenient x-values. The values 0, 1, and -1 often make calculation of y easy.

List x-values, y-values, and ordered pairs in three columns.

$y = x^2 - 4x - 3$		
x	y	(x, y)
-1	2	$(-1, 2)$
0	-3	$(0, -3)$
1	-6	$(1, -6)$
2	-7	$(2, -7)$
3	-6	$(3, -6)$
4	-3	$(4, -3)$

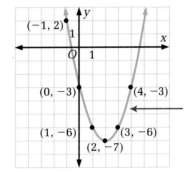

Plot the ordered pairs. Connect them.

Make a table and graph each function.

1. $y = -2x + 5$

2. $y = \dfrac{x}{2} - 1$

3. $y = x^2 - 5$

4. $y = x^2 + x - 2$

5. $y = |x - 2|$

6. $y = 3 - \dfrac{|x|}{2}$

7. $y = 2|x + 2| - 3$

8. $y = \dfrac{x^3}{4}$

9. $y = x^3 - x$

Toolbox

To graph an inequality in one variable on a number line, you shade the part of the number line that contains those x-values that make the inequality true.

Example   **a.** Graph $x < 4$.

Draw a ray to the left to include all points less than 4.

Use an open circle to show that 4 is not included.

```
 ←——+——+——+——+——⊕——+——+——+——→
    0   1   2   3   4   5   6   7   8
```

b. Graph $x \geq 5$.

Use a closed circle to show that -5 is included.

Draw a ray to the right to include all points greater than -5.

```
 ←—●——+——+——+——+——+——+——+——+——+——→
  -5  -4  -3  -2  -1   0   1   2   3   4   5
```

To graph a system of inequalities in two variables, you shade the region whose points make *both* inequalities true.

Example   Graph this system of inequalities: $y \geq -x + 4$
$2x - y > -2$

1 Graph the inequality $y \geq -x + 4$.

Graph $y = -x + 4$ as a *solid line*.

Test the point $(0, 0)$.
$y > -x + 4$
$0 \overset{?}{>} -0 + 4$
$0 > 4$ (false)

$(0, 0)$ is not a solution. Shade the region on the *opposite side* of the line from $(0, 0)$.

2 Graph the inequality $2x - y > -2$ on the same set of axes.

Graph $2x - y = -2$ as a *dashed line*.

Test the point $(0, 0)$.
$2x - y > -2$
$2(0) - 0 \overset{?}{>} -2$
$0 > -2$ (true)

You may want to darken the region of overlap.

$(0, 0)$ is a solution. Shade the region on the *same side* of the line as $(0, 0)$.

3 Find the solution region for the system. The points inside the region of overlap make both inequalities true.

Graph each inequality.

1. $x > -3$ **2.** $x \leq 4$ **3.** $x < 1$ **4.** $x \geq -2$

Graph each system of inequalities in a coordinate plane.

5. $y \leq 3x - 3$
$y > -\frac{1}{2}x + 2$

6. $y < 3x$
$3y - 2x \geq 9$

7. $x < 2$
$x + 2y > -2$

8. $y - 3x \geq 5$
$2y + 5x < 7$

650   **Student Resources**

A **quadratic function** is a function of the form $f(x) = ax^2 + bx + c$, where $a \neq 0$.

The graph of a quadratic function is always a U-shaped curve called a **parabola.** The coefficients a, b, and c help you draw the parabola in a coordinate system.

***y*-intercept of the parabola:** the number c

line of symmetry of the parabola: the vertical line whose equation is $x = -\dfrac{b}{2a}$

Example Find the *y*-intercept and the equation of the line of symmetry of the graph of $f(x) = 3x^2 - 5x + 2$.

In the given equation, $c = 2$, so the *y*-intercept is 2.

In the given equation, $a = 3$ and $b = -5$, so the equation of the line of symmetry is

$$x = -\frac{b}{2a} = -\frac{-5}{2(3)}, \text{ or } x = \frac{5}{6}.$$

The parabola determined by a quadratic function $f(x) = ax^2 + bx + c$ can open upward or downward.

If the number a is positive, the parabola opens upward, and the function has a minimum value.

If a is negative, the parabola opens downward, and the function has a maximum value.

Example Graph the function $y = -1.5x^2 + 6x + 3$.

In this function, $a = -1.5$, $b = 6$, and $c = 3$.

The *y*-intercept is 3.

The equation of the line of symmetry is

$$x = -\frac{6}{2(-1.5)}, \text{ or } x = 2.$$

Since $a < 0$, the graph opens downward and y has a maximum value.

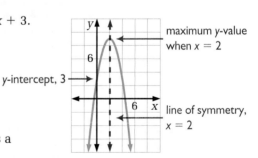

Find the y-intercept and the equation of the line of symmetry for each quadratic function. Then sketch the graph.

1. $y = x^2 - 4$

2. $y = -2x^2 + 7$

3. $y = -0.5x^2 + 3x$

4. $y = 0.25x^2 - 2x - 1$

5. $y = 3x^2 - 12x - 10$

6. $y = -0.75x^2 + 4.5x + 6$

Toolbox

➤ Geometry and Measurement

Formulas and Relationships

A = area B = area of base   S.A. = surface area V = volume

Parallelogram $A = bh$	**Triangle** $A = \frac{1}{2}bh$	**Trapezoid** $A = \frac{1}{2}(b_1 + b_2)h$

Circle

diameter

d r

radius

Circumference $= 2\pi r = \pi d$
$A = \pi r^2$

Sector

central angle

arc →

$\dfrac{\text{central } \angle}{360°} =$

$\dfrac{\text{arc length}}{\text{circumference}} = \dfrac{\text{area of sector}}{\text{area of circle}}$

Prism

h

base area B

S.A. = areas of two bases + areas of faces

$V = Bh$

Cylinder

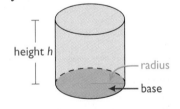

height h

radius

base

S.A. $= 2\pi r^2 + 2\pi rh$
$V = Bh = \pi r^2 h$

Pyramid

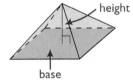

height

base

S.A. = area of base + areas of faces

$V = \frac{1}{3}Bh$

Cone

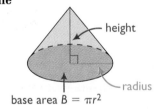

height

base area $B = \pi r^2$

radius

$V = \frac{1}{3}Bh = \frac{1}{3}\pi r^2 h$

Sphere

radius

S.A. $= 4\pi r^2$ $V = \frac{4}{3}\pi r^3$

Equation of Circle with Center (0, 0)

(x, y)

r

O x

$x^2 + y^2 = r^2$

Equation of Sphere with Center (0, 0, 0)

z (x, y, z)

r

O y

x

$x^2 + y^2 + z^2 = r^2$

Example Find the area of the trapezoid shown.

$A = \frac{1}{2}(b_1 + b_2)h$ ← Write the formula for the area of a trapezoid.

$A = \frac{1}{2}(21 + 33)13$ ← Substitute **21** for b_1, **33** for b_2, and **13** for h.

$= \frac{1}{2}(54)13 = 351$

The area is 351 cm². ← cm × cm = cm²

Find the area of each figure.

1. a parallelogram of height 10 ft with a base of length 16 ft

2. a trapezoid of height 3 in. with bases of length 5 in. and 8 in.

3. a sector with central angle 40° and radius 9 in.

Find the surface area of each space figure.

4. a rectangular prism with dimensions 18 in., 12 in., and 4.5 in.

5. a cylinder of height 20 cm and with a base of radius 5 cm

Find the volume of each space figure.

6. a triangular prism whose height is 8 cm and whose base area is 25 cm²

7. a cylinder of height 8.5 m and with a base of radius 2 m

8. a pyramid of height 12 in., whose base is a square with sides of length 10 in.

Skill 30   Using Special Triangle Relationships

Triangle Sum Theorem	**Pythagorean Theorem**
$y°$ $x°$ $z°$ $x + y + z = 180$	b c a $a^2 + b^2 = c^2$
45-45-90 Right Triangle	**30-60-90 Right Triangle**
a $a\sqrt{2}$ 45° a	b 60° $2b$ 30° $b\sqrt{3}$

Example Find the length of the hypotenuse in the right triangle.

$$c^2 = 6.4^2 + 12^2 \quad \longleftarrow \quad \text{Use the Pythagorean theorem: } c^2 = a^2 + b^2.$$

$$c^2 = 184.96$$

$$c = \sqrt{184.96} \quad \longleftarrow \quad \text{Find the positive square root.}$$

$$c = 13.6$$

12

6.4

Example Find the missing sides of the right triangle.

$$QR = a = 10 \quad \longleftarrow \quad \text{Use the pattern for 30-60-90 triangles.}$$

$$PR = a\sqrt{3} = 10\sqrt{3}$$

$$PQ = 2a = 2 \cdot 10 = 20$$

Q

$60°$ 10

$30°$

P R

**Find the length of the missing side of a right triangle with legs of length
a and b and hypotenuse of length c.**

1. $a = 3, b = 4, c = \underline{\ ?\ }$ **2.** $a = 7, c = 25, b = \underline{\ ?\ }$ **3.** $b = 8, c = 11, a = \underline{\ ?\ }$

4. Find the lengths of the missing sides of a 30-60-90 triangle when
the side opposite the 60° angle is 12 cm long.

Skill 31   Using the Distance and Midpoint Formulas

When you know the coordinates of two points (x_1, y_1) and
(x_2, y_2), you can find the distance between the points by using
the Pythagorean theorem or the **distance formula:**

$X_2 - X_1$

$$d = \sqrt{(\textbf{change in x})^2 + (\textbf{change in y})^2} = \sqrt{(x_2 - x_1)^2 + (y_2 - y_1)^2}$$

Example Find the distance between the points $(-4, 6)$ and $(0, 3)$.

$$\text{distance} = \sqrt{(x_2 - x_1)^2 + (y_2 - y_1)^2} \quad \longleftarrow \quad \text{Use the distance formula.}$$

$$= \sqrt{(0 - (-4))^2 + (3 - 6)^2} \quad \longleftarrow \quad \text{Substitute } (-4, 6) \text{ for } (x_1, y_1) \text{ and } (0, 3) \text{ for } (x_2, y_2).$$

$$= \sqrt{4^2 + (-3)^2}$$

$$= \sqrt{25}$$

$$= 5$$

The distance between the two points is 5 units.

The Midpoint Formula

The midpoint of a segment with endpoints (x_1, y_1) and (x_2, y_2) has coordinates

$$\left(\frac{x_1 + x_2}{2}, \frac{y_1 + y_2}{2} \right).$$

the mean of the x's ↗   ↖ the mean of the y's

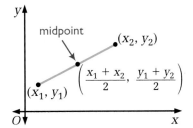

Example Find the coordinates of the midpoint of the segment whose endpoints are (9, −14) and (3, 4).

Let (x_1, y_1) be $(9, -14)$ and let (x_2, y_2) be $(3, 4)$.

The x-coordinate of the midpoint is $\dfrac{x_1 + x_2}{2} = \dfrac{9 + 3}{2} = 6$.

The y-coordinate of the midpoint is $\dfrac{y_1 + y_2}{2} = \dfrac{-14 + 4}{2} = -5$.

The coordinates of the midpoint are (6, −5).

Find the distance between each pair of points.

1. (2, 7) and (5, 3)   **2.** (4, −1) and (−8, 4)   **3.** (−2, 7) and (3, 9)

Find the coordinates of the midpoint of a segment with the given endpoints.

4. (3, 8) and (7, 4)   **5.** (−2, 1) and (6, −9)   **6.** (3, −4) and (8, −5)

Skill 32   Recognizing Similar Figures

Two polygons are **similar** if and only if their vertices can be matched up so that (1) corresponding angles are equal in measure and (2) corresponding sides are in proportion.

For *triangles*, condition (1) alone is enough to guarantee similarity. In fact, all you need are *two* pairs of angles that are equal in measure.

Example $m\angle C = m\angle F$ and $m\angle B = m\angle E$, so the triangles are similar.

Corresponding sides: AB and DE
BC and EF
CA and FD

Equal ratios: $\dfrac{AB}{DE} = \dfrac{BC}{EF} = \dfrac{CA}{FD}$.

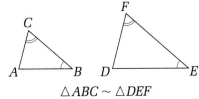

$\triangle ABC \sim \triangle DEF$

Explain why the triangles in each pair are similar. Name all pairs of corresponding sides and angles.

1.

2.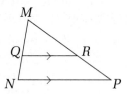

3. △MQR is similar to △XYZ. QR = 9, RM = 8, MQ = 12, and ZX = 16. Find YZ.

| Skill 33 | **Recognizing Congruent Figures** |

Two polygons are **congruent** if and only if their vertices can be matched up so that the *corresponding parts* (angles and sides) are equal in measure.

For *triangles,* you can prove congruence when only three pairs of corresponding parts are known to be equal in measure. See the list of postulates and theorems about triangles on page 670.

Example Name the congruent triangles. Explain why they are congruent.

△ABC ≅ △DEF by ASA.

Two pairs of angles and the included sides are equal in measure:

$m\angle B = m\angle E$, $m\angle A = m\angle D$, $AB = DE$.

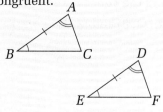

For each pair of triangles, tell whether there is enough information to prove that the triangles are congruent. Write Yes or No. Explain.

1.

2.

3.

4.

5. Name the corresponding sides and angles. Find the value of x.

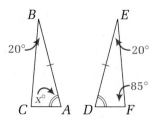

Student Resources

Logical Reasoning

A statement of the form $p \rightarrow q$ (read "p implies q" or "if p, then q") is called an **implication** or **conditional**. The statement represented by p is the **hypothesis** of the implication, and the statement represented by q is the **conclusion.**

Example   The statement "All prairie dogs are rodents" can be rewritten in the following equivalent ways:

• *Every* prairie dog is a rodent.

• The fact that an animal is a prairie dog *implies* that it is a rodent.

• *If* an animal is a prairie dog, *then* it is a rodent.

    hypothesis   conclusion

The **converse** of an implication is formed by reversing the hypothesis and the conclusion.

Example   The converse of the statement "If an animal is a prairie dog, then it is a rodent" is the statement: "If an animal is a rodent, then it is a prairie dog."

Since mice are also rodents, the converse is *false.*   ←——— The converse of a true inplication may be false.

The conjunction of a statement and its converse is called a **biconditional.** Biconditionals are often stated using "if and only if."

Example   The biconditional "Today is Tuesday if and only if yesterday was Monday" can be rewritten as the conjunction: "If today is Tuesday, then yesterday was Monday, and if yesterday was Monday, then today is Tuesday."

Rewrite each implication in an equivalent form using the key word(s) given.

1. If a figure is a rhombus, then its diagonals are perpendicular. (*all*)

2. A figure is a square only if it is a rhombus. (*implies*)

3. Whenever it is Saturday, it is a day of the weekend. (*every*)

4. If a figure is a cylinder, then the formula for its volume is $V = \pi r^2 h$. (*only if*)

Write each conjunction as a biconditional using "if and only if."

5. A polygon is a quadrilateral if it has four sides, and a polygon has four sides if it is a quadrilateral.

6. If $5x = 20$, then $x = 4$, and if $x = 4$, then $5x = 20$.

Toolbox

A **rule of logic** consists of two given statements, called **premises,** and a statement, called a **conclusion,** that follows from them.

RULES OF LOGIC

Direct Argument

If p is true, then q is true.
p is true.

Therefore, q is true.

$p \to q$
p

$\therefore q \leftarrow$ Read "Therefore q."

Indirect Argument

If p is true, then q is true.
q is not true.

Therefore, p is not true.

$p \to q$
not q

$\therefore$ not p

Chain Rule

If p is true, then q is true.
If q is true, then r is true.

Therefore, if p is true, then r is true.

$p \to q$
$q \to r$

$\therefore p \to r$

Or Rule

p is true or q is true.
p is not true.

Therefore, q is true.

p or q
not p

$\therefore q$

Example What conclusion can you reach when both premises are true?

a. Premise 1: If an animal is an insect, then it has exactly six legs.
Premise 2: A spider does not have exactly six legs.

b. Premise 1: If a polygon is a square, then it is a rectangle.
Premise 2: If a polygon is a rectangle, then it is a parallelogram.

Translate each premise into its symbolic form.

a. *insect* $\to$ *six legs*   These are the premises $p \to q$
    not *six legs*   of an indirect argument.   not q

    $\therefore$ not p

Conclusion: A spider is not an insect.

b. *square* $\to$ *rectangle*   These are the premises $p \to q$
    rectangle $\to$ *parallelogram*   of a chain rule argument. $q \to r$

    $\therefore p \to r$

Conclusion: If a polygon is a square, it is a parallelogram.

Arguments that do not use rules of logic are considered errors, or **invalid arguments.**

 Explain why each of the following arguments is invalid.

   a. *Argument:* All multiples of 20 are multiples of 5. Sam's locker number is a multiple of 5. Therefore, Sam's locker number is a multiple of 20.

   b. *Argument:* Every member of YHC likes to travel. Indira is not a member of YHC. Therefore, Indira does not like to travel.

Write the premises as if-then statements. Use symbols to examine the argument:

   a. If a number is a multiple of 20, then it is a multiple of 5. $p \rightarrow q$

   Sam's locker number is a multiple of 5. $\underline{\quad q \quad}$

   Therefore, Sam's locker number is a multiple of 20. $\therefore p$

   This argument does not use a rule of logic. If the first premise were the converse, "$q \rightarrow p$," instead of "$p \rightarrow q$," this argument would be valid. This is called a *converse error.*

   b. If a person is a member of YHC, then the person likes to travel. $p \rightarrow q$

   Indira is not a member of YHC. $\underline{\text{not } p}$

   Therefore, Indira does not like to travel. $\therefore \text{not } q$

   This argument would be valid if the first premise were the inverse, "not $p \rightarrow$ not q," instead of "$p \rightarrow q$." This is an example of *inverse error.*

Tell which rule of logic is used in these valid arguments.

1. John is in his room or John is in the kitchen. John is not in the kitchen. Therefore, John is in his room.

2. If I take the Number 10 bus, then I can get to the mall. If I can get to the mall, then I can go to the movies. Therefore, if I take the Number 10 bus, then I can go to the movies.

3. If Manuela has guacamole, then she has tasted avocado. Manuela has eaten guacamole. Therefore, she has tasted avocado.

What conclusion can you reach when both premises are true?

4. If an animal has a backbone, it is a vertebrate. A horse has a backbone.

5. If a triangle is isosceles, then it has at least two angles equal in measure. $\triangle ABC$ does not have at least two angles equal in measure.

6. If $2x + 3 = 21$, then $2x = 18$. If $2x = 18$, then $x = 9$.

7. If $P(A) = 0$, then A is an impossible event. A is not an impossible event.

Trigonometry

Suppose $\angle A$ is one of the acute angles of a right triangle. The **trigonometric ratios** for $\angle A$ are ratios of the measures of the sides of the triangle.

Sine of $\angle A$ $\sin A = \dfrac{\text{leg opposite } \angle A}{\text{hypotenuse}} = \dfrac{BC}{AB}$

Cosine of $\angle A$ $\cos A = \dfrac{\text{leg adjacent to } \angle A}{\text{hypotenuse}} = \dfrac{AC}{AB}$

Tangent of $\angle A$ $\tan A = \dfrac{\text{leg opposite } \angle A}{\text{leg adjacent to } \angle A} = \dfrac{BC}{AC}$

Example   Write each trigonometric ratio as a fraction and as a decimal rounded to the nearest hundredth.

a. $\sin P$ **b.** $\cos P$ **c.** $\tan P$

d. $\sin Q$ **e.** $\cos Q$ **f.** $\tan Q$

a. $\sin P = \dfrac{\text{leg opposite } \angle P}{\text{hypotenuse}} = \dfrac{15}{17} \approx 0.88$

b. $\cos P = \dfrac{\text{leg adjacent to } \angle P}{\text{hypotenuse}} = \dfrac{8}{17} \approx 0.47$

c. $\tan P = \dfrac{\text{leg opposite } \angle P}{\text{leg adjacent to } \angle P} = \dfrac{15}{8} \approx 1.88$

d. $\sin Q = \dfrac{\text{leg opposite } \angle Q}{\text{hypotenuse}} = \dfrac{8}{17} \approx 0.47$

e. $\cos Q = \dfrac{\text{leg adjacent to } \angle Q}{\text{hypotenuse}} = \dfrac{15}{17} \approx 0.88$

f. $\tan Q = \dfrac{\text{leg opposite } \angle Q}{\text{leg adjacent to } \angle Q} = \dfrac{8}{15} \approx 0.53$

Use the triangle at the right. Find the value of each trigonometric ratio.

1. $\sin A$ **2.** $\cos A$ **3.** $\tan A$

4. $\sin B$ **5.** $\cos B$ **6.** $\tan B$

Draw and label a right triangle that fits each description.

7. $\triangle ABC$ with $\sin A = \dfrac{\text{leg opposite } \angle A}{\text{hypotenuse}} = \dfrac{3}{5}$

8. $\triangle XYZ$ with $\cos X = \dfrac{\text{leg adjacent to } \angle X}{\text{hypotenuse}} = \dfrac{5}{13}$

You can use the trigonometric ratios to find missing lengths in right triangles. Scientific calculators are programmed to find these ratios. A table of trigonometric ratios is on page 667.

Example Find the missing length in the triangle at the right.

Use the tangent ratio.

$$\tan 61° = \frac{49}{x}$$

$$1.804 \approx \frac{49}{x}$$ ⟵ Use the **tan** key on your calculator.

$$1.804 \cdot x \approx \frac{49}{x} \cdot x$$ ⟵ Multiply both sides by x.

$$1.804x \approx 49$$

$$\frac{1.804x}{1.804} \approx \frac{49}{1.804}$$ ⟵ Divide both sides by 1.804.

$$x \approx \frac{49}{1.804} \approx 27.2$$

Example Find the altitude to side $\overline{AB}$ of $\triangle ABC$.

Let h = the altitude to $\overline{AB}$.

$$\sin 20° = \frac{h}{10}$$

$$h = 10 \sin 20°$$ ⟵ Multiply both sides by 10.

$$\approx 10(0.3420)$$ ⟵ Use the **sin** key on your calculator.

$$\approx 3.42$$

Find each missing length.

1.

2.

3.

4. Find the length of the altitude to side $\overline{PQ}$ in $\triangle PQR$ at the right.

A **transformation** is a procedure by which a new geometric figure is produced from a given figure according to a definite rule.

Translation

A **translation** slides a figure vertically and/or horizontally without changing its size or shape and without turning it. Each point of the figure moves the same distance and in the same direction.

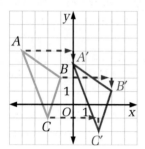

$\triangle A'B'C'$ is the translation of $\triangle ABC$ 4 units to the right and 1 unit down.

Rotation

A **rotation** moves each point of a figure through a circular arc about a common point, called the **center of rotation.** Each point of the figure is rotated by the same number of degrees.

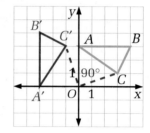

$\triangle A'B'C'$ is the 90° counterclockwise rotation of $\triangle ABC$ about the origin.

Dilation

A **dilation** transforms a figure into a similar figure. Each point of the figure is transformed along a line connecting it to the **center of dilation.** The ratio of any length in the transformed figure to the corresponding length in the original figure is the **scale factor.**

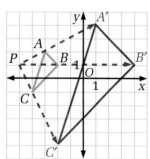

$\triangle A'B'C'$ is the dilation of $\triangle ABC$ with center P and scale factor 3.

Reflection

A **reflection** is a flip over a line. The line is called the **line of reflection.** The reflected figure is congruent to the original figure, but its orientation is reversed.

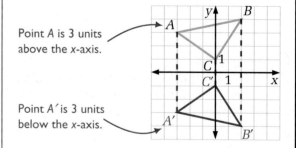

Point A is 3 units above the x-axis.

Point A′ is 3 units below the x-axis.

$\triangle A'B'C'$ is the reflection of $\triangle ABC$ over the x-axis.

Draw the figure produced by each transformation of the figure at the right.

1. translation by 3 units to the right and 1 unit down

2. translation by 2 units to the left and 2 units up

3. a 90° counterclockwise rotation about the origin

4. a 180° rotation about the origin

5. a dilation about the origin with a scale factor 2

6. a dilation about the origin with a scale factor 0.5

7. a reflection over the *x*-axis   **8.** a reflection over the line *y* = *x*

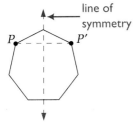

line of symmetry

A figure that looks the same after reflection over a line has **reflection symmetry.** The line over which the figure is reflected is called the **line of symmetry.**

Each point *P* corresponds to a point *P′* in such a way that the line of symmetry is the perpendicular bisector of the segment $\overline{PP'}$.

A figure that looks the same after a rotation through an angle, clockwise or counterclockwise, has **rotational symmetry.** The center of rotation is called the **point of symmetry.**

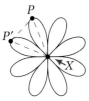

Each point *P* corresponds to a point *P′* in such a way that all the triangles *PXP′* are similar isosceles triangles, when *X* is the point of symmetry.

$m \angle PXP' = 45°$

Example   The regular hexagon at the right has three lines of symmetry: *l*, *m*, and *n*, as well as 60° rotational symmetry about point *X*.

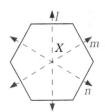

Name the type(s) of symmetry each figure has. Copy the figure and indicate lines and points of symmetry. For rotational symmetry, name the angle of the symmetry.

1.

2.

3.

Toolbox

Table of Measures

Time

60 seconds (s) = 1 minute (min)
60 minutes = 1 hour (h)
24 hours = 1 day
7 days = 1 week
4 weeks (approx.) = 1 month

365 days
52 weeks (approx.) $\Big]$ = 1 year
12 months
10 years = 1 decade
100 years = 1 century

Metric

Length

10 millimeters (mm) = 1 centimeter (cm)
100 cm
1000 mm $\Big]$ = 1 meter (m)
1000 m = 1 kilometer (km)

Area

100 square millimeters = 1 square centimeter
(mm^2) (cm^2)
10,000 cm^2 = 1 square meter (m^2)
10,000 m^2 = 1 hectare (ha)

Volume

1000 cubic millimeters = 1 cubic centimeter
(mm^3) (cm^3)
1,000,000 cm^3 = 1 cubic meter (m^3)

Liquid Capacity

1000 milliliters (mL) = 1 liter (L)
1000 L = 1 kiloliter (kL)

Mass

1000 milligrams (mg) = 1 gram (g)
1000 g = 1 kilogram (kg)
1000 kg = 1 metric ton (t)

Temperature — Degrees Celsius (°C)

0°C = freezing point of water
37°C = normal body temperature
100°C = boiling point of water

United States Customary

Length

12 inches (in.) = 1 foot (ft)
36 in.
3 ft $\Big]$ = 1 yard (yd)
5280 ft
1760 yd $\Big]$ = 1 mile (mi)

Area

144 square inches (in.^{2}) = 1 square foot (ft^2)
9 ft^2 = 1 square yard (yd^2)
43,560 ft^2
4840 yd^2 $\Big]$ = 1 acre (A)

Volume

1728 cubic inches (in.^{3}) = 1 cubic foot (ft^3)
27 ft^3 = 1 cubic yard (yd^3)

Liquid Capacity

8 fluid ounces (fl oz) = 1 cup (c)
2 c = 1 pint (pt)
2 pt = 1 quart (qt)
4 qt = 1 gallon (gal)

Weight

16 ounces (oz) = 1 pound (lb)
2000 lb = 1 ton (t)

Temperature — Degrees Fahrenheit (°F)

32°F = freezing point of water
98.6°F = normal body temperature
212°F = boiling point of water

Table of Symbols

Tables

Table of Squares and Square Roots

No.	Square	Sq. Root	No.	Square	Sq. Root	No.	Square	Sq. Root
1	1	1.000	51	2,601	7.141	101	10,201	10.050
2	4	1.414	52	2,704	7.211	102	10,404	10.100
3	9	1.732	53	2,809	7.280	103	10,609	10.149
4	16	2.000	54	2,916	7.348	104	10,816	10.198
5	25	2.236	55	3,025	7.416	105	11,025	10.247
6	36	2.449	56	3,136	7.483	106	11,236	10.296
7	49	2.646	57	3,249	7.550	107	11,449	10.344
8	64	2.828	58	3,364	7.616	108	11,664	10.392
9	81	3.000	59	3,481	7.681	109	11,881	10.440
10	100	3.162	60	3,600	7.746	110	12,100	10.488
11	121	3.317	61	3,721	7.810	111	12,321	10.536
12	144	3.464	62	3,844	7.874	112	12,544	10.583
13	169	3.606	63	3,969	7.937	113	12,769	10.630
14	196	3.742	64	4,096	8.000	114	12,996	10.677
15	225	3.873	65	4,225	8.062	115	13,225	10.724
16	256	4.000	66	4,356	8.124	116	13,456	10.770
17	289	4.123	67	4,489	8.185	117	13,689	10.817
18	324	4.243	68	4,624	8.246	118	13,924	10.863
19	361	4.359	69	4,761	8.307	119	14,161	10.909
20	400	4.472	70	4,900	8.367	120	14,400	10.954
21	441	4.583	71	5,041	8.426	121	14,641	11.000
22	484	4.690	72	5,184	8.485	122	14,884	11.045
23	529	4.796	73	5,329	8.544	123	15,129	11.091
24	576	4.899	74	5,476	8.602	124	15,376	11.136
25	625	5.000	75	5,625	8.660	125	15,625	11.180
26	676	5.099	76	5,776	8.718	126	15,876	11.225
27	729	5.196	77	5,929	8.775	127	16,129	11.269
28	784	5.292	78	6,084	8.832	128	16,384	11.314
29	841	5.385	79	6,241	8.888	129	16,641	11.358
30	900	5.477	80	6,400	8.944	130	16,900	11.402
31	961	5.568	81	6,561	9.000	131	17,161	11.446
32	1,024	5.657	82	6,724	9.055	132	17,424	11.489
33	1,089	5.745	83	6,889	9.110	133	17,689	11.533
34	1,156	5.831	84	7,056	9.165	134	17,956	11.576
35	1,225	5.916	85	7,225	9.220	135	18,225	11.619
36	1,296	6.000	86	7,396	9.274	136	18,496	11.662
37	1,369	6.083	87	7,569	9.327	137	18,769	11.705
38	1,444	6.164	88	7,744	9.381	138	19,044	11.747
39	1,521	6.245	89	7,921	9.434	139	19,321	11.790
40	1,600	6.325	90	8,100	9.487	140	19,600	11.832
41	1,681	6.403	91	8,281	9.539	141	19,881	11.874
42	1,764	6.481	92	8,464	9.592	142	20,164	11.916
43	1,849	6.557	93	8,649	9.644	143	20,449	11.958
44	1,936	6.633	94	8,836	9.695	144	20,736	12.000
45	2,025	6.708	95	9,025	9.747	145	21,025	12.042
46	2,116	6.782	96	9,216	9.798	146	21,316	12.083
47	2,209	6.856	97	9,409	9.849	147	21,609	12.124
48	2,304	6.928	98	9,604	9.899	148	21,904	12.166
49	2,401	7.000	99	9,801	9.950	149	22,201	12.207
50	2,500	7.071	100	10,000	10.000	150	22,500	12.247

Student Resources

Table of Trigonometric Ratios

Angle	Sine	Cosine	Tangent	Angle	Sine	Cosine	Tangent
1°	.0175	.9998	.0175	46°	.7193	.6947	1.0355
2°	.0349	.9994	.0349	47°	.7314	.6820	1.0724
3°	.0523	.9986	.0524	48°	.7431	.6691	1.1106
4°	.0698	.9976	.0699	49°	.7547	.6561	1.1504
5°	.0872	.9962	.0875	50°	.7660	.6428	1.1918
6°	.1045	.9945	.1051	51°	.7771	.6293	1.2349
7°	.1219	.9925	.1228	52°	.7880	.6157	1.2799
8°	.1392	.9903	.1405	53°	.7986	.6018	1.3270
9°	.1564	.9877	.1584	54°	.8090	.5878	1.3764
10°	.1736	.9848	.1763	55°	.8192	.5736	1.4281
11°	.1908	.9816	.1944	56°	.8290	.5592	1.4826
12°	.2079	.9781	.2126	57°	.8387	.5446	1.5399
13°	.2250	.9744	.2309	58°	.8480	.5299	1.6003
14°	.2419	.9703	.2493	59°	.8572	.5150	1.6643
15°	.2588	.9659	.2679	60°	.8660	.5000	1.7321
16°	.2756	.9613	.2867	61°	.8746	.4848	1.8040
17°	.2924	.9563	.3057	62°	.8829	.4695	1.8807
18°	.3090	.9511	.3249	63°	.8910	.4540	1.9626
19°	.3256	.9455	.3443	64°	.8988	.4384	2.0503
20°	.3420	.9397	.3640	65°	.9063	.4226	2.1445
21°	.3584	.9336	.3839	66°	.9135	.4067	2.2460
22°	.3746	.9272	.4040	67°	.9205	.3907	2.3559
23°	.3907	.9205	.4245	68°	.9272	.3746	2.4751
24°	.4067	.9135	.4452	69°	.9336	.3584	2.6051
25°	.4226	.9063	.4663	70°	.9397	.3420	2.7475
26°	.4384	.8988	.4877	71°	.9455	.3256	2.9042
27°	.4540	.8910	.5095	72°	.9511	.3090	3.0777
28°	.4695	.8829	.5317	73°	.9563	.2924	3.2709
29°	.4848	.8746	.5543	74°	.9613	.2756	3.4874
30°	.5000	.8660	.5774	75°	.9659	.2588	3.7321
31°	.5150	.8572	.6009	76°	.9703	.2419	4.0108
32°	.5299	.8480	.6249	77°	.9744	.2250	4.3315
33°	.5446	.8387	.6494	78°	.9781	.2079	4.7046
34°	.5592	.8290	.6745	79°	.9816	.1908	5.1446
35°	.5736	.8192	.7002	80°	.9848	.1736	5.6713
36°	.5878	.8090	.7265	81°	.9877	.1564	6.3138
37°	.6018	.7986	.7536	82°	.9903	.1392	7.1154
38°	.6157	.7880	.7813	83°	.9925	.1219	8.1443
39°	.6293	.7771	.8098	84°	.9945	.1045	9.5144
40°	.6428	.7660	.8391	85°	.9962	.0872	11.4301
41°	.6561	.7547	.8693	86°	.9976	.0698	14.3007
42°	.6691	.7431	.9004	87°	.9986	.0523	19.0811
43°	.6820	.7314	.9325	88°	.9994	.0349	28.6363
44°	.6947	.7193	.9657	89°	.9998	.0175	57.2900
45°	.7071	.7071	1.0000				

Postulates and Theorems

Postulates of Algebra

Postulate 1   **Addition Property of Equality** If the same number is added to equal numbers, then the sums are equal. *(Book 2)*

Postulate 2   **Subtraction Property of Equality** If the same number is subtracted from equal numbers, then the differences are equal. *(Book 2)*

Postulate 3   **Multiplication Property of Equality** If equal numbers are multiplied by the same number, then the products are equal. *(Book 2)*

Postulate 4   **Division Property of Equality** If equal numbers are divided by the same nonzero number, then the quotients are equal. *(Book 2)*

Postulate 5   **Reflexive Property of Equality** A number is equal to itself. *(Book 2)*

Postulate 6   **Substitution Property** If values are equal, then one value may be substituted for the other. *(Book 2)*

Postulate 7   **Distributive Property** An expression of the form $a(b + c)$ is equivalent to $ab + ac$. *(Book 2)*

Postulates and Theorems of Geometry

Angles

Theorem   If two angles are supplements of the same angle, then they are equal in measure. *(Book 2)*

Theorem   If two angles are complements of the same angle, then they are equal in measure. *(Book 2)*

Postulate   If the sides of an angle form a straight line, then the angle is a straight angle with measure 180°. *(Book 2)*

Postulate   For any segment or angle, the measure of the whole is equal to the sum of the measures of its non-overlapping parts. *(Book 2)*

Theorem   Vertical angles are equal in measure. *(Book 2)*

Theorem   The sum of the measures of the angles of a triangle is 180°. *(Book 2)*

Theorem   An exterior angle of a triangle is equal in measure to the sum of the measures of its two remote interior angles. *(Book 2)*

Theorem   If two sides of a triangle are equal in measure, then the angles opposite those sides are equal in measure. *(Book 2)*

Theorem   If two angles of a triangle are equal in measure, then the sides opposite those angles are equal in measure. *(Book 2)*

Theorem   If a triangle is equilateral, then it is also equiangular, with three 60° angles. *(Book 2)*

Theorem   If a triangle is equiangular, then it is also equilateral. *(Book 2)*

Theorem 3.4   The sum of the angle measures of an n-gon is given by the formula $S(n) = (n - 2)180°$. *(p. 161)*

Theorem 3.5   The sum of the exterior angle measures of an n-gon, one angle at each vertex, is 360°. *(p. 161)*

Lines

Postulate   If two parallel lines are intersected by a transversal, then corresponding angles are equal in measure. *(Book 2)*

Theorem   If two parallel lines are intersected by a transversal, then alternate interior angles are equal in measure. *(Book 2)*

Theorem   If two parallel lines are intersected by a transversal, then co-interior angles are supplementary. *(Book 2)*

Postulate   If two lines are intersected by a transversal and corresponding angles are equal in measure, then the lines are parallel. *(Book 2)*

Theorem   If two lines are intersected by a transversal and alternate interior angles are equal in measure, then the lines are parallel. *(Book 2)*

Theorem   If two lines are intersected by a transversal and co-interior angles are supplementary, then the lines are parallel. *(Book 2)*

Theorem   If two lines are perpendicular to the same transversal, then they are parallel. *(Book 2)*

Theorem   If a transversal is perpendicular to one of two parallel lines, then it is perpendicular to the other one also. *(Book 2)*

Postulate   Through a point not on a given line, there is one and only one line parallel to the given line. *(Book 2)*

Theorem   If a point is the same distance from both endpoints of a segment, then it lies on the perpendicular bisector of the segment. *(Book 2)*

Postulate   A segment can be drawn perpendicular to a given line from a point not on the line. The length of this segment is the shortest distance from the point to the line. *(p. 182)*

Triangles

Postulate   If two angles of one triangle are equal in measure to two angles of another triangle, then the two triangles are similar. (AA Similarity) *(Book 2)*

Theorem   If a line is drawn from a point on one side of a triangle parallel to another side, then it forms a triangle similar to the original triangle. *(Book 2)*

In a triangle, a segment that connects the midpoints of two sides is parallel to the third side and half as long. *(Book 2)*

Theorem   If two angles and the included side of one triangle are equal in measure to the corresponding angles and side of another triangle, then the triangles are congruent. (ASA) *(Book 2)*

Theorem   If two angles and a non-included side of one triangle are equal in measure to the corresponding angles and side of another triangle, then the triangles are congruent. (AAS) *(Book 2)*

Postulate   If two sides and the included angle of one triangle are equal in measure to the corresponding sides and angle of another triangle, then the triangles are congruent. (SAS) *(Book 2)*

Postulate   If three sides of one triangle are equal in measure to the corresponding sides of another triangle, then the triangles are congruent. (SSS) *(Book 2)*

Theorem   If the altitude is drawn to the hypotenuse of a right triangle, then the two triangles formed are similar to the original triangle and to each other. *(Book 2)*

Theorem   In any right triangle, the square of the length of the hypotenuse is equal to the sum of the squares of the lengths of the legs. *(Book 2)*

Theorem   If the altitude is drawn to the hypotenuse of a right triangle, then the measure of the altitude is the geometric mean between the measures of the parts of the hypotenuse. *(Book 2)*

The sum of the lengths of any two sides of a triangle is greater than the length of the third side. *(p. 9)*

Theorem 3.2   In an isosceles triangle, the medians drawn to the legs are equal in measure. *(p. 150)*

Quadrilaterals

In a parallelogram, the diagonals have the same midpoint. *(Book 2)*

In a kite, the diagonals are perpendicular to each other. *(Book 2)*

In a rectangle, the diagonals are equal in measure. *(Book 2)*

In a parallelogram, opposite sides are equal in measure. *(Book 2)*

Theorem   If a quadrilateral is a parallelogram, then consecutive angles are supplementary. *(Book 2)*

Theorem   If a quadrilateral is a parallelogram, then opposite angles are equal in measure. *(Book 2)*

Theorem   The sum of the measures of the angles of a quadrilateral is 360°. *(Book 2)*

Theorem   If both pairs of opposite angles of a quadrilateral are equal in measure, then the quadrilateral is a parallelogram. *(Book 2)*

Theorem 3.1   If the two diagonals of a quadrilateral bisect each other, then the quadrilateral is a parallelogram. *(p. 141)*

Theorem 3.3   In an isosceles trapezoid, (1) the legs are equal in measure, (2) the diagonals are equal in measure, and (3) the two angles at each base are equal in measure. *(p. 150)*

Circles

Theorem 3.6   The perpendicular bisector of a chord of a circle passes through the center of the circle. *(p. 166)*

Theorem 3.7   The measure of an inscribed angle of a circle is equal to half the measure of its intercepted arc. *(p. 174)*

Theorem 3.8   An inscribed angle whose intercepted arc is a semicircle is a right angle. *(p. 174)*

Theorem 3.9   If two inscribed angles in the same circle intercept the same arc, then they are equal in measure. *(p. 174)*

Theorem 3.10   If a line is tangent to a circle, then the line is perpendicular to the radius drawn from the center to the point of tangency. *(p. 183)*

Theorem 3.11   If a line in the plane of a circle is perpendicular to a radius at its outer endpoint, then the line is tangent to the circle. *(p. 183)*

Theorem 3.12   If two tangent segments are drawn from the same point to the same circle, then they are equal in measure. *(p. 183)*

Polyhedra

Postulate   In any convex polyhedron, the sum of the measures of the angles at each vertex is less than 360°. *(p. 194)*

Theorem 3.13   There are exactly five regular polyhedra: tetrahedron, octahedron, icosahedron, hexahedron, and dodecahedron. *(p. 195)*

Constant

Direct Variation

Linear

Absolute Value (Piecewise)

Quadratic

Square Root (Radical)

Cubic

Cube Root (Radical)

Reciprocal (Rational)

Exponential Logarithmic
(Inverse Functions)

Sine (Periodic)

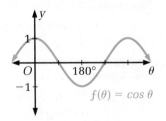

Cosine (Periodic)

Glossary

Student Resources

absolute value (p. 87) The distance that a number is from zero on a number line.

$$|x| = \begin{cases} x & \text{if } x \ge 0 \\ -x & \text{if } x < 0 \end{cases}$$

absolute value function (p. 88) A function that has a variable within the absolute value symbol.

algorithm (p. 4) A set of step-by-step directions for a process.

ambiguous case (p. 470) A situation where two triangles can be formed from the same side-side-angle information.

amplitude (p. 548) One half the difference between the maximum and minimum values of a periodic function.

arithmetic sequence (p. 229) A sequence in which the difference between any term and the term before it is a constant.

arithmetic series (p. 238) A series whose terms form an arithmetic sequence.

asymptote (p. 123) A line that a graph approaches more and more closely.

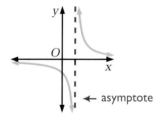

axis of a periodic function (p. 548) The horizontal line halfway between the minimum and maximum values of a periodic function.

bearing (p. 425) An angular direction given by a magnetic compass.

bimodal distribution (p. 332) A frequency distribution that has two distinct intervals or groups of intervals that contain the greatest frequencies.

binomial experiment (p. 411) An experiment with a fixed number of independent trials. For each trial there are two mutually exclusive outcomes, success and failure. Each trial has the same $P(\text{success})$, and $P(\text{success}) + P(\text{failure}) = 1$.

box-and-whisker plot (p. 17) A method for displaying the median, quartiles, and extremes of a data set.

cell of a periodic tessellation (p. 584) A fundamental unit of a periodic tessellation that can be copied and translated to generate the pattern.

central angle (p. 167) An angle with its vertex at the center of a circle.

chord (p. 166) A segment joining two points on a circle.

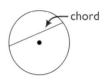

circumscribed circle (p. 166) A circle is *circumscribed* about a polygon when each vertex of the polygon lies on the circle. The polygon is *inscribed* in the circle.

circumscribed polygon (p. 187) A polygon is *circumscribed* about a circle when each side of the polygon is tangent to the circle. The circle is *inscribed* in the polygon.

common difference (p. 229) The value $a_n - a_{n-1}$ in an arithmetic sequence.

common logarithm (p. 302) A logarithm with base 10. It is usually written $\log x$.

common ratio (p. 229) The value $\frac{a_n}{a_{n-1}}$ in a geometric sequence.

complementary angles (p. 668) Two angles whose measures have the sum 90°.

complementary events (p. 386) Two mutually exclusive events that account for all possibilities.

composite of two functions (p. 126) The function whose value at x is $f(g(x))$ is the composite of the functions f and g. Also written as $(f \circ g)(x)$.

conclusion of an implication (p. 140) The *then* part of an *if-then* statement.

conclusion of a logical argument (p. 658) A statement resulting from the premises of a logical argument.

conditional probability (p. 396) The probability that an event will occur given that another event has occurred.

congruent (p. 656) Having the same size and shape.

conjecture (p. 139) A statement, opinion, or conclusion based on observation.

constraint (p. 54) Any condition that must be met by a variable or by a linear combination of variables.

contrapositive (p. 142) A statement obtained by interchanging and adding "not" to the *if* and *then* parts of an *if-then* statement.

converse (p. 142) A statement obtained by interchanging the *if* and *then* parts of an *if-then* statement.

coordinate proof (p. 147) A method of proof based on a coordinate system in which all points are represented by ordered pairs of numbers.

correlation coefficient (p. 352) A number between 1 and -1, inclusive, that describes how well a set of data points can be modeled by a line.

cosine function (p. 556) A function that measures the horizontal position of an object moving around a unit circle.

cycle (p. 548) The smallest portion of the graph that repeats.

damping function (p. 543) A function whose graph moves towards a constant value by alternately increasing and decreasing around that value.

defect (p. 194) The angle measure of the gap in a net for a polyhedron.

degree of a polynomial function (p. 103) The largest exponent, n, of a polynomial function.

direct variation function (p. 102) A function of the form $f(x) = kx^n$ where n is a positive integer and $k \neq 0$.

domain of a function (p. 70) All values of the control variable of a function.

edge of a network (p. 37) A line connecting two vertices of a network.

exclusive definition (p. 154) A definition that excludes some possibilities.

expected value (p. 404) If a situation has a gain or loss x_1 with probability $P(x_1)$, a gain or loss x_2 with probability $P(x_2)$, and so on, then the expected value is
$$x_1 \cdot P(x_1) + x_2 \cdot P(x_2) + \cdots + x_n \cdot P(x_n).$$

explicit formula (p. 217) A formula for a sequence that expresses the value of any term a_n using n, the position number of the term in the sequence $a_1, a_2, a_3, \ldots$.

exponential decay function (p. 270) An exponential function $y = ab^x$, where $0 < b < 1$.

exponential function (p. 267) A function of the form $y = ab^x$.

exponential growth function (p. 270) An exponential function $y = ab^x$, where $b > 1$.

extraneous solution (p. 112) A solution of a simplified equation that is not a solution of the original equation.

fair (p. 405) A game or situation is considered fair if it has an expected value of 0.

feasible region (p. 54) The graph of the solution of a system of inequalities that meets all given constraints.

flow proof (p. 144) A proof written as a diagram using arrows to show the connections between statements. Numbers written over the arrows refer to a numbered list of the justifications for the statements.

frequency distribution (p. 332) A display of data that shows the number of occurrences of each data item.

frequency of a periodic function (p. 548) The reciprocal of the period.

function (p. 70) A relationship where there is only one value of the dependent variable for each value of the control variable. All the values of the control variable are the *domain*. All the values of the dependent variable over the domain are the *range*.

function notation (p. 71) The notation $y = f(x)$, which means that y represents the value of the function f for a value of x.

geometric mean (p. 232) The *geometric mean* of any two positive numbers a and b is $\sqrt{ab}$, since the sequence a, $\sqrt{ab}$, b is geometric.

geometric sequence (p. 229) A sequence in which the ratio of any term to the term before it is a constant.

geometric series (p. 245) A series whose terms form a geometric sequence.

histogram (p. 331) A type of bar graph that displays frequencies.

hyperbola (p. 123) The graph of a rational function where the degree of the polynomial in the numerator is zero or 1 and the degree of the polynomial in the denominator is 1.

hypothesis (p. 140) The *if* part of an *if-then* statement.

implication (p. 142) A statement with an *if* part and a *then* part. The *if* part is the *hypothesis* and the *then* part is the *conclusion*. Also called a *conditional*.

inclusive definition (p. 154) A definition that includes all possibilities.

independent events (p. 398) Two events are independent if and only if the occurrence of one does not affect the probability of the occurrence of the other.

indirect proof (p. 180) A method of proof in which you temporarily assume the opposite of what you want to prove and then show that this leads to an impossible situation or a contradiction of a known fact.

inscribed angle (p. 172) An angle formed by two chords intersecting at a point on a circle.

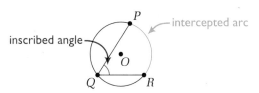

inscribed circle (p. 187) *See* circumscribed polygon.

inscribed polygon (p. 166) *See* circumscribed circle.

intercepted arc (pp. 167, 172) The arc that lies within an inscribed angle or central angle. *See also* inscribed angle and central angle.

inverse (p. 142) A statement obtained by adding "not" to both the *if* and *then* parts of an *if-then* statement.

inverse functions (p. 297) Two functions f and g are inverse functions if $g(b) = a$ whenever $f(a) = b$. The inverse of a function is written as $f^{-1}(x)$ or f^{-1}.

inverse matrices (p. 31) Two 2×2 matrices whose product is the matrix $\begin{bmatrix} 1 & 0 \\ 0 & 1 \end{bmatrix}$. The symbol A^{-1} is used to represent the inverse of matrix A.

isosceles trapezoid (p. 150) A trapezoid with a line of symmetry that passes through the midpoints of the bases.

kite (p. 155) A quadrilateral with two pairs of consecutive sides equal in measure. These pairs do not have a side in common.

law of cosines (p. 461) In any $\triangle ABC$:
$$a^2 = b^2 + c^2 - 2bc \cos A$$
$$b^2 = a^2 + c^2 - 2ac \cos B$$
$$c^2 = a^2 + b^2 - 2ab \cos C$$

law of sines (p. 467) In any $\triangle ABC$:
$$\frac{a}{\sin A} = \frac{b}{\sin B} = \frac{c}{\sin C}$$

least-squares line (p. 351) A linear model used to fit a line to a data set. The model minimizes the sum of the squares of the distances of the data points from the line.

least-squares parabola (p. 360) A quadratic model used to fit a curve to a data set.

limit of a sequence (p. 210) When the terms of a sequence get closer and closer to a single fixed number L, then L is called the *limit* of the sequence.

linear combination (p. 53) An expression in the form $ax + by$, where a and b are constants.

linear equation with three variables (p. 32) A linear equation of the form $ax + by + cz = d$.

linear function (p. 78) A function that has an equation of the form $f(x) = mx + b$, where m is the slope of its linear graph and b is the vertical intercept.

linear programming (p. 56) A process that uses a system of linear inequalities called *constraints* to solve certain decision-making problems where a linear combination is to be maximized or minimized.

logarithm (p. 302) The exponent a when a positive number x is written as a power of a positive base b, $(b \neq 1)$: $\log_b x = a$ when $x = b^a$.

logarithmic function (p. 302) The inverse of the exponential function $f(x) = 10^x$ and written as $f^{-1}(x) = \log_{10} x$.

logistic growth function (p. 290) A function whose rate of growth slows down after increasing or decreasing exponentially.

loop (p. 4) A group of steps that are repeated for a certain number of times or until some condition is met.

lower extreme (p. 17) In a data set, the smallest data item.

lower quartile (p. 17) In a data set, the median of the lower half of the data set.

magnitude (p. 441) The length of a vector.

major arc (p. 167) An arc of a circle with a measure greater than 180° and less than 360°.

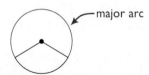

many-to-one function (p. 72) A function in which a member of the range may be paired with more than one member of the domain.

matrix (p. 632) An arrangement of numbers, called *elements*, in rows and columns. The number of rows and columns are the *dimensions* of the matrix.

matrix equation (p. 31) For a system of linear equations in two variables, a matrix equation has the form $A \begin{bmatrix} x \\ y \end{bmatrix} = B$.

maximum (p. 45) The greatest value.

mean (p. 16) The sum of the data in a data set divided by the number of items.

median (p. 17) In a data set, the middle number or the average of the two middle numbers when the data are arranged in numerical order.

median-median line (p. 352) A linear model used to fit a line to a data set. The line is fit only to summary points, key points calculated using medians.

median of a triangle (p. 147) A segment joining a vertex of a triangle to the midpoint of the opposite side.

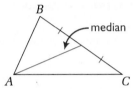

minimum (p. 45) The least value.

minor arc (p. 167) An arc of a circle with a measure less than 180°.

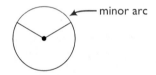

mound-shaped distribution (p. 332) A frequency distribution approximately symmetrical about a line passing through the interval or between the intervals with the greatest frequencies.

mutually exclusive events (p. 386) Events that cannot occur at the same time.

natural logarithm (p. 302) A logarithm with base e. It is usually written ln x.

net (p. 193) A set of polygons that can be used to make a polyhedron. *See also* defect.

normal distribution (p. 345) A distribution of data with a histogram that follows a bell-shaped curve, or *normal curve*, that reaches its maximum height at the mean.

one-to-one function (p. 72) A function in which each member of the range is paired with exactly one member of the domain.

opposite vectors (p. 443) Two vectors that have the same magnitude but opposite directions.

outlier (p. 332) In a data set, a value whose distance from the center of the data is much greater than the distances for other data values.

parabola (p. 95) The graph of $y = ax^2 + bx + c$, $a \neq 0$. The point where the curve turns is either the highest point or the lowest point and is called the *vertex*.

paragraph proof (p. 166) A proof whose statements and justifications are written in paragraph form.

parallelogram (p. 155) A quadrilateral with two pairs of parallel sides.

parametric equations (p. 453) Equations that express two variables in terms of a third variable, called the *parameter*.

partial sum (p. 252) The sum of the first n terms of an infinite series.

percentile (p. 523) A whole number between 1 and 100 that tells what percent of the data in a set are less than a given value.

period (p. 548) The length of one cycle.

periodic function (p. 543) A function whose graph repeats a pattern.

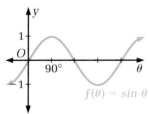

periodic tessellation (p. 584) A tessellation that matches itself exactly if it is translated.

perpendicular bisector (p. 165) A line, ray, or segment that bisects a segment and forms right angles with it.

piecewise function (p. 86) A function defined by two or more equations. Each equation applies to a different part of the function's domain.

polar coordinates (p. 425) A set of coordinates that use a distance from a reference point and an angle to describe a location.

polyhedron (p. 193) A space figure whose faces are polygons.

polynomial function (p. 103) A function of the form $P(x) = a_n x^n + a_{n-1} x^{n-1} + a_{n-2} x^{n-2} + \cdots + a_1 x + a_0$ where the coefficients are real numbers and n is a nonnegative integer.

premise (p. 658) A given statement in an argument.

probability distribution (p. 376) A histogram in which the relative frequencies on the vertical axis represent probabilities.

Pythagorean identity (p. 435) The relationship $\cos^2 \theta + \sin^2 \theta = 1$.

quadratic function (p. 95) A function of the form $f(x) = ax^2 + bx + c$ where a, b, and c are constants and $a \neq 0$.

quadrilateral (p. 155) A polygon with four sides. *See also* kite, parallelogram, rectangle, rhombus, square, and trapezoid.

radical function (p. 113) A function that has a variable under a radical symbol.

random numbers (p. 374) A sequence of numbers that has no pattern, and each number has an equally likely chance of appearing in the sequence.

range of a data set (p. 338) The difference between the greatest and least data values.

range of a function (p. 70) All values of the dependent variable.

rational expression (p. 120) The quotient of two polynomials.

rational function (p. 120) A function that is defined by a rational expression.

rectangle (p. 155) A quadrilateral with four right angles.

recursive formula (p. 223) A formula for a sequence that expresses the value of the nth term of a sequence, a_n, using the term before it, a_{n-1}.

regression (p. 351) The process of fitting a curve to a set of data.

regular polygon (p. 161) A polygon with all sides equal in length and all angles equal in measure.

regular polyhedron (p. 193) A space figure whose faces are all regular polygons of one type and which has the same number of faces at each vertex.

relative frequency histogram (p. 334) A histogram whose vertical scale shows the fraction or percent of the data values in each interval.

resultant vector (p. 442) The sum of two vectors. A vector from the tail of the first vector to the head of the second vector.

resultant vector

rhombus (p. 155) A quadrilateral with four sides of equal measure.

saturating function (p. 543) A function whose graph continually increases or decreases toward a constant value.

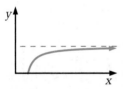

scalar multiple of a vector (p. 443) A vector $\mathbf{v} = k\mathbf{u}$ is called a *scalar multiple* of $\mathbf{u}$.

scatter plot (p. 18) A graph that shows the relationship between two data sets.

secant (p. 181) A line intersecting a circle in two points.

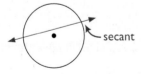

secant

semicircle (p. 167) An arc of a circle with a measure of 180°.

180° — semicircle

semiperimeter of a polygon (p. 188) Half the perimeter.

semiregular polyhedron (p. 193) A space figure whose faces are all regular polygons and which has the same number of faces of each type at each vertex.

sequence (p. 208) An ordered list of numbers called the *terms* of the sequence. A *finite sequence* has a last term. An *infinite sequence* has no last term.

series (p. 238) The indicated sum of the terms of a sequence. A *finite series* has a last term. An *infinite series* has no last term.

sigma notation (p. 238) A form of notation using the summation symbol Σ to express a series.

significance level (p. 413) In a probability model, a probability level that would be considered unusual if the results were due to chance.

similar triangles (p. 655) Two triangles whose vertices can be matched up so that corresponding angles are equal in measure and corresponding sides are in proportion.

simulation (p. 374) An experiment that models an actual event.

sine function (p. 555) A function that measures the vertical position of an object moving around a unit circle. (*See also* periodic function.)

skewed distribution (p. 332) A frequency distribution that has an interval or group of intervals that contains the greatest frequencies near one end.

slope (p. 78) The measure of the steepness of a line given by the ratio of rise to run for any two points on the line.

square (p. 155) A quadrilateral with four right angles and four sides of equal measure.

standard deviation (p. 339) A measure of the variability of a data set. The formula for the standard deviation σ (read *sigma*), where $\overline{x}$ is the mean and n is the number of data values, is

$$\sigma = \sqrt{\frac{\sum_{i=1}^{n}(x_i - \overline{x})^2}{n}}.$$

standard normal curve (p. 521) The parent graph of any normal distribution.

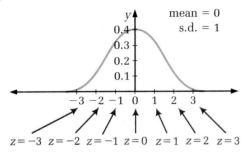

supplementary angles (p. 161) Two angles whose measures have the sum 180°.

synthetic proof (p. 140) A method of proof based on a system of postulates and theorems in which the properties of figures are studied, but not their actual measurements.

system of equations (p. 30) Two or more equations involving the same variables.

tangent (p. 181) A line in the plane of the circle that intersects the circle in exactly one point.

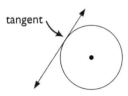

tessellation (p. 582) A design made up of regular polygons placed so their vertices touch without gaps or overlaps to cover a plane. A *regular* tessellation has only one kind of polygon. A *semiregular* tessellation has two or more kinds of polygons, and the arrangement at each vertex is the same.

transformation (p. 662) A change in the size or the position of a figure.

transformation matrix (p. 501) A matrix used to represent a transformation.

translation (p. 662) A transformation that moves each point of a figure the same distance in the same direction.

trapezoid (p. 154) A quadrilateral with at least one pair of parallel sides.

two-column proof (p. 141) A proof written in two columns. Statements are listed in one column and justifications in the other.

uniform distribution (p. 332) A frequency distribution where all the intervals have approximately equal frequencies.

upper extreme (p. 17) In a data set, the largest data item.

upper quartile (p. 17) In a data set, the median of the upper half of the data.

valid argument (p. 658) An argument that uses rules of logic.

vector (p. 441) A quantity that has both a length, or magnitude, and a direction.

vertex of a network (p. 37) In a network, the point where two edges meet.

x-intercept (p. 648) The x-coordinate of a point where a graph intersects the x-axis (where $y = 0$). Also called a *horizontal intercept*.

y-intercept (p. 648) The y-coordinate of a point where a graph intersects the y-axis (where $x = 0$). Also called a *vertical intercept*.

z-score (p. 520) The distance of a data value from the mean of a data set, measured in standard deviations.

zero of a function (p. 104) A value of x that makes $f(x)$ equal to zero.

Student Resources

inverse cosine, 463

least-squares line, 101, 351–352, 355–356, 359, 364, 500

least-squares parabola, 360, 362–363

inverse functions, 300, 526, 601

logarithmic equations, 309, 312, 319

logarithms, 302

matrices, 31, 33, 43, 361, 603, 604

maximums and minimums, 46

mean, 606

parametric equations, 454–455, 602

piecewise functions, 90

quadratic modeling, 46, 95–97, 360

radicals, 114, 286

random numbers, 374–376, 390, 410

rational function, 122

recursion equations, 224

scatter plot, 21, 101, 605

statistics, 339–340, 352–354, 358, 364, 484, 497, 605, 606

standard deviation, 606

trigonometric function, 555, 560

using TABLE feature, 599

using ZOOM feature, 599

See also Computer, Technology Handbook, *and* Technology Notes.

Career

architect, 42, 126

astronaut, 125, 494

atmospheric scientist, 20

biologist, 285, 476, 552

boat designer, 117

chemist, 126, 464

designer, 465

engineer, 98, 126

farmer, 59

financial consultant, 530

market researcher, 400

mathematician, 577

pediatrician, 524

pet groomer, 14 (Ex. 16)

pharmacist, 273

photographer, 306

physicist, 451

plasterer, 483

scientist, 20, 234, 320 (Ex. 9)

social scientist, 21, 108

surveyor, 74, 472

zoologist, 49

Catenary curve, 293

Cell of a periodic tessellation, 584

Center of a regular polygon, 586

Central tendency, 332

Checkpoints, 22, 93, 118, 158, 178, 236, 295, 349, 394, 452, 509, 576

Chord, perpendicular bisector of, 166

Circle

arc of, 167, 172–173, 652

area and circumference of, 652

central angle of, 167, 652

chord of, 166

equation of, 652

inscribed angle of, 172–174

secant, 181

tangent, 181, 183

unit, 555

Circumscribing, 155–166, 167, 188, 197

Coefficient matrix, 31

Collaborative learning

See Explorations, Group activities, *and* Projects.

Talk it Over and Look Back questions for group discussion occur in each section.

Combinations, counting, 629

Communication

reading, 6, 13, 19, 26, 34, 41, 49, 57, 73, 75, 81, 89, 97, 105, 115, 124, 129, 143, 150, 157, 162, 175, 183, 189, 195, 214, 219, 225, 234, 241, 247, 257, 271, 277, 285, 291, 299, 305, 313, 320, 324, 335, 340, 341, 347, 354, 362, 378, 387, 392, 399, 406, 407, 415, 427, 436, 444, 449, 456, 463, 471, 486, 492, 498, 505, 514, 523, 530, 534, 545, 550, 557, 563, 572, 580, 585

writing, 5, 8, 14, 15, 19, 21, 22, 28, 35, 43, 44, 49, 58, 59, 60, 62, 74, 75, 76, 84, 90, 93, 98, 100, 115, 118, 124, 125, 129, 130, 134, 143, 145, 151, 152, 158, 163, 164, 168, 178, 186, 190, 191, 200, 214, 219, 220, 226, 235, 236, 242, 248, 256, 258, 260, 261, 277, 279, 280, 287, 294, 295, 299, 300, 305, 307, 314, 315, 316, 322, 324, 333, 335, 336, 340, 341, 342, 343, 348, 349, 355, 356, 357, 362, 363, 366, 367, 378, 387, 392, 394, 400, 401, 402, 408,

416, 419, 436, 444, 449, 451, 452, 457, 458, 463, 465, 487, 488, 493, 499, 500, 509, 511, 515, 525, 530, 532, 534, 545, 546, 552, 557, 559, 564, 574, 575, 576, 588, 590

See also Discussion, Explorations, Group activities, *and* Projects.

Talk it Over and Look Back questions for group discussion occur in each section.

Complementary events, 386

Complex numbers, 643

Composite of two functions, 127

Computer

CAD (computer-aided drafting), 328

using graphing software, 21 (Ex. 21), 49 (Ex. 9), 50 (Ex. 11), 105, 108 (Ex. 29), 300 (Exs. 26, 27), 320 (Exs. 17–19), 321 (Ex. 23), 489, 563 (Exs. 2–5)

using spreadsheet software, 191, 215 (Ex. 32), 225, 607

using statistics software, 355 (Exs. 5–7), 356 (Exs. 8–10), 358 (Ex. 18), 362 (Ex. 4), 363 (Exs. 9, 11–12), 364 (Ex. 14)

See also Calculator *and* Technology Handbook.

Conditional probability, 396–397

Connections

art, 306

biology, 49, 130, 226, 234, 242, 285, 315, 552

business education, 271

chemistry, 464

earth science, 565, 574

geography, 169, 437

history, 8, 249, 272, 278, 573

literature, 83, 248, 321, 348, 408, 428, 466, 515, 566

music, 487

physics, 35, 91, 124, 257, 451

science, 27, 125, 213, 291, 388, 428, 473, 499

social studies, 145, 170, 379

sports, 43

See also Applications, By the Way, Careers, Economics, History, Literature, Multicultural connections, Projects, Research, *and* Science.

Constant matrix, 31

Constraint, 54

Continuous outcomes, 382–383

Control variable, 69

Converse, 142

Cooperative learning
See Explorations, Group activities, and Projects.
Talk it Over and Look Back questions for group discussion occur in each section.

Coordinate systems
polar, 430–431, 434, 448
rectangular, 147–149, 430–431, 434, 448, 501–502
three-dimensional, 32

Corner-point principle, 56, 57

Cosine(s)
function, 556
graphing, 556
law of, 459–463

Counting techniques
combinations, 629
Pascal's triangle, 630
permutations, 628

Critical thinking
See Logic, Reasoning, and Visual thinking.

Cross-curriculum connections
See Connections.

Data analysis, See Statistics.

Data display
box-and-whisker plot, 17
histogram, 331–332, 627
linear graph, 16
matrix, 31
network diagram, 37–40, 46–48
range, 338
scatter plot, 18, 605
spreadsheets, 191, 215, 225, 607
table, 649
tree diagram, 384, 395–397, 405, 579
Venn diagram, 384, 386

Decay graph, 270

Deductive reasoning
contrapositive, 142
converse, 142
implications, 142
inverse, 142

Degree, of a polynomial, 103

Dependent events, 397

Dependent variable, 69

Deviation
from the mean, 338
standard, 338–340, 498, 520

Diagonal, bisecting theorem, 141

Diagrams, using in problem solving, 38–44, 47–48, 50, 95, 384, 395–397, 405, 528
See also Data display.

Direct variation function, 102

Discrete mathematics
algorithms, 6–7, 10–11, 377
combinations, 9–12, 13 (Exs. 12, 13), 15 (Ex. 19), 22 (Ex. 3)
counting techniques, 628–629
decision-making, 11–12, 13 (Exs. 14, 15), 14 (Exs. 16–18), 15 (Ex. 19), 24–25, 27 (Exs. 17, 18), 30, 33, 36, 38, 40, 50 (Ex. 11), 55–56, 328, 339, 413
discrete vs. continuous, 267, 272 (Exs. 10, 11), 378 (Exs. 1–8), 389 (Ex. 27), 382–383
Euler's formula, 196 (Exs. 5, 6)
expected value, 404–405
fractals, 222–223, 227, 256, 259
graph theory, 184 (Ex. 9)
limits, 122, 123, 210, 543
linear programming, 55–57 (Ex. 1), 58 (Exs. 7, 8), 59 (Exs. 10–12)
logic, 142, 155, 160, 364
matrices, 31, 33, 361, 501, 502, 504 (Exs. 1–12), 505 (Exs. 13, 14), 537
network diagrams, 37–40, 46–48
patterns in discrete data sets, 18–21, 159, 163, (Ex. 15), 164 (Ex. 16), 191 (Ex. 11), 207, 211–214
permutations, 628
probability, 382–386, 395–398, 405, 410–414
recursion, 4–6, 8 (Exs. 13–15), 22 (Ex. 2), 218, 220 (Ex. 13c), 222–227, 230–231, 249 (Ex. 19), 272 (Exs. 14–16), 273 (Exs. 20–23)
sequences, 208–210, 216–221, 228–231, 301
series, 238–243, 244–250, 251–258
tree diagrams, 395–397, 405, 579
Venn diagrams, 384, 386
See also Data display, Probability, and Statistics

Discussion
Can we talk? 2, 68, 138, 206, 266,

330, 372, 424, 482, 540
Look Back and Talk it Over discussion questions occur in each section.

Distance formula, 149, 460

Distribution
bimodal, 332
defined, 332
mound-shaped, 332
normal, 344, 345
skewed, 332
uniform, 332

Doubling
See Exponential function(s).

Dual of a tessellation, 586

e, 288–290

Economics, 13, 14, 25–27, 29, 36, 59, 89, 90, 93, 204–206, 218, 220, 243, 286, 292, 321, 336, 349, 357, 368, 400, 403, 404, 407, 420, 493, 499, 506, 509, 515, 530

Edge of a network diagram, 37

Ellipse, 505

Equation(s)
for a line, 648
linear, solving, 25, 644
matrix, 31, 33
parametric, 453–455, 541–542, 602
polynomial, 647
quadratic, solving, 645
rational, solving, 646
system of, 24, 29–33, 361, 644
with three variables, 32
writing, 639, 648

Estimation
of area from circumference, 364
of boundary region of an inequality, 5
of value of e^n, 291 (Exs. 2–5)

Euler's formula, 196

Event(s)
dependent, 397
independent, 397–398

Exclusive/inclusive, 154

Expected value, 403–406

Experimental probability, 412

Explicit formula, 217

Explorations
adding constants to translate a graph, 489
circumscribing circles, 165

in Ongoing Assessment, 51, 198, 364

Map
four-color problem, 184 (Ex. 9)
network diagrams, 37, 39, 46–48

Mathematical argumentation
See Logic, Proof, Reasoning, Writing, *and Talk it Over questions in each unit.*

Mathematical modeling
See Modeling.

Matrix (matrices)
adding and subtracting, 633–634
calculator with, 31, 33, 361
coefficient, 31
constant, 31
inverse, 31
operations with, 632–634
representing a data set, 632
to solve system of equations, 33, 361
transformation, 501

Maximizing
using linear programming, 53–57
using quadratic functions, 46

Mean
arithmetic, 233
geometric, 232
statistical, 16, 269, 332, 338, 345, 485, 498, 520, 626

Measures
of angles of polygons, 159–161
of angles at each vertex of a polyhedron, 194
of inscribed angles, 174

Median(s)
statistical, 16, 332, 345, 352, 485, 498, 626
summary points, 352
of a triangle, 147–148

Median-median line, 352–353

Minimizing, 46–48, 53–57

Mode, 626

Modeling
feasible region, 54
to find maximum and minimum, 46, 53–57, 95–97, 360
exponential, 267–270, 275–276, 281–282
geometric, 390–391
least-squares line, 101, 351–352, 359–360
linear, 25, 53–54, 77–78, 90,

350–352, 359
logarithmic, 309, 312, 319
parametric, 453–455
quadratic, 46, 94–97, 359–361
with sine and cosine, 568–571
with system of inequalities, 53–54
trigonometric, 555, 560
See also Manipulatives *and* Multiple Representations.

Multicultural connections, xxvi, 1, 3, 5, 6 (Ex. 2), 7 (Ex. 5), 8 (Exs. 13, 14), 16, 32, 42 (Exs. 11–13), 56, 66, 67, 77, 80, 83, 94, 97, 99 (Exs. 12–15), 107, 110, 111, 119, 125, 130, 142, 144 (Exs. 16–18), 162 (Exs. 5–10), 184, 194, 195, 205, 212, 216, 219 (Ex. 11), 220, 234 (Ex. 23), 237, 241 (Ex. 7), 248, 264, 265, 271, 292, 293, 299 (Ex. 9), 304, 305 (Ex. 2), 318, 320 (Ex. 22), 325 (Exs. 30, 31), 329, 336 (Ex. 9), 350, 354 (Ex. 3), 355 (Ex. 7), 357 (Ex. 12), 362 (Ex. 4), 370–372, 381, 387, 389 (Exs. 27, 28), 393, 394, 402, 409, 417, 422–424, 437, 445 (Exs. 18, 19), 460, 465 (Exs. 14–17), 467–469, 471 (Ex. 2), 480, 481, 494, 496, 497, 510, 514, 530, 539, 574 (Ex. 12), 577, 579, 583, 584

Multiple representations, 18, 31, 38–40, 42, 46, 121–122, 142, 209, 224–225, 268, 302, 333, 334, 338, 350, 351, 359, 395, 425, 483, 496, 521–522, 550, 569–570
See also Data display, Graphs, and Manipulatives.

Multiplication
of data by a constant, 496, 498
Egyptian, 8
matrix, 43
of polynomials, 638
scalar, of vectors, 443

Mutually exclusive events, 386

Negative exponents, 637

Net, 193

Network diagram, 37–40, 46–48

Ongoing Assessment
See Assessment.

Open-ended problems
in Exercises, 6, 7, 19, 20, 27, 34, 44, 60, 75, 82, 124, 129, 145, 157, 177, 184, 190, 197, 212, 234, 242, 249,

272, 286, 292, 336, 347, 356, 389, 399, 401, 428, 436, 444, 457, 464, 504, 545, 574, 580, 587, 588
in Ongoing Assessment, 36, 51, 92, 108, 152, 171, 214, 221, 243, 250, 274, 337, 343, 394, 429, 445, 495, 532
in Review and Assessment, 63, 134, 200, 201, 261, 324, 367, 477, 535, 591
in Unit Project, 76, 100, 349, 358, 409, 419

Or, 384

Outcomes, 382–383

Outliers, 332

Parabola, 46, 72–73, 95, 102, 297, 360, 489, 506 (Exs. 23–26), 529, 598, 599, 601, 649, 651, 672

Parameter, 453

Parametric equation(s), 453–455, 602

Pascal's triangle, 237, 630

Patterns
in discrete data sets, 18–21, 159, 207
in sequences, 207–208
in tessellations, 195, 582–584
from transformations, 577–578

Percentile, 523

Periodic function graph, 548, 549

Periodic tessellations, 582–584

Permutations, counting, 628

Perpendicular bisector of a chord, 166

Piecewise function, 85–87

Polar coordinates, 425–426, 430–435

Polygon(s)
area of circumscribed, 188
center of regular, 586
diagonals of circumscribed, 188
diagonals of, 108 (Ex. 28)
diagonals of inscribed, 166, 167
regular, 161
semiperimeter of, 188
sum of exterior angles, 161
sum of interior angles, 161
See also Triangle(s).

Polyhedron
convex postulate, 194
dihedral angle of, 465

regular, 193, 195
semiregular, 193
types of, 195
See also Prism(s).

Polynomial(s)
binomial theorem, 639
factoring, 640
operations on, 636, 638, 641

Polynomial function
degree of, 103
factored form, 104
graphing, 104
standard form, 103–105
zero of, 104

Postulates and Theorems, 668–671

Prediction, *See* Probability *and* Statistics.

Prism(s)
surface area and volume of, 652
types of, 196

Probability
binomial experiments, 410–412
combinations, 629
complementary events, 386
conditional, 396–397
continuous outcomes, 382–383
decision making, 413
dependent events, 397
discrete outcomes, 382–383
distribution, 412
of an event, 631
experimental, 412, 631–632
geometric models for, 390–392
independent events, 397–398
mutually exclusive events, 386, 631–632
permutations, 628
significance level, 413
theoretical, 411, 631–632
of two events, 382–383, 385
using Pascal's triangle, 630
using a tree diagram, 395–397, 405

Problem solving strategies
breaking problem into parts, 86–87, 121
finding a trend, 210
looking for a pattern, 208–209, 229
making a systematic list, 10, 11
using algebra, 5, 25, 30, 78, 111, 112, 128
using a diagram, 37–41, 46–48, 95, 384, 395, 397, 405, 528
using an equation, 33, 102, 268,

276, 281, 289, 311
using a formula, 46, 97, 111, 161, 231, 238, 245, 318, 339, 405, 414, 431, 434, 461, 468, 484, 520
using a graph, 5, 17–18, 24–25, 46, 54, 56, 96, 104, 111–112, 121, 268, 270, 276, 295, 333–334, 351–352, 391, 503, 544, 549–550, 570
using a graphics calculator, 105, 122, 224, 339, 484, 497
using a matrix, 31, 33, 39, 361
using recursion, 268
using a calculator, 431, 434, 484
using a spreadsheet, 225
using a tree diagram, 395, 397, 405
using vectors, 442, 446, 448, 454

Programming, linear, 53–57

Projects
Alternative
Analyzing Advertising Claims, 418
Applying Exponential and Logarithmic Functions, 323
Consumer Economics and Maintenance Agreements, 418
Falling Objects, 132
Fractal Patterns, 259
Graphs, 132
Is It Normal? 365
Management Science, 61
Mathematics and My Musical Instrument, 323
Ocean Navigation, 475
Orienteering, 475
Penrose Tiles, 589
Predict Future Trends, 589
Put on a Mock Trial, 199
Re-scaling the SAT Test, 533
Research a Famous Case, 199
Secret Codes, 61
Sequences and Series in Everyday Things, 259
Transformations of Functions, 533
TV Ratings, 365
Unit 1, Plan a Park, xxvi, 1–2, 8, 15, 22, 28, 36, 44, 52, 60, 61
Unit 2, Make a Pedal Pitch, 66–68, 76, 84, 92, 100, 109, 118, 125, 131, 132
Unit 3, State Your Case, 136–138, 146, 152, 158, 164, 171, 178, 186, 191, 198, 199
Unit 4, Save for the Future,

204–206, 215, 221, 227, 236, 243, 250, 258, 259
Unit 5, Making Music with Mathematics, 264–266, 274, 280, 287, 295, 300, 308, 316, 322, 323
Unit 6, The Mean Machine, 328–330, 337, 343, 349, 358, 364, 365
Unit 7, Rules of the Game, 370–372, 381, 389, 394, 402, 409, 417
Unit 8, Plan a Treasure Hunt, 422–424, 429, 439, 445, 452, 458, 466, 474, 475
Unit 9, Job Interview, 480–482, 488, 495, 500, 509, 518, 525, 532, 533
Unit 10, Make a Functional Scrapbook, 538–540, 547, 553, 559, 567, 575, 581, 588, 589

Proof
contrapositive, 142
converse, 142
coordinate, 147–149
counterexample, 145
implications, 142, 657
indirect, 179–182, 364
inverse, 142
mathematical induction, 160
synthetic, 140
valid arguments, 657
See also Reasoning.

Pythagorean identity, 435

Pythagorean theorem, 653

Quadratic formula, 97, 645

Quadratic function
graphing, 95–96, 651
least-squares parabola, 360
line of symmetry of parabola, 46, 651
modeling with, 46, 94–97, 360–361
standard form, 95

Radical expressions, simplifying, 642

Radical function, 113–114, 286

Random sampling, 374–376, 390, 410

Range, 338, 485, 498

Rates of change, 544

Ratio, 229

Credits

DESIGN

Book Design: Two Twelve Associates, Inc.
Cover Design: Two Twelve Associates, Inc. Photographic collage by Susan Wides; student photography by Ken Karp.
Electronic Technical Art: American Composition & Graphics, Inc.

ACKNOWLEDGMENTS

20 Data from "The Best and Worst According to Nielsen," *TV Guide*, June 11, 1994. **248** From *The Mythology of All Races*, Volume 1: Greek and Roman, by William Sherwood Fox, A.M., Ph.D. Originally published in 1916 by Marshall Jones Company, copyright renewed 1944 by Macmillan Publishing Company. **249** From *The Oxford Dictionary of Nursery Rhymes*, edited by Iona and Peter Opie, Oxford University Press, 1983. **321** From *The Andromeda Strain*, by Michael Crichton. Copyright ©1969 by Centesis Corporation. Reprinted by permission of Alfred A. Knopf, Inc. **348** From *Jurassic Park* by Michael Crichton. Copyright ©1990 by Michael Crichton. Reprinted by permission of Alfred A. Knopf, Inc. **408** From *The Promise*, by Chaim Potok. Copyright ©1969 by Chaim Potok. Reprinted by permission of Alfred A. Knopf, Inc. **466** Cipher from *The Gold-Bug*, by Edgar Allen Poe. **515** From *Starbridge*, by A.C. Crispin. Copyright ©1989 by A.C. Crispin. Reprinted by permission of The Putnam Berkley Group. **566** From "The Parson's Tale" from *The Canterbury Tales*, by Geoffrey Chaucer, translated by Nevill Coghill, published by Penguin Books, 1977.

STOCK PHOTOGRAPHY

viii © Richard Megna/Fundamental Photographs (tl); **viii** Superstock (tr); **vii** The *Polyhedron Earth* found on page vii was designed and invented by R. Buckminster Fuller. © 1938, 1967, 1982 & 1992 Buckminster Fuller Institute, Santa Barbara, CA. All Rights Reserved.; **ix** Courtesy of the Playing Card Museum, The United States Playing Card Company, Cincinnati, Ohio; **xi** Murray Alcosser/The Image Bank; **xiii** Richard E. Smalley (b); **xiii** Lester Lefkowitz/Tony Stone Images/Chicago Inc. (t); **xxvi** Shinichi Kanno/FPG International Corp. (t); **xxvi** Superstock (bl); **xxvi** The Bettmann Archive (br); **xxvi** Portrait by William A. Smith, courtesy of Silvio Bedini and Landmark Enterprises (br); **1** Terry Qing/FPG International Corp. (bl); **1** Fort Worth Star-Telegram/Steve Gariepy (br); **2** © Bob Daemmrich (tl); **3** Dallas & John Heaton/Westlight; **5** NASA (l); **7** From *The Living Legend of Maria Martinez*, by Susan Peterson, Kodansha International © 1977, © 1989 (tl, tc, tr, bl, bc, br); **7** © Jerry Jacka. All Rights Reserved (br); **14** © 1994 Reneé Stockdale (tr); **14** Blair Seitz/Photo Researchers, Inc. (tl); **16** © The Stock Market/Otto Rogge (r); **16** Superstock (l); **16** © The Stock Market/Tom Van Sant 1993 (c); **19** Superstock; **20** NASA; **21** Bob Daemmerich/Stock Boston; **23** Tony Stone Images/Chicago Inc. (b); **23** The Bettmann Archive (t); **28** Copyright © David Smart/Stock South/Atlanta; **29** Henley & Savage/Uniphoto; **34** Ken Ross/FPG International Corp. (inset); **34** Copyright Tom Van Sant/Geosphere Project, Santa Monica/Science Photo Library/Photo Researchers, Inc. (b); **34** NASA (b); **36** Alex MacLean/Landslides (br); **36** © Kindra Clineff (bl); **37** FPG International Corp.; **37** Reproduced by permission of the Massachusetts Bay Transportation Authority, John J. Haley, Jr., General Manager (r); **39** Terry Donnelly/Tony Stone Images/Chicago Inc. (c); **43** Jerry Austin/The Picture Cube; **48** Martin Rogers/Uniphoto (bl); **49** Vance Tucker (r); **50** Per Breiehagen/Black Star (r); **52** David J. Sams/Tony Stone Images/Chicago Inc. (b); **53** Alan Becker/The Image Bank (r); **53** Mike Mazzaschi/Stock Boston (bl); **53** Don Smetzer/Tony Stone Images/Chicago Inc. (tr); **56** AT&T Archives (t); **57** Stamp designs © 1995 United States Postal Service. All Rights Reserved.; **59** Andy Sacks/Tony Stone Images/Chicago Inc. (r); **59** David R. Frazier/Tony Stone Images/Chicago Inc. (l); **66** Superstock (t); **66** The Bettmann Archive (bfr); **66** FPG International Corp. (bcr); **66** Ackerman/Mary Evans Picture Library (bfl); **66** Mary Evans Picture Library (bcl); **66** © Rob Crandall (m); **67** Eric Roth/The Picture Cube (bfl); **67** Courtesy Major Taylor Velodrome (m); **67** Indiana State Museum (t); **67** Mark Richards/PhotoEdit (bfr); **67** Duomo (bcr); **67** Lori Adamski Peek/Tony Stone Images/Chicago Inc. (bcl); **69** Superstock; **73** Jane Reed; **74** J. Goell/The Picture Cube (l); **74** Peter Pearson/Tony Stone Images/Chicago Inc. (r); **77** F. St. Clair-Renard/Photo Researchers; **83** Robert Caputo/Stock Boston (br); **83** From *The Albert N'yanza, Great Basin of the Nile, and exploration of the Nile Sources,* vol.1, by Samuel White Baker, © 1866, London: Macmillan and Co. (tr, mr); **85** Bill Bachman/Stock Boston; **91** Cathlyn Melloan/Tony Stone Images/Chicago Inc. (tr); **92** Chris Noble/Tony Stone Images/Chicago Inc.; **94** © Arthur & Elaine Morris/BIRDS AS ART (t); **94** Carr Clifton/Tony Stone Images/Chicago Inc. (b); **96** Superstock; **97** Reproduced by permission of the Lacrosse Foundation and Hall of Fame Museum, Balimore, MD and Time-Life Books Inc.; From *American Indians: Realm of the Iroquois*. Photograph by Larry Sherer © 1993 Time-Life Books Inc. (l); **99** John Running/Stock Boston; **102** © Animals Animals/Zig Leszczynski; **106** ABB Traction, Inc.; **107** Professors P.M. Motta & S. Correr/Science Photo Library/Photo Researchers; **108** Elena Rooraid/PhotoEdit; **109** Tim Davis/Tony Stone Images/Chicago Inc.; **110** Art Resource, NY (m); **110-111** © The Stock Market/Darrell Jones 1987; **116** © The Stock Market/Joe Towers 1991 (tl); **117** © Allsport USA/Ken Levine, 1992; **118** Gerard Vandystadt/Photo Researchers, Inc.; **125** NASA; **126** Solar Design Associates, Harvard MA; **130** © Animals Animals/Arthur Gloor (tl); **130** © Animals Animals/Joe McDonald (ml); **130** © The Stock Market/Michele Burgess 1991 (mr); **130** Stan Osolinski/Tony Stone Images/Chicago Inc. (br); **130** Chris Harvey/Tony Stone

423 The Bridgeman Art Library (bl);   425 Alcosser Murray/The Image Bank (br);   425 Courtesy Colorado Historical Society F13,238 (tl);   428 Map adapted from THE FELLOWSHIP OF THE RING by J.R.R. Tolkien. Copyright © 1954, 1965 by J.R.R. Tolkien. Copyright © renewed 1982 by Christopher R. Tolkien, Michael H.R. Tolkien, John F.R. Tolkien and Priscilla M.A.R. Tolkien. Reprinted by permission of Houghton Mifflin Co. All rights reserved. (b);   436 © The Stock Market/H.P.Merten 1991;   437 Archive Photos;   438 Alex MacLean/The Picture Cube;   442 Alex MacLean/Landslides;   446 Copyright © Jack Gardner/Stock South/Atlanta;   451 Jerome Shaw/FPG International Corp.;   451 Phoebe Hearst Museum of Anthropology, University of California at Berkeley (tr);   452 John Terence Turner/FPG International Corp.;   453 © Richard Megna, Fundamental Photographs, NY;   456 NASA (lc);   457 © Kirk Schlea/Sports Photo Masters, Inc.;   459 Superstock;   464 Eureka! ® Tent;   465 Roddy Mims/Uniphoto (tl);   465 Everett C. Johnson/Folio, Inc. (tr);   467 David Ball/The Picture Cube (tl);   476 © Animals Animals/Oxford Scientific Films/Stephen Dalton;   477 Alfred Gescheidt/The Image Bank (tr);   480 David Joel/Tony Stone Images/Chicago Inc. (t);   480 Philip & Karen Smith/Tony Stone Images/Chicago Inc. (l);   481 Eddie Stangler/The Picture Cube (r);   481 Robert Frerck/Odyssey Productions/Chicago (br, bl, m);   487 Courtesy NFL Properties, Inc. (b);   494 NASA;   497 J.M. Charles/Black Star/Rapho (l);   497 Jeff Dunn/The Picture Cube (r);   507 Bob Daemmrich/Stock Boston (l);   507 Donald Dietz/Stock Boston (r);   510 Steve Weinrebe/The Picture Cube (l);   510 Jean-Marc Truchet/Tony Stone Images/Chicago Inc. (r);   519 Steve Dunwell/The Image Bank;   523 Superstock;   524 Lee Balterman/The Picture Cube;   534 James Balog/Tony Stone Images/Chicago Inc.;   538 E. Carlin/The Picture Cube (t);   538 © Animals Animals/Patti Murray (bl);   538 © Animals Animals/Patti Murray (br);   539 Steve McCurry/Magnum Photos (tl);   539 Steve McCurry/Magnum Photos (tr);   539 David Young-Wolff/PhotoEdit (b);   540 © Bob Daemmrich;   541 Harlen Hunter/Indiana Motor Speedway (tl);   541 Ron McQueeny/Indiana Motor Speedway (bl);   541 Frank Cezus/FPG International Corp. (br);   542 Ann Purcell/Uniphoto (mr);   542 David Young-Wolff/PhotoEdit (br);   542 David Young-Wolff/PhotoEdit (tr);   542 Diane Schiumo/Fundamental Photo (tl);   542 Stuart Krasner/Uniphoto (bl);   549 Courtesy Vicki Sans;   553 Superstock;   554 The Bettmann Archive;   566 Reproduced by permission of The Huntington Library, San Marino, California;   570 Arnulf Husmo/Tony Stone Images/Chicago Inc.;   573 Richard Nowitz/FPG International Corp.;   573 Courtesy of the Massachusetts Historical Society;   575 © Bob Daemmrich;   577 Eleni Mylonas/Viesti Associates, Inc. (b);   583 Robert Frerck/Odyssey;   584 © 1995 M.C. Escher/Cordon Art—Baarn—Holland. All Rights Reserved.;

ASSIGNMENT PHOTOGRAPHERS
Ken Karp **vi**
Richard Haynes   **v, vi** (b), **x, xiv, xv, 9, 10, 11, 12, 14** (l), **27, 32, 35, 51, 57, 58, 61, 64, 68, 69** (b), **70, 100, 101, 115, 132, 139, 153, 154, 164, 165, 175, 176, 190, 198, 199, 206, 207, 230, 241, 251, 259, 266, 269, 282, 289** (t), **295, 323, 330, 331, 364, 365, 372, 382, 393, 395, 418, 424, 432, 439, 440, 450, 451** (bl), **462, 469, 475, 480** (r), **482, 483, 485, 504, 526, 532, 533, 542** (m), **560, 582, 589, 591**
Banta Digital Group   **162** (tc, bc), **179, 192-193**

ILLUSTRATIONS
Jana Brenning   **388, 422**
Chris Costello   **4, 17, 15, 91** (m), **95, 98, 126, 138** (b), **151, 152** (l), **182, 220, 237, 248, 264-266, 274, 293, 379, 427** (b), **450, 466** (mr), **476, 493, 564, 577, 578, 579** (m), **580, 591**
Steve Cowden   **xii, 6, 76, 84, 116, 454**
Christine Czernota   **161**
Dartmouth Publishing, Inc.   **16, 18, 20, 22, 23, 29, 30, 33, 35** (r), **37, 38,** (t, c, b), **40, 42** (t, b), **44, 45, 52, 53, 58, 62, 137** (t), **138** (t), **157, 159, 163, 187** (r), **196** (m), **281, 287, 288, 295, 331, 333, 340, 342, 344, 346, 348, 350** (bl, tr, br), **352, 373, 374, 376** (tl), **387** (t), **408** (tl), **425** (m), **426, 427** (tr, tl), **429, 439, 449, 451, 456, 457, 459** (l), **460, 464, 465** (ml, mr), **466** (tr), **471, 472, 473** (m), **474, 477, 511, 514, 528, 530, 541, 543** (lm), **545, 547, 548, 550, 551, 554, 558** (t), **561, 568, 570, 571, 572, 574** (b), **575, 579** (t, b) **582, 583, 584, 585, 586, 587, 588**
DLF Group   **3, 46, 80, 111** (t), **119** (b), **142, 144, 152** (r), **184** (b), **278-279, 286, 320, 430, 437, 565, 567, 569**
Bruce Holloway   **291, 315, 322, 552, 574** (t)
Piotr Kaczmareck   **169, 186** (r), **201, 213, 428** (t), **473** (tr, br), **499**
Aggie Kenny   **136-137**
Joe Klim   **91** (b), **308, 408** (m)
Ellen Kuzdro   **119** (m), **325, 440, 444, 445, 467, 468**
Andrew Myer   **180, 277** (r), **480**
Steve Patricia   **558** (b)
Neil Pinchin   **267, 277** (l), **296, 301, 321**
Photo manipulations by Lisa Rahon   **296, 317**
Glenn Reid   **51, 82, 350** (tl), **354, 359, 362, 357**
Michael Smith   **1, 2, 61**

TYPOGRAPHIC TITLES
Chris Costello   **136**
Frank Loose Design   **0, 3, 9, 16, 23, 29, 37, 45, 53, 69, 77, 85, 94, 101, 110, 119, 126, 139, 147, 153, 159, 165, 172, 179, 187, 192, 207, 216, 222, 228, 237, 244, 251, 267, 275, 281, 288, 296, 301, 309, 317, 331, 338, 344, 350, 359, 373, 382, 390, 395, 403, 410, 425, 430, 440, 446, 453, 459, 467, 483, 489, 496, 501, 510, 519, 526, 541, 548, 560, 568, 577, 582**
Piotr Kaczmareck   **422, 424**

Unit 1

Pages 3–6 Talk it Over

1. Answers may vary. An example is given. Walk south on Horikawa-dori Ave. to Shichijo-dori Ave. Turn left at Shichijo-dori Ave. and walk east. **2.** Answers may vary. Examples are given. **a.** Michiko's **b.** Michiko's **c.** Jiro's **d.** (1) Jiro's; Michiko's directions give no idea of how long to walk along Horikawa-dori Ave. and I'd think I missed the temple. (2) Michiko's; I wouldn't have to make decisions at as many intersections as with Jiro's directions. **3.** Steps 1, 6, and 7 **4.** End the first loop when a space is found that the car will fit in and in which it may be legally parked. End the second loop when there is enough space for the car to be backed in parallel to the curb. End the third loop when the car is parallel to the curb and less than 1 foot from it. **5.** In Step 4, turn the front wheels all the way to the left. In Step 6, turn the steering wheel all the way to the right. **6.** Answers may vary. An example is given for solving an inequality of the form $ax + b < c$. **Step 1:** If $b = 0$, go to Step 3. **Step 2:** Add the opposite of b to both sides of the inequality. **Step 3:** If $a = 1$, go to Step 6. **Step 4:** Multiply both sides of the inequality by the reciprocal of a. **Step 5:** If $a < 0$, reverse the inequality symbol. **Step 6:** Simplify if necessary. **7.** Yes; **Step 1:** Graph $y = 4$. **Step 2:** Graph $y = -3x + 9$. **Step 3:** Estimate the x-coordinate of the intersection point.

Pages 6–8 Exercises and Problems

5. E, F, C, A, B, B **7, 9.** Solution methods may vary. Solutions are given. **7.** $x > 1274$ **9.** $x \le -4\frac{2}{5}$

11. a. Answers may vary. An example is given. I prefer Ryan's algorithm because it requires fewer steps and calculations. If the server didn't add the sales tax to the check, then I'd use Susan's algorithm. **b.** Divide the bill, with tax, by 7. Divide the bill, without tax, by 6. **c.** Answers may vary. An example is given. I prefer Ryan's algorithm because multiplying is easier than dividing. My algorithm is less complicated than Susan's. **17.** $(3x + 7)(x - 1)$ **18.** $3(x + 3)(x + 2)$ **19.** $(3x - 8)(3x + 8)$ **20.** $(4x + 7)(4x + 7)$ **21.** 24 **22.** 360 **23.** 15,120 **24.** 21 **25.** 792 **26.** 5

Pages 10–12 Talk it Over

1. If one side is 1 unit long, the other two sides have lengths x and $11 - x$ for some integer x. Because of the triangle inequality, all of the following must be true: $x + 1 > 11 - x$, $x + (11 - x) > 1$, and $1 + (11 - x) > x$. For all three to be true, x must be greater than 5 and less than 6. There is no such integer x. **2.** The algorithm begins with the smallest possible length for one side and considers all possible lengths of each of the other two sides in order (from least to greatest for the second side and greatest to least for the third). **3.** No; first, there is no relationship among letters similar to inequality with numbers. If you were to use "≤" to mean "is the same or comes before in alphabetical order" the algorithm would still not be successful. In the given algorithm, order does not matter. It would in producing different ordering of letters. Also, in Sample 1, side lengths can repeat in a single triangle; in determining possible orders of letters, each letter would be used only once in each grouping. **4.** Answers may vary. An example is given. Beginning with 10 for the length of side 1, list all possible lengths for sides 2 and 3 that add up to 12 and also satisfy this inequality: length of side 1 ≥ length of side 2 ≥ length of side 3. Cross out all the combinations that do not satisfy the triangle inequality. **5.** Assign the first task to a mechanic. The second task would take that mechanic past 8 h, so assign it to a new mechanic. Similarly, assign the third task to a third mechanic. For each succeeding task, determine if any of the first three mechanics (in order) can complete the task. If not, assign another mechanic. **6.** Even if Paula Hernandez does not need to use the least number of mechanics, the second algorithm may be more reasonable, because each mechanic's time is used more efficiently. Three of the four will be working all day. With the first algorithm, four are working 6 h or less and two are working less than 5 h. **7.** Answers may vary. An example is given. Look for the most time-consuming job and assign it to mechanic 1. Then find a smaller job to fill his or her 8 hours. Then take the next most time-consuming job and assign it to mechanic 2. Then find smaller jobs to fill his or her 8 hours. Continue this until all the jobs are assigned. This method should result in the least number of mechanics. **8.** If some customers need to pick up their cars by noon, Paula would have to assign those tasks so that they could be completed in time, then schedule the others. If two or more mechanics are needed for some tasks, they would have to be assigned first. Then the remaining tasks would have to be assigned to individual mechanics as they become available.

Pages 13–15 Exercises and Problems
1. The sum of the lengths of any two sides must be greater than the length of the third side. This relationship is called the triangle inequality. **3.** Yes. **5.** Yes. **7.** No.

13. a.

Side 1	Side 2	Side 3
8	8	14
9	9	12
10	10	10
11	11	8
12	12	6
13	13	4
14	14	2

b. the triangle with sides lengths of 10, 10, and 10
15. Answers may vary. An example is given.
(1) 57 lb; (2) 43 lb 9 oz, 26 lb 7 oz; (3) 38 lb 12 oz, 30 lb 7 oz; (4) 34 lb 8 oz, 30 lb 6 oz; (5) 25 lb 5 oz, 22 lb 8 oz, 18 lb 14 oz **17. a.** Six breaks are needed. Plans may vary. An example is given. Run two pairs of 60 s commercials, and two pairs of one 90 s and one 30 s commercials. Run the remaining three 30 s and the two 15 s commercials together. Run the 40 s, 20 s, and 45 s commercials together. **b.** Answers may vary. An example is given. I grouped numbers with a sum of 120. There were five such groups. I grouped the remaining commercials together, since their running time was less than 2 min. **19.** She needs four boards. Plans may vary. An example is given. She could cut two 12 ft boards into three pieces each, one $6\frac{1}{2}$ ft long and the other two $2\frac{1}{2}$ ft long. The third board could be cut into four pieces, two 4 ft long and two 2 ft long. She would need a $6\frac{1}{2}$ ft piece from the fourth board. **21.** $x < 4\frac{1}{4}$ **22.** $x >$ -48 **23.** $x \le -2$ **24.** $x \ge 2\frac{1}{2}$ **25.** 45 **26.** 110 **27.** 7 **28.** 12 **29.** If there is heavy traffic in the city, Corey will have to wait until the first act ends to be seated.

Pages 16–18 Talk it Over
1. Caracas **2.** Answers may vary. Examples are given. Caracas in both January and July; the temperature is at or near 70°F during both months in Caracas, but not in Alice Springs. **3. a.** No; it means that, on average, Caracas is rainier than Alice Springs.
b. Answers may vary. An example is given. Yes; if it rains a lot, then my activities could be limited.
4. No; the graph would still rise to the right, indicating the same relationship between increasing

employment percentages and increasing tuition.
5. Estimates may vary. about 90%

Pages 19–21 Exercises and Problems
3. Mexico City: about 16.3°; Shanghai: about 16.6°
5. a, b. Answers may vary. An example is given.
a. Of the 13 points on the scatter plot, 9 appear to lie near the line $y = 80$, which indicates that the annual cost of operating a top-freezer refrigerator is fairly constant, about $80, no matter what the cost of the refrigerator. **b.** No; four of the data points lie fairly far from the line, indicating that four of the refrigerators cost somewhat more or less than $80 per year to operate. **7.** Fox **9.** ABC; ABC has the highest upper extreme as well as the highest median.

16.

Side 1	Side 2	Side 3
1	6	6
2	5	6
3	4	6
3	5	5
4	4	5

17.

Side 1	Side 2	Side 3
2	6	6
3	5	6
4	4	6
4	5	5

18.

Side 1	Side 2	Side 3
2	8	8
3	7	8
4	6	8
4	7	7
5	5	8
5	6	7
6	6	6

19.

Side 1	Side 2	Side 3
2	12	12
3	11	12
4	10	12
4	11	11
5	9	12
5	10	11
6	8	12
6	9	11
6	10	10
7	7	12
7	8	11
7	9	10
8	8	10
8	9	9

20. a. $x = -\frac{3}{8}$ **b.** 8 **21. a.** $x = 1\frac{5}{6}$ **b.** 0 **22. a.** $x = \frac{5}{14}$

b. 1 **23.** $\left(-5\frac{1}{5}, -13\frac{4}{5}\right)$ **24.** $\left(-2\frac{4}{7}, -7\frac{5}{7}\right)$ **25.** $\left(-\frac{10}{23}, 1\frac{6}{23}\right)$

26. $\left(14\frac{5}{7}, 2\frac{1}{7}\right)$

Page 22 Checkpoint

1. Answers may vary. An example is given. Box-and-whisker plots let you compare the extremes and the quartiles. For example, you can determine which of the data sets contains the largest or smallest number. You can also compare which half of its data grouped more closely about the median, or which is spread out more. You can also tell how the upper and lower quartiles of the data compare. **2.** Answers may vary. An example is given. **Step 1:** Decide which movies are showing at the theater you plan to go to. **Step 2:** Decide which movie you would all like to see. If you do not agree on a movie, discuss your preferences, toss a coin , or compromise until a movie is selected. **Step 3:** Decide what times the movie is showing and whether any one time is suitable for all of you. If not, go back to the previous step to choose another movie. **3.** garden salad, small cole slaw, small herbal tea **4.** about 75% both years
5. Answers may vary. An example is given. Generally, usage is up slightly. Every specific point on the graph is higher in 1990 than it was in 1980.

Pages 23–26 Talk it Over

1. There were more workers employed in agriculture than in any of the other three sectors. **2. a.** They intersect. **b.** about 1905 **3. a.** the Industrial Age **b.** about 1954 **4.** the Information Age; More workers are employed in Information than in any of the other three sectors. **5.** The x-coordinates represent the number of checks Camille will write. The y-coordinates indicate the total monthly charge for the number of checks indicated by the x-coordinate. **6.** At that point, both the graph of $y = 3 + 0.75x$ and the graph of $y = 10$ are above the graph of $y = 6 + 0.35x$. The monthly charges at Main St. Bank and Co-op Bank would be higher for that number of checks than for the same number of checks at Central Bank.
7. Both graphs involve the same control variable and independent variable. **8.** Find the solutions of the three pairs of equations $y = 6 + 0.35x$ and $y = 3 + 0.75x$, $y = 6 + 0.35x$ and $y = 10$, and $y = 3 + 0.75x$ and $y = 10$. Check which bank is least expensive on each of the four intervals determined by the x-values of the three solutions. Answers may vary. Examples are given. The graphing solution to Sample 1 is easier to interpret. The algebra solution to Sample 2 is quicker.

Pages 26–28 Exercises and Problems

1. You can determine the intervals where the values of one function are less than, greater than, or equal to the values of another function.

3. B **5.** \$25,000 per year **7.** Physicians' Services
9, 11. Estimates may vary.

9. about 333.3

11. about 26

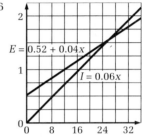

13. 22.7 **15.** 131.8 **24.** lower extreme: 25; lower quartile: 38; median: 48; upper quartile: 63.5; upper extreme: 83 **25.** lower extreme: 80; lower quartile: 90; median: 98.5; upper quartile: 115; upper extreme: 140 **26.** $TR = 4$; $RS = 4\sqrt{3}$
27. $DE = 11$; $DF = 11\sqrt{2}$ **28.** $KL = 10$; $JL = 5$

29. $XY = ZY = 11\sqrt{2}$ **30.** $\begin{bmatrix} 12.6 & 78 & 28 \\ 10 & 70 & 9 \end{bmatrix}$

Pages 29–33 Talk it Over

1. the seating capacity of the auditorium **2.** premier; These seats are closer to the stage. **3.** Answers may vary. Examples: average ticket prices in the area; local sales of the band's music; how much of a profit the promoter can reasonably expect on each ticket
4. a. Yes; when the given values of x and y are substituted in the equation, the result is a true statement. $3(-1) + 4(2) = -3 + 8 = 5$✓ **b.** Yes; when the given values of x, y, and z are substituted in the equation, the result is a true statement. $3(-1) + 4(2) + 2(3) = -3 + 8 + 6 = 11$✓ **c.** No; when the given values of x, y, and z are substituted in the equation, the result is not a true statement. $3(-1) + 4(2) + 2(-3) = -3 + 8 + (-6) = -1$; $-1 \neq 11$ **5. a.** Yes; $(-1, 2)$ is a solution of both equations. **b.** No; $(-1, 2, 3)$ is not a solution of the second equation or the third. **6. a.** Yes; methods may vary. An example is given. Substitute $y + z$ for x in the first equation to get $2y + 2z = 10,000$. Next, substitute $y + z$ for x in the second equation to get $16y + 20z = 88,000$. Then solve the system of equa-

tions in y and z to get $z = 2000$. Use this value to get $y = 3000$ in one of the two equations. Finally, use $z = 2000$ and $y = 3000$ in $x = y + z$ to get $x = 5000$.
b. No; it is only possible to graph equations in two variables on a graphics calculator.

Pages 34–36 Exercises and Problems
3. $(-1, 2)$ **5.** $(-0.5, 1.5)$ **7.** $(5000, 2000)$ **9.** $(4.7, 1.7)$
11. $(112, -170)$ **13.** No; the planes have no common point of intersection. **15.** No; the planes have no common point of intersection. **17.** $(0, 7, 1)$
19. $(-2, 4, 1.5)$ **21.** $(-3, 10, 1)$ **29.** 311.7 **30.** 59.9
31. 56.1 **32.** 27

33.

34. ◄—+—+—●—+—+—+—+—+—+—►
        -4   -2   0   2   4   6

35. ◄—+—+—○—+—+—+—+—+—►
        -2 -1   0   1   2

36. $\dfrac{2}{c^{1/2}}$ **37.** 0 **38.** $\dfrac{6}{n^5}$ **39.** $-3r^4$

Pages 37–41 Talk it Over
1. The transportation map is easier to read. Summaries may vary. The labels are clearly written in horizontal lines. The labels on the street map are written within boundary lines in varying directions.
2. stations; There is a transportation line connecting the two stations. There is no transportation line directly connecting the two stations. **3.** Answers may vary. An example is given. I would take the Green Line from the Museum station to Government Center, then take the Blue Line to the Airport. The Airport would be the twelfth stop. **4.** Kenmore, Hynes, Copley, Arlington, Boylston, Park St., Government Center, Haymarket, North Station, Science Park; 9 edges **5.** No. **6.** Summaries may vary. Both maps indicate locations in the city of Boston. The street map shows the actual layout of the streets, with distances to scale. The transportation map shows transportation routes around the city. Distances are not to scale and streets are not shown. The street map would be helpful if you were walking or driving around the city. The transportation map would be of little help when walking and driving, other than indicating relative positions of some locations. **7.** 2 nonstop flights; 4 nonstop flights; Count the arrows coming out of the vertex for the indicated city; add the 1's in the row for the indicated city.
8. Answers may vary. An example is given. It is very easy to read the number of nonstop departing flights from either the diagram or the matrix. It is easier to read the number of roundtrip nonstop flights from the diagram because you only have to look for arrows going both ways between two vertices.

9. Answers may vary. An example is given.

Meeting time A	Meeting time B	Meeting time C
band	student council	science club
honor society	language club	school newspaper
drama club		

10. Answers may vary. An example is given. Use each vertex as a starting point and find all possible colorings for the vertex. Record all resulting schedules and eliminate any duplicates.

Pages 41–44 Exercises and Problems
1. The vertices labeled "Cárdenas" and "volleyball" each have four edges connected to them. The number of edges connected to a story indicates the number of people who can cover it. The number of edges connected to a name indicate the number of stories the reporter can cover.

3.

5. Y W X   **7.** K   L
[diagram with vertices Y, W, X, Z]   [diagram with vertices K, L, M, N, J]
    Z   N   J

9. Answers may vary. Examples are given. children's hospital: Joyce, Becka; food pantry: Miguel, Hannah; homeless shelter: Desmond, Marissa; community center: Kirby, John **19.** Schedules may vary. An example is given. scheduling sequence: math; chemistry and history; economics and American literature; French and Spanish **22.** $(-2, 1, -1)$ **23.** $(-1, -3, 5)$
24. $(-1, 0, -4)$ **25.** $2\sqrt{5} \approx 4.5$ **26.** $2\sqrt{5} \approx 4.5$
27. $5\sqrt{2} \approx 7.1$ **28.** $\sqrt{73} \approx 8.5$ **29.** $2\sqrt{26} \approx 10.2$
30. $\sqrt{5} \approx 2.2$

Pages 45–48 Talk it Over
1. It increases initially, reaches a maximum at about 35 mi/h, and then begins to decrease. **2.** Yes; there must be a maximum. For example, there could be no speed at which a car achieves 200 MPG. The maximum appears to occur at about 35 mi/h. **3.** Yes; clearly the MPG cannot be less than 0.
4. a. St. Louis to Effingham to Champaign to Danville; 201 mi **b.** Answers may vary. An example is given. I used trial and error. **5.** 201 mi; They are

equal.   **6.** St. Louis is the starting point. There is no edge leading into this vertex.   **7.** 7 times   **8.** Yes. Yes. In both cases, you are able to do so, but it is unnecessarily complicated, since the shortest routes are fairly apparent.

Pages 49–52 Exercises and Problems
3. a. minimum   **b.** 2   **c.** −11   **5. a.** maximum   **b.** −3
c. 25.5   **7. a.** maximum   **b.** $\frac{1}{8}$ **c.** $\frac{49}{96}$
13. $A - D - E - Z$; 24
16.

$\begin{array}{c|ccccc} & A & B & C & D & E \\ \hline A & 0 & 1 & 0 & 0 & 0 \\ B & 0 & 0 & 1 & 0 & 0 \\ C & 0 & 1 & 0 & 0 & 0 \\ D & 1 & 0 & 1 & 0 & 1 \\ E & 0 & 0 & 1 & 1 & 0 \end{array}$

17.

18.

19.

20.

21.

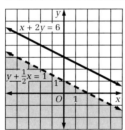

Pages 53–55 Talk it Over
1. Answers may vary. An example is given. I think more people listen to the radio in the morning than in the afternoon or evening, because people listen while getting ready for and going to work or school.
2. Answers may vary.   **3. a.** 22 ads; $2600
b. 16 ads; $1700   **c.** 18 ads; $2400   **d.** 22 ads; $1400
4. a. the total number of ads   **b.** the total cost of x A.M. ads and y P.M. ads   **5.** $200x + 50y$; $x + y$ **6.** b, c, and d; b   **7.** No; x and y represent numbers of ads, which are always nonnegative.   **8.** O: 0 ads, $0; A: 20 ads, $1000; B: 20 ads, $2200; C: 11 ads; $2200
9. No; only points with both coordinates whole numbers.   **10. a.** 300,000 people   **b.** 300,000 people
c. 300,000 people   **11. a.** the total number of listeners   **b.** on the line labeled T = 300,000 in the figure (the line with equation $90,000x + 30,000y = 300,000$)
c. (3, 1)   **12. a–c.** Answers may vary. Examples are given.   **a.** 4 A.M. ads, 8 P.M. ads   **b.** 8 A.M. ads, 9 P.M. ads   **c.** 8 A.M. ads, 12 P.M. ads   **d.** The line T = 1,260,000 does not intersect the feasible region.

None of the combinations will reach that many listeners.   **13. a.** It moves to the right and both intercepts increase.   **b.** All other points in the feasible region fall below the graph of $90,000x + 30,000y =$ 1,080,000. That is, for all other points in the feasible region, T < 1,080,000.   **c.** 8 A.M. ads and 12 P.M. ads; 1,080,000 listeners

Pages 57–60 Exercises and Problems
1. a. $0.45a + 0.30p$ **b.** $0.45a + 0.30p \le 8.10$
c. $a + p \ge 8$ **d.** $a \ge 0$; $p \ge 0$
e.

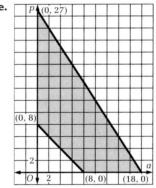

f. Answers may vary. An example is given. For (10, 6), the total cost is $6.30.
3.

5.

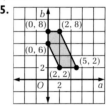

11. 35 kg of silicon carbide and 150 kg of silicon tetrachloride; $48,700   **15.** maximum height: about 13 ft; distance traveled: about 14 ft   **16.** $\frac{1}{36} \approx 0.03$
17. $\frac{1}{12} \approx 0.08$ **18.** $\frac{1}{4} \approx 0.25$ **19.** S.A. ≈ 254.5 cm^2;
$V \approx 381.7$ cm^3 **20.** S.A. $\approx 16,286$ in.^{2};
$V \approx 195,432$ in.^{3} **21.** S.A. ≈ 1017.9 m^2;
$V \approx 3053.6$ m^3 **22.** S.A. ≈ 2123.7 ft^2; $V \approx 9202.8$ ft^3

Pages 62–63 Unit 1 Review and Assessment
1. Answers may vary. Examples are given for two equations in x and y.   **a.** *Method 1:* **Step 1:** Solve for y in the first equation. **Step 2:** Substitute the resulting value for y in the second equation. **Step 3:** Solve the resulting equation for x. **Step 4:** Substitute the value of x in the first equation. **Step 5:** Solve the resulting equation for y. *Method 2:* **Step 1:** Graph both equations on a graphics calculator. **Step 2:** Use TRACE to determine the point of intersection and find x and y.
b. The results will be the same (although the first may result in a fractional answer, while the second gives a decimal approximation). Neither algorithm is significantly easier to use.

2. *Method 1:*

$3x > 7 + 10x$

$-7x > 7$ ← Subtract $10x$ from both sides.

$x < -1$ ← Divide both sides by -7, and reverse the inequality sign.

Method 2: Graph $y = 3x$ and $y = 7 + 10x$ on the same set of axes.

X = −1   Y = −3

The solution of the inequality is all values of x for which the graph of $y = 7 + 10x$ is below the graph $y = 3x$, that is $x < -1$.

3.

Side 1	Side 2	Side 3
2	10	10
3	9	10
4	8	10
4	9	9
5	7	10
5	8	9
6	6	10
6	7	9
6	8	8
7	7	8

4. Answers may vary. Examples are given.   **a.** In general, as the weight of an SLR Camera zoom lens increases, the price increases.   **b.** No; although the points lie close to the line $y = 3x$, they do not all lie on the line. So, for example, there is a 17 oz lens that costs less than a 16 oz lens.   **5. a.** less than about 110 min or between about 128 min and about 238 min   **b.** less than about 178 min   **c.** If Robert expects to spend less than about 110 min or between about 128 min and about 238 min on local calls, he should get Measured Service. If he expects to spend between about 110 min and about 128 min on local calls, he should get Measured Circle Service. If he plans to spend more than 238 min on local calls, then he should get Unlimited Service.   **6.** $(2, 1, -2)$
7. $(-2, -4, 5)$ **8.** $(-3, 0, 2)$ **9. a.** Answers may vary. Example: The access graph might represent five towns and their connections by direct train service.

b.

$$\begin{array}{c} \\ A \\ B \\ C \\ D \\ E \end{array} \begin{array}{c} \begin{array}{ccccc} A & B & C & D & E \end{array} \\ \left[\begin{array}{ccccc} 0 & 1 & 1 & 0 & 0 \\ 1 & 0 & 1 & 1 & 0 \\ 1 & 1 & 0 & 0 & 0 \\ 0 & 1 & 0 & 0 & 1 \\ 0 & 0 & 0 & 1 & 0 \end{array} \right] \end{array}$$

10. three colors

11. a. minimum   **b.** $1\frac{1}{4}$ **c.** $7\frac{7}{8}$ **12. a.** maximum
b. $1\frac{1}{2}$ **c.** $\frac{1}{4}$ **13. a.** maximum   **b.** about -2
c. about 6.9   **14.** She should spend 50 days in Arizona and 120 days in New Mexico for a sales volume of $486,000.

Unit 2

Pages 70–72 Talk it Over
1. walking speed   **2.** all real numbers except 0   **3.** all 366 days of the year   **4.** $C(r) = 2\pi r$ **5.** Answers may vary. An example is given. B(George Washington) = February 22   **6. a.** Answers may vary. An example is given. Let m be the minimum stopping distance function; $m(x) = x + \frac{x^2}{20}$.   **b.** 0; The point $(0, 0)$ is on the graph. That is, for $x = 0$, $m(x) = 0$.

Pages 73–76 Exercises and Problems
1. a. the relation that pairs words and meanings in the dictionary   **b.** The word *friendly* on page 69, for example, is paired with several meanings.   **3.** No; the domain values Giles and Kalisha are both paired with two range values.   **9. a.** $\frac{1}{3}$ **b.** $-\frac{1}{3}$ **c.** $\frac{1}{a + b + 1}$

11. a. 2   **b.** 4   **c.** $|a + b|$ **13. a.** 11   **b.** 77   **c.** $4a^2 + 8ab + 4b^2 - 3a - 3b + 1$ **17.** 1   **19.** 1   **21.** Yes.
23. Yes.   **25.** B and C are functions, since no member of either domain is paired with more than one member of the range. B is many-to-one, since two members of the domain are paired with the same member of the range. C is one-to-one, since every member of the range is paired with exactly one member of the domain. A is not a function, since 0 is paired with three different members of the range.   **27.** one-to-one; No horizontal line intersects the graph in more than one point.   **29.** one-to-one; Each value y of the range is paired with exactly one x-value.   **31.** all real numbers; all real numbers greater than or equal to 1
34.

35.

36.

37. Answers may vary. An example is given.
Step 1: I make sure I have my homework assignment.
Step 2: I read over my notes if necessary. **Step 3:** I do
my math homework. If I can't complete it, I reread
my notes and my math text and work through sample
problems. **Step 4:** I complete my homework. If there
are problems I still can't do, I ask for help at home, or
make a note to ask my teacher for help. **Step 5:** I put
my homework, my notebook and textbook, a pencil
and, if necessary, a calculator together in one place
so I will be ready for the next math class.
38. $x > 6$ **39.** -3.75

Pages 77–79 Talk it Over
1. The points appear to
lie in a line. As altitude
increases, the boiling
temperature of water
decreases.

2. The graph appears to represent a function. It
appears that no two points on the graph lie on the
same vertical line. **3. a.** Estimates may vary.
Example: about 200°F **b.** Estimates may vary.
Example: about 2800 ft

4. 212; the boiling temperature of water at an altitude
of 0 ft, or sea level **5.** The coefficient of a is negative. The slope of the graph is negative, so as a
increases, $T(a)$ decreases. As the values in the second
column (altitudes) increase, the values in the third
column (temperatures) decrease. **6.** Cathie used the
form of a linear function with the calculated value of
m and substituted the a and $T(a)$ values from one of
the pairs in the table. She solved the resulting equa-

tion for b. **7.** Answers may vary. An example is
given. For Kimberley and Colorado Springs, the value
of m is $\frac{201 - 205}{6012 - 4013} = -\frac{4}{1999} \approx -0.002$ and the
equation is $T(a) = -0.002a + 212$. The equation will
vary only slightly, since for any two points in the
table, the value of m rounded to three decimal places
is -0.002. **8.** Yes; the equation is written in the form
$f(x) = mx + b$ with $m = \frac{1}{2}$ and $b = -13$. **9.** Yes; the
equation is written in the form $f(x) = mx + b$ with
$m = 4$ and $b = 0$. **10.** No; the equation cannot be
written in the form $f(x) = mx + b$. **11.** Substitute
10,000 for a; $T(10,000) = 212 + (-0.0018)(10,000) =$
194; 194°. **12.** Substitute 185 for $T(a)$; $185 = 212 +$
$(-0.0018)a$; $a = 15,000$; 15,000 ft.

Pages 81–84 Exercises and Problems
1. Its graph is a line. Its equation can be written in
the form $y = mx + b$. **3.** Yes. **5.** Yes. **7.** No.
9. Yes; 24, -16, $4 + 10a + 10b$ **11.** Yes; 7, 1,
$\frac{3}{2}a + \frac{3}{2}b + 4$ **17.** $f(x) = -5x - 6$ **19.** $f(x) = \frac{1}{2}x - 1$
21. a. $C(T) = 4T - 156$ **b.** 204; the number of times
per minute a snowy tree cricket chirps at 90°F
c. $39 \le T \le 105$; $0 \le C(T) \le 264$ **27. a.** $g(y) + g(z) =$
$3y + 2 + 3z + 2 = 3y + 3z + 4$; $g(y + z) = 3(y + z) + 2 =$
$3y + 3z + 2$ **b.** There are values of y and z for which
$g(y) \cdot g(z) = g(y \cdot z)$. However, the statement is not
true in general. Consider $y = 1$ and $z = 2$: $g(1) \cdot g(2) =$
$(3(1) + 2)(3(2) + 2) = 40$; $g(1 \cdot 2) = g(2) = 3(2) + 2 = 8$
30. 120; 0; $8a^3 - 2a$ **31.** When a linear programming
problem is represented by a system of linear inequalities in x and y, any maximum or minimum value of a
linear combination $ax + by$ will occur at one of the
vertices of the feasible region. **32.** $-10 \le x < 5$
33. $x \ge 0$ **34.** $x < 2$

Pages 85–88 Talk it Over
1. A person's heart rate decreases steadily over the
first 20 years of life, then remains constant after the
age of 20. **2.** Yes; no two points have the same first
coordinate and different second coordinates. **3.** No;
the first part of the graph clearly has an equation of
the form $f(x) = mx + b$, where m is negative and b is
positive. The second part of the graph clearly has an
equation of the form $g(x) = c$, for a constant c.
4. 104 beats/min; 82 beats/min; 72 beats/min
5. a. $90 = -2a + 112$ **b.** 11; Etenia is 11 years old.
6. a.

The graphs have the
same shape; the graph of
$y = |x| + 2$ is the graph of
$y = |x + 2|$ shifted 2 units
to the right and up 2
units. **b.** all x greater
than or equal to 0

7. The graphs are identical. Each of the two sections of the graph of $y = |2x|$ and $y = 2|x|$ has slope twice that of the corresponding section of the graph of $y = |x|$.

8. Each graph is the image of the other reflected across the x-axis. Each of the two sections of the graph of $y = |-2x|$ has slope twice that of the corresponding section of the graph of $y = |x|$. Each of the two sections of the graph of $y = -2|x|$ has slope twice that of the corresponding section of the graph of $y = -|x|$, which is the graph of $y = |x|$ reflected across the x-axis.

Pages 89–92 Exercises and Problems

1. Heart rate is a piecewise function of age. If a person's age is 20 or less, the heart rate is given by $h(a) = -2a + 112$. If his or her age is greater than 20, the heart rate is given by $h(a) = 72$.

3. $y = \begin{cases} -\dfrac{3}{2}x + 3 & \text{if } 0 \le x \le 2 \\ x - 4 & \text{if } x > 2 \end{cases}$

5.

7.

13.

15.

17.

23. $f(x) = 3x - 4$ **24.** $f(x) = -\dfrac{1}{2}x + 5$ **25.** kite

26. rectangle **27.** parallelogram **28.** about −0.38; about −2.6 **29.** about 1.6; about −1.1

Page 93 Checkpoint

1. If any vertical line drawn through the graph intersects the graph in more than one point, the graph does not represent a function. If a vertical line intersects the graph in more than one point, there are two points on the graph with the same first coordinate and different second coordinates. Then the graph does not represent a function. **2.** Yes. The domain consists of the numbers 12, 20, and 32. The range consists of the numbers 0.75, 1, and 1.5. **3. a.** $V(r) = 3\pi r^2$ **b.** about 59 units^3; about $462x^2$ units^3 **4.** many-to-one; For every real number x except 0, $x \ne -x$ but $f(x) = f(-x)$. **5. a.** Let n be the number of movies ordered and $C(n)$ the cost in dollars; $C(n) = 4.99n + 24.28$. **b.** $49.23 **c.** 4 movies **d.** He will be able to order 3 movies per month. (If he carries over the $2.75 he has left to the next month, he can order 4 movies every other month.) **6.** $f(x) = -\dfrac{1}{3}x + 5$ **7.** Let w be the weight of the chicken in pounds and $c(w)$ be the cost in dollars;

$c(w) = \begin{cases} 2.5w & \text{if } 0 < w \le 5 \\ 2w & \text{if } w > 5 \end{cases}$

8. The graphs are translations of the graph of $y = |x|$. The graph of $y = |x -3|$ is a translation 3 units to the right; the graph of $y = |x| - 3$ is a translation 3 units down.

Pages 94–97 Talk it Over

1. a. 4 ft; 12 ft; 20 ft **b.** No. If d were a linear function of t, the clam would have fallen the same distance in every 0.5-second period. **c.** Yes; the graph is a curve, not a line.

Distance
Clam Falls

Distance (ft) / Time (s)

2. a. $d(t) = kt^2$ **b.** Using the point (1, 16) gives $d(1) = 16$; $k \cdot 1^2 = 16$; $k = 16$. **3.** Answers may vary. An example is given. I like using a graphics calculator because it is simpler than using the quadratic formula. **4.** after about 1.4 s; about 38.6 ft **5.** No; it shows the height of the ball as a function of time and does not give any information about the angle of the ball with respect to the horizontal. **6.** No; every height but the maximum is paired with two times.

Pages 97–100 Exercises and Problems

1. 36 ft

3. a. quadratic; 25; 7;
$2a^2 + 4ab + 2b^2 + 3a + 3b - 2$
b.

5. a. quadratic; –58; –58;
$5 - 7a^2 - 14ab - 7b^2$
b.

7. a. quadratic; 1;
49; $a^2 + 2ab - 8a + b^2 - 8b + 16$
b.

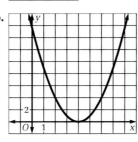

18. 80.3; 82.5; none

19.

20.

21. $(x + 6)(x - 4)$ **22.** $(3a - 5)(2a + 3)$
23. $25x(x + 2)(x - 2)$

Pages 102–105 Talk it Over

1. Each function has the form $f(x) = kx^n$; the degrees of the equations (from left to right) are 1, 2, 3, 4, and 5. **2.** $y = x$; $y = x^3$; $y = x^5$ **3.** $y = x$, $y = x^3$, and $y = x^5$ have rotational symmetry of 180° about the origin; $y = x^2$ and $y = x^4$ have symmetry about the y-axis.
4. They are one-to-one and have 180° rotational symmetry about the origin. Their domain and range are all real numbers. **5.** They are many-to-one and are symmetric about the y-axis. Their domain is all real numbers, and their range is all nonnegative real numbers. **6. a.** Yes; 1; linear. **b.** 6 **7. a.** Yes; 2; quadratic. **b.** 0, 3 **8.** Answers may vary. An example is given. You could graph the function and see that there is no value for which $P(x) = -1$. **9.** the points in the first quadrant **10.** Draw the graph of $y = 40$ on the same axes and determine the x-coordinate of the point where the graphs intersect. ($x = 2$)

Pages 105–109 Exercises and Problems

3. No. **5.** $f(x) = 0.8x^3$ **7.** $f(x) = \frac{1}{2}x^4$ **9.** $w(d) =$
$0.41d^3$ **13.** Yes. **15.** No; in a polynomial function, the exponents are positive whole numbers. **17. a.** 2; polynomial function of degree 2 and quadratic function **b.** 10; $1\frac{3}{4}$ **c.** 0, –3 **19.** 4; 1 **21.** 4; 2

23. a. 1, 3
b.

25. a. 0, 2
b.

30. Let t be the time in seconds after the fall and $h(t)$ the height in feet of the pebble; $h(t) = -16t^2 + 75$.
31. No. **32.** Yes. **33.** Yes. **34.** True.

Pages 110–114 Talk it Over

1. a.

Depth d (ft)	Speed $s(d)$ (mi/h)
100	38.6
200	54.6
346	71.8
5000	272.9
10,000	386
20,000	545.9
34,600	718

b. The speed at a depth of 10,000 ft is 10 times that at 100 ft. The speed at a depth of 34,600 ft is 10 times that at 346 ft. **2. a.** $s(100d) = 3.86\sqrt{100d} = 38.6\sqrt{d}$
b. The speed is 10 times greater at a depth 100 times as deep. **c.** Yes. **3.** The graphs do not intersect the x-axis at $x = -3$. **4.** $\sqrt{x + 7}$ is not a real number if $x < -7$. **5.** The domain of the function is all possible values of the control variable. Jane knows that $x + 1$ must be nonnegative for $\sqrt{x + 1}$ to be a real number. **6.** The first function's domain is limited by the fact that for $x < -1$, $\sqrt{x + 1}$ is not a real number. The range is limited by the fact that $\sqrt{x}$ is nonnegative for every real number x. For the second function, $\sqrt[3]{x + 1}$ is a real number for every real number x, and for every real number y, there is a real number z such that $y^3 = z$.

Pages 115–117 Exercises and Problems

1. 6.3 **3.** 5 **5.** 1.2 **7.** Table values may vary. The functions are the same. $\sqrt{25x} = \sqrt{25} \cdot \sqrt{x} = 5\sqrt{x}$
9. False. The statement is only true if $a = 0$ or $b = 0$.

11. 0, $\frac{1}{4}$ **13.** 4, 3 **15.** –2, –1 **19.** $8|x|$ **21.** $7p$

23. 2 **25.** $5\sqrt{3}|x|$

27. 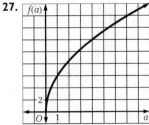 domain: all real numbers greater than or equal to 0; range: all real numbers greater than or equal to 0

29. domain: all real numbers greater than or equal to 9; range: all real numbers greater than or equal to 0

31. domain: all real numbers greater than or equal to −1; range: all real numbers greater than or equal to 0

33. all real numbers less than or equal to 0 **35.** all real numbers; all real numbers **37.** all real numbers greater than or equal to 0; all real numbers less than or equal to 1 **39.** all real numbers; all real numbers

45. a. 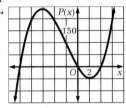 **b.** −10, 0, 4

46. lower extreme: 0.171; lower quartile: 0.190; median: 0.224; upper quartile: 0.2735; upper extreme: 0.325 **47.** $x = 1$; If $x = 1$, $1 - x = 0$ and $\frac{1}{1 - x}$ is not defined.

Page 118 Checkpoint

1. Summaries may vary. An example is given. The graphs of quadratic functions and square root functions are both curves. The graph of a quadratic function is a parabola. The graph of a square root function is a curve that resembles half of a parabola. **2. a.** Let t be the time in seconds and $h(t)$ the height in feet. $h(t) = -16t^2 + 60$

b.

3. a. $h(t) \approx -16t^2 + 3.14t + 4$ **b.** about 0.5 s

4. a. −162; $64b^3 - 144b^2 + 72b$

b.

5. about 2267.57 **6.** 1 **7.** 3

8. domain: all real numbers greater than or equal to 3; range: all real numbers greater than or equal to 0

9. all real numbers; all real numbers

Pages 119–123 Talk it Over

1.

Speed s (miles per hour)	Time t (hours)
25	12
40	7.5
55	5.45
65	4.62

2. a. distance = speed × time or $d = st$ **b.** $t = \frac{d}{s}$; the rate of speed **c.** In a polynomial function, exponents of the control variable are whole numbers in $t = ds^{-1}$, the exponent of s is a negative number. **3.** to produce a quadratic equation in standard form **4.** You get a fraction with denominator 0. **5.** The average is the sum divided by 2, so the sum is 2 · 63. **6.** The function becomes $a(t) = \frac{74 + 100t}{t + 1}$. **7.** No fraction with numerator 1 is equal to 0. **8.** Note that $\frac{1}{1 - x}$ is not defined when $1 - x = 0$, that is, when $x = 1$. **9.** $y = 0$ **10.** A vertical asymptote $x = k$ indicates that the domain of the function is all real numbers except k. A horizontal asymptote $y = n$ indicates that the range is all real numbers except n.

Pages 124–125 Exercises and Problems

1. to show that the graph may not cross those lines, they are not part of the graph **3.** $\frac{11}{3}$ **5.** 4 **7.** 9, −1 **9.** 3 tests

11. a.
b. $x = 1$; $y = 0$
c. domain: all real numbers except 1; range: all real numbers except 0

13. a.
b. $x = 0$; $y = 2$
c. domain: all real numbers except 0; range: all real numbers except 2

15. a.
b. $x = 1$, $x = -1$, $y = 0$
c. domain: all real numbers except 1 and -1; range: all real numbers greater than or equal to 1 or less than 0

17. a.
b. $y = -2$ **c.** domain: all real numbers; range: all real numbers greater than -2 and less than or equal to 0

23. 5, 4 **24.** 1 **25.** $f(x) = \begin{cases} 3x - 12 & \text{if } x \geq 4 \\ -3x + 12 & \text{if } x < 4 \end{cases}$

26. $a + 1$

Pages 126–128 Talk it Over
1. $s(A) = 1000A$ **2.** $p(s) = 0.12s$ **3.** $p(A) = 120A$
4. 240 W **5.** The domain of $(h \circ k)(x)$ is those numbers in the domain of $h(x)$ that are also in the range of $k(x)$. **6.** Sandra found the value of $k\left(\frac{1}{3}\right)$ and substituted that value in the equation for h. She found $k\left(\frac{1}{3}\right) = 2$, then $h(2) = 6$. **7. a.** $(f \circ g)(x) = 4x^2 - 4x$
b. $(g \circ f)(x) = 3 - 2x^2$ **c.** No; the given functions $f(x)$ and $g(x)$ provide a counterexample, since $4x^2 - 4x \neq 3 - 2x^2$ for all x. **8.** the number of bottles and the cost; the number of people and the number of bottles; the number of people and the cost; $b(p)$ and $(C \circ b)(p)$
9. Answers may vary. An example is given. I disagree. The range of the number of bottles function is even numbers greater than 10. The domain of the cost function is positive whole numbers. However, every number in the range of the number of bottle functions is in the domain of the cost function.

Pages 128–131 Exercises and Problems
1. $\sqrt{2x}$ **3.** $12x^2 - 2$ **5.** 20 **7.** f of g of x; the composite of f and g **15.** $x^2 - 3x + 2$ **17.** $\frac{x-4}{2}$, $x \neq 1$

20. domain: all real numbers except 2; range: all real numbers except 0 **21.** 2; $4a^2 - 6a + 2$ **22.** SSS, ASA, AAS, SAS

Pages 133–134 Unit 2 Review and Assessment
1. Yes; for every number in the domain, there is only one value in the range. **2. a.** $C(g) = 1.17g$
b. $0 \leq g \leq 12$; $0 \leq C(g) \leq 14.04$ **3.** 1; $\frac{2}{a-b+4}$
4. $f(x) = \frac{1}{9}x + 4$ **5.** $f(x) = -\frac{3}{2}x + 6$
6. $f(x) = \begin{cases} -3 & \text{if } -4 < x \leq -1 \\ 2 & \text{if } -1 < x < 2 \\ x + 1 & \text{if } x \geq 2 \end{cases}$
7. a. $h(t) = -16t^2 + 4$ **b.** about 3 ft **c.** after about 0.35 s **8.** 0; -20 **9.** $V = \frac{\pi}{6}d^3$ **10. a.** 4 **b.** -9
11. $2\sqrt{3}|a|$ **12.** 1 **13. a.** $-\frac{10}{19}$ **b.** about -1.93; about 52.93 **14.** No; she would need to score 46 points. It is unlikely she could do so, with an average of 22 points per game. **15.** $(f \circ g)(x) = \frac{3}{x}$

16. a. domain: all real numbers; range: all real numbers greater than or equal to 0

 domain: all real numbers greater than or equal to -1; range: all real numbers greater than or equal to 0

 domain: all real numbers except 5; range: all real numbers except 0

 domain: all real numbers; range: all real numbers

b. Answers may vary. Examples are given. The first consists of two rays, the second is half of a parabola, the third is a hyperbola, and the fourth is an S-shaped curve.

17. Answers may vary. Examples are given. Every direct variation function is a polynomial function. No absolute value function is a direct variation function. Some rational functions are polynomial functions.

Pages 140–141 Talk it Over
1. If the diagonals of a quadrilateral bisect each other, then the quadrilateral is a parallelogram; True. Since vertical angles are equal in measure, two pairs of congruent triangles are formed (SAS). If two lines are intersected by a transversal and alternate interior angles are equal in measure, the lines are parallel. This fact can be used with the pairs of congruent triangles to show that both pairs of opposite sides of the quadrilateral are parallel. **2.** If the diagonals of a quadrilateral are equal in length, then the quadrilateral is a rectangle; False. The diagonals must also bisect each other. **3.** Steps 1–5 **4.** Steps 1 and 6–9

Pages 143–146 Exercises and Problems
5. a. Yes. **b.** SSS **7. a.** No. **9. a.** If two parallel lines are intersected by a transversal, then alternate interior angles are equal in measure. **b.** True.
11. ❶ definition of parallelogram; **❷** If two ∥ lines are intersected by a transversal, then alternate interior ∡ are equal in measure; **❸** Reflexive property of equality; **❹** ASA; **❺** Corres. parts of ≅ ▵ are = in measure.
13. a. If opposite sides of a quadrilateral are equal in measure, then the quadrilateral is a parallelogram.
b. *Given:* Quadrilateral $ABCD$ with $AB = CD$ and $BC = AD$ *Prove:* $ABCD$ is a parallelogram.

Statements (Justifications)
1. $AB = CD$ and $BC = AD$ (Given)
2. $DB = DB$ (Reflexive property of equality)
3. $\triangle ABD \cong \triangle CDB$ (SSS)
4. $m\angle 1 = m\angle 2$; $m\angle 3 = m\angle 4$ (Corres. parts of ≅ ▵ are = in measure.
5. $\overline{AB} \parallel \overline{CD}$ and $\overline{BC} \parallel \overline{AD}$ (If two lines are intersected by a transversal and alternate interior ∡ are = in measure, then the lines are ∥.)
6. $ABCD$ is a parallelogram. (Definition of parallelogram)
15. *Given:* Parallelogram $ABCD$ is a rectangle. *Prove:* $AC = BD$

Statements (Justifications)
1. $ABCD$ is a rectangle. (Given)
2. $ABCD$ is a parallelogram and $m\angle A = m\angle B = m\angle C = m\angle D = 90°$. (Definition of rectangle)
3. $AD = BC$ (If a quadrilateral is a parallelogram, then opposite sides are = in measure.)
4. $AB = AB$ (Reflexive property of equality)
5. $\triangle DAB \cong \triangle CBA$ (SAS [Steps 2, 3, and 4])
6. $AC = BD$ (Corres. parts of ≅ ▵ are = in measure.)

17. Answers may vary. Examples are given.
a. If you are in Queensland, then you are in Australia. **b.** If you are not in Australia, then you are not in Queensland. **19.** Converse: If two lines form right angles, then the lines are perpendicular; True. Inverse: If two lines are not perpendicular, then the lines do not form right angles; True. Contrapositive: If two lines do not form right angles, then the lines are not perpendicular; True. **27.** Implication: $p \to q$ (If today is Monday, then tomorrow is Tuesday.) Converse: $q \to p$ (If tomorrow is Tuesday, then today is Monday.) Inverse of the converse: not $q \to$ not p (If tomorrow is not Tuesday, then today is not Monday.) Contrapositive: not $q \to$ not p (If tomorrow is not Tuesday, then today is not Monday.) **29.** Inverse: not $p \to$ not q (If today is not Monday, then tomorrow is not Tuesday.) Inverse of the inverse: not (not p) $\to$ not (not q) or $p \to q$ (If today is Monday, then tomorrow is Tuesday.) The inverse of the inverse is the original implication. **31.** $(f \circ g)(x) = x^2 + 1$
32. $(-4, 6)$ **33.** $(3, 0)$ **34.** $(-a, b)$ **35.** $3\sqrt{5} \approx 6.7$

Page 147 Talk it Over
1. Answers may vary. An example is given. Yes. I think $ADEC$ should be called an isosceles trapezoid because it appears to have two sides that are equal in measure, just like an isosceles triangle. **2.** $E(2, 3.5)$; $A(-5, 0)$ **3.** Use the distance formula and the coordinates of A, C, D, and E. **4.** Use the midpoint formula and the coordinates of A and B to find the coordinates of the midpoint of $\overline{AB}$ to determine if they are the same as the coordinates of D (they are not). Repeat for $\overline{CB}$ and E. $\overline{DC}$ and $\overline{AE}$ are not medians.

Pages 150–152 Exercises and Problems
3. $\overline{DC}$ has endpoints $(-2, 3.5)$ and $(5, 0)$ and length $\sqrt{(5 - (2))^2 + (0 - 3.5)^2} = \sqrt{61.25}$. AE has endpoints $(2, 3.5)$ and $(-5, 0)$ and length $\sqrt{(2 - (-5))^2 + (3.5 - 0)^2} = \sqrt{61.25}$. The supports are the same length. **5. ❶** Division property of equality; **❷** Definition of median; **❸** Substitution property; **❹** Base ∡ of an isosceles triangle are = in measure; **❺** Reflexive property of equality; **❻** SAS; **❼** Corres. parts of ≅ ▵ are = in measure. **7.** One side has endpoints $(-9, 56)$ and $(-34, 0)$ and length $\sqrt{(-9 - (-34))^2 + (56 - 0)^2} = \sqrt{3761}$. The other side has endpoints $(9, 56)$ and $(34, 0)$ and length $\sqrt{(9 - 34)^2 + (56 - 0)^2} = \sqrt{3761}$. The sides are the same length. **9.** It would make it difficult, if not impossible, to get into the swing.
11. a. $PS = \sqrt{(-b - (-a))^2 + (c - 0)^2} = \sqrt{(-b + a)^2 + c^2}$ $= \sqrt{(a - b)^2 + c^2}$; $QR = \sqrt{(b - a)^2 + (c - 0)^2} = \sqrt{(b - a)^2 + c^2}$; since $(a - b)^2 = (b - a)^2$, $PS = QR$.

Integrated Mathematics

b. $PR = \sqrt{(b - (-a))^2 + (c - 0)^2} = \sqrt{(b + a)^2 + c^2}$;
$QS = \sqrt{(-b - a)^2 + (c - 0)^2} = \sqrt{(-b - a)^2 + c^2}$; since
$(b + a)^2 = (-b - a)^2$, $PR = QS$.
c. Form of proof may vary. An example is given.

Given: PQRS is an isosceles trapezoid. The y-axis is a line of symmetry of PQRS, passing through the midpoints of its bases.

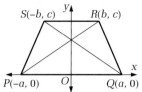

Prove: $m \angle SPQ = m \angle RQP$ and $m \angle PSR = m \angle QRS$

Statements (Justifications)
1. PQRS is an isosceles trapezoid. (Given)
2. $PS = QR$ (Definition of isosceles trapezoid)
3. $PR = QS$ (In an isosceles trapezoid, the diagonals are = in measure.)
4. $SR = SR$ and $PQ = PQ$ (Reflexive property of equality)
5. $\triangle SPQ = \triangle RQP$ and $\triangle QRS = \triangle PSR$ (SSS)
6. $m \angle SPQ = m \angle PQR$ and $m \angle QRS = m \angle RSP$ (Corres. parts of $\cong$ $\triangle$s are = in measure.)

13.

a. $\left(\dfrac{2d + 0}{2}, \dfrac{2e + 0}{2} \right) = (d, e)$

b. $\left(\dfrac{2a + 2b}{2}, \dfrac{2c}{2} \right) = (a + b, c)$

c. $a + b$; c

d.

The coordinates of R are $(2a + 2b, 2c)$. $\overline{OQ}$ is on the x-axis, so the slope of $\overline{OQ}$ is 0. The slope of $\overline{RS}$ is
$\dfrac{2c - 2c}{2a + 2b - 2b} = \dfrac{0}{2a} = 0$,

so $\overline{OQ} \parallel \overline{RS}$. The slope of $\overline{SO}$ is $\dfrac{2c - 0}{2b - 0} = \dfrac{c}{b}$. The slope of $\overline{RQ}$ is $\dfrac{2c - 0}{2a + 2b - 2b} = \dfrac{c}{b}$. Then $\overline{SO} \parallel \overline{RQ}$ and OQRS is a parallelogram. **17.** If a quadrilateral is not a rectangle, then it is not a square. **18. a.** All squares are rhombuses. **b.** All parallelograms are quadrilaterals. **c.** All rectangles are parallelograms. **19.** Answers may vary. An example is given. A quadrilateral is a parallelogram if and only if both pairs of opposite sides are parallel.

Pages 153–154 Talk it Over
1–3. Answers may vary. Examples are given.
1. Among the terms that may need to be defined in order to interpret the city ordinance are: *commercial establishment, meals,* and *premises.* **2.** A commercial establishment could be defined as any place of business that offers goods or services for sale. The bookstore is a commercial establishment. A meal could be defined as any food consumed in one sitting or as a substantial serving of food as opposed to a snack or light refreshment. Premises could be defined as land owned by a business and the buildings on the land, or as the building occupied by a business. **3.** If a meal is defined as any food consumed in one sitting and premises are defined as land owned by a business and the buildings on the land, then the bookstore manager must apply for a license. If a meal is defined as a substantial serving of food as opposed to a snack or light refreshment or if premises are defined as only the building occupied by a business, then the owner does not have to apply for a license. **4.** Answers may vary. **5–7.** Answers may vary. Examples are given. **5.** Yes; MNRS fits the given definition of trapezoid. **6.** Yes; the definition does not exclude the possibility of two pairs of parallel sides. **7.** disagree; I don't think a quadrilateral can be both a parallelogram and a trapezoid. **8.** True. **9.** True. **10.** True. **11.** False.

Pages 156–158 Exercises and Problems
3. exactly one **5.** at least one **7. a.** I, II, III, V **b.** I, III **11.** True. **13.** False. **15.** In a rectangle, either pair of opposite sides may be considered the bases. A rectangle is a parallelogram, so each pair of opposite sides is equal in measure. The second property was proved in Ex. 15 on page 144. (If a parallelogram is a rectangle, then its diagonals are equal in measure.) All four angles of a rectangle are equal in measure, so the two angles at each base are equal in measure. **17.** Answers may vary. An example is given. A quadrilateral is an isosceles trapezoid if and only if it has at least one pair of parallel sides and a line of symmetry that passes through the midpoints of the bases. **21.** $PQ = \sqrt{(-1 - 0)^2 + (-2 - 0)^2} = \sqrt{5}$;
$QR = \sqrt{(2 - 0)^2 + (1 - 0)^2} = \sqrt{5}$;
$RS = \sqrt{(1 - 2)^2 + (-1 - 1)^2} = \sqrt{5}$;
$PS = \sqrt{(1 - (-1))^2 + (-1 - (-2))^2} = \sqrt{5}$;
Since $PQ = QR = RS = PS$, PQRS is a rhombus.
22. Answers may vary. An example is given.
Step 1: Determine the author's last name. **Step 2:** Look in the card catalog under the author's last name and find the reference number. **Step 3:** If you know the general location of the book, go to Step 5. **Step 4:** Find the general location of the book. If necessary, ask the librarian. **Step 5:** Use the reference number to locate the book.
23.

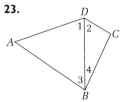

a. 180°; 180°; $m \angle 2$; $m \angle ABC$

b. $m \angle A + m \angle ABC + m \angle C + m \angle CDA = m \angle A + (m \angle 3 + m \angle 4) + m \angle C + (m \angle 1 + m \angle 2)$ (Substitution property) $= (m \angle A + m \angle 1 + m \angle 3) + (m \angle C + m \angle 2 + m \angle 4)$ (Associative and commutative properties of addition) $= 180° + 180°$ (Substitution property) $= 360°$ **c.** The sum of the measures of the angles of a quadrilateral is $360°$.

Page 158 Checkpoint

1. In the inverse of an implication, the "if" and the "then" are in the same order as in the original implication. In the contrapositive, they are in reverse order. In both cases, the "if" and the "then" are negated. **2.** If a quadrilateral is not a rectangle, then its diagonals are not equal in measure; False.

3. $FD = \sqrt{(0 - (-6))^2 + (3 - 0)^2} = 3\sqrt{5}$; $FE = \sqrt{(0 - 5)^2 + (3 - 0)^2} = \sqrt{34}$; $ED = \sqrt{(5 - (-6))^2 + (0 - 0)^2} = 11$. $\triangle DEF$ is not isosceles, since no two sides are equal in measure. $\triangle DEF$ has no line of symmetry, so $\triangle DEF$ is not isosceles.

4. $JK = \sqrt{(-4 - 0)^2 + (5 - (-2))^2} = \sqrt{65}$; $LK = \sqrt{(4 - 0)^2 + (5 - (-2))^2} = \sqrt{65}$; Since two sides of $\triangle JKL$ are equal in measure, $\triangle JKL$ is isosceles. $\triangle JKL$ is an isosceles triangle because it has a line of symmetry, the y-axis. **5.** True. **6.** False.

Pages 159–161 Talk it Over

1. $360°$; $540°$; $720°$; $900°$

2.

Name of polygon	Number of sides, n	Sum of angle measures, $S(n)$
Triangle	3	$180° = (180°)$
Quadrilateral	4	$360° = 2(180°)$
Pentagon	5	$540° = 3(180°)$
Hexagon	6	$720° = 4(180°)$
Heptagon	7	$900° = 5(180°)$
Octagon	8	$1080° = 6(180°)$

3. $S(n) = (n - 2)(180°)$ Answers may vary. An example is given. Every time another side is added, another triangle can be formed, so $180°$ is added to the sum of the angle measures. For example, the formula is true for octagons, $S(8) = (8 - 2)(180°) = 6(180°) = 1080°$. When a ninth side is added, $180°$ is added and the sum of the measures of the angles is $1260° = 7(180°) = (9 - 2)(180°)$. **4.** $(k - 2)180° + 180° = (k - 2)180° + (1)180° = (k - 2 + 1)180°$ **5.** Answers may vary. An example is given. I know the formula is true for $n = 3$. Since I can show that whenever it is true for n, it is true for $n + 1$, I am convinced that it is true for all values of n greater than 3.

1. Yes. All the sides of a square are equal in measure, and all four angles are right angles and thus equal in measure. So a square is a regular polygon. **3. a.** Yes; a square is a rectangle that is a regular polygon. **b.** Yes; a square is a rhombus that is a regular polygon. **c.** Yes; a square is a trapezoid that is a regular polygon. **5.** about $128.6°$; about $51.4°$ **7.** $140°$; $40°$ **9.** about $147.3°$; about $32.7°$ **11. a.** At each vertex, the interior angle and one exterior angle form a linear pair. Angles that form a linear pair are supplementary. **b.** $n(180°)$ **c.** $(n - 2)180° + E(n) = n(180°)$; $E(n) = n(180°) - (n - 2)180° = 2(180°) = 360°$

13. a. $X(n) = \dfrac{360°}{n}$; $I(n) = \dfrac{(n - 2)180°}{n}$ **b.** rational

c.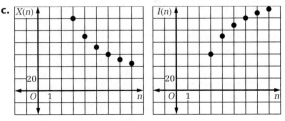

18. True. **19.** True. **20.** 4 **21.** b ($\overleftrightarrow{RS}$ is perpendicular to $\overline{PQ}$ and passes through its midpoint); c ($\overleftrightarrow{RS}$ is perpendicular to $\overline{PQ}$ and its intersection with $\overline{PQ}$ forms two congruent triangles (HL), so $\overleftrightarrow{RS}$ bisects $\overline{PQ}$.)

Page 167 Talk it Over

1. $\triangle ODE$, $\triangle OEF$, $\triangle OFG$, and $\triangle OGH$, and $\triangle OHD$ ($\triangle OED$, $\triangle OFE$, $\triangle OGF$, $\triangle OHG$, and $\triangle ODH$ are all congruent to the five given triangles as well.) All ten triangles are congruent by SSS. The sides that are radii of the circle are equal in measure. The bases that are sides of the regular polygon are equal in measure as well. **2.** $72°$

1. **3.** agree; The statement is true because every triangle has a circumscribed circle, the center of which is equidistant from all three vertices.

5. a. $(0, 4)$; $(3, 1)$ **b.** $y = 4$ **c.** $y = -3x + 10$ **d.** $(2, 4)$ **e.** $2\sqrt{5} \approx 4.5$; $(x - 2)^2 + (y - 4)^2 = 20$ **f.** $y = x + 2$; $4 = 2 + 2$, so the perpendicular bisector of $\overline{ST}$ passes through H. **7.** $45°$ **9. a.** 21,600 nautical miles **b.** about 24,840 statute miles; about 7907 statute miles **13. a.** $120°$ **b.** $120°$ **c.** $30°$ **d.** $120°$ **19.** about $152.3°$ **20.** Corresponding angles are equal in measure and corresponding sides are in proportion. **21.** $43°$; $86°$; $51°$

Pages 172–173
1. A; C **2.** Yes; let X and Y be the endpoints of the stage. Consider a circle of which $\overline{XY}$ is a chord and B a point on the circle. The points with the same viewing angle are on $\overset{\frown}{XBY}$.   **3.** $\overset{\frown}{AB}$ **4.** a semicircle
5. They are inscribed angles that intercept the same arc, so each has measure $\frac{1}{2}\overset{\frown}{KL}$.

Pages 175–178 Exercises and Problems
1. The vertex of an inscribed angle of a circle is on the circle, so the sides of an inscribed angle are chords of the circle. The vertex of a central angle is at the center of the circle, so the sides of a central angle are radii of the circle.   **3.** $m\overset{\frown}{KF} = 180°$; $m\overset{\frown}{MF} = 130°$; $m\angle K = 65°$; $m\angle F = 25°$

7.

In $\triangle ABC$, $2x + 2y = 180°$. In $\triangle BOC$, $2y + m\angle BOC = 180°$. So $m\angle BOC = 2x$. Consequently, $m\angle BOC = 2m\angle BAC$. Since the measure of an arc is equal to the measure of its central angle, $m\overset{\frown}{BC} = m\angle BOC = 2m\angle BAC$. Therefore, $m\angle BAC = \frac{1}{2}m\overset{\frown}{BC}$.

11. The slope of $\overline{PR}$ is $\frac{y-0}{x-(-r)} = \frac{y}{x+r}$. The slope of $\overline{QR}$ is $\frac{y-0}{x-r} = \frac{y}{x-r}$. Since $x^2 - r^2 = -y^2$, the product of the slopes is $\left(\frac{y}{x+r}\right)\left(\frac{y}{x-r}\right) = \frac{y^2}{x^2-r^2} = \frac{y^2}{-y^2} = -1$. Then $\overline{PR} \perp \overline{QR}$ and $\angle PRQ$ is a right angle.   **17.** 45°
18. Tanya eats taco salad for lunch.   **19.** Akio used a black pen or a blue pen to fill out the application.
20. The odd integers can be written $2k + 1$ and $2n + 1$ for integers k and n. Their sum is $2k + 1 + 2n + 1 = 2k + 2n + 2 = 2(k + n + 1)$, which is even.

Page 178 Checkpoint
1. a regular 19-gon; a regular 18-gon; The measure of an interior angle of a regular n-gon is $\frac{(n-2)180°}{n} = 180° - \frac{360°}{n}$, which increases as n increases. The measure of an exterior angle of a regular n-gon is $\frac{360°}{n}$, which decreases as n increases.
2. Construct the perpendicular bisectors of two of the sides. The point where the bisectors intersect is the center of the circumscribed circle. The radius is the distance from the center to any vertex of the triangle.
3. $m\overset{\frown}{AC} = 150°$; $m\angle A = 45°$; $m\angle B = 75°$; $m\angle C = 60°$
4. $m\overset{\frown}{DGE} = 180°$; $m\overset{\frown}{DF} = 90°$; $m\angle D = 45°$; $m\angle E = 45°$
5. $m\angle I = 70°$; $m\overset{\frown}{JI} = 150°$; $m\overset{\frown}{HJ} = 140°$; $m\overset{\frown}{HI} = 70°$

Pages 179–182
1. 62 squares; 32 black squares, 30 red squares
2. 31 dominoes   **3.** red   **4.** 31 black; 31 red   **5.** No; there are only 30 red squares to be covered. There are 32 black squares.   **6.** the point of tangency   **7.** C

Pages 183–186 Exercises and Problems
1. Sample 1: Line j is not parallel to line k; Sample 2: All three numbers in a Pythagorean triple are odd; Sample 3: $\overline{OP}$ is perpendicular to line t.   **3.** Suppose quadrilateral $ABCD$ has four acute angles. Then $m\angle A < 90°$, $m\angle B < 90°$, $m\angle C < 90°$, and $m\angle D < 90°$. Then $m\angle A + m\angle B + m\angle C + m\angle D < 360°$. This contradicts the fact that the sum of the measures of the interior angles of a quadrilateral is 360°. So the assumption that a quadrilateral can have four acute angles must be false. Therefore, no quadrilateral can have four acute angles.   **7.** Suppose there is a Pythagorean triple with two even numbers and one odd number. There are two possibilities. One, either a or b is odd, and two, c is odd. Suppose a is odd and b and c are even. Then a^2 is odd and b^2 is even, so $a^2 + b^2 = c^2$ is odd, since it is the sum of an even number and an odd number. This contradicts the assumption that c is even. Suppose a and b are even and c is odd. Then a^2 and b^2 are even, so $a^2 + b^2 = c^2$ is even, since it is the sum of two even numbers. This contradicts the assumption that c is odd. The assumption that there is a Pythagorean triple with two even numbers and one odd number must be false. Therefore, there is no Pythagorean triple with two even numbers and one odd number.   **11.** Since $\overline{OA} \perp m$, $\angle A$ is a right angle. Since $\triangle OAB$ is isosceles, its base angles are equal in measure and $m\angle B = 90°$. Then since $m\angle AOB > 0$, $m\angle AOB + m\angle A + m\angle B > 180°$. This contradicts the triangle sum theorem. The assumption that m is not tangent to the circle must be false. Therefore, m is tangent to circle O.
19. Figures may vary. An example is given.
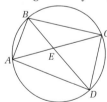
$\triangle ABE \sim \triangle DCE$ and $\triangle BEC \sim \triangle AED$. Both triangles can be proved to be similar using Theorem 3.9 (If two inscribed angles in the same circle intercept the same arc, then they are equal in measure) and AA. $\angle BAC$ and $\angle CDB$ both intercept $\overset{\frown}{BC}$, so they are equal in measure and $\angle ABD$ and $\angle DCA$ both intercept $\overset{\frown}{AD}$, so they are equal in measure. Then $\triangle ABE \sim \triangle DCE$ by AA. $\angle CBD$ and $\angle DAC$ both intercept $\overset{\frown}{CD}$, so they are equal in measure and $\angle BCA$ and $\angle ADB$ both intercept $\overset{\frown}{AB}$, so they are equal in measure. Then $\triangle BEC \sim \triangle AED$ by AA.   **20. a.** $-\frac{1}{3}$ **b.** 1, -2
21. circumference: 9π m, or about 28.3 m; area: 20.25π m², or about 63.6 m²

Pages 187–189 Talk it Over

1. 45°; all arcs whose endpoints are consecutive points on the circle O **2.** Answers may vary. An example is given. $OR = OR$ (The measure of a segment is equal to itself.) $OF = OE$ (All radii of a circle are equal in measure.) $FR = FE$ (If two tangent segments are drawn from the same point to the same circle, then they are equal in measure.) Then $\triangle OER \cong \triangle OFR$ by SSS. **3.** $22\frac{1}{2}°$; If $\overline{OG}$, $\overline{OH}$, $\overline{OI}$, $\overline{OJ}$, $\overline{OK}$, and $\overline{OD}$ were drawn, the sixteen central angles produced would all have measure $22\frac{1}{2}°$. **4.** $\triangle EOR \cong \triangle FOR$, so $FR = ER$ and $m \angle ORF = m \angle ORE$. (Corresponding parts of congruent triangles are equal in measure.) $OR = OR$ (Reflexive property of equality) Then $\triangle SOR \cong \triangle ROQ$ by ASA. **5.** Using the same methods as in questions 1–4, you can prove that $\triangle SOR \cong \triangle ROQ \cong \triangle QOP \cong \triangle POW \cong \triangle WOV \cong \triangle VOU \cong \triangle UOT \cong \triangle TOS$. Then the sides of $PQRSTUVW$ are corresponding parts of congruent triangles and are equal in measure. Using the same property along with addition of angle measures, you can show that all the angles of $PQRSTUVW$ are equal in measure. **6.** about 3.312 m **7.** The octagon consists of eight congruent triangles. Let p be the perimeter of the octagon. Each triangle has height h (which is also the radius of the circle) and base $\frac{p}{8}$. The area of one triangle is $\frac{1}{2}h\left(\frac{p}{8}\right) = h \cdot \frac{p}{16}$. The area of the octagon is $8 \cdot h\frac{p}{16} = h \cdot \frac{p}{2}$. So the area of the octagon is equal to the radius times one half of the perimeter, which is the semiperimeter. **8.** The area of the circle is about 3.14 m²; the area of the circle is slightly less than that of the octagon. **9. a.** $s = \pi r$ **b.** $A = sr$ or $\frac{s^2}{\pi}$

Pages 189–191 Exercises and Problems

1. A semiperimeter of a figure is half the perimeter. **3.** 36°; 54° **5.** Method 1: $A = rs = 9\left(\frac{25 + 63 + 52}{2}\right) = $ 630 ft²; Method 2: Draw $\overline{OA}$, $\overline{OB}$, and $\overline{OC}$; $A =$ area of $\triangle AOB +$ area of $\triangle AOC +$ area of $\triangle BOC = \frac{1}{2} \cdot 9 \cdot 25 + \frac{1}{2} \cdot 9 \cdot 63 + \frac{1}{2} \cdot 9 \cdot 52 = 630$ ft² **13.** Suppose that $m \angle MOA = 25°$. Then the figure is an n-gon where $\frac{180}{n} = 25$ and $n = 7.2$. This contradicts the fact that n must be a whole number. The assumption that $m \angle MOA = 25°$ must be false. Therefore, $m \angle MOA$ can never be 25°. **14.** cylinder; cone; pentagonal prism **15.** Yes; −6; −2; 14

Pages 192–195 Talk it Over

1. two hexagons, one pentagon **2.** two 120° angles, one 108° angle **3.** 348° **4.** 12° **5.** The tessellation of hexagons has no defects; the sum of the measures of the angles at each vertex is 360°. **6.** Yes; Yes; No; No. The sum of the measures of the angles at each vertex must be less than 360°, so there can be no more than five equilateral triangles at each vertex. **7.** No; No. The sum of the measures of the angles at each vertex must be less than 360°, so there can be no more than three squares or three pentagons at each vertex. **8.** No. The measure of each angle of a regular hexagon is 120°. The sum of the measures of three such angles is 360°.

Pages 195–198 Exercises and Problems

1. a space figure with faces that are all regular polygons of at least two types, with the same number of faces of each type at each vertex

5.

	Number of Faces (F)	Number of Vertices (V)	Number of Edges (E)
tetrahedron	4	4	6
hexahedron	6	8	12
octahedron	8	6	12
dodecahedron	12	20	30
icosahedron	20	12	30

tetrahedron: $4 + 4 = 6 + 2$; hexahedron: $6 + 8 = 12 + 2$; octahedron: $8 + 6 = 12 + 2$; dodecahedron: $12 + 20 = 30 + 2$; icosahedron: $20 + 12 = 30 + 2$ **9.** 720°
11. 720° **13.** Suppose that there is a regular polyhedron with faces that have more than five sides. That is, the faces are regular n-gons with $n \geq 6$. The measure of each angle of the n-gon is $\frac{(n-2)180°}{n} = $ $180° - \frac{360°}{n}$. Since $n \geq 6$, the measure of each angle is greater than or equal to 120°. There are at least three n-gons at each vertex of the polyhedron, so the sum of the measures of the angles at each vertex is greater than or equal to 360°. This contradicts the convex polyhedron postulate. The assumption that there is a regular polyhedron with faces that have more than five sides must be false. Therefore, there is no regular polyhedron with faces that have more than five sides. **15.** at least **17.** at least **19. a.** $r = 1$ m; $R = \sqrt{3}$ m $\approx$ 1.7 m **b.** The inner sphere has surface area 4π m² or about 12.6 m². The outer sphere has surface area 12π m² or about 37.7 m². The cube has surface area 24 m². **c.** The inner sphere has volume $\frac{4}{3}\pi$ m³ or about 4.2 m³. The outer sphere has volume $4\sqrt{3}\pi$ m³ or about 21.8 m³. The cube has volume 8 m³. **23. a.** prism: $500\sqrt{3}$ cm³ ≈ 866 cm³; cylinder: 250π cm³ ≈ 785.4 cm³ **b.** Its volume is greater than that of the cylinder but less than that of the hexagonal prism. **24.** 13 **25.** $x < -4$ **26.** 2; 1.5

27. a.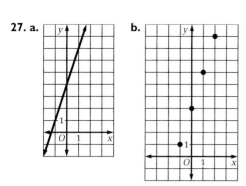

b.

c. Yes; answers may vary. An example is given. Neither graph includes two points with the same first coordinate and different second coordinates.

Pages 200–201 Unit 3 Review and Assessment
1. a. *ABCD* is a parallelogram and $\overline{AC} \perp \overline{BD}$ (Given); $\angle DEC$ and $\angle BEC$ are right angles (Def. of $\perp$ lines); $\angle DEC$ and $\angle BEC$ are equal in measure (Def. of right angles); $\overline{AC}$ and $\overline{BD}$ bisect each other (The diagonals of a parallelogram bisect each other.); *DE* = *BE* (Def. of segment bisector); *CE* = *CE* (Reflexive property of equality); $\triangle DEC \cong \triangle BEC$ (SAS)   **b.** Answers may vary. An example is given. I would use the proof to show that $\overline{DC}$ and $\overline{BC}$ are corresponding parts of congruent triangles and are equal in measure. Since *ABCD* is a parallelogram, we already know that $\overline{DA}$ and $\overline{CB}$ are equal in measure and $\overline{AB}$ and $\overline{DC}$ are equal in measure. It would then follow that all four sides of *ABCD* are equal in measure and *ABCD* is a rhombus.   **2. a.** Converse: If the diagonals of a quadrilateral are perpendicular, then the quadrilateral is a kite. Inverse: If a quadrilateral is not a kite, then its diagonals are not perpendicular. Contrapositive: If the diagonals of a quadrilateral are not perpendicular, then the quadrilateral is not a kite.   **b.** The converse and the inverse are false. Counterexample: Consider a quadrilateral whose diagonals are perpendicular, but whose intersection is not the midpoint of either diagonal. The contrapositive is true.
3. a. *Q*(6, –2); *S*(4, 6); *U*(–7, 2)   **b.** *QRSTUV* can be formed by joining *QVUR* and *UTSR*, which are isosceles trapezoids, since both have one pair of parallel sides ($\overline{TS}$, $\overline{UR}$, and $\overline{VQ}$ are all parallel to the *x*-axis) and both have a line of symmetry (the *y*-axis).
4. There are no longer segments joining parallelograms to trapezoids or rectangles to trapezoids and isosceles trapezoids.   **5.** Answers may vary. Among the terms or phrases which may need to be defined in order to interpret the by-laws are *member, in good standing, appropriate account,* and *reliable financial institution.* Sample definitions are given. A member in good standing is one who has paid dues for the last membership year and has been absent from fewer than half of all meetings (unless those absences were

due to illness or for other causes found reasonable by the executive board). A reliable financial institution is one which is licensed by the state to do business and is insured by the Federal Deposit Insurance Corporation.   **6.** 8 sides   **7.** 12 sides   **8.** 8 cm; 8 cm; 17 cm   **9.** $m \stackrel{\frown}{GF} = 142°$; $m \stackrel{\frown}{EF} = 54°$; $m \angle G = 27°$; $m \angle F = 82°$ **10.** 22.5° (for example, $\angle BAC$); 45° ($\angle BAD$); 67.5° ($\angle BAE$); 90° ($\angle BAF$); 112.5° ($\angle BAG$); 135° ($\angle BAH$)   **11.** Suppose that *P* is a regular *n*-gon with an exterior angle measuring 150°. *P* has *n* such exterior angles and their sum is 360°. (The sum of the exterior angles of an *n*-gon is 360°.) Then $150n = 360$ or $n = \frac{360}{150} = 2.4$. This contradicts the fact that *n* must be a whole number. So the assumption that a regular polygon can have an exterior angle measuring 150° must be false. Therefore, no regular polygon has an exterior angle measuring 150°.   **12. a.** about 900 mi
b. If a line is tangent to a circle, then it is perpendicular to the radius from the center to the point of tangency. In any right triangle, the square of the length of the hypotenuse is equal to the sum of the squares of the lengths of the legs.   **c.** Let *h* be the distance from *R* to *H*; $h = \sqrt{(4000 + d)^2 - (4000)^2} = \sqrt{8000d + d^2}$.   **13.** 50 in.^{2}; 100 in.^{2}; the circumscribed square   **14. a.** In a regular polyhedron, only one type of regular polygon is used for the faces.
b. 720° (There are 4 vertices with defects of 150° and one vertex with a defect of 120°.

Unit 4

Pages 209–211 Talk it Over
1. a. Each term is the cube of the position number.
b. 1000   **c.** Method 1   **2.** Yes. Answers may vary. An example is given. The graphs pass the vertical-line test.   **3.** Yes; the positive integers; ranges may vary.
4. The graph of a sequence is discrete because the domain is a set of distinct points.   **5. a.** (a) The sequence does not get close to any number. (b) 0
b. (a) The terms will increase steadily as you go farther out in the sequence. The points lie on the line with equation $y = 3x - 1$. (b) The graph will get closer and closer to, but never intersect, the *x*-axis as you go farther out in the sequence. The points lie on the curve with equation $y = \frac{1}{x}$.
6.   There is no single number to which the terms get close.

7. Answers may vary. An example is given. The limit of a sequence is a number that the sequence approaches but never reaches. The speed limit is a speed that the car approaches, reaches, and exceeds.

Pages 212–215 Exercises and Problems
3. a. 48, 96, 192 **b.** 6144 **c.** Answers may vary. An example is given. I noticed that each term is twice the term before it. I continued the pattern to find the 12th term. **5. a.** 360, 2160, 15,120 **b.** 1,437,004,800 **c.** Answers may vary. An example is given. I noticed that each term is the product of the term before it and the position number. I continued the pattern to find the 12th term. **7. a.** heptagon, octagon, nonagon **b.** 14-gon **c.** I noticed each term is the name of a figure with $n + 2$ sides, where n is the position number.
13. a.
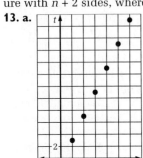
b. No; each term is 4 more than the term before it. The terms increase without limit.
15. a.

b. No; each term is −2 times the term before it. Odd-numbered terms decrease without limit, while even-numbered terms increase without limit.
17. a.

b. No; each term is 2 less than the term before it. The terms decrease without limit.
19. Yes; the terms decrease toward 0. **21.** Yes; odd-numbered terms increase toward 0, while even-numbered terms decrease toward 0. **27.** Each face of an octahedron is an equilateral triangle. Four faces meet at each vertex. Therefore, the sum of the measures of the angles at each vertex is 240°. The defect at each vertex is 360° − 240° = 120°. Since there are 6 vertices, the sum of the defects is 6 · 120° = 720°.
28. $\frac{1}{32}$ **29.** 1 **30.** $\frac{1}{343}$ **31.** −5; −17; 43

Pages 216–219 Talk it Over
1. $16\frac{2}{3}$ ft; 25 ft **2.** 48 ft; the width of the first terrace is 90 ft; that is, $a_1 = 90$. Each succeeding terrace is 7 ft narrower, so the width of the seventh terrace is 42 ft less, that is, $a_7 = 90 − 42 = 48$. **3.** eight times

4. For each value of n, there is a single value of $90 − (n − 1)(7)$. The control variable is the position number and the dependent variable is the term. The domain is the positive integers. The range is the set of numbers given by the sequence 90, 83, 76, 69, ...
5. $b_n = \frac{25n}{3}$ **6.** The domain of the explicit formula is the nonnegative integers rather than the positive integers. **7.** about $1161.62

Pages 219–221 Exercises and Problems
1. when the initial value of a sequence is the value before any changes take place **3.** 0, $\frac{1}{2}$, 1, $\frac{3}{2}$; $\frac{23}{2}$
5. 3, $\frac{1}{2}$, $\frac{1}{9}$, $\frac{1}{36}$; $\frac{1}{3^{22} \cdot 24} \approx 0.000000000001328$
7. $a_n = 3^n$ **9.** $d_n = n − 3$, where n is the number of vertices of the polygon
16. a.

b. Yes; odd-numbered terms increase toward 0, while even-numbered terms decrease toward 0.
17. 15 ways **18.** $11 + 3i$
19. −6 **20.** $24 + 10i$
21. $4i + 8$

Pages 222–225 Talk it Over
1. Summaries may vary. A fractal tree begins with a single branch; a tree has a trunk, which can be thought of as the first single branch. For both, new branches grow from existing branches. When you magnify any part of the fractal tree, what you see looks like the whole tree. This is not true of a real tree. **2.** 1, 3, 7, ..., 63 **3.** Each term is a power of 2 added to the previous term. The power is the position number of the previous term. **4. a.** $a_n = 1 \cdot 2 \cdot 3 \cdot ... \cdot n = n!$ **b.** Answers may vary. An example is given. I think the recursive formula was easier to find in this case. I don't think this will always be the case. In general, I think no one method will always be easier. **5.** the sixth dose; 30 h **6.** The first term would be 1000 rather than 650. The recursion equation would be the same.

Pages 225–227 Exercises and Problems
1. the value of the first term and a recursion equation, a formula showing how to find each term from the term(s) before it. **3.** $a_1 = −3$; $a_n = −3a_{n−1}$ **5.** $a_1 = 8.32$; $a_n = a_{n−1} + 0.12$ **7.** $a_1 = \frac{1}{2}$; $a_n = (2a_{n−1})\left(\frac{n}{n+1}\right)$
9. 0.5, 0.1, 0.02, 0.004, 0.0008, 0.00016

11. $5, \frac{5}{2}, \frac{5}{6}, \frac{5}{24}, \frac{1}{24}, \frac{1}{144}$ **13.** 1, 2, 2, 4, 8, 32 **19.** $\frac{3}{6}, \frac{9}{7},$
$\frac{27}{8}, \frac{81}{9}; \frac{19{,}683}{14}$ **20.** $\frac{1}{2}$ **21. a.** 80, 160, 320 **b.** 2560
c. Answers may vary. An example is given. I used an explicit formula, $a_n = 5 \cdot 2^{n-1}$; $a_{10} = 5 \cdot 2^9 = 2560$.
22. a. 25, 30, 35 **b.** 50 **c.** Answers may vary. An example is given. I used an explicit formula,
$a_n = 5 \cdot n$; $a_{10} = 5 \cdot 10 = 50$.

Pages 228–233 Talk it Over
1. a. $a_1 = 1$; $a_n = a_{n-1} + 7$ **b.** $a_1 = 1$; $a_n = a_{n-1} - \frac{1}{4}$
c. $a_1 = 2$; $a_n = a_{n-1} + 2$ **2. a.** $a_1 = 32$; $a_n = \frac{3}{4}a_{n-1}$
b. $a_1 = 1$; $a_n = \frac{1}{2}a_{n-1}$ **c.** $a_1 = 2$; $a_n = 2a_{n-1}$
3. Answers may vary. An example is given. The recursion equations for all the sequences in Group 1 involve adding the same number to the previous term. The recursion equations for all the sequences in Group 2 involve multiplying the previous term by the same number. The graphs of Group 1 functions are linear; the graphs of Group 2 functions are curves.
4. a. $a_n = 12 - 2.5(n-1)$ or $a_n = 14.5 - 2.5n$
b. $(n-1)$ times **5. a.** $a_n = 27\left(\frac{1}{3}\right)^{n-1}$ or $a_n = \frac{81}{3^n}$
b. $(n-1)$ times
6. a.
 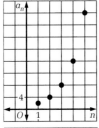
The graph of the first sequence is linear; the graph of the second is a curve.
b.

The graph of the first sequence is linear; the graph of the second is a curve.
c. The graph of an arithmetic sequence is part of a line. The graph of a geometric sequence is part of a curve. **7. a.** 2 sequences; 3, $3\sqrt{6}$, 18; 3, $-3\sqrt{6}$, 18
b. $\sqrt{6}$; $-\sqrt{6}$ **c.** $18\sqrt{6}$; $-18\sqrt{6}$ **8. a.** 10.5 **b.** 1 sequence; 7.5 **c.** 10.5 **d.** The arithmetic mean and the mean are the same.

Pages 233–235 Exercises and Problems
1. arithmetic **3.** neither **5.** neither **7.** arithmetic
9. neither **11.** arithmetic **13. a.** geometric
b. $a_1 = 64$; $a_n = \frac{1}{4}a_{n-1}$ **15. a.** arithmetic **b.** $a_1 = 5$;
$a_n = a_{n-1} - 2$ **17. a.** arithmetic **b.** $a_1 = 550$;
$a_n = a_{n-1} + 550$ **19.** 18 terms **21.** 33 terms

27. a. $\sqrt{35}$ or $-\sqrt{35}$ **b.** $\frac{\sqrt{35}}{5}$ or $-\frac{\sqrt{35}}{5}$ **c.** $\frac{7\sqrt{35}}{5}, \frac{49}{5},$
$\frac{49\sqrt{35}}{25}$ or $-\frac{7\sqrt{35}}{5}, \frac{49}{5}, -\frac{49\sqrt{35}}{25}$ **29. a.** -12 **b.** $4\sqrt{5}$ or
$-4\sqrt{5}$ **31. a.** 10 **b.** 8 or -8 **33.** $8\sqrt{3} \approx 13.9$
36. 15, 18, 23, 30, 39, 50 **37.** $\frac{68}{7} \approx 9.7$ **38.** 42

Page 236 Checkpoint
1. a. If the inside ring is considered the first ring, the number of parallelograms in each ring is 8 times the ring number. The number of parallelograms in the rings forms the sequence 8, 16, 24, 32, …. **b.** 40 parallelograms for the fifth ring and 48 parallelograms for the sixth ring, for a total of 88 parallelograms; If the color begins to repeat, Kiyoski will need 40 golden and 48 violet parallelograms.
2. a. **3. a.**
b. No.
b. Yes; 0.
4. $a_n = \frac{3n-2}{4n-3}$ **5.** $a_n = \frac{3n-5}{n}$ **6.** $a_1 = 6$; $a_n = a_{n-1} + 7$
7. $a_1 = 1$; $a_n = a_{n-1} + 2n - 1$ **8.** geometric **9.** neither
10. arithmetic **11.** neither

Pages 237–240 Talk it Over
1. 1, 2, 3, 4, …, n **2.** 21 reeds **3.** It is the sum of the first six terms of the sequence. **4.** $1 + 2 + 3 + 4 + … + n$ **5. a.** 101; 101; 101; 101 **b.** 50 sums; There are 100 numbers altogether and they are grouped in pairs. **c.** $\frac{100}{2} \cdot 101 = 5050$ **6. a.** Yes; Yes; Yes; Yes, except that the middle term will not be paired with another term. **7.** Answers may vary. An example is given. I think it was easier to use the formula. I think deciding which method is easier depends on several things, including the number of terms in the series and the types of numbers. For example, if the terms involved fractions or both positive and negative numbers, I think it would be easier to use the formula. **8.** The series is not arithmetic.

Pages 241–243 Exercises and Problems
1. the first term, the last term, and the number of terms **3.** 1248 **5.** 119 **13.** 144 **15.** -21
17. $\sum_{n=1}^{8} [28 + (n-1)(-5)] = \sum_{n=1}^{8} (33 - 5n)$ **19.** $\sum_{n=3}^{10} \frac{1}{2^n}$

24. $2\sqrt{3}$ or $-2\sqrt{3}$ **25.** $AB = \begin{bmatrix} 14 & 2 \\ 7.5 & 1 \end{bmatrix}$;

$BA = \begin{bmatrix} -5 & -8.5 & -6 \\ 2 & 16 & -6 \\ 2 & 1 & 4 \end{bmatrix}$ **26. a.** geometric **b.** 189

Pages 244–246 Talk it Over
1. a. 32, 16, 8, 4, 2, 1; geometric **b.** 32 + 16 + 8 + 4 + 2 + 1 **c.** 63 games **2. a.** She multiplied each term of the series by the common ratio, 2. The new series has the same terms as the original series except that it does not include the first term of the original and has a new last term, 192. When she subtracts, all but the first term of the original series and the last term of the new series cancel out, leaving $S - rS = a_1 - ra_n$. She then divides both sides by $1 - r$. Her answer is correct. **b.** $S = 32 + 16 + 8 + 4 + 2 + 1$; $\frac{1}{2}S = 16 + 8 + 4 + 2 + 1 + \frac{1}{2}$; $S - \frac{1}{2}S = 32 - \frac{1}{2}$; $S = 64 - 1 = 63$; Yes.
3. Alternating terms of the sequence are negative.
4. the first and last terms and the common ratio
5. a. Answers may vary. An example is given. $3 + 3 + 3 + 3 + 3 + 3$ **b.** Since $r = 1$, $1 - r = 0$ and $\frac{a_1 - a_n r}{1 - r}$ is not defined. **c.** Since all the terms are the same, multiply the first term by the number of terms. $3 \cdot 6 = 18$

Pages 247–250 Exercises and Problems
1. the number of terms and an explicit formula for the related geometric sequence, for which you need to know the first term and the common ratio **3.** 684
5. about 28.24 **7.** 102 **9.** about 5.99
11. a. arithmetic **b.** 105 **13. a.** geometric
b. 0.134375 **15. a.** geometric **b.** 182 **22.** 935
23. $AB = BC = 5$ **24.** $EF = 3$; $DF = 3\sqrt{3}$ **25.** No; there is no single number to which the terms of the sequence get close. **26.** Yes; the odd-numbered terms decrease toward 0 and the even-numbered terms increase toward 0.

Pages 253–254 Talk it Over
1. Yes; each partial sum S_n is defined in terms of S_{n-1}.
2. a. Answers may vary. An example is given. For the sequence 1, 0, −1, −2, −3, …, the common difference is −1 and the sequence of partial sums is 1, 1, 0, −2, −5, … . The series has no sum. (This will be true for any such example.) **b.** No. No arithmetic sequence with $d \neq 0$ will have a sum. The sequence of partial sums will increase (if $d > 0$) or decrease (if $d < 0$) without limit. **3.** $\frac{3}{1 - \left(-\frac{1}{2}\right)} = 2$; Yes. **4. a.** Answers may vary. An example is given. For the sequence 2, 4, 8, 16, …, the common ratio is 2 and the sequence of partial sums is 2, 6, 14, 30, … .

The series has no sum. (This will be true for any such example.) **b.** No. No geometric series with $|r| > 1$ will have a sum. The sequence of partial sums behaves as did the one in Sample 1(b) if $r < -1$ and increases without limit if $r > 1$.

Pages 255–258 Exercises and Problems
1. a.

3. a.

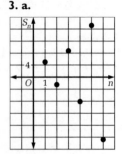

b. No.   **b.** No.
5. Yes; 8. **7.** No. **11.** those for which $|r| < 1$
13. Yes; 40.5. **15.** Yes; −2. **17.** No. **19.** 66 **21.** no sum **23.** 12.5 **29.** 555.55555 **30.** 51 **31.** 8 cm; The longest chord of a circle is a diameter. The length of a diameter is twice the length of a radius.
32. a. No vertical line intersects the graph in more than one point. **b.** all real numbers; all positive real numbers

Pages 260–261 Unit 4 Review and Assessment
1. a. 121, 364, 1093 **b.** 29,524 **c.** Answers may vary. An example is given. I noticed that the terms increase by powers of 3. I continued the pattern to find the 10th term. **2. a.** 78, 158, 318 **b.** 2558
c. Answers may vary. An example is given. I noticed that the second term is 5 more than the first, and each increase after that is twice the previous increase. I continued the pattern to find the 10th term.
3. a. AE, AF, AG **b.** AJ **c.** Answers may vary. An example is given. I noticed that the terms follow a pattern. The first letter is always A. The second letters are in alphabetical order. The tenth letter of the alphabet is J.
4. a.

5. a.

b. No. The terms appear to increase without limit.

b. Yes; the terms appear to approach 1.

Integrated Mathematics

6. a.

b. Yes. the terms appear to approach 0.

7. $a_n = 3^{3-n}$ **8.** $a_n = \dfrac{1}{n+2}$

9. 2, 1, 0, 1; 14

10. 17, 8, 5, $\dfrac{7}{2}$; $\dfrac{1}{17}$

11. a. $a_n = 200 + 30n$
b. \$60

12. 3, 4, 3, 4, 3 **13.** 6, −3.6, 2.16, −1.296, 0.7776
14. $a_1 = 11$; $a_n = a_{n-1} + 13$ **15. a.** 48π, 80π, 112π, 144π, 176π, 208π, 240π, 272π, 304π **b.** recursive: $a_1 = 48\pi$, $a_n = a_{n-1} + 32\pi$; explicit: $a_n = 48\pi + 32\pi(n-1)$ **c.** 304π cm$^2 \approx 955$ cm^2 **16. a.** neither
b. $a_1 = 10$; $a_n = 2a_{n-1} + 1$ **17. a.** neither **b.** $a_1 = \dfrac{2}{3}$; $a_n = (a_{n-1})^2$ **18. a.** arithmetic **b.** $a_1 = \dfrac{1}{8}$; $a_n = a_{n-1} + \dfrac{3}{8}$ **19.** 1643 **20.** 84 **21.** $\displaystyle\sum_{n=1}^{20}(100 - 5n)$

22. Maps will vary. An example is given.

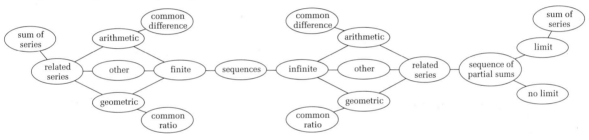

23. 333.33333 **24.** about 5.33

25. a.

b. Yes; 625.

26. a.

b. No.

27. no sum **28.** −8 **29.** Answers may vary. Examples are given. $\displaystyle\sum_{n=1}^{\infty}\left(\dfrac{1}{2}\right)^n$ has a sum. (The sum is 1.)

$\displaystyle\sum_{n=1}^{\infty} 2^n$ has no sum.

Unit 5

Pages 267–269 Talk it Over
1. a. 32 ancestors **b.** the positive integers; all numbers 2^n for n an integer and $n \geq 1$ **c.** The number of generations and the number of ancestors must both be positive whole numbers. **2.** Estimates may vary. An example is given; about 4 billion people. **3.** The model assumes that the growth rate will remain unchanged during the time period in question. The growth rate may not stay the same. For example, it might increase (for example, in response to an economic boom in the state) or decrease (for example, in response to a decline in available natural resources).
4. For the same value of a, the greater the value of b, the steeper is the graph of $y = ab^x$.

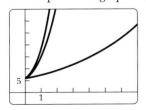

Pages 271–274 Exercises and Problems
1. a represents the initial amount, b represents the rate of change, x represents the time interval, and y represents the amount after x time intervals. **3.** A
11. a. discrete **b.** $y = 48{,}000(1.05)^x$ **c.** in 2027
15. about \$104,245,000,000 **19. a.** Both functions are exponential functions, that is, both have the form $y = ab^x$. For the first equation, $b > 1$, so the first function models exponential growth. For the second equation, $0 < b < 1$, so the second function models exponential decay.
b.

Both curves are exponential. The first models exponential growth; the second models exponential decay. The graphs have the point (0, 3) in common.

21. a.   **b.** 492.5 ng/mL
c. about 2.9 h
d. about 14.5 h

25. The sum does not exist. **26.** 1 **27.** $-\dfrac{5}{0.997} \approx$
-5.015 **28.** No; if such a polygon existed, the number, n, of sides of the polygon would satisfy the equation $(n-2)180° = 655$. The solution to this equation is not a whole number. **29.** $\dfrac{15}{x}$ **30.** $5s^2t^2$ **31.** $\dfrac{p^2}{q^2}$

Page 275 Talk it Over
1. 1984; 1987; 1992 **2.** 7 **3.** about \$1,014,000
4. −1 **5.** about \$114,000 **6.** about \$38,000
7. about \$12,750

Pages 277–280 Exercises and Problems
3. $y = (0.5)(0.125)^x$ **5. a.** 1985; 1980; 2000 **b.** The graph declines and moves toward the x-axis; the graph rises and moves away from the x-axis.
c. y-values increase; Yes; a percent can be any real number. **7. a.** about 162,132 **b.** 0 **c.** For years represented by negative values of x, there was no cellular phone system, and so no subscribers.
16. $y = (132,000,000)(1.013)^x$, where x is the number of years since 1940 **17.** −2 **18.** 1 **19.** $3d^3$ **20.** $2|x|$
21. a. ± 123 **b.** 3 **c.** $\pm 1107, 3321, \pm 9963$

Pages 282–283 Talk it Over
1. $f(x) = (40)\left(\dfrac{1}{2}\right)^x$, where x is the number of 2-hour periods since the beverage was consumed **2.** It takes 5780 years for half of a given amount of carbon 14 to decay. **3.** $6^{2/5}$ **4.** $18^{3/2} = (2 \cdot 3^2)^{3/2} = 2^{3/2} \cdot 3^{2 \cdot 3/2} = 2^{1 + 1/2} \cdot 3^3 = 2 \cdot 2^{1/2} \cdot 3^3 = 54\sqrt{2}$

Pages 285–287 Exercises and Problems
1. For integers m and n with $n > 0$ and any positive real number a, $a^{1/n} = \sqrt[n]{a}$, and $a^{m/n} = (\sqrt[n]{a})^m = \sqrt[n]{a^m}$. Examples may vary. **3.** $\sqrt[5]{13}$ **5.** $\sqrt[3]{15^5}$ or $\sqrt[3]{759,375}$ or $15\sqrt[3]{225}$ **7.** $12^{1/4}$ **9.** $21^{4/3}$ **11.** $4\sqrt[4]{2}$ **13.** $\sqrt[6]{243}$
15. $\dfrac{512}{125} = 4\dfrac{12}{125}$ **17.** $800\sqrt{5}$ **19. a.** $f(t) = 0.1(1.35)^t$
b. about 0.11 g; about 0.15 g **c.** nonnegative real numbers; Yes. **d.** after about 2.3 h **23.** $|x|\sqrt{x}$
25. $7v^2\sqrt{v}$ **27.** $6z^{-2}$ **29.** 1 **37.** 1,000,000,000
39. $\dfrac{16}{25} = 0.64$ **42.** $\left(\dfrac{1}{b}\right)^x = b^{-x}; \left(\dfrac{1}{b}\right)^x = \dfrac{1^x}{b^x} = \dfrac{1}{b^x}$
43. Methods may vary. An example is given.
Step 1: Find the product of the two first terms.
Step 2: Find the product of the two outside terms.
Step 3: Find the product of the two inside terms.
Step 4: Find the product of the two last terms.
Step 5: Add your results from Steps 1 through 4.
Step 6: Simplify if necessary.
44. exponential decay **45.** exponential growth
46. exponential decay **47.** exponential growth

Page 289 Talk it Over
1. about \$35.63
2. Answers may vary. An example is given. Since the rate of change is greater than 1, the function models exponential growth. The graph lies completely above the x-axis, approaching the x-axis as x decreases and increasing exponentially as x increases. It has a y-intercept of 2.62.

Pages 291–294 Exercises and Problems
1. irrational; about 2.718281828 **3.** C **5.** A
7. about $2.95 \cdot 10^{-6}$ **13.** \$106.17 **15. a.** \$7430.90
b. \$7404.56 **c.** He will earn more in the account in which interest is compounded continuously; the added \$10 in the other account does not make up for the interest lost by compounding quarterly rather than continuously. **26.** 5 **27.** 10,000 **28.** $7|x|\sqrt{2x}$
29. $4|b^3|c^2\sqrt[4]{c^2}$ or $4|b^3|c^2\sqrt{|c|}$
30. **31.**

32. **33.**

Page 295 Checkpoint
1. Exponential growth functions and exponential decay functions both have the form $y = ab^x$. For an exponential growth function, $b > 1$. For an exponential decay function, $0 < b < 1$.
2. a. $y = 15,112,000(1.16)^x$, where x is the number of 5-year periods after 1980 **b.** about 27,360,000
c. about 11,231,000 **3.** 9 **4.** 243 **5.** 8 **6.** \$286.23
7. \$287.45 **8.** \$287.57

1.

Distance (km)	Number of laps
10	25
5	12.5
3	7.5
1.5	3.75
1	2.5
0.5	1.25

2. $L(D) = \dfrac{D}{0.4} = 2.5D$

3. $D(L) = 0.4L$

4. The domain of L consists of the numbers 0.5, 1, 1.5, 3, 5, and 10, while the range consists of the numbers 1.25, 2.5, 3.75, 7.5, 12.5, and 25. The domain of D consists of the numbers 1.25, 2.5, 3.75, 7.5, 12.5, and 25, while the range consists of the numbers 0.5, 1, 1.5, 3, 5, and 10. The domain of L is the range of D and the range of L is the domain of D.

5. Each graph is the image of the other after reflection over the line $L = D$.
6. Yes; No; the inverse does not pass the horizontal line test.
7. Yes; Yes; the inverse passes the horizontal line test.

8. Yes; No; the inverse does not pass the horizontal line test. **9. a.** nonnegative real numbers; nonnegative real numbers **b.** the portion of the graph in the first quadrant **c.** Yes; the function $y = x^2$ with the domain restricted to $x \geq 0$ has an inverse. Its graph passes the horizontal line test. The graph of the inverse is the first-quadrant portion of the inverse function shown in Sample 1(b).

1. The domain of $f(x)$ is the range of $f^{-1}(x)$ and the range of $f(x)$ is the domain of $f^{-1}(x)$.

3. Yes.
5. No. Answers may vary. An example is given.

7. Yes.
11. $y = -x + 6$
13. $y = x$
15. $y = \sqrt[5]{\dfrac{x+3}{2}}$
17. $y = -\dfrac{x}{2}, x \geq 2$
19. $y = x - b$
21. $y = x^{b/a}$
23. No. **25.** No.

29. about 6.2 billion transactions **30.** Answers may vary. An example is given. Use the distance formula to find OR, OP, RQ, and QP.
$OR = \sqrt{(a - 0)^2 + (b - 0)^2} = \sqrt{a^2 + b^2}$,
$OP = \sqrt{(a - 0)^2 + (b - 0)^2} = \sqrt{a^2 + b^2}$,
$RQ = \sqrt{(c - a)^2 + (0 - b)^2} = \sqrt{(c - a)^2 + b^2}$, and
$QP = \sqrt{(c - a)^2 + (0 + b)^2} = \sqrt{(c - a)^2 + b^2}$. Therefore, $OR = OP$ and $RQ = QP$. By the definition of a kite, $OPQR$ is a kite. **31.** $2.91 \cdot 10^{-6}$ **32.** $4.7 \cdot 10^7$ **33.** $4.829 \cdot 10^5$

1. The scale number is the same as the number of zeroes in the relative size. **2.** about 125,893 **3.** No; the relative size of an earthquake that measures 8 on the Richter scale is 100,000,000. The relative size of an earthquake that measures 2 on the Richter scale is 100. The size of the larger earthquake is a million times the size of the smaller quake. **4.** arithmetic; geometric **5.** Yes; the graph passes the horizontal line test. **6.** because 1 raised to any power is 1
7. a. $5^2 = 25$ **b.** $4^1 = 4$ **c.** $10^{-2} = 0.01$
8. a. $\log (100{,}000) = 5$ **b.** $\log_4 8 = \dfrac{3}{2}$ **c.** $\log_7 1 = 0$
9. more acidic **10.** less acidic

1. For any positive number b, $f(x) = \log_b x$ and $g(x) = b^x$ are inverse functions. **3.** $\log_7 y = x$
5. $\ln e = 1$ **7.** $\log_2 \left(\dfrac{1}{8}\right) = -3$ **9.** $\log_8 1 = 0$ **11.** $6^0 = 1$
13. $10^4 = 10{,}000$ **15.** $e^1 \approx 2.718$ **17.** 2 **19.** 1
21. 2.30 **23.** 0 **25. a.** Estimates may vary; about 3.25. **b.** Answers may vary. An example is given. 10 is about one-quarter of the way between 8 and 16.
27. $\dfrac{1}{2}$ **29.** 1.32 **31.** 2.30 **40.** $y = \dfrac{1}{4}(x - 1)$ **41.** $\dfrac{16x^4}{y}$
42. $5t$ **43.** $\dfrac{9}{4a^6 b^{12}}$ **44.** $\dfrac{1}{m^3 n^6}$ **45.** Answers may vary.
An example is given. The graph of $y = -16x^2 + 20$ is a parabola that opens down. Its vertex is at (0, 20).

1. No; as the sample shows, doubling the intensity of a sound increases the loudness by about 3 decibels. The loudness would double only if the original loudness were 3 decibels. **2.** increase in loudness =
$L_2 - L_1 = 10 \log \dfrac{2I}{I_0} - 10 \log \left(\dfrac{I}{I_0}\right) = 10\left(\log \dfrac{2I}{I_0} - \log \dfrac{I}{I_0}\right) =$
$10\left(\log\left(\dfrac{2I}{I_0} \div \dfrac{I}{I_0}\right)\right) = 10 \log \left(\dfrac{2I}{I_0} \cdot \dfrac{I_0}{I}\right) = 10 \log 2 \approx 3$
3. Find $3^{1.893}$. **4.** $\log_3 8 = \dfrac{\ln 8}{\ln 3} \approx \dfrac{2.0794}{1.0986} \approx 1.893$

5. Graph $y = \dfrac{\ln x}{\ln 6}$. This graph is identical to the graph of $\dfrac{\log x}{\log 6}$ from Sample 5.

Pages 313–316 Exercises and Problems

3. $3 \log M$ **5.** $7 \log M - 5 \log N$ **7.** $\dfrac{4}{5} \log M$ **9.** $\ln \dfrac{2}{343}$

11. $\log_4 35$ **13.** $\ln 4$ **15.** 1 **17.** -2 **19.** $-3x$

23. 3.459 **25.** 0.921 **27.** -0.102 **33.** Let $\log_b M = x$. Then $M = b^x$, so that $\log_b M^k = \log_b (b^x)^k = \log_b b^{kx} = kx = k \log_b M$.   **35.** Let $\log_b M = x$. Then $M = b^x$, so that $\log_c M = \log_c b^x = x \log_c b = \log_b M \cdot \log_c b$; so $\log_b M = \dfrac{\log_c M}{\log_c b}$.   **39.** $3^4 = 81$ **40.** $e^{1.61} \approx 5$ **41.** $2^6 = 64$ **42.** 145 **43.** 14 **44.** $7\dfrac{3}{4}$ **45.** $0; \dfrac{1}{9}$ **46.** 1 **47.** 3

Pages 318–319 Talk it Over

1. Take the common logarithms of both sides of the equation to express the equation in logarithmic form. Use the power property of logarithms to express $\log (0.883)^t$ as $t \log 0.883$. Finally, divide both sides of the equation by $\log 0.883$.   **2.** Yes. Using logarithms with any base will result in the same answer.
3. Take the common logarithms of both sides of the equation. Use the power property of logarithms to express $\log 5^x$ as $x \log 5$. Divide both sides of the equation by $\log 5$; $x \approx 2.05$.   **4.** Graph the equation $y = 0.883^t$ and use TRACE to find the t-value when $y = 0.37$.   **5.** Graph $y = \dfrac{\log x + \log (x - 2)}{\log 2}$ and $y = 3$ on the same screen and use TRACE to find the x-coordinate of the intersection point.   **6.** Graph both equations on the same screen and use TRACE to find the x-coordinate of the intersection point; $x \approx 1.9$, $y \approx 5.2$.

Pages 320–322 Exercises and Problems

1. $\log_2 x + \log_2 (x - 2)$ is not defined for $x = -2$.
3, 5, 7. Answers are given to the nearest hundredth.   **3.** 0.56 **5.** 1.82 **7.** -0.90 **11.** 8 **13.** 2
15. no solution   **25.** $\log_5 9$ **26.** $\log_b \dfrac{p^{17}}{q}$ **27.** $w^3 - w$
28. $4a^2 + 2a - 23$ **29.** $x^2 - x$ **30.** mean: 76; median: 81   **31.** mean: 3.05; median: 2.85

Pages 324–325 Unit 5 Review and Assessment

1. The growth factor would be 1.05, so the equation would be $y = a(1.05)^x$. The decay factor would be 0.95, so the equation would be $y = a(0.95)^x$.   **2.** about 22 billion dollars   **3.** Answers may vary. Examples are given. value of an investment at a fixed rate of interest over a period of time; amount of carbon 14

left in organic material over time   **4.** A   **5.** B   **6.** C
7. a. $y = 10586000(1.485)^x$, where x is the number of decades since 1950   **b.** about 1,466,000
8. $y = (20)(5^x)$ **9.** 125 **10.** $10\sqrt[3]{2}$ **11.** $2x^4\sqrt[4]{4}$
12. 27 **13. a.** 0.94 L/min   **b.** about 18 mi/h
14. $y = 0$; $y = 5$

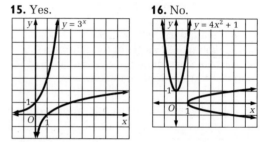

15. Yes.   **16.** No.

17. Yes; $y = 4x - 8$.   **18.** -5 **19.** 1.79 **20.** 3 **21.** 11
22. -4 **23.** 1.54 **24.** $7 \log N$ **25.** $\log M + 5 \log N$
26. $\dfrac{1}{2} \log M - 6 \log N$ **27.** $\log \left(13\dfrac{1}{3}\right)$ **28.** 2.579
29. 8 **30.** about 2.65 billion dollars   **31.** about 3.7%

Unit 6

Pages 332–334 Talk it Over

1. Answers may vary. An example is given. The telephone-digit data set shows a uniform distribution.
2. Estimate the total heights of all the bars and divide by 2. The median will be in the bar that contains the item of data that corresponds to this quotient.
3. Answers may vary. An example is given. I think measures of central tendency describe how numbers relate to a central, or average, value.   **4. a.** An outlier might show as a bar separated from the rest of the bars. If the intervals are large enough, the histogram might not show the outliers at all.   **b.** The median is determined by the numerical order of the numbers in a data list, not by how large or small they are, so an outlier has no effect on the median. For example, for the data 3, 5, 6, 7, 7, 7, 8, 12, if the last data point were 1750 instead of 12, the median would still be 7. Since the outlier may significantly change the sum of the data, the mean would be affected.   **5.** Each histogram in Sample 2 is identical to the corresponding one in Sample 1 except for the scale on the vertical axis.   **6.** 38.7% (about 40%); 90.3% (about 90%)

Pages 335–337 Exercises and Problems

1. In a skewed distribution, the interval or intervals that contain the greatest frequencies are at one end. In a mound-shaped distribution, the interval with the greatest frequency is in the middle of the histogram. **3.** Answers may vary. As the widths of the intervals change, the shape of the histogram will change. **5. a.** Estimates may vary. Monday, Wednesday, and Thursday: about 48; Tuesday: 50; Friday: about 45; Saturday: about 42; Sunday: 40 **b.** Yes; it seems reasonable that there is no particular day of the week on which more births occur. Therefore, it is reasonable to expect a uniform distribution.

11. a.

b. about 39%

13. a.

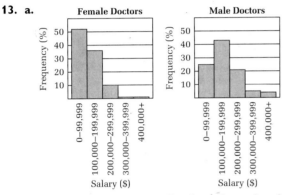

b. Both distributions are basically skewed. **c.** female doctors: 46%; male doctors: 64% **d.** Answers may vary. Examples are given. It appears that the salaries of male doctors are significantly higher than those of female doctors. Over half of the female doctors earn less than $100,000 per year, while 75% of all male doctors earn more than $100,000 per year. Also, while only 2% of all female doctors earn more than $300,000 per year, 11% of male doctors earn that much. Both the mean and median salaries are higher for male doctors. **15.** about 2.16 **16.** No. **17.** −63

Pages 338–340 Talk it Over
1. The San Francisco distribution is fairly uniform, while the Kansas City distribution is basically mound-shaped. **2.** about 56.8° for both cities; No. Although the histograms show that the monthly mean temperatures for the two cities are very different, the mean annual temperature is the same for both cities. **3.** San Francisco: 11.3°; Kansas City: 49.8° **4.** Answers may vary. An example is given. I think the mean and range together are better than the mean alone. Given both, I can tell that there is a greater variation in the temperature in Kansas City.

5. San Francisco: −6.1, −3.8, −2.1, −1.1, 0.6, 2.3, 2, 2.6, 5.2, 4.6, 0.6, −4.3; Kansas City: −25.1, −21, −13.5, −1.1, 8.8, 19.1, 24.7, 23, 14.5, 3.4, −12.2, −21; San Francisco average: about 0.04; Kansas City average: about −0.03 **6.** Kansas City; The standard deviation for Kansas City, about 17.4, is greater than that for San Francisco, about 3.4. Also, the range for Kansas City, 49.8, is greater than the range for San Francisco, 11.3. **7.** San Francisco: 60.2, 53.4; 58.3% of the temperatures are within one standard deviation of the mean; Kansas City: 74.2, 39.4; 50% of the temperatures are within one standard deviation of the mean.

Pages 341–343 Exercises and Problems
1. 2, the least and the greatest; all the data items **3. a.** 282.4 **b.** 13 **c.** 3.9 **d.** 60% **5. a.** 8.2 **b.** 7 **c.** 1.7 **d.** 84.6% **11.** Answers may vary depending on intervals chosen. In the example shown, the data are not grouped into intervals.

12. −3, −5 **13. a.** mound-shaped **b.** Estimates may vary; about 42%.

Pages 345–346 Talk it Over
1. about 68.5 in. **2.** about 71% **3.** normal; Most heights and weights approximate normal distributions. **4.** Both distributions have the same mean, but the distribution described by the shorter, wider bell-shaped curve has a greater standard deviation than the distribution described by the narrower curve. **5.** The 68-95-99.7 rule applies only to normal distributions. **6.** 5%

Pages 347–349 Exercises and Problems
1, 3. Answers may vary depending on interval size chosen. Examples are given.
1. a, b. **c.** No.

3. a, b.

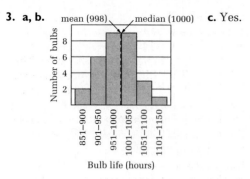

mean (998) median (1000) **c.** Yes.

Bulb life (hours)

7. a. 144 and 200 **b.** about 34% **c.** about 2.5%
9. about 2.5% **13.** 13.4°; 10.5° **14.** $y = 0.5x - 1$
15. $y = 4x + 3$ **16.** $\begin{bmatrix} 2\frac{2}{3} \\ -5\frac{2}{3} \end{bmatrix}$

Page 349 Checkpoint

1. Answers may vary. An example is given. The graph of a normal distribution has the same shape as the data set gets larger, no matter how small the interval size. For a normal distribution, a known percentage of the data falls within one, two, or three standard deviations of the mean. In a true normal distribution, the mean and median of the data are equal and fall at the line of symmetry of the distribution's bell-shaped curve. **2. a.** Answers may vary depending on the intervals chosen. Examples are given. See histograms below. **b.** financial: basically bimodal; communications: basically mound-shaped
c. financial: 50%; about 42%; communications: about 44.5%; about 55.5%

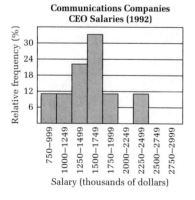

d. The range of salaries for financial institutions is greater than that for communications companies, so there is more variation for financial institutions. The two groups appear to have similar median salaries, but it appears that, overall, salaries are higher in financial institutions. **3.** about 3601; 3031; about 775 **4.** between 67 and 83

Pages 350–353 Talk it Over

1. distance from NYC vs. airfare; Jan. low temp. vs. population **2.** latitude vs. Jan. low temp.; distance from NYC vs. airfare **3.** The point is not near either the least-squares line or the median-median line. **4.** the least-squares line; The slope of the least-squares line is determined using actual data points, while the slope of the median-median line is determined using points whose coordinates are means of the coordinates of summary points. **5.** Answers may vary. An example is given. I think the point will be closer to the median-median line. That line is less affected by the point (11, 914) than is the least-squares line. **6.** the median-median line

Pages 354–358 Exercises and Problems

1. No; if the correlation coefficient of a data set is close to 0, the distribution of the data set is nearly random. A line would not model the data well.

3. a. $\frac{1}{2} < r \le 1$ **b.**

Yes; the data show a general upward trend, but the data points are somewhat scattered.

11. a–c.

(15,207, 1204)

d. Answers may vary due to rounding; $y = 0.13x - 639.54$.
e. Answers may vary. An example is given. I think the median-median line is a better fit than the least-squares line. The data point for the United States appears to be an outlier.

13. a–c.

d. $\left(\dfrac{4 + 11 + 9}{3}, \dfrac{9 + 16 + 11}{3}\right) =$ (8, 12)

15. about 81.5%

16. −3, −1, 3, 11, 27

17. $\begin{bmatrix} 2 & 3 & -1 \\ -1 & 5 & 8 \\ 5 & -1 & 0 \end{bmatrix} \begin{bmatrix} x \\ y \\ z \end{bmatrix} = \begin{bmatrix} 16 \\ 16 \\ -7 \end{bmatrix}$

b. $\begin{bmatrix} 1 & 1 & 1 \\ 1 & -1 & 1 \\ 4 & -2 & 1 \end{bmatrix} \cdot \begin{bmatrix} a \\ b \\ c \end{bmatrix} = \begin{bmatrix} 16 \\ 16 \\ -32 \end{bmatrix}$ **c.** $y = -16x^2 + 32$

14. a.

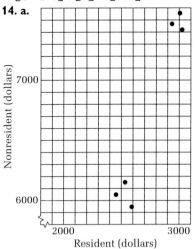

b. linear; The points appear to lie near a line.

c. $y = 2.6814x - 608.36$

Pages 359–361 Talk it Over

1. a. Answers may vary due to rounding; $y = -1.16x + 121.6$.

b–d.

	y-values		Deviation	
x	Actual	Model	*d*	d^2
20	108	98.4	9.6	92.16
25	91	92.6	−1.6	2.56
30	81	86.8	−5.8	33.64
35	74	81	−7	49
40	71	75.2	−4.2	17.64
45	70	69.4	0.6	0.36
50	71	63.6	7.4	54.76

e. 250.12   **2.** Yes; a parabola.   **3.** There are three unknowns: *a*, *b*, and *c*.   **4.** In Sample 1, all the points were used to find the least-squares parabola. In Sample 2, a curve that passes through 3 of the points was found.   **5.** No; only if all the points actually are on the same curve as the points in Sample 2.   **6.** Choose the quadratic equation for which the sum of the squares of the distances from the curve is the least.

Pages 362–364 Exercises and Problems

1. Graph points to see if they appear to lie on a line or on a curve.

3. a.

b. Answers may vary depending on whether the matrix method or technology is used. An example is given; $y = (-4.13 \times 10^{-6})x^2 + 0.039x - 19.2$.   **c.** about 4718 rpm   **5. a.** $4a + 2b + c = 20$; $25a + 5b + c = 56$; $9a - 3b + c = 0$ **b.** $\begin{bmatrix} 4 & 2 & 1 \\ 25 & 5 & 1 \\ 9 & -3 & 1 \end{bmatrix} \cdot \begin{bmatrix} a \\ b \\ c \end{bmatrix} = \begin{bmatrix} 20 \\ 56 \\ 0 \end{bmatrix}$

c. $y = x^2 + 5x + 6$

7. a. $a + b + c = 16$; $a - b + c = 16$; $4a - 2b + c = -32$

15. Suppose that $\angle B$ is a right angle. Then, since $m \angle C > 0$, $m \angle A + m \angle B + m \angle C = 100° + 90° + m \angle C > 190°$. This is not possible, since the sum of the measures of the angles of a triangle is 180°. So the assumption that $\angle B$ is a right angle is false. Therefore, $\angle B$ is not a right angle.   **16.** 0.5

Pages 366–368 Unit 6 Review and Assessment

1. a. A: mound-shaped; B: skewed; C: uniform
b. A: 7.55, 8; B: 8.85, 9; C: 7.77, 8
2. a. Intervals may vary; bimodal.

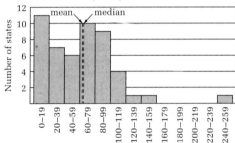

b. 254   **c.** mean: 61.64; median: 62.5; See graph.
d. 18%   **3. a.** sons: 2.15, 8; daughters: 1.46, 6
b. 2.05; 1.47   **c.** The mean is the sum of the means;

$$\frac{\text{number of children}}{\text{number of presidents}} = \frac{\text{number of daughters}}{\text{number of presidents}} + \frac{\text{number of sons}}{\text{number of presidents}}.$$ The standard deviation is greater when the numbers are combined because the presidents had so many more sons than daughters.
4. a. 43 yr to 67 yr   **b.** 47.5%; 34%
5. a–c. Sketches may vary.
a, b.

c.

d. If the standard deviation is unchanged and the mean is increased (or decreased), the curve retains the same shape but shifts to the right (or left). If the mean is unchanged and the standard deviation increases (or decreases), the line of symmetry of the curve is unchanged, but the curve becomes flatter and wider (or steeper and narrower).

6. a. $P = 0.0723A + 0.23$ **b.** 314 in.^{2}; $22.93

7. Answers may vary. An example is given.

a. $y = -186.14x^2 + 2201.7x + 23,895$, where x is the number of years since 1986 **b.** $23,895

Unit 7

Pages 373–378 Talk it Over

1. 20%, or $\frac{1}{5}$ **2.** 5; If an infinite number of tickets were printed, then no number of tickets would guarantee winning a T-shirt. But in this example, only a finite number of tickets will be printed. Since it is equally likely that each letter will appear, there must be an equal number of tickets, n, with each letter. Since there are 5 different letters, buying $4n + 1$ tickets guarantees getting one of each letter, thus winning a T-shirt. **3.** Answers may vary. **4.** The random sequence produced will consist of integers between 0 and 9. **5.** The random sequence produced will consist of integers between 3 and 11. **6.** int (20*rand) + 10 **7.** int (2*rand) + 1 **8.** Yes; 15 of the random numbers represent passengers who do not take the flight, and 85 represent passengers who do.

9.

General model	Model applied to T-shirt problem
State the problem clearly.	Find out how many tickets must be purchased in order to win a T-shirt.
Define the key question.	Select a letter. Does that letter show up on one of your tickets?
State the underlying assumptions.	The probability that any given letter appears on a ticket is 20%. The appearance of a letter on one ticket has no effect on any other ticket.
Choose a model to the answer the key question.	Generate random numbers from 1 to 5 inclusive. Each of the numbers represents one of the 5 letters.
Define and conduct a trial.	Generate a sequence of random numbers until each of the digits 1–5 has appeared once.
Record the observation of interest.	How many numbers had to be generated before each of the digits 1–5 appeared once?
Repeat the last two steps several times.	Generate a sequence as described above several times.
Summarize the information and draw conclusions.	Make a table or graph; determine the measures of central tendency of the data. Analyze and interpret the results.

Pages 378–381 Exercises and Problems

3. No. Since there is no restriction on the range of numbers, a random distribution cannot be achieved. Responses would tend to be positive one- or two-digit numbers. Also, by saying the numbers out loud, some students' responses might be affected by others' responses. **5.** Yes; a sequence of the letter "A" and random numbers between 2 and 10 would be produced (or 1–10 if aces are counted as ones). Each of the numbers occurs with the same frequency in the deck. **7.** int(100*rand) + 1 **9.** int(19*rand) + 11

11. a. It will increase the number of tickets needed. **b.** Answers may vary. An example is given. Use the function int(25*rand) + 1 to generate a sequence of random numbers from 1 to 25. Assign, say, the numbers 1–6 to the letter U, 7–12 to the letter S, and so on, and the number 25 to the letter M. For each trial, generate random numbers until each letter is represented once. **13.** Estimates may vary; about 45%.

15. Methods of simulation and results may vary. Use the function int(12*rand) + 1. Let the numbers 1–12 represent the months in order. (1 = January, and so on) For each trial, generate random numbers until the number for your birth month appears. Analyze the data. **22.** $y = x^2 + 2x - 8$ **23.** 160°; 20° **24.** $\frac{1}{8}$, or 12.5%

Pages 382–386 Talk it Over

1. a. die: 1, 2, 3, 4, 5, 6; dial: all real numbers greater than 0 and less than 6 **b.** die: discrete (exactly six possible outcomes); dial: continuous (the number of outcomes cannot be counted) **2.** $\frac{5}{6} \approx 0.83$;

$\frac{\text{number of favorable outcomes}}{\text{number of possible outcomes}} = \frac{5}{6}$ **3.** Since the outcomes are continuous, measurements can be used to compare the ratio of favorable outcomes to possible outcomes. **4. a.** $\frac{1}{2} = 0.5$ **b.** $\frac{1}{3} \approx 0.33$ **c.** $\frac{1}{6} \approx 0.17$

5. To find $P(A \text{ or } B)$ for the given situation, you can add $P(A)$ and $P(B)$ and subtract $P(A \text{ and } B)$ so no outcomes are counted twice. $P(A \text{ or } B) = \frac{1}{2} + \frac{1}{3} - \frac{1}{6} = \frac{2}{3} \approx 0.67$ **6.** the square region bounded by the x- and y-axes and the lines $x = 5$ and $y = 5$ **7. a.** $\frac{1}{6} \approx 0.17$

b. $\frac{3}{6} = \frac{1}{2} = 0.5$ **c.** $\frac{4}{6} = \frac{2}{3} \approx 0.67$ **d.** 0 **8.** Part (b) becomes $\frac{5}{6}$, or about 0.83; part (c) becomes 1; part (d) remains 0. **9.** If A and B are mutually exclusive events, then $P(A \text{ and } B) = 0$, so $P(A \text{ or } B) = P(A) + P(B) - P(A \text{ and } B) = P(A) + P(B) - 0 = P(A) + P(B)$.

10. A and not A are complementary events, so A and not A are mutually exclusive, which means that $P(A \text{ and not } A) = 0$. Also, A and not A account for all possibilities, so $P(A \text{ or not } A) = 1$. Then $P(A \text{ or not } A) = P(A) + P(\text{not } A) - P(A \text{ and not } A)$. Then $1 = P(A) + P(\text{not } A) - 0$ and $P(\text{not } A) = 1 - P(A)$.

When necessary, probabilities are rounded to the nearest hundredth. **1.** Use measurements such as length or area to determine the sizes of favorable outcomes and possible outcomes. **3. a.** discrete **b.** $\frac{1}{12} \approx 0.083$ **5. a.** continuous **b.** $\frac{1}{12} \approx 0.083$ **7. a.** continuous **b.** $\frac{8}{48} = \frac{1}{6} \approx 0.17$ **9.** $\frac{67}{72} \approx 0.93$ **11.** $\frac{32}{52} = \frac{8}{13} \approx 0.62$ **20.** int(13*rand) **21.** int(35*rand) + 1 **22.** int(16*rand) + 47

23. **24.**

25.

26. a. between 326 and 442 **b.** about 34%

1. Answers may vary. **2.** May is right. She describes $y = x$ and the two boundary lines. The region *does* represent the friends arriving at the same time ($y = x$) and all times *within* 10 minutes of that event, for the region inside the box. **3.** Answers may vary. An example is given. Divide the shaded region into a rectangle and two congruent triangles. Then the area of the shaded region is $10\sqrt{2}(20\sqrt{2}) + 2\left(\frac{1}{2}\right)(10)(10)$ or 500 square units. **4.** The region of the graph would be bounded by the inequalities $y < x + 20$ and $y > x - 20$. The probability would be about 0.89.

3. $\frac{275}{900} \approx 0.31$

5. 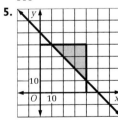 x is the amount of one sister's check; y is the amount of the other sister's check; the square represents all possible sums of the two checks written; the account is overdrawn if $x + y > 50$, that is, if the sum of the checks is more than was deposited.

$P(\text{overdrawn check}) = \frac{450}{1600} = \frac{9}{32} \approx 0.28$

7.

area of square = 100
area of shaded region = 36

Let x be time in minutes after the beginning of the ten-minute period when Janelle starts ringing up the sale and y the time in minutes when Abby starts ringing up the sale. The sales overlap if $x - 2 < y < x + 2$. The rectangle represents all possible times within the 10-minute interval when one of the clerks starts using the register for the indicated sale. The shaded area represents the possible times when the clerks would be using the register at the same time, that is, the time when one clerk would have to wait. $P(\text{one of them will have to wait}) = \frac{36}{100} = 0.36$.

10. $\frac{10}{36} = \frac{5}{18} \approx 0.28$ **11.** $\frac{13}{36} \approx 0.36$ **12.** $\frac{8}{36} = \frac{2}{9} \approx 0.22$ **13.** $\frac{10}{36} = \frac{5}{18} \approx 0.28$ **14.** $f(x) = -2x + 11$ **15.** $f(x) = 0$ **16. a.** $\frac{4}{12} = \frac{1}{3} \approx 0.33$ **b.** $\frac{9}{12} = \frac{3}{4} = 0.75$

1. Answers may vary. Examples are given. I used a formula in Exercise 10 on page 387 to find the probability that one of two events that are not mutually exclusive will occur. The formula $P(A \text{ or } B) = P(A) + P(B) - P(A \text{ and } B)$ is used by finding the individual probabilities and subtracting the probability that both events occur. I also used the formula for the area of a triangle in Exercise 6 on page 393. Areas are used when finding probability of an event with continuous outcomes. **2.** int(20*rand) **3.** int(7*rand) + 6 **4.** For each trial, use the function int(20*rand) + 1 to generate a sequence of 60 random numbers between 1 and 20. Let the number 1 represent a cancelled order and the numbers 2–20 represent orders that are not cancelled. Analyze the number of sequences for which the number 1 appears three or more times. **5.** $\frac{1}{2} = 0.5$ **6.** $\frac{16}{32} = \frac{4}{13} \approx 0.31$ **7.** $P(\text{one person will have to wait}) = \frac{1.75}{4} = 0.4375$

area of square = 4
area of shaded region = 1.75

1. It was given that the student selected is male. There are 19 male students. **2.** $\frac{9}{17} \approx 0.53$ **3.** Tree 1 determines probabilities such as $P(\text{allergic | male})$, while Tree 2 determines probabilities such as $P(\text{male | allergic})$. **4. a.** $P(\text{male and allergic}) = P(\text{male}) \cdot P(\text{allergic | male})$; $P(\text{male and allergic}) = P(\text{allergic}) \cdot P(\text{male | allergic})$

b. Answers may vary. An example is given.
$P(\text{female}) = \frac{17}{36}$; $P(\text{not allergic} \mid \text{female}) = \frac{8}{17}$;
$P(\text{not allergic}) = \frac{15}{36}$; $P(\text{female} \mid \text{not allergic}) = \frac{8}{15}$;
$P(\text{female and not allergic}) = \frac{8}{36}$. The relationship
holds. **5.** with replacement: $\frac{4}{25} = 0.16$; without
replacement: 0.1 **6.** situation (b), in which the first
ball was not replaced

Pages 399–402 Exercises and Problems
3. $\frac{160}{400} = \frac{2}{5} = 0.4$ **5.** $\frac{25}{110} = \frac{5}{22} \approx 0.23$ **7.** $\frac{175}{400} = \frac{7}{16} = $
0.4375 **11.** $\frac{1}{3}$ **17.** $\frac{30}{50} = \frac{3}{5} = 0.6$ **19.** $\frac{12}{20} = \frac{3}{5} = 0.6$
21. $\frac{21}{50} = 0.42$ **30.** $\frac{2475}{8100} \approx 0.31$ **31.** $2 \log M + 3 \log N$
32. 1540 groups

Page 404 Talk it Over
1. a. Answers may vary. An example is given. In both
cases, each average claim is multiplied by the number of such claims and divided by 10,000 and the
results are added. The order of the operations is different for the two methods. **b.** Answers may vary.
c. $\left(\frac{1}{10,000}\right)[\$200,000(1) + (\$20,000)(10) +$
$(\$2000)(200) + (\$0)(9789)] = \frac{\$200,000(1)}{10,000} +$
$\frac{(\$20,000)(10)}{10,000} + \frac{(\$2000)(200)}{10,000} + \frac{(\$0)(9789)}{10,000}$
2. Answers may vary. An example is given. I think it
makes sense to share the cost evenly unless a policy-
holder has repeated claims. Then I think that policy-
holder should pay more, being more of a risk.

Pages 406–409 Exercises and Problems
5. $3.50 **7.** No; the person running the game.
15. $3.30 **17.** No; if the game were fair, the expected
value would be 0. **19.** $\frac{2}{3}$ **20.** 90° **21. a.** $(a + b)^3 =$
$1a^3 + 3a^2b + 3ab^2 + 1b^3$; $(a + b)^4 = 1a^4 + 4a^3b +$
$6a^2b^2 + 4ab^3 + 1b^4$ **b.** Answers may vary. Examples
are given. The coefficients of the expanded form of
$(a + b)^n$ are the numbers in row n of Pascal's triangle.
The powers of a in the expanded form of $(a + b)^n$
begin at n and decrease to 0, while the powers of b
begin at 0 and increase to n. The sum of the powers
of a and b in each term equals n.

Pages 412–413 Talk it Over
1. Answers may vary. Responses are given based on
the sample results from step 2 of the Exploration. The
results predict a 4% probability, while theoretically
the probability is 7.6%. **2.** Answers may vary. Examples are given. Use a systematic list, or use Pascal's triangle. The number in row 10 and diagonal 8

of Pascal's triangle is $_{10}C_8$. **3.** 0.55^{10}, or about 0.25%
4. a. step 2 and step 3 since $P(\text{man}) = 0.3$ and
$P(\text{woman}) = 0.7$ **b.** about 0.14%; This probability is
about $\frac{1}{50}$ of the probability found in Sample 1.
5. Six men are hired. **6.** mound-shaped **7. a.** about
0.17 **b.** about 0.265 **c.** The events are mutually exclusive. **8.** No. **9. a.** Yes. **b.** Yes. **c.** Yes. **d.** No.

Pages 415–417 Exercises and Problems
3. about 0.00000525 **5.** about 0.00042 **7.** There are
exactly two outcomes for each trial. The trials are
independent. Each trial has the same probability of
success. The experiment has a fixed number of trials.
9. a. $\frac{11}{20} = 0.55$ **b.** $\frac{10}{19} \approx 0.53$ if the first person hired
is male, and $\frac{11}{19} \approx 0.58$ if the first person hired is
female **c.** The trials are not independent, so the trials do not all have the same probability of success.
11. a. 0.3125 **b.** 0.15625 **c.** 0.03125 **d.** 0.50
15, 17, 19. Estimates may vary. **15.** about 0.29;
about 0.23; The values are different because
$P(\text{senior has a job}) > P(\text{junior has a job})$. **17.** about
0.33 **19.** about 0.96 **25.** −25¢ **26.** 170.8; 37.7
27. 10 **28.** 13 **29.** $5\sqrt{2} \approx 7.07$

Pages 419–420 Unit 7 Review and Assessment
1. If the numbers given to the students were originally assigned in a random manner (for example, by
putting all the names in a hat and assigning 1 to the
first name, and so on), then the procedure described
would give a random sampling. If the numbers were
not originally assigned at random (for example, if the
numbers were given out in sequence by someone
who simply visited all the areas of the school), then
the sequence produced would not be random, since it
is likely that friends would have numbers assigned at
the same time and would arrive together, as would
groups of athletes, band members, and so on.
2. int(100*rand) **3.** int(10*rand) + 1 **4. a.** Add the
frequencies; divide each frequency by the sum.
b. Answers may vary. Examples are given. If a call is
selected at random, the probability that it was received between 4 P.M. and midnight is about 55%. If
a call is selected at random, it is most likely to be in
the 8 P.M.–midnight category. **5.** For each trial, use
the function int(100*rand) + 1 to generate a sequence
of 10 random numbers. Let the numbers 1–60 represent people with previous experience and the numbers 61–100 represent people with no previous experience. Count the number of sequences generated and
the number in which 7 numbers greater than 60
appear. Analyze the data. **6.** $\frac{5}{18} \approx 0.28$ **7.** $\frac{1}{6} \approx 0.17$
8. $\frac{5}{12} \approx 0.42$ **9.** Answers may vary. Examples are
given. Two dice are rolled. Their sum is less than 5 or

greater than 7. Both events cannot occur at the same time, so they are mutually exclusive. However, they account for only 21 of the 36 possible outcomes, so the events are not complementary. **10. a.** True.
b. False. **11.** $\frac{7}{16} = 0.4375$ **12. a.** Two events are independent if the occurrence of one of the events does not affect the probability of the occurrence of the other. **b.** Events A and B are independent if the probability that B occurs given that A has occurred is exactly the same as the probability of B alone.
13. $\frac{7}{12} \approx 0.58$ **14.** $\frac{7}{15} \approx 0.47$ **15.** No. P(female) = $\frac{20}{32} = \frac{5}{8}$; P(female | in the band) = $\frac{7}{15}$; $\frac{5}{8} \neq \frac{7}{15}$

16. a.

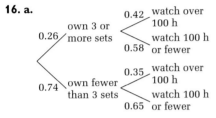

0.26 own 3 or more sets
— 0.42 watch over 100 h
— 0.58 watch 100 h or fewer

0.74 own fewer than 3 sets
— 0.35 watch over 100 h
— 0.65 watch 100 h or fewer

	Watch over 100 h	Watch 100 h or less	Total
Own 3 or more sets	0.109	0.151	0.26
Own fewer than 3 sets	0.259	0.481	0.74
Total	0.368	0.632	1

b. No; P(over 100 hours per week | three or more televisions) ≈ 0.11; P(over 100 hours per week) ≈ 0.37
17. −40¢ **18. a.** 278 **b.** 278 Calories **19.** ≈ 0.16
20. ≈ 0.00000018

Unit 8

Pages 426–427 Talk it Over
1. For each pair, $r = 0.4$ and $\theta = 330° + n(360°)$ for some integer n. For −30°, $n = -1$; for 690°, $n = 1$.
2. Answers may vary. Examples are given.
(0.8, −185°); (0.8, 535°) **3.** Answers may vary. An example is given. Use the same r-coordinate and find $\theta + n(360°)$ for integer values of n. **4.** Answers may vary. An example is given. I think it is easier to use negative angles when the negative angles are small.
5. You can measure distances using a ruler or compass and measure angles using a protractor. You must first designate a reference point.

Pages 427–429 Exercises and Problems
3. 180°; 270° **5.** 45°; 45° **7.** 225°; 225°

17, 19, 21.

23. Mt. Erebor **25, 27.** Estimates may vary.
25. (about 260, about 92°)
27. (about 560, about −30°) **36.** about 0.38
37. $\frac{1}{2} = 0.5$ **38.** Measure the length of the hypotenuse. To find the cosine of an acute angle, measure the length of the leg adjacent to the angle and divide by the length of the hypotenuse. To find the sine of the acute angle, measure the length of the leg opposite the angle and divide by the length of the hypotenuse.

Pages 431–435 Talk it Over
1. $r = 2.5$ and $\theta = 53.1°$; $x = r \cos \theta \approx 2.5(0.6) = 1.5$ and $y = r \sin \theta \approx 2.5(0.8) = 2$ **2. a.** The three pairs of polar coordinates describe the same point.
b. (5.3, 37.6); (5.3, 37.6) **3.** 90°; 270° **4.** 0°; 180°;
360° **5.** 116.6°; 296.6° **6.** $\sin^{-1} \frac{y}{r} = \sin^{-1} \frac{-7}{7.616} =$
$\sin^{-1} (-0.9191) = -66.8°$; The polar angle in Quadrant III with this sine value is 246.8°.
7. $\tan^{-1} \frac{y}{x} = \tan^{-1} \frac{-7}{-3} = \tan^{-1} (2.333) = 66.8°$; The polar angle in Quadrant III with this tangent value is 246.8°. **8.** Method 1: Use the Pythagorean theorem to find r and use the inverse trigonometric feature of a calculator to find θ. $r^2 = \sqrt{5^2 + (-8)^2}$; $r \approx 9.434$;
$\cos^{-1} \frac{x}{r} = \cos^{-1} \frac{5}{9.434} \approx 58°$. The polar angle 57.99° has the correct cosine value but is in the first quadrant. The polar angle in Quadrant IV with this cosine is 302.01°. The polar coordinates of (5, −8) are about (9.43, 302.01). Method 2: Use a graphics calculator.

Pages 436–439 Exercises and Problems
1. If a perpendicular is constructed from the point with polar coordinates (r, θ) to the x-axis and a line is drawn from the origin to the point, a right triangle is formed with acute angle θ and hypotenuse r. The horizontal leg has length x and the vertical leg has length y, so $\cos \theta = \frac{x}{r}$ and $\sin \theta = \frac{y}{r}$. Then $x = r \cos \theta$ and $y = r \sin \theta$. **3.** (1, 2); Drive 1.5 mi east on Five Mile Rd., 2 mi north on Farmington, and then 0.5 mi west on Seven Mile Rd. **5.** (1, 0) **7.** (0.71, 0.71)
9. (16.2, 22.5°) and (16.2, 67.5°)
13. $\tan \theta = \frac{y}{x} = \frac{y/r}{x/r} = \frac{\sin \theta}{\cos \theta}$

15. about (−482, 688); Belgrano II is about 482 mi "west" and 688 mi "north" of the South Pole.
23. opposite **25.** the same **27.** 215° **29.** 10°, 350°
31. 195°, 345 **33.** 155° **35.** 350° **37.** 100°, 280°
39. 152.87°, 207.13° **41.** 311.41°, 228.59°
43. (5.7, 45°) **45.** (28.0, 173.84°) **47.** (4.3, 180°)
49. (2, 120°) **51.** C(1.4, 0°), B(3.4, 49.8°), A(0, 90°), E(3.4, 130.2°), D(1.4, 180°) **53.** $-\frac{4}{5}$ **55.** −0.9772
57. (2, 0°) or (2, 120°) **58.** 2000, 4140, 6429.8, 8879.886, 11,501.47802, 14,306.58148 **59.** 5

Pages 441–442 Talk it Over
1. The (−4, −3) on the left of the diagram indicates the rectangular coordinates of the point in the plane that is 4 units to the left of the y-axis and 3 units below the x-axis. The (−4, −3) on the right indicates the vector with horizontal shift −4 and vertical shift −3.
2. a. (2, 3) **b.** (5, 126.9°) **3. a.** u and w **b.** t and v
4. a. No. **b.** Answers may vary. An example is given. The figure shows the vectors added in both orders, beginning at the same point. The resulting figure is a parallelogram whose diagonal is the resultant vector from both additions, $a + b$ and $b + a$. **5. a.** The magnitude of u is twice that of v; the direction is the same. **b.** w has magnitude three times that of v and the same direction as v; t has magnitude half that of v and the same direction as v. **c.** $(−1)v$ has the same magnitude as v. Its direction is opposite that of v.

Pages 444–445 Exercises and Problems
5, 7, 9.

11.

(8.5, 135°); (−6, 6)

13.

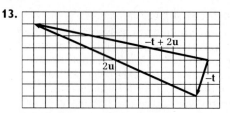

(15.3, 168.7°); (−15, 3)
15.

(6.8, −102.8°); (−1.5, −6.6)
21. (8.7, −33.69°) **22.** 0.588
23. (1.56, −12.70)

Pages 447–449 Talk it Over
1. The horizontal component of the airplane's speed is its speed relative to the ground, or *ground speed*. The vertical component of the airplane's speed is the rate at which it is climbing, or *rate of climb*.
2. a. (200, 15°); its actual speed through the air and its angle of ascent **b.** (193.19, 51.8); the horizontal and vertical distances of the jet from its takeoff point after 1 h **3. a.** $\sqrt{34}$; 60; $\sqrt{34}$; 60 **b.** 5; 3; $\frac{3}{5}$ **4.** The methods are the same. **5.** so the vectors could be added by adding coordinates **6.** to find the bearing of the airplane **7. a.** decreases **b.** Yes; with a bearing of 30°, the wind would increase the airplane's speed. **c.** 40°; 220°

Pages 449–452 Exercises and Problems
3. (6.32, 161.57°) **5.** (3.5, 6.06) **7.** (2.05, −1.43)
9. (4, 3) **11.** $(2\sqrt{2}, 1)$ **13.** (85.10, −93.96°)
15. about 246.2 mi/h; about 43.41 mi/h **22.** (−6, 15)
23. about 11.9 **24.** 11 **25. a.** $h(t) = -16t^2 + 34t + 6$
b. after about 2.3 s

Page 452 Checkpoint
1. No; the magnitude of $u + v$ will be $r_1 + r_2$ only if u and v have the same direction. **2.** C **3.** F **4.** G
5. (6.4, 128.66°) **6.** (4.24, −45°) **7.** (4, 0°)
8. (−2.74, 7.52) **9.** (5.83, −59.04°) **10.** 51.37°; 308.63° **11.** 0.8722 **12.**

13. (3, 14) **14.** (6.0, −68.4°)

Pages 453–455 Talk it Over

1. a. The golf ball on the left has no horizontal motion. The golf ball on the right moves horizontally at a steady rate as it falls. **b.** The golf balls move vertically at the same rate. **c.** No; the vertical motion of the two golf balls is the same. **2. a.** $a \approx$ −4.9 **b.** $x = 2t$ **3. a.** −3 **b.** after about 0.71 s
4. Yes. **5.** Answers may vary. An example is given. The skateboard will not achieve the same height and will hit the ground slightly sooner.

Pages 456–458 Exercises and Problems
5. $y = 1.36x$ **7.** $y = 0.35x - 0.06x^2$ **9.** $x^2 + y^2 = 12.96$ or $y = \pm\sqrt{12.96 - x^2}$ **11. a.** $x = 33.88t$; $y = 26.47t - 4.9t^2 + 1$

b. $y = 0.78x - 0.0043x^2 + 1$

c. **d.** The graphs are essentially the same. They may not be identical due to rounding.

e. Answers may vary. An example is given. The parametric equations allow you to determine the horizontal and vertical positions of the ball at any given time t. The single equation allows you to determine the height of the ball at any given horizontal distance x from the point where the ball was hit. **29.** If $a \neq c$, the graph is an ellipse centered at (b, d) with one axis $2a$ units high on the line $x = b$, and one axis $2c$ units wide on the line $y = d$. If $a = c$, the graph is a circle with radius a and center (b, d). **31.** $x = 6 \cos t + 3$; $y = 6 \sin t - 2$ **35. a.** $(3, -2)$ **b.** $(1, -12)$
36. a. $(3, -3)$ **b.** $(7, -9)$ **37.** $5\sqrt{5} \approx 11.18$ cm
38. about 7.28 units

Page 461 Talk it Over
1. because of the Pythagorean identity, which states that for every angle θ, $\cos^2 \theta + \sin^2 \theta = 1$ **2.** Answers may vary due to measurement or rounding; 1: 1230 ft; 2: 1140 ft; 3: 940 ft; They are the same. **3.** Yes; since the term $2ab \cos C = 0$, the formula simplifies to $a^2 + b^2 = c^2$. The Pythagorean theorem is a special case of the law of cosines for $\theta = 90°$.

Pages 463–466 Exercises and Problems
1. the lengths of two sides and the measure of the included angle **3.** Measurements may vary slightly. Calculated value is given to the nearest tenth. 9.9 cm
11. Answer is given to nearest tenth. 3.5 in. **17.** The angle at the vertex marked by the Lincoln Memorial is 44.4°; the third angle is 10.4°. **23.** Answer is given to the nearest tenth. 109.5° **29.** $x = 5 \cos \theta$; $y = 5 \sin \theta$ **30. a.** True. **b.** True. **31.** 14

Page 469 Talk it Over
1. from Aisyālukharka: about 29,030 ft; from Mayām: about 28,720 ft **2.** SAS

Pages 471–474 Exercises and Problems
3, 5, 7, 9. Measurements are given to the nearest tenth. **3.** $m \angle Z = 57°$; $x = 16.7$ m; $y = 21.3$ m
5. $m \angle A = 104°$; $a = 40.3$ m; $b = 21.4$ m

	$m \angle A$	$m \angle B$	$m \angle C$	a	b	c
7.	109°	46°	25°	58	44.1	25.9
9.	90°	38°	52°	30.9	19	24.3

11. a. 39.249° **b.** 7.359 km; 8.124 km **c.** 2.518 km **d.** 2.520 km **e.** 2.519 km **f.** (a) 40° (b) 7.21 km; 8.000 km (c) 2.443 km (d) 2.483 km (e) 2.463 km; The estimate is decreased about 2.2%.
17. If $a \leq b$, no triangle is formed. If $a > b$, one triangle is formed.

19. 1 triangle **21.** no triangle **23.** no triangle
25, 27. Answers are given to the nearest tenth. Answers may vary slightly due to rounding or to solution method. **25.** $m \angle B = 24.6°$; $m \angle C = 44.4°$; $b = 5.4$ **27.** not possible **29, 31, 33.** Solution methods may vary; examples are given. Answers are given to the nearest tenth. Answers may vary slightly due to rounding or to solution method. **29.** $m \angle S = 69°$; $r = 12.3$ km; $s = 10.5$ km; law of sines **31.** $m \angle R = 46°$; $r = 11.1$ in.; $s = 13.5$ in.; law of sines
33. $m \angle S = 72°$; $s = 10.4$ km; $t = 10.9$ km; law of sines **35.** $x^2 = y^2 + z^2 - 2yz \cos X$; $y^2 = x^2 + z^2 - 2xz \cos Y$; $z^2 = x^2 + y^2 - 2xy \cos Z$ **36.** Methods may vary. An example is given. Suppose a regular n-sided polygon has an interior angle whose measure is 80°. Then the measure of an exterior angle is $180° - 80° = 100°$. The measure of each exterior angle of a regular n-sided polygon is $\frac{360°}{n}$, so $100° \cdot n = 360°$ and $n = 3.6$. This contradicts the fact that n must be an integer. The assumption that there is a regular polygon with an interior angle whose measure is 80° is false. Therefore, no regular polygon has an interior angle whose measure is 80°. **37.** Answers may vary. An example is given. data: 75, 66, 84, 82, 88, 71, 72, 87; standard deviation: 7.67

1. (180, 180°) **2.** (180, 202.5°) **3.** (180, 225°)
4. (−180, 0) **5.** about (−166.3, −68.9)
6. about (−127.3, −127.3)

7.   **8.**

9.   **10.**

11. (−166.3, −68.9) **12.** (−127.3, −127.3) **13.** (0, 0)
14. a circle with radius 1 centered at the origin
15. a circle with radius 1 centered at (4, −5)
16. an ellipse with its center at the origin, 8 units
wide, 10 units high **17.** about 78.6 in.
18.   2.35 in.

19.

20. about 3562 paces
21. about 2574 paces
22. about 2:28

Unit 9

1. The number in each row of the third column is 14
more than the number in the corresponding row of
the second column. **2.** about 66.7; about 80.7; The
mean of the heights with stilts is 14 more than the
mean of the heights without stilts. **3.** 66; 80; The
median of the heights with stilts is 14 more than the
median of the heights without stilts. **4.** 12; 12; The
ranges are the same. **5.** The histograms have exactly
the same shape. The second is the first shifted to the
right. **6.** Answers may vary. An example is given.
The standard deviation is a measure of spread. The
data in both cases are spread out in exactly the same

manner. Let x_i represent the first data points and X_i
represent the second. For every i, $X_i = x_i + 14$, so
$X_i - \overline{X} = (x_i + 14) - (\overline{x} + 14) = x_i - \overline{x}$). Since the sum
of the deviations is the same, the variance and stan-
dard deviation are the same. **7. a.** decrease; When
the same constant value is added to each value in a
data set, the mean is translated by the constant value,
in this case, a negative number. **b.** decrease; When
the same constant value is added to each value in a
data set, the median is translated by the constant
value, in this case, a negative number. **c.** stay the
same; When the same constant value is added to each
value in a data set, the range remains the same.
d. stay the same; When the same constant value is
added to each value in a data set, the standard deviation remains the same. **8.** left; When the same
constant value is added to each value in a data set,
the graph of the distribution is translated by the constant value, in this case, a negative number.

3. The median, lower extremes, and upper extremes
for the heights with 18-in. stilts are each 18 more
than the corresponding values for the heights without
stilts. The ranges are the same. **5.** 160; about 40.2
7. 156.5; 40.2 **20.** about 20.78 cm **21.** (7, −1)
22. (15, −4) **23.** (17, −8)

24.
domain: all real numbers;
range: all real numbers greater
than or equal to 0

25.
domain: all real numbers;
range: all real numbers greater
than or equal to 3

26.
domain: all real numbers;
range: all real numbers
greater than or equal to 0

1. (0, 0); (2, 1); (2, 1) **2.** b and c; a and c; The graph
of $y - k = f(x - h)$ is the graph of $y = f(x)$ translated
k units up if $k > 0$, k units down if $k < 0$, h units to
the right if $h > 0$, and h units to the left if $h < 0$.
3. a. $x + h$; $y + k$ **b.** $\begin{bmatrix} h \\ k \end{bmatrix}$ **4.** $9 + 1 = 10^{4-3}$, $10 = 10$ ✓
5. The origin is not part of the graph of $y = 10^x$.

6. The domain of the parent function is all real numbers greater than or equal to 0. The domain of the function in part (a) is all real numbers greater than or equal to −4. If you think of the domain of the parent function as an interval of the *x*-axis, the domain of the second function is the interval with the endpoint shifted 4 units to the left.   **7.** The asymptote of the graph in part (b) is the asymptote of the parent graph translated 1 unit down.

Pages 492–495 Exercises and Problems
1. $y = x^2$; (−2, 7)   **3.** $y = 10^x$; (−9, 0)

5.   **7.**

15. $y + 3 = x^3$ **17.** $y - 2 = \sqrt{x - 1}$ **19.** $y - 2 = 10^x$
21. a. $h = 3$; $k = 1$ **b.** $x = 3$; $y = 1$ **26.** 82; 9

27. about 1.6   **28.** $\begin{bmatrix} 5 & 0 \\ 0 & 8 \end{bmatrix}$ **29.** $\begin{bmatrix} 1\frac{3}{5} & 0 \\ 0 & \frac{1}{2} \end{bmatrix}$

30. $\begin{bmatrix} 6 & 9 & 6 & 12 \\ 2 & 0 & 4 & 2 \end{bmatrix}$

Pages 496–497 Talk it Over
1. 0.2; 0.2 dollars to 1 franc   **2. a.** 1500   **b.** 300
c. 0.2   **3. a.** 1550   **b.** 310   **c.** 0.2   **4. a.** 750   **b.** 150
c. 0.2   **5.** The columns are the same height. The columns in the second histogram are five times as wide as the columns in the first. The endpoints of each column in the second histogram are 5 times the endpoints of the corresponding column in the first.
6. 0.2   **7.** Predictions will vary. Each will be multiplied by 4. For the original data, the mean is 8, the median is 7, the range is 15, and the standard deviation is about 4.94. For the transformed data, the mean is 32, the median is 28, the range is 60, and the standard deviation is about 19.76.

Pages 498–500 Exercises and Problems
3. a. 7.3; 6.7; 4.5; about 1.8   **b.** 21.9; 20.1; 13.5; about 5.4   **c.** Data intervals may vary.

5. a. $d > 1$ **b.** $d < 1$ **7. a.** about 0.000126
b. Answers are rounded to the nearest tenth. 3.5; 1.0; 11.0; 3.9   **c.** Aaron used the fact that the value of *d* for Earth is the median; Yolanda used the fact that the value of *d* for Earth is significantly less than the mean.

10.   **11.**

12.   **13.** 2.322   **14.** 0.565
15. −2.066   **16.** −0.120

17. $y \approx 2.8x^2 - 13.5x + 18.7$ or $y = \frac{17}{6}x^2 - \frac{27}{2}x + \frac{56}{3}$

18. $y \approx -0.08x^2 + 0.2x + 1.1$ or $y = \frac{-7}{88}x^2 + \frac{19}{88}x + \frac{47}{44}$

Page 503 Talk it Over
1. a. The parent graph is stretched horizontally by a factor of 2.   **b.**

2. a. $\frac{y}{3} = 2x(2x - 2)(2x + 3)$ **b.** the origin

Pages 504–508 Exercises and Problems
1. a. $\begin{bmatrix} 0 & 8 & 8 & 4 & 0 \\ 0 & 0 & 3 & 5 & 3 \end{bmatrix}$ **b.** The polygon is stretched vertically by a factor of $\frac{1}{2}$.

3. a. $\begin{bmatrix} 0 & 8 & 8 & 4 & 0 \\ 0 & 0 & 12 & 20 & 12 \end{bmatrix}$

b. The polygon is stretched vertically by a factor of 2.

5. a. The matrix on the left produces a horizontal stretch by a factor of 4. The matrix on the right produces a vertical stretch by a factor of 3.   **b.** The product matrix $\begin{bmatrix} 4 & 0 \\ 0 & 3 \end{bmatrix}$ produces a horizontal stretch by a factor of 4 and a vertical stretch by a factor of 3.

9. $\begin{bmatrix} 9 & 0 & -9 \\ 0 & 9 & 0 \end{bmatrix}$; The transformation produces a horizontal stretch by a factor of 3 and a reflection over the y-axis. **11.** $\begin{bmatrix} 9 & 0 & -9 \\ 0 & -4\frac{1}{2} & 0 \end{bmatrix}$; The transformation produces a horizontal stretch by a factor of 3, a vertical stretch by a factor of $\frac{1}{2}$, and reflections over both axes.

17. a.

New Rates

b. $\frac{y}{2} = f(x)$ or $y = 2(f(x))$

23. A **25.** D

27.

35. $y = \left(\frac{x}{2}\right)^3$

37. $y - 2 = |x - 3|$

39. Both are multiplied by 0.8. **40.** 310° **41.** 225°

42. 120° **43.** 25° or 335°

44. $y + 2 = |x - 4|$

Page 509 Checkpoint

1. When the same constant value is added to each value in a data set, the same value is added to the mean and the median. The range and standard deviation are unchanged. When each value in a data set is multiplied by the same positive constant, the mean, the median, the range, and the standard deviation are all multiplied by the same constant. **2.** 29; 10

3.

4.

5.

6. $154.88; $94.50

7. $\frac{y}{1.05} = 0.05x$ or $y = 0.0525x$

8. $\frac{y}{0.75} = 0.05x$ or $y = 0.0375x$

Pages 510–514 Talk it Over

1. how Celsius and Fahrenheit temperatures are related **2.** about 11.3°C; slightly lower **3.** Answers may vary. Examples are given. elevation, nearness to the ocean, prevailing wind patterns **4.** The resulting function is $y = 2(2^{x-1}) = 2^x$. The graph is unchanged.

5. $y = \left(\frac{2}{3}x\right)^3 + 2$

6. a. $\frac{2}{3}$ **b.** $y - 2 = \left|\dfrac{x-7}{\frac{2}{3}}\right|$ or $y - 2 = \left|\dfrac{3(x-7)}{2}\right|$ **c.** Yes.

Pages 514–518 Exercises and Problems

1. stretching and translating; stretching **3. a.** 1969, 1974, 1976, and 1977; 1965, 1966 and 1975 **b.** No. **c.** part (a) above: 1961, 1973, and 1975; below: 1965, 1976, 1979, and 1980; part (b) No. **7.** $31,790; about $11,347 **13.** a vertical stretch by a factor of 16 and a translation 160 units up

19. $y = -3|x - 3| + 2$

21. $y = \sqrt{\dfrac{x+1}{2}} + 1$

23. $y = 3 \log x + 5$

25. The graph is the graph of $y = x(x + 3)(x + 3)$ with a horizontal stretch by a factor of $\frac{1}{2}$.

26. 0.682256

27. the randomly selected group; the randomly selected group; Journalists are more likely to have better training in writing correctly and are more likely to perform well as a group. The randomly selected people are more likely to include both people who are poor writers and people who are good writers.

Page 519–523 Talk it Over

1. No; it is unreasonable to compare the two because of the age difference. **2. a.** Georgia: 6.55 min; Texas: 14.94 min **b.** Both are above; below. A lower time indicates a faster run. **c.** Georgia: 0.30 above; Texas: 0.56 above **d.** The Georgia woman did better. She was only 0.30 standard deviation above the mean for her division, while the Texas woman was 0.56 standard deviation above the mean for her division.

3. above; below; The score and the mean are the same.
4. A lower z-score means a better performance relative to a particular age group, so z-scores for different age groups can be compared.   **5.** 5% of the heights are less than Sara's height.   **6.** 50th percentile

Pages 523–525 Exercises and Problems

1. Answers may vary. An example is given; in situations where you want to compare data from different categories; z-scores standardize results so that results from different categories can be compared.
3. Answers are given to the nearest thousandth.
a. 31.657; 2.900   **b.** −1.371; −1.171; −1.047; −0.796; −0.344; 0.473; 0.811; 0.953; 1.204; 1.287   **c.** 0; 1; These are the mean and standard deviation of the normal distribution.

5. a.   **7. a.**

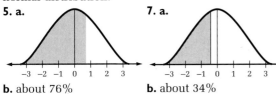

b. about 76%   **b.** about 34%
9. about −0.7   **11.** about 0.3   **13.** Stretch curve 1 horizontally by a factor of 2 and vertically by a factor of $\frac{1}{2}$.

18.

19.

Answers may vary. An example is given. Consider the point (1, 2), which is on the graph of $y = 2^x$. If the functions were inverses, (2, 1) would be on the graph of $y = \left(\frac{1}{2}\right)^x$, which it is not, since $\left(\frac{1}{2}\right)^2 = \frac{1}{4}$, not 1. The graphs are reflections of one another over the y-axis   **20.** (0, 1)

Page 529 Talk it Over

1. Write the equation as $\frac{y + 3}{\frac{1}{2}} = -|x - 6|$. Reflect the graph of the parent function $y = |x|$ over the x-axis to get the graph of $y = -|x|$. Stretch the graph of $y = -|x|$ vertically by a factor of $\frac{1}{2}$. Finally, translate the graph by the vector (6, −3).   **2. a.** 2500 ft   **b.** 5.2 min

Pages 530–532 Exercises and Problems

1. domain: all real numbers less than or equal to 4; range: all real numbers greater than or equal to 1

3.

5.

7.

13. $y = 10^{-(x - 1)}$
15. $y - 7 = -2\sqrt{-x - 3}$
17. $y = -2 \log x$ **20.** 0.75

21. $PQ = \sqrt{x - (-r)^2 + (y - 0)^2} = \sqrt{(x + r)^2 + y^2}$; $QR = \sqrt{(x - r)^2 + (y - 0)^2}$; $\overline{PR}$ is a diameter, so $PR = 2r$. Then $(PQ)^2 + (QR)^2 = (x + r)^2 + y^2 + (x - r)^2 + y^2 = x^2 + 2xr + r^2 + y^2 + x^2 - 2xr + r^2 + y^2 = 2(x^2 + y^2 + r^2) = 2(2r^2) = 4r^2 = (PR)^2$. By the converse of the Pythagorean theorem, $\triangle PQR$ is a right triangle and $\angle PQR$ is a right angle.

Pages 534–535 Unit 9 Review and Assessment

1. a. 545.6; 517; 280; about 112

b.

Name of building	Height (ft)
Amoco Building	5728
Anaconda Tower	5787
Arco Tower	5807
First Interstate Tower North	5714
Mountain Bell Center	5989
1999 Broadway	5824
Republic Plaza	5994
17th Street Plaza	5718
Stellar Plaza	5717
United Bank of Denver	5978

c. 5825.6; 5797; 280; about 112

2.

3.

4.

(graph)

5. Answers may vary. An example is given. (1) Determine the mean and standard deviation of the model heights and multiply both by 100 to determine the actual mean and standard deviation. (2) Multiply each model height by 100 and then calculate the mean and standard deviation of the actual heights.

6. $\begin{bmatrix} 0 & 20 & 24 & 4 \\ 0 & 0 & 3 & 3 \end{bmatrix}$; horizontal stretch by a factor of 4

7. $\begin{bmatrix} 0 & 5 & 6 & 1 \\ 0 & 0 & 1 & 1 \end{bmatrix}$; a vertical stretch by a factor of $\frac{1}{3}$

8. $\begin{bmatrix} 0 & 10 & 12 & 2 \\ 0 & 0 & 15 & 15 \end{bmatrix}$; a horizontal stretch by a factor of 2 and a vertical stretch by a factor of 5

9. **10.**

11.

12. about 19.3°C; about 0.7°C **13.** Answers may vary. An example is given. $f(x) = \frac{5}{3}x - 5$. The range of the actual scores is 24 and we want it to be $100 - 60 = 40$, so $m = \frac{40}{24} = \frac{5}{3}$. Since $\frac{5}{3} \cdot 39 = 65$ and we want a 39 to be scaled to a 60, $b = -5$. **14.** $y + 3 = \frac{1}{2}|x - 4|$

15. $y - 1 = \left(\frac{x}{2}\right)^3$ **16. a.** about 73% **b.** about 10%

17. about 16% **18.**

19. a. $g(t) = 80 - f(t)$
b.

Pages 541–545 Talk it Over

1. time and speed; There appears to be little relationship between the two. **2.** The car accelerates to 230 mi/h, races in the 220–230 mi/h range, slows to 80 mi/h for 30 s, accelerates to resume normal racing speed, slows and stops for 10 s, and finally accelerates back into the race. The two similar-looking sections appear to be the normal racing section of the graph, with speeds varying slightly due to turns. The slowdown from 60 s to 90 s could be due to a caution condition on the track, perhaps because of an accident. The stop from 155 s to 165 s could be a pit stop.
3. B **4.** E **5.** D **6.** A **7.** C **8.** F **9.** Answers may vary. An example is given. **a.** E **b.** B, F **c.** A **d.** C **e.** A, B **f.** D **10.** The results are not exactly the same but are similar. 4^x grows fastest, followed by x^4, then $4x$. The differences in y-values for $y = 4x$ are constant, the differences for $y = x^4$ are increasing, and the differences for $y = 4^x$ are increasing in a geometric sequence. **11.** $y = \frac{1}{2}x$ increases fastest, followed by $y = \sqrt{x}$, and then $y = \log_2 x$.
12. a. slowly at the start and quickly at the end of this interval **b.** slowly over the whole interval

Pages 545–547 Exercises and Problems

1. a. The elevator goes to the second floor and returns to the ground floor. It goes to the fifth floor, stopping at every floor, and returns to the ground floor. It does this 3 times. Then it stops at the ground floor for 40 minutes and goes to the fifth floor. **b.** 8:15 to 8:30; In each period, the elevator takes the same time to fill, go up while stopping at each floor, then return to the ground floor and await the next trip. **c.** between 8:15 and 8:25 **3.** The graphs are alike in that they alternate between high values and low values. They are different in that the graph in question 5 does not repeat values, while the graph in question 7 does repeat values. **7, 9, 11.** Answers may vary. Examples are given. **7.** decreasing or saturating **9.** decreasing **11.** periodic **13.** 11 **15.** 9 **17.** $y = 3^x$ grows fastest, followed by $y = x^3$, and then $y = 3x$.

19. $y = 2 - x$ decays fastest, followed by $y = 2^{-x}$, and then $y = \frac{2}{x}$. **26. a.** **b.** Reflect it over the x-axis.

27. 16 **28.** $5\sqrt[6]{5^5}$ **29.** $\frac{27}{125}$

Integrated Mathematics

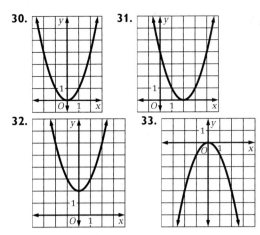

30. **31.** **32.** **33.**

34. $y = (x - 2)^2$: transformation by (2, 0) or shift 2 units to the right; $y - 2 = x^2$: transformation by (0, 2) or shift 2 units up; $y = -x^2$: reflection over the x-axis

Pages 548–549 Talk it Over

1. 4 min   **2.** 15; $\frac{1}{4}$; the frequency   **3.** 7   **4.** start of the second cycle; middle of the wash and rinse part of the cycle; wash and rinse   **5.** The amplitude for Jennifer's graph is 8.5 and the axis is $y = 11.5$.   **6.** The amplitude and the period would decrease, the axis would be lower, and the frequency would increase.

Pages 550–553 Exercises and Problems

1. The period and the frequency are reciprocals.
3. 24 h   **5.** 3 P.M.; 4:30 A.M.   **7.** Answers may vary. An example is given.

11. about 21 times   **13. a.** 4   **b.** $\frac{1}{4}$

c. $y = -1$ **d.** 2   **15. a.** 6   **b.** $\frac{1}{6}$ **c.** $y = 2.5$ **d.** 1.5

17. **19.**

31. $y = 5^x$ grows fastest, followed by $5x^2$, then $5x$.

32. a. 90°   **b.** $\sin A = \frac{a}{c}$ **c.** $\cos B = \frac{a}{c}$

33. $b \approx 6.2$ cm, $m \angle A \approx 23.8°$, and $m \angle C \approx 126.2°$
34. $a \approx 16.2$ cm; $m \angle C \approx 6.7°$, and $m \angle B \approx 63.3°$

35. $m \angle B = 100°$, $a \approx 22.8$ cm, and $c \approx 35$ cm
36. $m \angle A = 63°$, $a \approx 15.2$ cm, and $b \approx 6.4$ cm

Pages 554–556 Talk it Over

1. a. **b.** **c.** **d.** **e.** **f.**

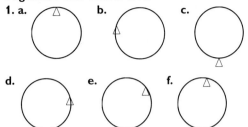

2. It increases and decreases in cycles, going from a low of 5 ft to a high of 55 ft.
3. A: a. at the top   **b.** 90°   **c.** $\frac{1}{4}$ **B: a.** on the left side, 30 ft up   **b.** 180°   **c.** $\frac{1}{2}$ **C: a.** at the bottom   **b.** 270°

c. $\frac{3}{4}$ **D: a.** on the right side, 30 ft up   **b.** 360°   **c.** 1
E: a. on the right side, 30 ft up   **b.** 720°   **c.** 2   **F: a.** at the top   **b.** 810°   **c.** $2\frac{1}{4}$ **4.** 360°; one turn of the wheel   **5.** 25 ft; the radius of the Ferris wheel
6. a. 30 s   **b.** 2   **c.** It would be stretched horizontally by a factor of $\frac{2}{3}$.   **7.** I: the x-coordinate starts at 1 and ends up at 0. II: the x-coordinate starts at 0 and ends up at −1. III: the x-coordinate starts at −1 and ends up at 0. IV: the x-coordinate starts at 0 and ends up at 1.
8.

Pages 557–559 Exercises and Problems

1. The unit circle is a circle with radius 1 centered at the origin. If an object moves counterclockwise around the unit circle, the sine function indicates the vertical position and the cosine function indicates the horizontal position of the object.   **3.** neither
5. sine   **7.** both (The horizontal intercepts of the sine function occur at multiples of 180°; the horizontal intercepts of the cosine function occur at odd multiples of 90°.)   **9.** sine   **11.** 12   **13.** The period of the function is 20 s; 27 s.   **20.** Answers may vary. An example is given.

21. $f(g(x)) = \left(\dfrac{x}{2}\right)^2 = \dfrac{x^2}{4}$ **22.** $h(f(x)) = \sqrt{x^2 - 1}$ or $|x| - 1$

23. 16   **24.** 2

25.

27.

26.

Pages 563–567 Exercises and Problems

1. Answers may vary. An example is given. $|A|$ is the amplitude, $\dfrac{360°}{|B|}$ is the period, C is the horizontal shift from the graph of $y = \sin \theta$, and D is the vertical shift.

7. D   **9.** F   **11.** E   **13. a.** 3; 360°; $\dfrac{1}{360°}$

b.

15. a. 1; 360°; $\dfrac{1}{360°}$

b.

23. a. 1; 180°; $\dfrac{1}{180°}$

b.

27. C   **31, 33.** Answers may vary. Examples are given.   **31.** $y = 2 \sin (\theta - 45°) + 1$
33. $y = \sin 2(\theta + 30°) - 3$ **44.** −300.7°; −239.3°; 59.3°; 120.7° (in general, $\theta = 59.3° + n \cdot 360°$ or $\theta = 120.7° + n \cdot 360°$ for any integer n)   **45.** no sum
46. $\dfrac{100}{199} \approx 0.5$ **47.** 1800°; 30°

Pages 569–571 Talk it Over
1. a. 30 ft   **b.** 30 ft   **c.** about 8.35 ft
2. $h(t) = 25 \cos (12(t - 7.5))° + 30$ **3.** 9

4.

The graph crosses the horizontal axis.

Pages 572–575 Exercises and Problems
3. a.

b. every 30 s after the start
c. $(30n, 30)$, where n is a positive integer

5. a. The axis is now $h = 29$; the graph is shifted down 1 unit.   **b.** $h = 25 \sin (12t)° + 29$
7. a. $h(t) = 20 \sin (120(t - 0.75))° + 30$

b.

c. near 0.75 s and every 3 s after that
d. near 2.25 s and every 3 s after that
e. every 1.5 s

15. Answers may vary. An example is given.
$N = 438.5x + 49821$, where N is the number (in thousands) of women employed and x is the number of years since 1989.   **16.** 0.75   **17.** vertical reflection symmetry   **18.** none of these   **19.** 180° rotational symmetry   **20.** all three

Page 576 Checkpoint
1. $45° < \theta < 225°$; In this interval, the graph of $y = \sin \theta$ is above the graph of $y = \cos \theta$.   **2.** $y = 5^x$ grows the fastest, followed by $y = x^5$, and then by $y = 5x$.
3. Answers may vary. An example is given.

4. both   **5.** cosine   **6.** both   **7.** sine
8. 180°; 1; $\dfrac{1}{180°}$; $y = \sin 2(\theta - 30°)$
9. 360°; 1; $\dfrac{1}{180°}$; $y = 3 \sin (\theta - 45°) + 2$

10.

11. a.

a sine curve; The points appear to lie on a sine curve.

b, c. Answers may vary. An example is given.

b. $y = 17.2 \cos (30(x - 6))° + 73.3$

c.

My graph fits the data fairly well. I think no graph will fit all the data points exactly because ice cream production reflects sales and sales are dependent on human behavior, which is not entirely predictable.

Page 577 Talk it Over

1. Each pattern repeats the same figure over and over.
2. a. A, C, and D   **b.** B and D   **c.** C, D, E, and F

Pages 580–581 Exercises and Problems

1. A translation is used in each pattern.   **3.** 180° rotational   **5.** translation   **7.** vertical   **9.** horizontal
11. a. If a border pattern has a rotational symmetry of θ, the image of each edge under a rotation of θ must be the other edge. Since the edges are parallel, θ must be 180°.   **b.** If a line is a line of symmetry of a border pattern, then the image of each edge under reflection over the line must be the same edge or the other edge. Then the line of symmetry must be parallel to or perpendicular to the edges.   **15.** glide reflection; 180° rotation and vertical reflection; horizontal and vertical reflection   **17.** glide reflection; horizontal reflection; horizontal and vertical reflection
20. Answers may vary. An example is given.
$y = 22.3 \cos (30(x - 7))° + 40.6$ **21.** (8.06, 150.3°)
22. (4.53, −2.11)   **23.** 120°; 60°

Page 584 Talk it Over

1. Any regular tessellation is periodic. For a tessellation consisting of squares or hexagons, the basic figure is a cell. For a tessellation consisting of triangles, a hexagon-shaped cluster of triangles is a cell.
2. Answers may vary.   **3.** The four angles at each vertex are congruent to the four angles of each parallelogram. The sum of the measures of the interior angles of a parallelogram is 360°.   **4.** The six triangles around each vertex have congruent sides matched so that four congruent parallelograms are formed. So, by the answer to question 3, the sum of the measures of the six angles is 360°.

Pages 585–588 Exercises and Problems

1. A regular tessellation uses only one kind of regular polygon, while a semiregular tessellation uses two or more regular polygons.   **3.** 3.12.12
5.

7.

9. Suppose regular pentagons and equilateral triangles tessellate a plane. Let p = the number of regular pentagons at each vertex and let t = the number of equilateral triangles at each vertex. The measures of interior angles of regular pentagons and equilateral triangles are 108° and 60°, so $108p + 60t = 360$. The only solution with nonnegative integer values is (0, 6). Since there is no combination of regular pentagons and triangles that can surround a vertex, the assumption that regular pentagons and triangles tessellate a plane is false.   **15.** region A   **32.**

33. $y = \dfrac{x^2}{16} - 5$

34. a. 3   **b.** 0   **c.** 1.61

Pages 590–591 Unit 10 Review and Assessment

1. periodic   **2.** increasing   **3.** constant
4. decreasing   **5.** $y = 4^x$ grows fastest, followed by $y = x^4$, and then by $y = 4x$.
6. Answers may vary. An example is given.

7. a. Answers may vary. An example is given. the part of the graph from 0 to 4 on the horizontal axis **b.** 4 **c.** $\frac{1}{4}$ **d.** 3 **e.** $y = 1$ **8.** A sine wave is any graph that has an equation of the form $y = A \sin B (\theta - C) + D$ or $y = A \cos B (\theta - C) + D$. It can be obtained by transforming the graph of $y = \sin \theta$ or $y = \cos \theta$.

9. 3; 360°; $\frac{1}{360°}$

10. 1; 180°; $\frac{1}{180°}$

11. $\frac{1}{2}$; 120°; $\frac{1}{120°}$

12, 13. Answers may vary. Examples are given.
12. $y = 1.5 \cos 2\theta - 3$ **13.** $y = 3 \sin (\theta - 45°) + 2$

14. a.

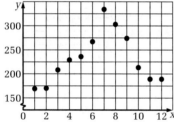

b. Answers may vary. An example is given. $y = 75 \cos (30(x - 7))° + 235$ **c.** A periodic function that can be modeled by a sine wave. The given data are periodic. **15.** vertical **16.** vertical and 180° rotation **17.** horizontal, vertical, and 180° rotation **19.** Yes. **20.** No. **21.** Suppose regular 9-gons and squares tessellate a plane. Let n = the number of regular 9-gons at each vertex and let s = the number of squares at each vertex. The measures of interior angles of regular 9-gons and squares are 140° and 90°, so $140n + 90s = 360$. There is no solution with non-negative integer values. Since there is no number of regular 9-gons and squares that surround a vertex, the assumption that 9-gons and squares tessellate a plane is false.

Page 596 Try This
1. a. 3.5 **b.** 32 **c.** about 0.966 **d.** 60° **e.** 4 **f.** 120 **g.** 20 **h.** 924

Page 597 Try This
2. a.

b.

c.

d.

3. Answers may vary. An example is given. [–5, 30] and Xscl=5 for x, [–10, 75] and Yscl=5 for y.
4. Answers may vary. An example is given. [–7.5, 7.5] and Xscl=1 for x, [–5, 5] and Yscl=1 for y.

Page 598 Try This
5. about 1.59 **6.**

TI-82: window of [–4, 4.4] and Xscl=0.5 for x, and [–2, 2] and Yscl=0.5 for y. Graph crosses at 0.4 and –2.4. TI-81: window of [–4, 5.5] and Xscl=0.5 for x, and [–2, 2] and Yscl=0.5 for y. Graph crosses at 0.4 and –2.4.

Page 600 Try This
7. between –2.41 and –2.42
8.

9.

Page 601 Try This

10. Enter Y₁={1,−1,0.5,2}X.

11. a.

b.

12. a.

b.

c.

Page 602 Try This

13. a.

b. 1.25 seconds

Page 604 Try This

14.

```
[A]+[B]
        [[8  15]
         [3  0 ]]
```

15.

```
[B]−[C]
        [[−4   8 ]
         [−15 −11]]
```

16.

```
2[A]
        [[6   8 ]
         [12  14]]
```

17.

```
[A][B]
        [[3  5 ]
         [9  17]]
```

18. not defined

19.

```
[C][D]
    [[33  21  −63  36]
     [44  28  −84  48]]
```

20.

```
[A]⁻¹
    [[−2.33  1.33 ]
     [2      −1   ]]
```

21. not defined

Page 606 Try This

22. b.

c. $y = 12.43x + 31.64$
d. $y = 12.4x + 31.6$
e. 75.14; 12.48

Extra Practice

Pages 608–610 Extra Practice Unit 1

1. a. finding the least common multiple of A and B **b.** Yes; testing multiples of B until one is found that is evenly divisible by A. **3, 5, 7.** Solution methods may vary. **3.** $x = 5$ **5.** $x \leq -5$ **7.** $x \geq 6$ **9.** Yes. **11.** No. **13.** No. **15.**

Municipal Library Systems

17. Weefixit: $y = 16x + 25$; Appliance Rehab: $y = 19x + 18$ **19.** 3 **21.** 8.0 **23.** (2.2, −2.8) **25.** (2, −1, 4) **27.** (3.2, 1.4, 0.8)

29.
$$\begin{array}{c} \\ P \\ Q \\ R \\ S \\ T \end{array} \begin{array}{c} \begin{array}{ccccc} P & Q & R & S & T \end{array} \\ \left[\begin{array}{ccccc} 0 & 1 & 1 & 1 & 1 \\ 1 & 0 & 1 & 0 & 0 \\ 1 & 1 & 0 & 1 & 0 \\ 1 & 0 & 1 & 0 & 1 \\ 1 & 0 & 0 & 1 & 0 \end{array} \right] \end{array}$$

31.

Central Sq. ⇄ Veterans' Plaza
Downtown
Zoo → Northside Mall

33. 3; 11; maximum **35.** −4.5; 41.5; maximum **37.** 9 walkers and 6 washers ($111 raised)

1. 25; 0; $a^2 + 2ab + b^2 + 4a + 4b + 4$ **3.** $\frac{11}{2}$; 8;

$7 - \frac{a + b}{2}$ **5.** 2; 7; $|a + b - 5|$ **7.** Yes; many-to-one.

9. Yes; one-to-one. **11.** Yes; -4; 11; $-3a + 3b + 2$.
13. No. **15.** Yes; 5; 25; $13 - 4a + 4b$.

17. $f(x) = \frac{1}{2}x + \frac{9}{2}$ **19.** $f(x) = 2x + 7$ **21.** $f(x) = \frac{3}{2}x + \frac{9}{4}$

23. **25.**

27. a. quadratic; -2; $-\frac{9}{2}$, $-\frac{a^2 - 2ab + b^2}{2}$

b.

29. not quadratic **31. a.** quadratic; $\frac{1}{4}$; 4; $\frac{(a - b - 1)^2}{4}$

b.

33. $f(x) = 3x^5$ **35.** $f(x) = 48x^4$ **37.** $f(x) = 1125x^3$

39. **41.**

43. 3 **45.** 12 **47.** 4 **49.** all real numbers; all real
numbers **51.** all real numbers greater than or equal
to 3; all real numbers less than or equal to 0 **53.** all
real numbers; all real numbers

55. a.   **b.** $x = 2$; $y = 0$
c. all real numbers except
2; all real numbers except
0

57. a.   **b.** $x = -3$; $y = 1$
c. all real numbers
except -3; all real
numbers except 1

59. a.   **b.** $x = 4$; $y = 0.5$
c. all real numbers except
4; all real numbers except
0.5

61. a. $(7x^2 + 1)\sqrt{x}$ **b.** all real numbers greater than
or equal to 0 **63. a.** $\sqrt{7x^2 + 1}$ **b.** all real numbers

65. a. $\frac{(7x^2 + 1)(2x + 1)}{x}$ **b.** all real numbers except 0 or $\frac{1}{2}$

67. a. $7x + 1$ **b.** all real numbers greater than or
equal to 0

1. True. If two sides of a triangle are equal in measure, then two angles of the triangle are equal in measure; True. If no two angles of a triangle are equal in
measure, then no two sides of the triangle are equal
in measure; True. If no two sides of a triangle are
equal in measure, then no two angles of the triangle
are equal in measure; True. **3.** True. If n is a positive
odd integer, then n is a prime number greater than 2;
False. If n is not a prime number greater than 2, then
n is not a positive odd integer; False. If n is not a positive odd integer, then n is not a prime number
greater than 2; True. **5.** The midpoints are $J(a, 0)$,
$K(a + b, c)$, $L(b + d, c + e)$, $M(d, e)$. The slope of both
$\overline{JK}$ and $\overline{ML}$ is $\frac{c}{b}$; the slope of both $\overline{KL}$ and $\overline{MJ}$ is $\frac{e}{d - a}$.
Thus, by definition, $JKLM$ is a parallelogram. **7.** Yes.
9. No. **11.** about 128.6°; about 51.4° **13.** 157.5°;
22.5° **15.** 72° **17.** 72° **19.** 108° **21.** 110° **23.** 35°
25. 120° **27.** They are the same, since each is equal
to the sum of the radii of the two circles. **29.** 60°
31. $12\sqrt{3} \approx 20.8$ units² **33.** 840 units² **35.** Assume
temporarily that a regular polyhedron with octagonal
faces exists. Then at each vertex at least three regular
octagons meet. This is impossible, since each has
interior angles that measure 135°, and $3 \cdot 135 =
405° > 360°$.

1. a. 6, -7, 8 **b.** -11 **3. a.** 8, 5, 2 **b.** -7 **5. a.** 4, 2, 1
b. 4 **7.** Yes; 1. **9.** Yes; $\frac{2}{3}$. **11.** $\frac{1}{2}, \frac{4}{3}, \frac{9}{4}, \frac{16}{5}; \frac{400}{21}$

13. $\frac{1}{3}, \frac{3}{5}, \frac{5}{7}, \frac{7}{9}; \frac{39}{41}$ **15.** $a_n = 3 + 2n$ **17.** $a_n = 1500\left(\frac{1}{10^n}\right)$

19. $a_n = 625\left(\tfrac{1}{5}\right)$

$4, \tfrac{1}{2}, 4, \tfrac{1}{2}$ **25.** $10, 2, 6, \tfrac{8}{3}, \tfrac{19}{4}, \tfrac{\ldots}{19}$

b. $a_1 = 16$; $a_n = \tfrac{5}{4}a_{n-1}$ **29. a.** geometric **b.** $u_1 = 8$;

$a_n = \tfrac{1}{10}a_{n-1}$ **31. a.** arithmetic **b.** $a_1 = \tfrac{1}{2}$; $a_n = a_{n-1} - 2$

33. a. -14.5 **b.** ± 10 **35. a.** 51 **b.** $\pm 10\sqrt{2}$

37. a. -151.5 **b.** ± 30 **39.** 105 **41.** 364

43. $\displaystyle\sum_{n=1}^{12}(6 + 10n)$ **45.** $\displaystyle\sum_{n=1}^{9}(9n - 21)$ **47.** 513

49. 55.55555 **51. a.** geometric **b.** $\dfrac{-189}{64} = -2.953125$

53. a.   **b.** Yes; 20.

55. a.   **b.** No.

57. a.   **b.** Yes; 120.

Pages 615–617 Extra Practice Unit 5

1.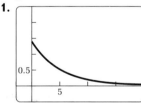

3. 3.49 h **5.** $y = 320(1.15)^x$, where x is the number of years since 1990 **7.** 0 computers **9.** 3 **11.** $\dfrac{5\sqrt{5}}{8}$

13. $2ab^2\sqrt[3]{a}$ **15.** $\sqrt[3]{w}$ **17. a.** 0.30 **b.** 0.03

19. $\$2203.99$ **21.** $\$2237.74$ **23.** $y = \dfrac{3}{7x}$

25. $y = (x-2)^2$, $x \ge 2$ **27.** $y = \dfrac{x}{2}$, $x \ge 0$ **29.** $y = \sqrt[3]{x-1}$

31. 4 **33.** -3 **35.** 0 **37.** 2.5 **39.** 0.20 **41.** 1

43. 0.56 **45.** $\log_3 56$ **47.** $\log_7 A + 0.5 \log_7 B$

49. $0.25(\log_7 A + 5 \log_7 B)$ **51.** 1 **53.** 1.95

55. 26.40 **57.** $\dfrac{7}{17}$ **59.** $4, 20$

Pages 617–619 Extra Practice Unit 6

1. Histograms may vary. An example is given. **3.** 182.1; 182.5

5.   **7.** 60%

9. mean ≈ 1.33; range $= 0.09$; $\sigma \approx 0.024$ **11.** Bars of the the second would be shifted to the right and more closely bunched around the mean. **13. a.** Histogram may vary depending on intervals chosen. An example is given.

  b. mean $= 7.8$; median $= 8$ **c.** Yes.

15. 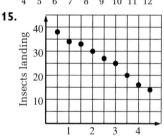 **17.** $y = -6x + 40.7$

19, 21.

Pages 619–620 Extra Practice Unit 7

1. int($6 *$ rand) $+ 1$ **3.** On a calculator, choose groups of 5 random integers from 1 to 13. Count the number of duplicate integers in each group. Perform a large number of trials. The experimental probability is

$$\frac{\text{number of times at least two integers match}}{\text{number of trials}}.$$

5. $\frac{4}{13}$ **7.** $\frac{2}{9}$ **9.** $\frac{5}{18}$ **11.** $\frac{7}{8}$ **13.** $\frac{1}{3}$; $\frac{7}{30}$; $\frac{7}{90}$ **15.** $\frac{1}{4}$ **17.** $\frac{3}{7}$

19. The average expected advance from picking a card is 2.5 spaces. You should pick the card unless rolling the die is an option. Rolling the die has a greater expected advance. **21.** 0.146

Pages 621–622 Extra Practice Unit 8
Answers may vary due to rounding.

1, 3, 5.

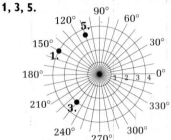

7. $(0, -7)$
9. $(-2.83, -2.83)$
11. $(-1.81, -0.85)$
13. $(-3.94, 3.08)$
15. $(4, 120°)$
17. $(5, -36.9°)$
19. $(5.4, 141°)$
21. $(4, 2)$
23. $(-2, 3)$
25. $(2, 6)$

27. $(5, 5)$ **29.** $(-6, 2)$ **31.** $(9, 90°)$; $(0, 9)$
33. $(7.74, 71.2°)$; $(2.5, 7.33)$ **35.** $(7.55, -131.5°)$;
$(-5, -5.66)$ **37.** $(-2, 0)$ **39.** $(-1.4, -1.5)$
41. $(-1.7, -1.3)$ **43.** $(3.30, -101.2°)$ **45.** $(1, -20°)$
47. $(6.07, 129.1°)$ **49.** $x = 55.6t$; $y = 29.6t - 4.9t^2$
51. $y = 0.37x - 0.065x^2$ **53.** $(x - 1)^2 + (y - 2)^2 = \frac{1}{4}$
55. $\frac{(x - 3)^2}{36} + \frac{(y + 1)^2}{25} = 1$ **57.** 19.8 **59.** 108.6°
61. $a = 6.72$, $m \angle C = 86°$, $b = 9.69$ **63.** $m \angle C = 43.9°$,
$m \angle A = 64.1°$, $a = 8.0$ **65.** $m \angle A = 51.5°$,
$m \angle B = 14.5°$, $b = 6.9$ **67.** 0 **69.** 2

Pages 622–624 Extra Practice Unit 9
1. 66.7; 62.5; 34.9 **3.** $y = 10^x$; $(1, -2)$ **5.** $y = \log x$;
$(9, 0)$ **7.** $y = |x|$; $(0, -8)$

9. $y - 4 = (x - 3)^3$

11. $y + 5 = |x - 3|$

13. $y + 5 = (x - 1)^2$

15. a. 29.9, 34, 34, 12.1 **b.** 44.8, 51, 51, 18.1
c.

17. $\begin{bmatrix} 16 & 24 \\ 0 & 2 & 6 \end{bmatrix}$; horizontal stretch by a factor of 4

19. $\begin{bmatrix} 4 & 6 & 2 \\ 0 & 0.5 & 1.5 \end{bmatrix}$; vertical stretch by a factor of $\frac{1}{4}$

21. $y = 2 \log (x + 3)$

23. $y = \frac{1}{2}|x - 4|$

25. a.

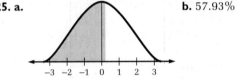

b. 57.93%

27. a.

b. 1.79%

29. 0.1 **31.** -2.3 **33.** 0.3; 38 **35.** -0.7; 57.2

37.

39.

41.

Pages 624–625 Extra Practice Unit 10
1. periodic **3.** damping **5. a.** 4 **b.** $\frac{1}{4}$ **c.** $y = 2.5$
d. 1.5 **7. a.** 0 **b.** 1 **9. a.** $-1 \le y \le 1$ **b.** $-1 \le y \le 1$
11. 220° **13.** 295° **15. a.** 5, 180, $\frac{1}{180}$
b.

17. a. 1, 180, $\frac{1}{180}$

b.

19. a. 2.5, 120, $\frac{1}{120}$

21. $y = 15 \sin(18t) + 20$ **23.** horizontal reflection

25. vertical reflection

27.

29.

Page 626 Skill 1
1. about 22.7   **2.** 21   **3.** 10, 18, and 24   **4.** 32

Page 627 Skill 2
1. 30   **2.** 100   **3.** 10 or 11   **4.** \$20,000–29,000; \$50,000 or over

Page 628 Skill 3
1. 120   **2.** 5040   **3.** 120   **4.** 1,814,400   **5.** 210
6. 6720   **7.** 3024   **8.** 720   **9.** 1680   **10.** 840
11. 3024

Page 629 Skill 4
1. 15   **2.** 56   **3.** 21   **4.** 126   **5.** 462   **6.** 792

Page 630 Skill 5
1. 6   **2.** 10   **3.** 20   **4.** 15   **5.** Add the two numbers together.   **6.** The numbers in diagonal 2 of Pascal's triangle are called triangular numbers because they can be represented by dots arranged to form equilateral triangles.   **7.** The sum of any two consecutive numbers in diagonal 2 of Pascal's triangle is a perfect square. These numbers are called square numbers because they can be represented by dots arranged in a square.

Page 631 Skill 6
1. about 16%   **2.** about 35%   **3.** about 48%
4. about 8%   **5.** about 77%   **6.** 0   **7.** 100%

Page 632 Skill 7
1. $\frac{1}{6}$ **2.** $\frac{5}{12}$ **3.** $\frac{7}{12}$ **4.** $\frac{2}{3}$

Page 632 Skill 8
1. 2×3 **2.** \$4.50; \$5.50

Page 633 Skill 9
1. $\begin{bmatrix} 5 & 20 \\ 35 & 0 \\ 30 & 10 \end{bmatrix}$ **2.** $\begin{bmatrix} 0.5 & 0.5 & 0 & 0.5 \\ 1.5 & 1 & 2 & 3 \end{bmatrix}$ **3.** $\begin{bmatrix} 30 & 45 & 10 \\ 15 & 60 & 5 \end{bmatrix}$

Pages 633–634 Skill 10
1. $\begin{bmatrix} 9 & 2 & -1 \\ 15 & 1 & 6 \end{bmatrix}$ **2.** $\begin{bmatrix} 17 & 9 \\ 7 & -9 \\ 5 & 29 \\ 0 & -4 \end{bmatrix}$ **3.** $\begin{bmatrix} -1 & 2.4 \\ 1.9 & -1.3 \end{bmatrix}$

4. $[110 \ \ 180 \ \ 70]$

Page 634 Skill 11
1. $[3]$ **2.** $\begin{bmatrix} 16 & 27 \\ 12 & 26 \\ 8 & 12 \end{bmatrix}$ **3.** $\begin{bmatrix} 9 & -2 & 7 & -2 \\ 12 & 16 & -20 & -8 \\ 9 & 5 & -4 & -4 \end{bmatrix}$

Page 635 Skill 12
1. 0   **2.** 94   **3.** −21   **4.** −4   **5.** 478   **6.** −72   **7.** −24
8. 6   **9.** −200   **10.** −396   **11.** −416   **12.** −256

Pages 635–636 Skill 13
1. $-a^2 - a + 2$ **2.** $3x^2 + 2y^2$ **3.** $2x^3 - 3x^2 - 1$
4. $-2c^2 - 6cd - 5d^2 - 1$

Pages 636–637 Skill 14
1. $27t^{13}$ **2.** $\frac{3}{4}a^8$ **3.** $\frac{-20}{r}$ **4.** $\frac{5}{a^2}$ **5.** $\frac{5}{u^5}$ **6.** $\frac{12}{m^2 n^4}$ **7.** $\frac{-6}{y^2}$
8. $\frac{2v^2}{3w}$ **9.** $\frac{2}{x^6 y^9}$

Page 638 Skill 15
1. $a^2 - 4$ **2.** $a^2 + 4a + 4$ **3.** $a^2 - 4a + 4$
4. $21k^2 + 22k - 8$ **5.** $25x^2 + 20xy + 4y^2$
6. $49c^2 - 36d^2$ **7.** $81w^2 - 72w + 16$
8. $20x^3 - 56xy + 15y^2$ **9.** $a^3 - a^2 - 5a + 2$
10. $9x^2 + 12xy + 4y^2$ **11.** $x^3 + x^2 - 2x + 12$
12. $4n^3 - 16n^2 + 11n + 10$

Page 639 Skill 16
1. $x^5 + 5x^4 y^1 + 10x^3 y^2 + 10x^2 y^3 + 5xy^4 + y^5$
2. $16r^4 + 96r^3 + 216r^2 + 216r + 81$ **3.** $p^{12} + 6p^{10}q + 15p^8 q^2 + 20p^6 q^3 + 15p^4 q^4 + 6p^2 q^5 + q^6$
4. $8n^3 - 12n^2 m + 6nm^2 - m^3$ **5.** $c^5 + 50c^4 d + 1000c^3 d^2 + 10,000c^2 d^3 + 50,000cd^4 + 100,000d^5$
6. $v^8 + 8v^6 w^2 + 24v^4 w^6 + 32v^2 w^9 + 16w^{12}$

Page 640 Skill 17

1. $(x-10)(x-10)$ **2.** $(5y+9z)(5y-9z)$

3. $(a-7)(a+2)$ **4.** $(c+5)(2c-1)$ **5.** $(3x-y)(x-2y)$

6. $(7m+5n)(7m+5n)$ **7.** $2x^2(2x^3-x^2+8)$

8. $3p^2(3pq+5)$ **9.** $9x^2y(5x-2y^4)$

Page 641 Skill 18

1. $\dfrac{1}{y+5}$ **2.** $\dfrac{x+1}{x+2}$ **3.** $\dfrac{a-3}{a+3}$ **4.** $\dfrac{14}{3x}$ **5.** $\dfrac{1}{2x-10}$

6. $\dfrac{2-x}{x^2+x}$

Page 642 Skill 19

1. $3\sqrt{5}$ **2.** $10\sqrt{3}$ **3.** $2\sqrt{19}$ **4.** $10\sqrt{3}$ **5.** $60\sqrt{5}$
6. $\sqrt{42}$ **7.** $3\sqrt{10}$ **8.** $4.2\sqrt{33}$ **9.** $24\sqrt{6}$ **10.** 6
11. 27   **12.** $12\sqrt{3}$ **13.** $60\sqrt{2}$

Page 643 Skill 20

1. $10i$ **2.** $0.5i$ **3.** $i\sqrt{17} \approx 4.12i$ **4.** $i\sqrt{83} \approx 9.11i$
5. -35 **6.** $6i$ **7.** $72+9i$ **8.** $21-84i$ **9.** $18-19i$
10. $-13+11i$ **11.** $10-7.5i$ **12.** $78-36i$
13. $-3.6+7.6i$ **14.** 116

Pages 644–645 Skill 21

1. $x=-3, y=-12$ **2.** $a=3, b=8$ **3.** $x=0, y=-1$
4. $a=\dfrac{37}{3}, b=-4$ **5.** $p=5, q=-\dfrac{3}{2}$ **6.** $c=5, d=5$

Pages 645–646 Skill 22

1. $5, -1$ **2.** $\dfrac{5}{2}, -1$ **3.** $\dfrac{1}{3}, -1$ **4.** about 3.7, about 0.27
5. about -2.8, about 1.25   **6.** about 1.77, about 0.23

Pages 646–647 Skill 23

1. $-\dfrac{2}{3}$ **2.** $2, -3$ **3.** 5   **4.** $3, 2$ **5.** $\dfrac{1}{4}$ **6.** 3

Page 647 Skill 24

1. $0, 2, 3$ **2.** $0, -1, -3$ **3.** $1, -3, \dfrac{1}{3}$ **4.** $0, -4, 1$
5. $0, 2, -2$ **6.** $2, -6$

Pages 648–649 Skill 25

1. $y=4x+7$ **2.** $y=-0.5x-2$ **3.** $y=-3x+11$
4. $y=-\dfrac{2}{3}x-\dfrac{1}{3}$ **5.** $y=-\dfrac{1}{2}x+\dfrac{3}{2}$

Page 649 Skill 26

1. Tables may vary. Examples are given.

x	y	(x, y)
-2	9	$(-2, 9)$
-1	7	$(-1, 7)$
0	5	$(0, 5)$
1	3	$(1, 3)$
2	1	$(2, 1)$

2.

x	y	(x, y)
-2	-2	$(-2, -2)$
-1	$-\dfrac{3}{2}$	$\left(-1, -\dfrac{3}{2}\right)$
0	-1	$(0, -1)$
1	$-\dfrac{1}{2}$	$\left(-1, -\dfrac{1}{2}\right)$
2	0	$(2, 0)$

3.

x	y	(x, y)
-2	-1	$(-2, -1)$
-1	-4	$(-1, -4)$
0	-5	$(0, -5)$
1	-4	$(1, -4)$
2	-1	$(2, -1)$

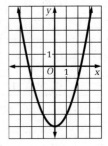

4.

x	y	(x, y)
-2	0	$(-2, 0)$
-1	-2	$(-1, -2)$
0	-2	$(0, -2)$
1	0	$(1, 0)$
2	4	$(2, 4)$

5.

x	y	(x, y)
-2	4	$(-2, 4)$
-1	3	$(-1, 3)$
0	2	$(0, 2)$
1	1	$(1, 1)$
2	0	$(2, 0)$
3	1	$(3, 1)$
4	2	$(4, 2)$

6.

x	y	(x, y)
-2	2	$(-2, 2)$
-1	2.5	$(-1, 2.5)$
0	3	$(0, 3)$
1	2.5	$(1, 2.5)$
2	2	$(2, 2)$

Integrated Mathematics

7.

x	y	(x, y)
−4	1	(−4, 1)
−3	−1	(−3, −1)
−2	−3	(−2, −3)
−1	−1	(−1, −1)
0	1	(0, 1)
1	3	(1, 3)
2	5	(2, 5)

8.

x	y	(x, y)
−3	−6.75	(−3, −6.75)
−2	−2	(−2, −2)
−1	−0.25	(−1, −0.25)
0	0	(0, 0)
1	0.25	(1, 0.25)
2	2	(2, 2)
3	6.75	(3, 6.75)

9.

x	y	(x, y)
−3	−24	(−3, −24)
−2	−6	(−2, −6)
−1	0	(−1, 0)
−0.5	0.325	(−0.5, 0.325)
0	0	(0, 0)
0.5	−0.325	(0.5, −0.325)
1	0	(1, 0)
2	6	(2, 6)
3	24	(3, 24)

Page 650 Skill 27

1.

2.

3.

4.

5.

6.

7.

8.

Page 651 Skill 28

1. y-intercept: −4; x = 0   **2.** y-intercept: 7; x = 0

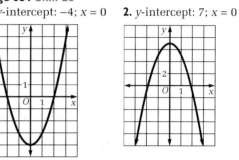

3. y-intercept: 0; x = 3   **4.** y-intercept: −1; x = 4

5. y-intercept: −10; x = 2   **6.** y-intercept: 6; x = 3

Pages 652–653 Skill 29
1. 160 ft² **2.** 19.5 in.² **3.** about 28.27 in.²
4. 702 in.² **5.** about 785.4 cm² **6.** 200 cm³
7. about 106.8 m³ **8.** 400 in.³

Pages 653–654 Skill 30
1. 5 **2.** 24 **3.** about 7.55 **4.** $b \approx 6.9$ cm, $c \approx 13.9$ cm

Pages 654–655 Skill 31
1. 5 **2.** 13 **3.** $\sqrt{29} \approx 5.4$ **4.** (5, 6) **5.** (2, −4)
6. (5.5, −4.5)

Pages 655–656 Skill 32

1. $m \angle CAB = m \angle DEB$ and $m \angle CBA = m \angle DBE$, so the triangles are similar. Corresponding angles are $\angle CAB$ and $\angle DEB$, $\angle CBA$ and $\angle DBE$, and $\angle BCA$ and $\angle BDE$; corresponding sides are $\overline{AC}$ and $\overline{ED}$, $\overline{BC}$ and $\overline{BD}$, and $\overline{AB}$ and $\overline{EB}$. **2.** $m \angle PNM = m \angle RQM$ and $m \angle NMP = m \angle QMR$, so the triangles are similar. Corresponding angles are $\angle PNM$ and $\angle RQM$, $\angle NMP$ and $\angle QMR$, and $\angle M$ and $\angle M$; corresponding sides are $\overline{NP}$ and $\overline{QR}$, $\overline{MN}$ and $\overline{MQ}$, and $\overline{MP}$ and $\overline{MR}$. **3.** 18

Page 656 Skill 33

1. Yes; by SSS. **2.** Yes; by AAS. **3.** Yes; by ASA. **4.** No. **5.** $CB = FE$, $AC = DF$, $AB = DE$, $m \angle A = m \angle D$, $m \angle C = m \angle F$, $m \angle B = m \angle E$; 75

Page 657 Skill 34

1. All rhombuses have perpendicular diagonals. **2.** The fact that a figure is a square implies that it is a rhombus. **3.** Every Saturday is a day of the weekend. **4.** A figure is a cylinder only if the formula for its volume is $V = Bh$. **5.** A polygon is a quadrilateral if and only if it has four sides. **6.** $5x = 20$ if and only if $x = 4$.

Pages 658–659 Skill 35

1. *or* rule **2.** chain rule **3.** direct argument **4.** A horse is a vertebrate. **5.** $\triangle ABC$ is not isosceles. **6.** If $2x + 3 = 21$, then $x = 9$. **7.** $P(A) \neq 0$.

Page 660 Skill 36

1. $\frac{4}{8.06} \approx 0.50$ **2.** $\frac{7}{8.06} \approx 0.87$ **3.** $\frac{4}{7} \approx 0.57$

4. $\frac{7}{8.06} \approx 0.87$ **5.** $\frac{4}{8.06} \approx 0.50$ **6.** $\frac{7}{4} \approx 1.75$

7.
8.

Page 661 Skill 37

1. $x \approx 26.8$ **2.** $x \approx 5.8$ **3.** $x \approx 26.6$ **4.** $h \approx 10.3$

Pages 662–663 Skill 38

1. **2.**

3. **4.**

5. **6.**

7. **8.**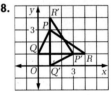

Page 663 Skill 39

1. 72° rotational symmetry about point X

2. reflection symmetry

3. reflection symmetry